# BIOLOGY
# 201/203

## HUMAN ANATOMY AND PHYSIOLOGY— A MODERN SYNTHESIS

## Vol. 1

Fall 2017

**C. DAVID BRIDGES**
PURDUE UNIVERSITY

Printed in the United States of America

10 9 8 7 6 5 4 3 2 1

ISBN 978-0-7380-9569-1

Macmillan Learning Curriculum Solutions
14903 Pilot Drive
Plymouth, MI 48170
www.macmillanlearning.com

Bridges 9569-1 F17

macmillan learning
curriculum solutions

**Sustainability**

Hayden-McNeil's standard paper stock uses a minimum of 30% post-consumer waste. We offer higher % options by request, including a 100% recycled stock. Additionally, Hayden-McNeil Custom Digital provides authors with the opportunity to convert print products to a digital format. Hayden-McNeil is part of a larger sustainability initiative through Macmillan Learning. Visit http://sustainability.macmillan.com to learn more.

bedford/st. martin's • hayden-mcneil
w.h. freeman • worth publishers

# TABLE OF CONTENTS

# SYLLABUS

## Introductory Information

**FIRST SEMESTER: BIOL 201** (2 cr., no lab), **203** (4 cr., with lab)

*"I believe that we are solely responsible for our choices, and we have to accept the consequences of every deed, word and thought throughout our lifetime."* Elisabeth Kubler-Ross

*"When you can measure what you are speaking about, and express it in numbers, you know something about it; but when you cannot measure it, when you cannot express it in numbers, your knowledge is a meagre and unsatisfactory thing; it may be the beginning of knowledge, but you have scarcely, in your thoughts, advanced to the stage of science."* Lord Kelvin "Popular Lectures and Addresses (1891–1894).

*"At its core, science is a way of thinking—making judgments, often creative ones, that are based on evidence, not on desires, received beliefs, or hearsay.... [T]he pursuit of evidence, through experiment and observation, is the lifeblood of science."* [Commencement address given at Harvard University on June 6, 1996, by Harold Varmus, Director of the National Institutes of Health. Published in the *FASEB Journal, 10*, 1237, September 1996.]

No student is permitted to take the examination before (or after) the scheduled time for *any* reason—there are absolutely no exceptions to this rule.

Your grade is computed according to the points system described in this syllabus. We do *not* calculate percentages, so there is no question of "rounding up" to the next full percentage point. *All grades are absolutely final and are not negotiable.* No matter how close your points total is to the next letter grade, there is no "extra credit" or any other device for improving on your grade.

## Schedule of Lectures and Exams

(Lectures are recorded and the audio/video available on Boilercast.)

---

BIOL 201: Two 50-minute lectures (Tues, Thurs), LILLY 1-105 (with quiz)

BIOL 203: Two 50-minute lectures (Tues, Thurs), LILLY 1-105 (with quiz)

One two-hour laboratory, LILLY G-130 (with quiz)

One 50-minute laboratory preparation lecture (with quiz)

---

**I am available to help you. The best way is for you to e-mail me and set up an appointment during my office hours. Formal pre-examination help sessions have been scheduled, and I will notify you of time and place, during lecture, and by class e-mail. They will be recorded. I also help individual students during office hours.**

---

No student will be permitted to take any examination before (or after) the scheduled time for any reason—there are absolutely no exceptions to this rule.

---

Unless an arithmetic error has been made, grades are absolutely final and non-negotiable.

---

---

STUDYING: YOU *MUST* TEST YOURSELF EFFECTIVELY. After you have completed your studying, you should be able to answer *on paper* all the objectives FROM MEMORY.

---

## Lecture Schedule—Fall Semester, 2017

| Date | Topic |
| --- | --- |
| Aug. 22 | Lecture 1 – Introduction to the Course and to the Human Body |
| Aug. 24 | Lecture 2 – Basic Chemistry and Biochemistry |
| Aug. 29 | Lecture 3 – Biology of the Cell I |
| Aug. 31 | Lecture 4 – Biology of the Cell II |
| Sept. 5 | Lecture 5 – Cell Metabolism I |
| Sept. 7 | Lecture 6 – Cell Metabolism II |
| Sept. 12 | Lecture 7 – Tissues of the Body |
| Sept. 14 | Lecture 8 – Membranes Found in the Body |
| Sept. 19 | Lecture 9 – Bones and Joints |
| TBA | Lecture Exam 1 – Date not set at time of printing. |
| Sept. 26 | Lecture 10 – Muscle I |
| Sept. 28 | Lecture 11 – Muscle II |
| Oct. 3 | Lecture 12 – Neurophysiology I |
| Oct. 5 | Lecture 13 – Neurophysiology II |
| Oct. 10 | No Class! Octoberbreak |
| Oct. 12 | Lecture 14 – Neurophysiology III: Somatic sensory receptors |
| Oct. 17 | Lecture 15 – Central Nervous System I: Spinal cord, spinal reflexes |
| Oct. 19 | Lecture 16 – Central Nervous System II: Meninges ventricles, cerebrospinal fluid, brain stem |
| Oct. 24 | Lecture 17 – Central Nervous System III: Cerebral cortex and basal ganglia |
| Oct. 26 | Lecture 18 – Central Nervous System IV: Neurotransmitters; cerebellum |
| Oct. 31 | Lecture 19 – Central Nervous System V: Integration of sensation, motor function, motivation |
| TBA | Lecture Exam 2 – Date not set at time of printing. |
| Nov. 2 | Lecture 20 – The Autonomic Nervous System |
| Nov. 7 | Lecture 21 – Special Senses I: The eye, olfaction and taste |
| Nov. 9 | Lecture 22 – Special Senses II: The ear – hearing and balance |
| Nov. 14 | Lecture 23 – Cardiovascular System I: Function, basic arrangement, blood vessels, the heart |
| Nov. 16 | Lecture 24 – Cardiovascular System II: Cardiac cycle, energy supply, cardiac output |
| Nov. 21, 23 | No Classes! Thanksgiving |
| Nov. 28 | Lecture 25 – Cardiovascular System III: Electrical properties of the heart, the electrocardiogram, dysrhythmias |
| Nov. 30 | Lecture 26 – Cardiovascular System IV: Blood vessels, capillaries and the control of blood pressure |
| Dec. 5 | Lecture 27 – Cardiovascular System V: Exercise, hemorrhage, hypertension, atherosclerosis, coronary circulation |
| Dec. 7 | Lecture 28 – Cardiovascular System VI: Heart disease |
| TBA | Lecture Exam 3 (week of December 11 through December 16) |

## Course Information

**Read this.** This section contains all the information you need to know about the course: staff, lecture outlines, required and recommended texts, lecture, laboratory, laboratory lectures, help sessions, examination schedules, examination and course policies, points, grades and makeup policies, etc.

### A. Course Description

The goal of this two-semester course is to give you a grasp of how the human body—YOUR body—is built and how it works.

In order to know what has gone wrong in disease, we must understand the normal, healthy body. Often this depends on working out many complex molecular events occurring within cells. To assist you in comprehending the exciting new developments in biomedical science, the course provides you with lectures on biochemistry and cell biology.

### B. Lectures, Laboratory Lectures and Labs

In BIOL 203 there are two one-hour lectures, one one-hour laboratory lecture, and one two-hour laboratory per week. See BIOL 203 Laboratory Policies for further details on the laboratory part of the course.

Audiovisual recordings of the lectures are available on Boilercast, accessible via Blackboard.

viii

This course calls for 1–2 hours of study per day, seven days a week.

### C. How to Handle Your Reading Assignments for Labs and Lectures

You MUST read the corresponding chapter BEFORE coming to lecture. Make sure you can pronounce the words. You can't memorize a word if you can't pronounce it. After the lecture, watch and listen to it on Boilercast.

### D. Subject Matter

My lectures will be mainly on the physiology, but I will also deal with essential features of the anatomy wherever necessary. Some of the subject matter in the notes will be repeated (but not necessarily identically) in the lectures themselves; some subject matter will be presented *only* in the lectures; some may not be given in the lecture at all.

That is why you need to attend the lectures and read the corresponding chapter *ahead of time.*

## E. Study Materials

Items 1 through 3 in <u>bold print</u> are required. Items 4 through 5 are recommended.

1. **Human Anatomy and Physiology—A Modern Synthesis, Vol. 1, 2017 Bridges – Hayden-McNeil – on sale at bookstores – required text.**

2. **Human Anatomy and Physiology—A Modern Synthesis, Vol. 1, Laboratory Manual 2017 – Hayden-McNeil – on sale at bookstores – required text for BIOL 203 students, not needed by BIOL 201 students.**

3. **Di Fiore's *Atlas of Histology* with functional correlations, any edition – required text for BIOL 203 students, useful for BIOL 201 students.**

4. Human Anatomy, any edition, F.H. Martini, M.J. Timmons; Prentice Hall – recommended text, but purchase is optional.

5. The Anatomy Coloring Book 4th Edition by Wynn Kapit, Lawrence M. Elson

   The Physiology Coloring Book (2nd Edition) by Wynn Kapit, Robert Macey, Esmail Meisami – recommended, although there are many guides like these that are equivalent.

You are also <u>required</u> to purchase an i-clicker for recording answers to questions in lectures, and a non-programmable calculator that is capable of calculating logarithms.

## F. Staff, Office Hours, Help, Course Discussion

1. **Lecture:**

   C. David Bridges, Ph.D., D.Sc.,
   Professor of Biological Sciences (Purdue University),
   Adjunct Professor of Physiology and Biophysics
        (Indiana University School of Medicine)
   Telephone 494-8153, room 1-230, Lilly Hall of Life Sciences.
   Home phone 765-427-3071
   e-mail: **bridgesc@purdue.edu**

2. **Laboratory:**

   Regina Shannon, M.S., Instructional Coordinator
   Lisa Kolo, Assistant Instructional Coordinator

3. **Graduate teaching assistants:** To be named

4. **Undergraduate teaching assistants:** To be named

5. **Course secretary:**

   Marcy Nevius, telephone 494-8157, room G-110
   (opposite the G-130 lab), Lilly Hall of Life Sciences

ix

6.  **Office hours** (Fall Semester):

    **David Bridges** – Tuesdays, 12:30–4:30; Thursdays, 12:30–4:30. Other times by appointment—schedule with Dr. Bridges by e-mail. It's a good idea to make an appointment by e-mail even when you want to come during my office hours. That is not mandatory, but you are guaranteed to see me at a particular time, and you won't have to wait if there is another student already with me.

    **Regina Shannon and Lisa Kolo** – Regular office hours will be announced in the laboratory (other times by appointment).

## G. Grading for BIOL 203 (Lecture, Laboratory Lectures and Laboratory, 4 Credits)

*Course Point Distribution*

The point distribution for the course is as follows:

| | | |
|---|---|---|
| 3 Lecture exams @ 350 pts each | = | 1050 |
| 25 Online post-lecture quizzes @ 10 pts each | = | 250 |
| TOTAL for lecture | = | 1300 |
| (Plus bonus points for i-clicker questions) | | |
| TOTAL for lab | = | 1100 |
| Total points for BIOL 203 | = | 2400 |

**A:** 2040–2400 points     **B:** 1800–2039 points

**C:** 1560–1799 points     **D:** 1320–1559 points

**F:** below 1320 points

1.  **Online POST-LECTURE QUIZZES are worth a total of 250 points.**

    There will be 25. The first will be next Thursday, after Lecture 4.

    Quiz will be made available online from 12 noon on the day of the lecture and will close at *five minutes before midnight ON THE FOLLOWING DAY.*

    You will have *10 minutes* to take the quiz.

    You may only take it *one time.*

    Each quiz consists of 10 multiple choice questions based on the material of the current lecture and POSSIBLY previous lectures. Each question is worth 1 point.

2. **Access to quizzes and problem solving**

- You must first register via the Hayden-McNeil URL provided.
- You must use the access code in your new BIOL 201/203 text. For the lab you must use the access code in your new laboratory manual.
- If you have a SOFTWARE problem, you must first call the 1-800 technical help number. *Only after you have done that should you contact me.*
- You must use Firefox or Internet Explorer as your browser.
- Do *not* attempt to use your smartphone.
- Be aware that if you choose to use your own computer rather than one of the University's computers YOU DO SO AT YOUR OWN RISK AND WE CANNOT HELP YOU IF YOU ENCOUNTER TECHNICAL PROBLEMS. TO REPEAT— IT IS WISE TO USE A UNIVERSITY COMPUTER.

## H. Your i-clicker

1. **Bring it to every class** – if you forget it I cannot help you.

2. Keep a set of **replacement batteries**.

3. *Register* your i-clicker on *Blackboard* (access with username and password). Do NOT register on the i-clicker website.

4. If you are having i-clicker problems, they won't go away on their own. It could just be a battery issue, or the frequency setting is the wrong one. It should be AA. ITAP may be able to fix other problems.

**i-clicker Lecture Bonus Points = About 40**

- **Attendance bonus points:** to earn attendance points, you must answer ALL i-clicker questions during the lecture (right or wrong). The points obtainable for just answering them are 0.9

- **Performance bonus points:** each correct answer is worth an *extra* 0.2 points. There are between 3 and 5 questions per lecture (total possible points for the course = 30–40)

- So if you arrive late or leave early and miss one question you will not earn attendance points. BUT, you can still pick up 0.2 performance points for each question answered correctly.

Lectures are *NOT* interchangeable except for special circumstances. Please check with me first. You can do this by e-mail if you like.

If you wish to change lecture time for the whole semester, you must do this through the registrar, but please let me know.

***THERE IS NO EXCUSED ABSENCE ALLOWANCE***

### I. Grading for BIOL 201 (Lecture Only, 2 Credits)

Your final grade will be based on three lecture exams, worth 350 points each, plus online quizzes associated with each lecture, adding up to a total of 250 points. Maximum points obtainable is therefore 1300. The third exam will be held during finals week, and will be non-comprehensive. Grades will be determined as follows:

**A:** 1105–1300 points

**B:** 975–1104 points

**C:** 845–974 points

**D:** 715–844 points

**F:** below 715 points

### J. Makeups

1. **Lecture Exams.**

    *Missing of lecture examinations is STRONGLY DISCOURAGED*. You must be **physically unable to attend.** Reasons for missing an exam do NOT include weddings, birthdays, anniversaries, funerals of *distant* relatives or *unrelated* individuals, oversleeping, wakeup alarm failure, not feeling ready or not having prepared adequately for the examination (whatever the reason), not knowing when or where the lecture exam is to be held, or just plain forgetting.

    It is wholly *your* responsibility to find out when and where lecture examinations will be held, and to attend them.

    If you miss one of the lecture examinations for an *acceptable* reason, you must *personally* request from Dr. David Bridges permission to take a makeup. This request must be made in person, NOT via my secretary, by note, nor by e-mail. **A condition of obtaining permission to take the makeup is that** *within two working days* **of missing the examination you must provide verifiable, documentary justification (e.g. a doctor's certificate, announcement of the funeral of a** *close* **relative, etc.).** *If* Dr. Bridges determines that your excuse is acceptable (and that is not guaranteed), you are eligible to take the makeup and your name will be placed on his makeup list. You will only be permitted to take the makeup if your name is on the makeup list. Note that the makeup is NOT the same as the exam that was missed.

    It is wholly *your* responsibility to find out when and where the makeup examination will be held.

    If you miss the final examination for a verifiable, documented, and acceptable reason (see above), the makeup will be an *essay* examination. Time and place will be determined by Dr. Bridges.

2. **Labs, Lab Exams, Lab Quizzes, Lab Worksheets, Laboratory Lecture Quizzes, Other.**
    See BIOL 203 Laboratory Policies for information.

## K. Finals

The date, time and place for our final examination will not be set by Purdue until later in the semester. That is out of my control. Be aware that it could be late on Saturday! Therefore, do NOT make travel plans that could conflict with your final examination schedule.

No student will be permitted to take any examination before (or after) the scheduled time for any reason—there are absolutely no exceptions to this rule.

An essay makeup will be given if you miss the *final* examination for a verifiable, documented, and approved reason. See above.

## Academic Dishonesty

*"The commitment of the acts of cheating, lying and deceit in any of their diverse forms (such as the use of substitutes for taking examinations, the use of illegal cribs, plagiarism and copying during examinations) is dishonest and must not be tolerated. Moreover, knowingly to aid and abet, directly or indirectly, other parties in committing dishonest acts is in itself dishonest."* [University Senate Document 72-18, December 15, 1972]

Cheating includes looking at a neighbor's paper, for any excuse or any reason whatsoever (e.g. "time management"), and *irrespective of whether any advantage has been gained from this action*. It not only includes written cribs, but also the use of **all forms** of electronic quipment, such as iPods and cell phones.

xiii

I believe that the vast majority of you are honest. Unfortunately, there are often one or two students who are prepared to cheat in order to elevate their grades. Let me tell you now that it just isn't worth it. **We are *dead serious* about this, and will apply *zero-tolerance* to any act of dishonesty.** It doesn't matter whether the cheating involves a 400-point examination, a 10-point quiz or a take-home assignment. All will be treated with equal severity. If the preponderance of the evidence shows you have cheated, the penalties are very severe.

***You can be dropped a letter grade or failed completely.***

If the case is of an unusually serious nature or magnitude, requires further investigation, or calls for a stronger penalty than punitive grading, the matter will be turned over to the Office of the Dean of Students for possible additional action.

## Some Advice on How to Study for BIOL 201/203

*"The difference between ordinary and extraordinary is that little extra."* Jimmy Johnson

This is not an easy course. There is an enormous amount of unfamiliar and specialized terminology you need to remember and there is a large amount of material you need to learn. But the real interest of this course is that we will be talking about the human body — *your* body. Not only will your knowledge be useful in your careers, it may also be important in the event of illness or emergency.

Many students earn an A in this course. There is no reason why you shouldn't, either. It takes organization, time-management, good study habits, hard work, and the *ability and desire to test yourself regularly.*

YOU MUST TEST YOURSELF EFFECTIVELY. By that, I mean being able to follow up your studying by answering all the objectives FROM MEMORY AND WITHOUT referring to the notes again.

## A. Suggestions for Studying

*Each of us has different ways of studying. Here are some suggestions.*

1. Objectives are e-mailed to the whole class before every lecture. Use them as your study guide.

2. Your goal should be to do the e-mailed objectives ON PAPER from MEMORY – challenge yourself!

3. Use Boilercast frequently and use it to go over difficult material.

4. Go to Supplemental Instruction sessions. SI leaders also have office hours.

5. Study the review materials and questions that will be sent out before the help sessions.

6. Watch the Boilercast recordings of the help sessions.

7. Study the i-clicker questions from each lecture.

8. A few days before the final, do the practice exam and see if you can identify any areas you need to brush up on.

9. When studying from the textbook or Boilercast, have a scrap pad and pencil handy. Write short notes, construct diagrams to make things easier to remember, put information in connected boxes, etc.

10. Answering multiple choice questions:

    a.   cover up the 4 options and study the question. Make sure you understand what is being asked, and then think about what you know about the topic.

    b.   Now uncover each option one at a time, and think about it.

    c.   Do not make a final decision until you have uncovered all four.

    d.   Sometimes you can find the most likely answer by a process of elimination.

    e.   If you have to calculate anything, write down the formula first and then substitute the numbers you have been given.

Feel free to come in and talk about this if you like. My best days are Tuesdays and Thursdays. Just e-mail me suggesting days/times.

---

Use my lecture notes, e-mailed objectives and my lectures as your *primary* source of information. If things are not clear, don't be shy. Come and talk to me about it, and I will try to help—I really will!

---

To summarize:

- Study my lecture notes, paying particular attention to my e-mailed objectives. Always have a notepad on the table and a pencil in your hand, and make outlines and diagrams as you go along. Prepare flash cards based on the e-mailed objectives, if you like. Make sure you can *pronounce* all the technical terms.

- **The self-test**. Read my e-mailed objectives again, and see if you can accomplish in writing all the tasks suggested. If not, reread the appropriate sections of the notes.

- A few days after reading my notes, scan my lecture outline and my e-mailed objectives. If some parts of it seem unfamiliar, reread the corresponding sections in my notes or listen to the relevant section of Boilercast.

## LECTURE ETIQUETTE

TURN OFF CELL PHONES—PLEASE!

BE CONSIDERATE: PRIVATE CONVERSATIONS CAN BE VERY ANNOYING TO THE STUDENTS AROUND YOU—KEEP THEM TO A MINIMUM AND KEEP THEM QUIET

ACT LIKE YOU WANT TO BE HERE: DON'T SLEEP, DON'T READ NEWSPAPERS OR DO ASSIGNMENTS FOR ANOTHER CLASS—THAT IS INSULTING TO THE LECTURER AND TO YOUR FELLOW STUDENTS

IF YOU NEED TO DO ANY OF THOSE THINGS, PLEASE DON'T COME TO LECTURE.

ARRIVING LATE OR LEAVING EARLY IS *DISCOURTEOUS* AND *INCONSIDERATE*, NOT ONLY TO THE LECTURER (ME) BUT ALSO TO YOUR FELLOW STUDENTS. Additionally, your lecture attendance will not count under these circumstances.

## B. Preparing for the Examinations

The exams cover material in my textbook and any additional material presented in the lecture itself. Be warned—questions will be very specific. You must be *dead serious* about every examination. You can't afford to do badly on the first, then spend the rest of the semester playing catch-up.

1. Do the practice exam.
2. Study the questions in the help session material.
3. Go through my objectives, and write out the answers from memory—this is your goal.
4. Study my help session material.
5. Don't cram at the last minute—you will panic and it won't work.
6. Stick to your study schedule and don't be tempted to go party when you should be studying.
7. Try to attend the help sessions. (They will be recorded on Boilercast as well.)

## C. How Am I Doing?

On xvii is a form that will help you to determine where you stand during the semester, and what grade you may reasonably expect. We can do this calculation because I use a straight grading system and do NOT curve the results of the exams.

Your points will be posted on BLACKBOARD. To access your secure records (and all the help session material), you will need a user name and a password.

## D. Finally — If You Are Having Problems, Come and Talk to Me

If you are having problems with the course—any problems at all—come and talk to me about them. If it concerns your grade, bring with you the form on the next page, complete with the results of your lecture and laboratory exams (including laboratory quizzes, homework, etc.).

Do this early on in the course. DON'T LEAVE IT UNTIL IT'S TOO LATE TO DO ANYTHING USEFUL (like coming to my office on the day before the final exam). I guarantee I will do my best to help you in any way I can.

## E. Grade Checks

If you need me to sign a grade check form, please calculate your grade from your total points (posted securely on BLACKBOARD), divide by total points possible, calculate the percentage, then bring your form to me for my signature.

**BIOL 203—Fall 2017**

**Form for Calculating Your Grade Status During the Semester**

(Use this if you need a grade check.)

*Your Name*

_____

*Your Points Are Listed on BLACKBOARD.*

*BE AWARE THAT BONUS POINTS ARE A PRIVILEGE, NOT A RIGHT.*

|  | Points obtained (include bonus points, if any) (a) | Maximum points possible (b) |
|---|---|---|
| Lecture exam 1 | | |
| Lecture exam 2 | | |
| Lecture exam 3 | | |
| Lecture online quizzes | | |
| Recitation | | |
| Laboratory | | |
| Bonus Points (e.g., i-clicker) | | |
| **Totals** | (= a) | (= b) |

You currently have 100a/b percent = _____   (% grade = ____ )

Points remaining = 2400 − b = _____

| Grade | Total Points | Percentage of remaining points you must get to obtain indicated grade |
|---|---|---|
| A | 2040 | $100 \times \dfrac{2040 - a}{2400 - b} =$ |
| B | 1800 | $100 \times \dfrac{1800 - a}{2400 - b} =$ |
| C | 1560 | $100 \times \dfrac{1560 - a}{2400 - b} =$ |
| D | 1320 | $100 \times \dfrac{1320 - a}{2400 - b} =$ |

xviii

# Chapter 1

## INTRODUCTION
Introduction to the Human Body

### CHAPTER OUTLINE

If you are taking BIOL 204, make sure you bring these notes back to campus next January. You will need them.

## DESCRIPTION AND INTRODUCTION

This book contains course details, followed by an introduction to the living human body and its needs.

In this chapter, we discuss *homeostasis*, which is essentially the principle whereby we maintain a tight control on our internal environment. Following homeostasis, we describe some general features of the human body and its various parts and cavities.

## OBJECTIVES

After listening to Lecture 1 and reading this chapter you should be able to:

1. Define anatomy and physiology and explain how they are related.
2. List and describe ten major characteristics of higher life forms.
3. Know the name of the writer of the earliest textbook of anatomy, and the name of the discoverer of the blood circulation.
4. List and describe the four most important **needs** of humans.
5. Explain the concept of **homeostasis** and explain its importance to survival.
6. Describe six factors that are under homeostatic **control** in the body.
7. Explain, define, and give examples of *negative feedback*.
8. List and explain the five levels of **organization** of the body.
9. State what a *homeotic* (*Hox*) gene does.
10. List the major body **cavities** and state their locations.
11. List the **organs** found in each major body cavity.
12. List the **membranes** associated with the thoracic and abdominopelvic cavities.
13. List the major organ **systems** and the organs comprising each of them.
14. Describe the role that each organ system plays in the **functioning** of the body.
15. Correctly use the terms that describe relative positions, body sections, and body regions.
16. List and explain the **planes** of the body.
17. Distinguish and describe what is meant by **invasive** and **non-invasive** techniques for exploring the interior regions of the body.
18. Describe five modern **non**-invasive techniques for exploring the interior of the body.
19. Define *endoscopy*.

## I. Introduction to Human Anatomy and Physiology

### A. Some Early History (Based on Rhoades & Pflanzer, Human Physiology) — Why Are Nearly All Our Terms in Anatomy and Physiology Either Greek or Latin?

Most anatomical and physiological terms are derived from Greek and Latin, predominantly the latter. This is because many of the early writings and descriptions were in Greek, and from Roman times into the eighteenth century the universal language of science was Latin. Nowadays the universal language of science is English (which is really a mixture of languages), but the original Greek and Latin terminology has been retained. Even new terms tend to be based on Greek and Latin roots.

## B. Andreas Vesalius, the First Textbook of Anatomy and the Visible Human Project

In 1543, at the age of 29, **Andreas Vesalius** (1514–1564) published in Latin the first "modern" anatomy textbook (*De Humani Corporis Fabrica,* Structure of the Human Body), which consisted of seven volumes and contained many illustrations of the dissected human body. Vesalius (as Andreas van Wesele) was born in Brussels in 1514. At the University of Louvain, he studied Latin and Greek. He started his medical studies in Paris, but returned to the University of Louvain, where he graduated in 1537. He then moved to Padua, where he was granted an MD degree. He was then appointed by the Venetian Senate to teach anatomy and surgery.

Vesalius was the first to note that without their bones, humans would be mushy blobs. More importantly, he established the importance of observation and investigation as the basis of our knowledge of human structure and function. For close to 1500 years before Vesalius' time, human anatomy teaching had consisted of teaching dogma. According to Gerald W. Friedland and Meyer Friedman, *De Humani Corporis Fabrica* "presented medicine with the precious gift of the scientific method with which to approach an infinite number of future medical problems." [Friedland and Friedman, *Medicine's 10 Greatest Discoveries,* Yale University Press, 1998].

As was common in those days, the initial letters in the chapters were "illuminated." That is, they were set into pictures and cartoons. In *De Humani Corporis Fabrica,* these cartoons depicted rather horrible cherub-like creatures (they call them "putti") engaged in grave robbing, dissection and other unpleasant activities. I took photographs of these cartoons when I was lucky enough to be allowed to examine a copy of the book at the University of Edinburgh in Scotland, and I share an unpublished example with you in this handout.

Richardson and Carman's translation of Vesalius' *De Humani* was published in 2003.

3

4

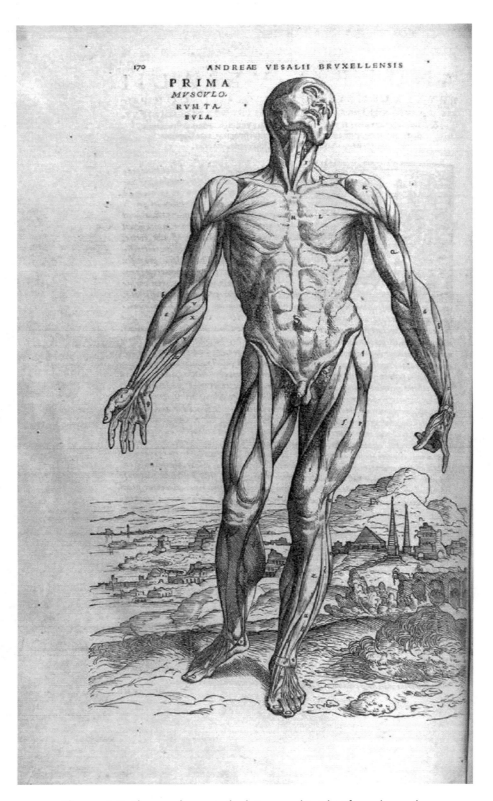

**Figure 1-1.** The muscles: note the letters used to identify each muscle. There was a key to aid in identification. This is a very "modern" device.

**Figure 1-2.**

In the year 2000, we acquired access to another important resource that provides information on human anatomy. It is the *VISIBLE HUMAN PROJECT*, first conceived by the US National Library of Medicine and carried out by the Colorado Health Science Center in Denver.

Two cadavers, one male and one female, have been imaged using CAT and MRI. Then the bodies were embedded in gelatin and sliced transversely. A total of 1871 cross sections were obtained for the male and 5189 for the female. The slices were then photographed and digitized, the data being stored on two CDs. These CDs are published by Springer-Verlag as "The Complete Visible Human."

## C. Harvey and the Discovery of the Blood Circulation

The English physician **William Harvey** (1578–1657) did for modern physiology what Vesalius had done for modern anatomy. He was born in 1578 during the reign of Queen Elizabeth I. He obtained his first degree from Cambridge University then went to the University of Padua, where Vesalius had also studied.

Harvey returned to England in 1602, where he was made a Fellow of the Royal College of Physicians (FRCP). In 1618 he was appointed as a physician to the court of James I. He was later appointed personal physician to Charles I, who was an enthusiastic sponsor of Harvey's studies on the circulation.

**Figure 1-3.** William Harvey M.D., FRCP (1578–1657) demonstrating on a dead deer to Charles I and the young heir to the throne. Charles I was beheaded at the instigation of Cromwell. The young prince became Charles II at the Restoration of the Monarchy after Cromwell's death.

6

An important aspect of Harvey's work was that he used the *experimental method* to deduce the circulation of blood. He introduced the notion that the heart was a pump that maintained a circular movement of blood. This was in direct contradiction to the traditional dogma of Galen, which held that the blood pulsed back and forth in the arteries. This idea had persisted for fifteen centuries. It is frightening to think of how long a misconception can survive, isn't it? It was Harvey's *experiments* that finally destroyed the speculation and dogma and established the truth. Harvey's work (published in Latin in 1628 under the title of *De Motu Cordis et Sanguinis in Animalibus,* On the Motion of the Heart and of Blood in Animals) was critical to the advancement of our thinking on how the human body functions. Friedland and Friedman wrote "What the authorized version of the Bible has been to the Church of England and the Shakespeare Folio to English literature, *'De Motu Cordis'* has been to medicine everywhere."

The only thing Harvey could not work out was how the blood passed from the arteries to the veins. The puzzle was solved a few years after Harvey's death when Malpighi discovered capillaries by observing them under the microscope, an instrument that had just been invented and therefore was not available to Harvey.

The following text is translated from *De Motu Cordis*, and is from the Internet Modern History Sourcebook, Paul Halsall, August 1998. It is reproduced here for educational purposes only.

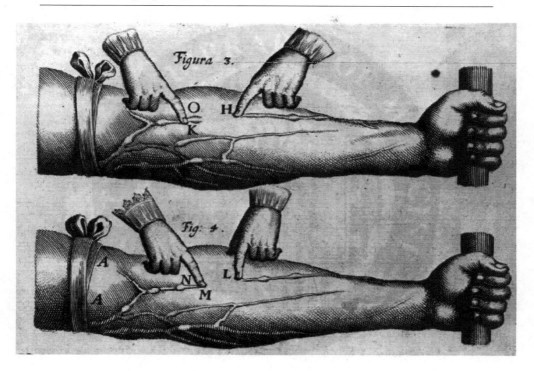

**Figure 1-4.**

*It would therefore appear that the function of the valves in the veins is the same as that of the three sigmoid valves which we find at the commencement of the aorta and pulmonary artery, viz., to prevent all reflux of the blood that is passing over them.*

### D. What Is Life?

All life forms can **replicate**, or produce copies of themselves. As we shall see, it is possible that during evolution, an early form of life consisted of molecules of RNA that could reproduce themselves.

"Higher" life forms, such as fish, reptiles, birds and mammals, have the ability to:

- move
- respond or react to a stimulus
- grow
- reproduce
- respire
- digest food
- absorb products of digestion
- circulate blood
- assimilate food products
- excrete unwanted or harmful materials

Living creatures also carry out two important biochemical processes—they **degrade** molecules to obtain energy, and they **synthesize** new molecules for the body's structural and functional components. The sum of all these chemical processes occurring in the body is called **metabolism**. We shall talk about the early origins of life on Earth in Chapter 2.

8

### II. Human Life – How Is It Sustained? The Concept of Homeostasis – That Is, the Control of the Body's Internal Environment

Human needs include food, water, oxygen and warmth (external and self-generated). These are the most important, but maybe you can think of a few others.

About 56% of the adult human body is fluid. About two thirds is inside cells, and is called **intracellular** fluid. The remaining one third is outside the cells, and is called **extracellular** fluid. All the cells of the body live immersed in this extracellular fluid, which is called the internal environment (or, in French, *milieu interior*, a term introduced a hundred years ago by the great 19th century French physiologist Claude Bernard).

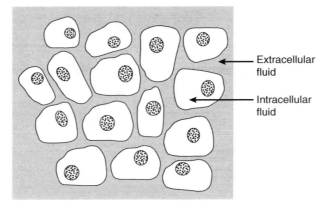

Extracellular fluid

Intracellular fluid

**Figure 1-5.**

Most of the body's activities are aimed at regulating the composition and properties of this extracellular fluid within narrow limits. If we lacked this ability to regulate (or control) the internal environment, the body's cells would fail to function properly, and would eventually die. This process of regulation is called **homeostasis**.

Six factors under homeostatic control in humans are:

- body temperature
- oxygen level in blood and tissues
- acidity or alkalinity (pH) of blood and body fluids
- salt content
- glucose level in the blood
- metabolic waste product levels

Other factors that have a vital bearing on this control of the internal environment are also regulated in a homeostatic manner. For example, it is important to maintain blood flow through the tissues, so that they are provided with oxygen and nutrients and so that carbon dioxide and waste products of metabolism are removed. In order to do this, blood pressure must be regulated.

We will encounter many other examples as this course proceeds.

In all these cases, homeostasis is maintained by a process that:

- Detects a deviation from normal, acceptable limits.
- If a deviation occurs, the system sets in train a series of events that returns conditions to normal.

    Since changes away from normal provoke changes in the opposite direction (back to normal), the homeostatic process is said to utilize *negative feedback*.

Negative feedback is operating when you set your room thermostat to a desirable room temperature. If both air conditioner and heater are hooked up and functioning at the same time, you have:

**THIS IS A _NEGATIVE FEEDBACK_ LOOP**

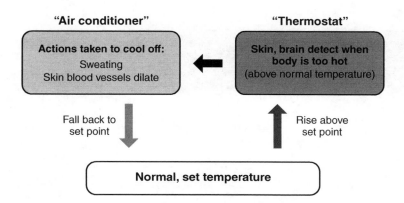

Negative feedback also operates when you control the temperature of your body. If your temperature rises, sensory receptors in the skin and brain cause sweating and increased blood flow to the skin. This increases heat loss via the skin, so bringing the temperature back to normal.

## III. The Human Body – From Atoms to Organ Systems (Levels of Organization)

The human body is composed of **atoms** of oxygen, hydrogen, carbon, nitrogen, etc. These atoms are organized progressively into:

- **Molecules** (e.g. water, two atoms of hydrogen linked to one atom of oxygen) and macromolecules ( = "large molecules," e.g. DNA)

- **Cells** (e.g. white blood cells, muscle cells, nerve cells), which contain cell organelles (e.g. mitochondria)

- **Tissues**, made up of cells (e.g. muscle tissue, nerve tissue)

- **Organs**, groups of tissues (e.g. liver, heart, kidney)

- **Systems**, groups of organs designed to do a specific job (e.g. the digestive system, reproductive system, nervous system)

Taken together, atoms, molecules and macromolecules represent the most basic level of organization of the human body—the chemical level.

10

## IV. The Plan of the Body Is Determined by Homeotic (Hox) Genes

We now know that the pattern of every animal body, whether we are dealing with fruit flies, lobsters, mice, or human beings, is determined by a special family of genes called **homeotic** genes (**Homeobox** or **Hox** genes). These Hox genes have played a central role in *evolution*, and also play a vital role in normal development and in determining what the adult animal will finally look like. Hox genes are found in most organisms. Four groups of similar Hox genes control related regions both in the human body and in the fruit fly.

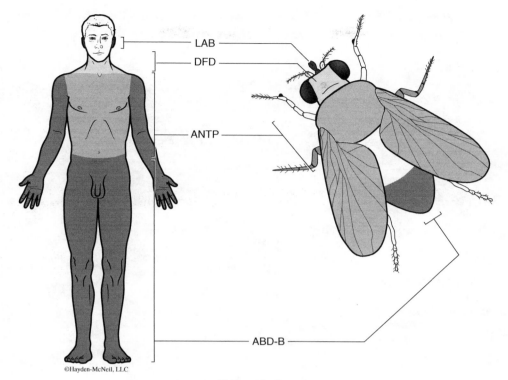

©Hayden-McNeil, LLC

**Figure 1-6.**

11

Hox genes play an important role in the development of the skeleton. If certain Hox genes are knocked out in mice, the animals made ribs all the way from the thoracic region through the tail. This arrangement is present in most fish and also in the dinosaurs. Mammals must have adapted the Hox genes to get rid of some of the ribs and increase their flexibility. Hox gene mutations are responsible for some deformations of the human skeleton, as will be discussed in the Lecture. Hox genes also regulate many aspects of how the neurons in the central nervous system are wired up.

The major features of the human body are discussed in the next section.

### V. The Human Body – Major Features – Cavities, Organ Systems, and Membranes That Line the Cavities and Cover the Organs

#### A. Cavities

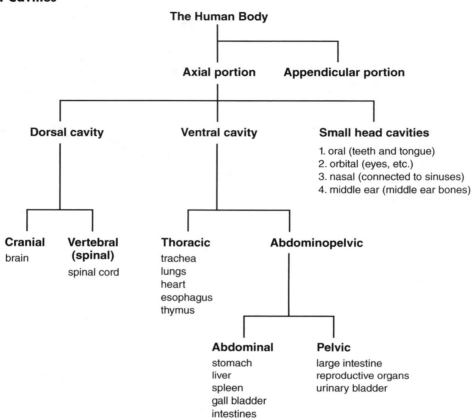

12

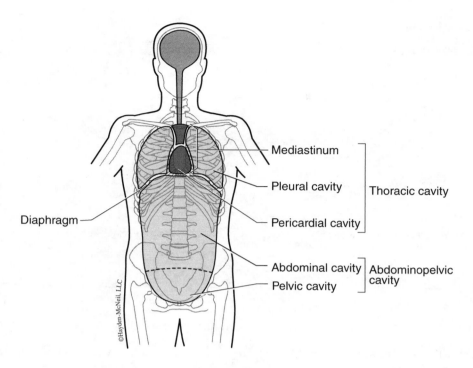

**Figure 1-7.** Body cavities – anterior view.

13

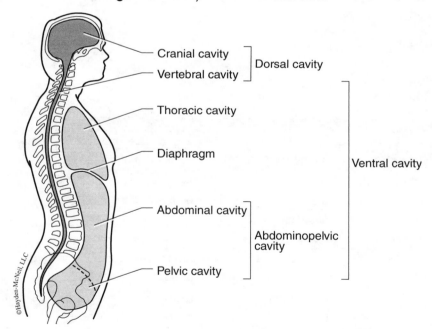

**Figure 1-8.** Body cavities – lateral view.

## B. Membranes

Line cavities and cover organs.

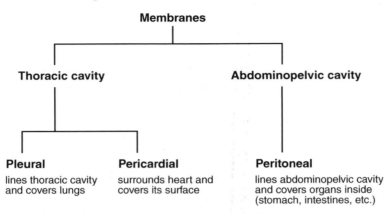

Inflammation of the pleural, pericardial, and peritoneal membranes is called *pleuritis*, *pericarditis*, and *peritonitis*.

The part of a membrane that lines the walls of the cavity is called the parietal part.

The part of a membrane that covers the surface of an organ is called the visceral part.

Spaces between the parietal and visceral portions of these membranes are called:

- pleural
- pericardial
- peritoneal

## C. Organ Systems

|  |  | **Examples of Components or Organs** |
|---|---|---|
| Body covering | **integumentary** system |  |
| Support, protection, and movement | **skeletal** system | skull, humerus, calcaneum |
|  | **muscular** system | biceps brachii, gastrocnemius |
| Integration and coordination | **nervous** system | brain, spinal cord |
|  | **endocrine** system | thyroid, pancreas, adrenals, pituitary |
| Processing and transporting | **digestive** system | esophagus, stomach, small intestine, liver |
|  | **respiratory** system | lungs |
|  | **circulatory** system | heart, arteries, veins |
|  | **lymphatic** system | lymph nodes, spleen |
|  | **urinary** system | kidney, bladder, ureters |
| Reproduction | **reproductive** system | testes, ovaries, uterus, penis, vagina |

## VI. Some New Language

### A. Relative Positions of Body Parts

You must learn the following descriptions of the relative positions of body parts.

**Superior/inferior**

*superior* = toward the head: "the thorax is superior to the abdomen"

*inferior* = away from the head: "the legs are inferior to the trunk"

**Anterior/posterior**

*anterior* (*ventral*) = toward the front: "the nipples are on the anterior side of the body"

*posterior* (*dorsal*) = toward the back: "the kidneys are posterior to the intestines"

**Medial/lateral**

*medial* = toward the midline: "the heart is medial to the lungs"

*lateral* = toward the side: "the ears are lateral to the head"

*ipsilateral* = same side

*contralateral* = opposite side

**Proximal/distal**

*proximal* = toward the main mass of the body: "the knee is proximal to the foot"

*distal* = away from the main mass of the body: "the hand is distal to the elbow"

**Superficial/deep**

*superficial* = toward the surface of the body: "the skin is superficial to the muscles"

*deep* = away from the surface of the body: "a deep wound"

**Central/peripheral**

*central* = at the center: "the brain and spinal cord are part of the central nervous system"

*peripheral* = around the outside: "the popliteal nerve is part of the peripheral nervous system"

### B. Planes of the Body and Sections Cut through Organs

You will often see references to *sagittal*, *transverse* and *coronal* body sections. These are just words that are used to define cuts along various parts of the body, and the directions the cuts are made.

*   **Sagittal** – divides the body into left and right portions. A mid-sagittal cut divides the body into equal right and left halves. The word derives from the Latin for arrow (the Zodiac sign for Sagittarius is a half-human with a bow and arrow). The left and right parietal bones of the skull are joined at the sagittal suture.

*   **Transverse** (across, horizontal) – any cut that divides the body into superior ("upper") and inferior ("lower") segments.

*   **Coronal** (= **frontal**) – a cut that divides the body into anterior ("front") and posterior ("back") portions.

Note that long tubular organs (such as the aorta) can be cut transversely, longitudinally, or obliquely, giving circular, rectangular or oval cross-sections.

15

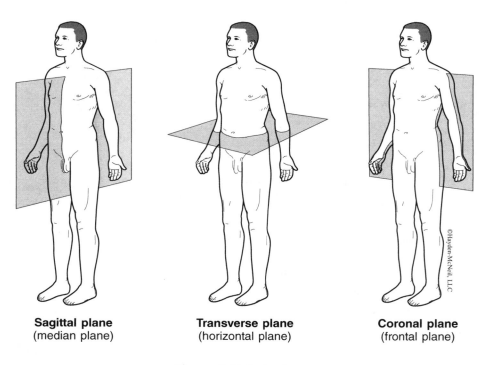

**Sagittal plane**
(median plane)

**Transverse plane**
(horizontal plane)

**Coronal plane**
(frontal plane)

**Figure 1-9.** Body planes.

## C. Regions of the Body

There are numerous terms used to define various *regions* of the body. A few examples are:

| | |
|---|---|
| **abdominal** | you can figure that one out (abdominal pain) |
| **acromial** | point of the shoulder (from Greek "akron," meaning peak) |
| **brachial** | upper arm |
| **antebrachial** | forearm |
| **cubital** | elbow (the ancient measure of length called the cubit was based on the distance from the elbow to the tip of the middle finger = usually about 18 inches but sometimes 21 inches or more)[1] |
| **antecubital** | space in front of elbow (antecubital fossa, an indentation in this region where blood is sometimes withdrawn) |
| **axillary** | armpit (axillary glands, axillary hairs) |
| **buccal** | cheek (the buccal cavity is the mouth cavity enclosed by the cheeks) |
| **carpal** | wrist (think of carpal tunnel syndrome) |
| **cephalic** | pertaining to the head |
| **cervical** | neck (cervical dislocation) |

16

---

[1] *"And there went out a champion out of the camp of the Philistines, named* Goliath *of Gath, whose height was six cubits and a span."* (1 Samuel 17).

| | |
|---|---|
| **costal** | ribs (intercostal space) |
| **digital** | finger (= digit) |
| **frontal** | forehead (frontal bone of the skull) |
| **genital** | you can figure that one out (genital herpes) |
| **lumbar** | you can figure that one out (lumbar pain) |
| **mammary** | breast (mammary glands; mammals, animals that suckle their young at the breast) |
| **nasal** | you can figure that one out (nasal spray) |
| **oral** | you can figure that one out (oral hygiene) |
| **pelvic** | you can figure that one out (pelvic examination) |
| **pectoral** | chest (pectoral muscles, "pecs") |
| **pedal** | foot (bicycle pedals; where you place your feet when riding a bicycle; quadruped, four-footed animal; biped, two-footed animal) |
| **plantar** | sole of foot |
| **umbilical** | navel (umbilical cord) |
| **vertebral** | the vertebra or spinal column (intervertebral discs) |

17

The **abdominal** area is subdivided into nine regions, three down the left side, three down the center, and three down the right side.

Right side (superior to inferior regions)
*Right hypochondriac*
*Right lumbar*
*Right iliac*

Center (superior to inferior regions)
*Epigastric*
*Umbilical*
*Hypogastric*

| RH | EPI | LH |
|----|-----|----|
| RL | UMB | LL |
| RI | HYP | LI |

Left side (superior to inferior regions)
*Left hypochondriac*
*Left lumbar*
*Left iliac*

Some people just divide the abdominal area into quarters, or quadrants. These are designated as right upper, right lower, left upper and left lower quadrants.

## VII. Clinical Techniques for Exploring the Body

A physician who needs to look inside the body has a number of options open to him or her. One way is to simply cut open the region of interest. Obviously, this has drawbacks. Another way is to use **endoscopes** that are inserted into body openings or into small surgical incisions. They have a glass fiber illumination system and an objective that gathers the light from the illuminated area and transmits it to a camera or small video monitor. *Endoscopy* allows surgery, often with microinstruments and lasers, that is far less invasive than traditional open surgery that involves making large incisions. Infrared illumination enables the observer to map temperature differences between different areas of tissue.

The above techniques are called **invasive**, because the body is invaded or penetrated in some way. Another group of techniques are called **non-invasive**. They include:

1. **X-rays** (can be used for determining the nature and extent of bone fractures, for detecting tumors, etc.).

2. **Computed axial tomography**, **CT** or **CAT** (also uses X-rays: detects blood clots, tumors, etc.).

3. **Positron-emission tomography** or **PET** (detects certain isotopes and can be used to determine metabolic activity in regions of an organ such as the brain: can show regions of decreased metabolic activity in parts of the brain of people suffering from mental disorders such as schizophrenia, depression and Alzheimer's disease). A closely-related technique is single-photon emission tomography (SPECT).

4. **Magnetic resonance imaging** or **MRI** (able to differentiate between normal and damaged myelin nerve sheaths, can detect atherosclerosis and certain brain tumors that are invisible on CAT scans, can assess damage to heart muscle after a heart attack and also the state of heart valves).

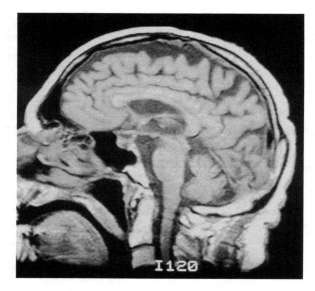

**Figure 1-10.** MRI scan of the brain.

18

**Functional magnetic resonance imaging** or **fMRI** uses the same technology as MRI, but also measures oxygen levels in the brain. Therefore, it is possible to detect areas of greatest activity which have high oxygen levels.

5.  **Ultrasonography** (uses ultrasound to visualize the heart in *echocardiography*, and is also used to visualize other organs such as the prostate as well as the fetus in the uterus). Doppler ultrasound measures the velocity of blood flow through the heart and blood vessels.

There are a number of variants of these techniques that some of you will learn about later in your training.

# CHAPTER 2

# THE ORIGIN OF LIFE, BASIC CHEMISTRY, AND BIOCHEMISTRY

## CHAPTER OUTLINE

## DESCRIPTION AND INTRODUCTION

We must understand the biochemistry of the normal human body if we are to understand and treat disease processes.

The goal of this chapter is to provide you with the knowledge that is essential for you to understand the molecular basis and activity of living matter, and how its various component molecules interact to confer the property of life. At the beginning of this chapter, we will discuss current ideas about how life may have originated on earth.

## OBJECTIVES

After listening to the lecture and reading the textbook, you should be able to:

1. Summarize current scientific thinking on how life may have originated on earth.
2. Describe what *matter* is composed of.
3. Describe what *atoms* are composed of, and draw a diagram showing the structures of the *hydrogen* atom and the *carbon* atom.
4. Explain what is meant by *ions, atomic number* and *atomic weight*.
5. Explain what is meant by an *isotope*.
6. Describe the three major types of atomic *bond*.
7. Distinguish between a *molecule* and an atom.
8. Describe the use of simple and structural formulas to represent chemical compounds.
9. Describe at least four types of chemical reaction.
10. Define *acids, bases, salts* and *electrolytes*.
11. Define *pH*.
12. List the major *inorganic* substances found in cells (Section III, Subsection A).
13. Describe four major groups of *organic* substances and their general role in the cell (Section III, Subsection B).
14. Describe what is meant by a *carbohydrate*: name three classes of carbohydrates and give an example of each.
15. Define a *lipid*, name three classes of lipids and give an example of each.
16. Define a *protein* and list at least three examples of proteins.
17. Describe what is meant by *denaturation* and what causes it.
18. List the three components of a *nucleotide*.
19. Know the chemical formulas of the substances listed in Section II, Subsection F.
20. Know the chemical formulas or chemical makeup for *glucose, sucrose, triglycerides, phospholipids, cholesterol* and the general structure of an *amino acid*.
21. Describe the basis of some *genetic diseases*.

## I. Origin of Life on Earth and the "RNA World" Hypothesis

### A. The Organic Soup

Life on this planet is believed to have originated in "a primordial ocean which contained all the ingredients necessary to form long, information-carrying polymers able to self-replicate, mutate and evolve." (*Nature 381*, 20, 1996). But how did the "organic soup" that made up the primordial ocean come about and where did its ingredients come from? Scientists have several basic hypotheses.

1.  The Russian scientist Oparin suggested that some 4 billion years ago, lightning or ultraviolet radiation initiated the synthesis of the first organic molecules in the Earth's primitive atmosphere. These molecules collected in the oceans.

2.  Instead of lightning or UV radiation, thermal vents in the oceans may have been the sites for organic molecule synthesis.

3.  As much as 30 percent of the mass of meteorites and comets can be made up of organic molecules. Therefore, many scientists have suggested that organic molecules were first formed in outer space and brought to Earth by meteorites.

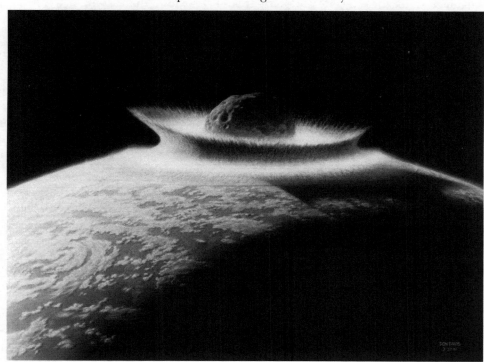

23

### B. The First Self-Replicating Molecules and the "RNA World" Hypothesis

The *"RNA world" hypothesis* proposes that early life developed by using **RNA** molecules, rather than proteins, to catalyze the synthesis of important biological molecules [Unrau and Bartel, 1998; see reference below].

It has been suggested that the "long, information-carrying polymers" were RNA-like replicating molecules, possibly the precursors of ribosomes, that finally produced **DNA** and **proteins**. At first, therefore, the world would have been an "RNA world." But what was the mechanism whereby the molecules in the organic soup of the primordial oceans became molecules of RNA? The surfaces of mineral substances such as clay could have promoted the development of very complex molecules from more simple ones. It has been demonstrated experimentally that such mineral surfaces can promote and catalyze the formation of chains of nucleotides and even amino acids such as glutamate and aspartic acid [Ferris et al., (1996) *Nature 381*, 59]. In recent research, it has been shown that synthetic RNA is capable of carrying out many of the reactions necessary for protein synthesis.

Even though the RNA world hypothesis is becoming stronger as new research findings are made, it is not the only one out there. It has been shown that a substance called carbonyl sulfide, present in volcanic gas, is capable of producing peptides by linking amino acids via peptide bonds. So it has been suggested that volcanic activity may have been responsible for forming the first proteins. We don't know how the amino acids got here in the first place. They may have arisen on Earth under prebiotic conditions, but they also occur on meteorites, so they could have been brought to Earth. Other hypotheses are predicated on the fact that in an oxygen-free world, the early oceans were rich in iron. Together with other metals and phosphate, metabolic reactions could have started to occur, pre-dating life itself.

### C. The Earliest Organisms

The Archaean eon lasted from about 4000 million to 2500 million years ago. There is now widespread evidence that during that time the earliest forms of bacteria evolved. On that scale, the evolutionary divergence of *humans* and *chimpanzees* from a common *primate* ancestor was very recent—estimates range from only 6 million to 9 million years ago.

### D. Life Elsewhere in the Universe?

There is no compelling scientific evidence for life elsewhere in the Universe. Recent findings from Mars Explorers suggest that water existed on the planet at some point in its history, but the probes on the surface and orbiting the planet have not uncovered any evidence of life. Nevertheless, there are other planets in the Universe, and some of them probably have conditions that have allowed for the evolution of life forms. The future development of probes to explore other planets may provide some answers.

## II. Structure and Properties of Matter

### A. Matter, Elements, and Atoms

1.  **Matter.**

    Matter occupies space and has weight, and includes all solids, gases and liquids in our environment and our bodies.

2.  **Elements.**

Simple substances called elements make up matter. There are 91 elements on earth, although a total of 106 are known. Examples of elements are *gold, silver, carbon, iron, zinc, uranium, oxygen, hydrogen, nitrogen, silicon, magnesium, phosphorus, platinum,* etc.

The four predominant elements in the human body are **carbon**, **hydrogen**, **oxygen** and **nitrogen**. Between them, they account for 95% of our body weight. Other elements found in the body include *calcium, phosphorus, potassium, sulfur, magnesium, iron* and *chlorine*.

| Elements in the human body (% by mass) | |
|---|---|
| Oxygen | 65 |
| Carbon | 18 |
| Hydrogen | 10 |
| Nitrogen | 3 |
| Calcium | 1.5 |
| Phosphorus | 1 |
| Potassium | 0.35 |
| Sulfur | 0.25 |

3.  **Atoms.**

Elements are composed of atoms. All the atoms found in one element are essentially the same, but the atoms of different elements are different. Gold atoms are not the same as carbon atoms, and carbon atoms are not the same as oxygen atoms, etc.

The old alchemists were always trying to find ways of changing (transmuting) the so-called base elements (e.g. iron, lead) into gold, but they searched for the Philosopher's Stone without success!

## B. Atoms Are Composed of Protons, Neutrons, and Electrons

An atom consists of a massive central nucleus composed of protons and neutrons. The nucleus, because it contains protons, is always positively charged. It is surrounded by an essentially weightless cloud of electrons that occur in various orbits or shells.

* **Electrons** are very light and are negatively charged.
* **Protons** are relatively heavy (massive) and are positively charged.
* **Neutrons** have the same mass as protons, but are uncharged (i.e. electrically neutral).

---

This is very simplified. Things are really far more complicated than that. For example, protons and neutrons are not really fundamental particles. They are composed of objects called *quarks* (three quarks for protons and three for neutrons) held together by "strong" force-carrying particles called *glutons*.

---

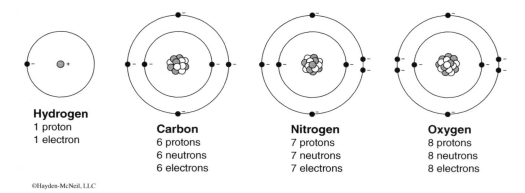

©Hayden-McNeil, LLC

**Figure 2-1.** Atomic structures of the four elements that make up
95% of the weight of our bodies.

### Ions.

In a complete atom the number of electrons equals the number of protons in the nucleus. Therefore, the complete atom is electrically neutral because the positive charges of the protons in the nucleus are neutralized by the same number of negatively charged electrons surrounding it.

If, for reasons to be discussed later, an atom loses one or more electrons, it becomes positively charged. Similarly, if the atom gains one or more electrons it acquires a net negative charge. In either case, it is called an ion. For example, if a sodium atom loses one electron it becomes a positively charged sodium ion. Likewise, if a chlorine atom gains one electron it becomes a negatively charged chloride ion. Positively charged ions are called cations, and negatively charged ions are called anions.

### Atomic number.

The atoms of different elements have different numbers of protons in their nuclei, and therefore different numbers of electrons to neutralize their charge. The number of protons in the atoms of a particular element is called its atomic number.

The atomic number is a characteristic of the element. Hydrogen has an atomic number of 1, carbon has an atomic number of 6, nitrogen has an atomic number of 7, and oxygen has an atomic number of 8.

### Atomic weight.

While the atomic number of an atom is determined by the number of protons in the nucleus, the atomic weight is determined by the number of protons and neutrons (the electrons are so light that they may be ignored).

Hydrogen, which has one proton and no neutrons, has an atomic weight of 1. Carbon, which has 6 protons and 6 neutrons, has an atomic weight of 12. Nitrogen, which has 7 protons and 7 neutrons, has an atomic weight of 14. Oxygen, which has 8 protons and 8 neutrons, has an atomic weight of 16.

What are the atomic number and atomic weight of sodium, which has 11 protons and 12 neutrons?

### C. What Is Meant by "Isotopes"?

The *isotopes* of an element are different varieties of that element. Different isotopes of a given element all have the **same number of protons in their nuclei**, and therefore the same atomic number. However, they have **different numbers of neutrons**, and therefore have different atomic weights. For example, the most abundant isotope of oxygen is oxygen-16, which has 8 protons and 8 neutrons. Another isotope is oxygen-18, which still has 8 protons but has two extra neutrons, making a total of 10 neutrons. Note that the atomic number for both isotopes is 8 (i.e. 8 protons, characteristic of oxygen), but one has an atomic weight of 16 (8 protons + 8 neutrons) and the other has an atomic weight of 18 (8 protons + 10 neutrons).

Therefore, the isotopes of an element all have the same atomic number (determined by the number of protons), but they have a variety of atomic weights (which are determined by the number of protons and neutrons: the electrons are always neglected, because their mass is negligible).

Many people think that all isotopes are radioactive. Not so. Some isotopes are stable, others are unstable (radioactive). Only the unstable ones undergo radioactive decay. In so doing, they emit a variety of radiations. Examples of such radiation are *gamma rays*, *alpha particles* (or rays) and *beta particles* (or rays).

### D. Molecules—Combinations of Atoms

When atoms *bond* together, either covalently or ionically as will be described below, they form *molecules*.

Two atoms of hydrogen (H) bond together to form a molecule of hydrogen ($H_2$). In many cases, particularly gases, the molecule is the predominant form of the element in nature. Examples are oxygen ($O_2$) and nitrogen ($N_2$).

Hydrogen and nitrogen molecules are made up of atoms of the same element. Sometimes, molecules contain different elements. In fact, this is very common. These substances are then called *compounds*. *Sodium chloride* (NaCl) is a compound, so is *methane* ($CH_4$). *Water* is a compound, formed by the bonding of two atoms of hydrogen to one of oxygen to form a molecule of $H_2O$. The molecule of hydrogen ($H_2$) is NOT a compound.

### E. How Atoms Bond with Each Other and How Ions Are Formed

Almost every atom can combine or *bond* with other atoms. There are three principal types of bond. Two types (covalent and ionic) are quite strong. The third type (hydrogen) is very weak, but is nevertheless quite important in maintaining the shapes of proteins and other large molecules such as DNA.

1.  **Covalent bonds** are formed when atoms **share electrons** with other atoms. An example of a covalent bond is found in water ($H_2O$). In this case, the oxygen atom shares two electrons with two hydrogen atoms. Another example is methane gas ($CH_4$), where the carbon atom shares four electrons with four hydrogen ions. If the two electrons are not shared equally, the result is a "polar covalent bond."

27

2. **Ionic bonds** (or *electrovalent bonds*) are formed when atoms either **donate electrons** to the other atoms, or **receive electrons** from the other atoms. An example of an ionic bond is found in the salt sodium chloride (NaCl), where the sodium atom has parted with its electron ($e^-$) and donated it to an atom of chlorine.

$$Na \xrightarrow{\text{e-}} Cl \longrightarrow Na^+ Cl^-$$
(usually written as NaCl)

Naturally, when sodium donates its electron to chlorine, the sodium atom must become positively charged and the chlorine atom negatively charged. They are now called sodium ions ($Na^+$) and chloride ions ($Cl^-$). Since they have opposite charges they are attracted to each other. An ionic bond is formed between them, and a *MOLECULE* (see below) of sodium chloride (NaCl) is formed. Many sodium chloride molecules form transparent, cube-shaped crystals of *table* salt. When crystals of sodium chloride are dissolved in water, the sodium and chloride ions *dissociate* and move around in solution, among the molecules of water.

$$NaCl \xrightarrow{\text{dissolved in water}} Na^+ + Cl^-$$
*dissociation*

Sodium ions and chloride ions are *very* different from free sodium (Na) and free chlorine ($Cl_2$). Free sodium is a soft, highly reactive and very dangerous metal to handle. Free chlorine (which exists as a molecule consisting of two chlorine atoms) is a greenish-yellow, choking, toxic gas that was used by Germany as a war gas in WWI. On the other hand, the *salt* sodium chloride is essential for life and is not toxic.

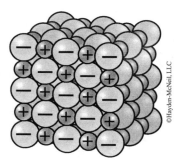
©Hayden-McNeil, LLC

**Figure 2-2.** Crystal of sodium chloride, illustrating ionic bonding.

3. **Hydrogen bonds** occur between hydrogen and certain other atoms, particularly oxygen and nitrogen. They are important in maintaining the shapes of proteins. Individually, these bonds are very weak (much, much weaker than proper covalent bonds), but if there are a lot of them their combined effect can be quite important. When hydrogen bonds are broken by heat, acid, or alkali, the protein loses the characteristic shape on which its function depends, and is said to be ***denatured***.

4. **Van der Waals forces** are very weak, short-range attractions between all atoms and molecules. They are responsible for the surface tension of water, for example.

## F. Molecules and Chemical Compounds—How Their Compositions and Arrangements Are Expressed in Terms of "Formulas"

1.  **Simple formulas.**

    The notations NaCl, $CH_4$, $H_2O$, $N_2$, $H_2$, $O_2$, etc. are all simple "formulas."

    The simple formula for *glucose* is $C_6H_{12}O_6$, meaning that one molecule of glucose contains six *carbon* atoms ($C_6$), twelve *hydrogen* atoms ($H_{12}$), and six *oxygen* atoms ($O_6$).

    The following is a short list of the simple formulas for some common substances that are important in the body.

    | | |
    |---|---|
    | $H_2O$ | water |
    | NaCl | sodium chloride |
    | KCl | potassium chloride |
    | $MgCl_2$ | magnesium chloride |
    | $CaCl_2$ | calcium chloride |
    | $MgSO_4$ | magnesium sulfate |
    | $H_3PO_4$ | phosphoric acid |
    | $NaH_2PO_4$ | monosodium phosphate |
    | $Na_2HPO_4$ | disodium phosphate |
    | $Na_3PO_4$ | trisodium phosphate |
    | $NH_3$ | ammonia |
    | $NH_4Cl$ | ammonium chloride |
    | $CO_2$ | carbon dioxide |
    | $O_2$ | oxygen |
    | $H_2CO_3$ | carbonic acid |
    | $H_2SO_4$ | sulphuric acid |
    | HCl | hydrochloric acid |
    | $NaHCO_3$ | sodium bicarbonate |
    | $CaCO_3$ | calcium carbonate |
    | $C_6H_{12}O_6$ | *glucose* |
    | $C_{12}H_{22}O_{11}$ | *sucrose* (ordinary sugar) |
    | $CO(NH_2)_2$ | *urea* |

2.  **Structural formulas.**

    For complex molecules, it is often convenient to use "structural formulas" which, in addition to giving the simple information on the numbers of different atoms present, also tell us something about how these atoms are arranged. Examples on the following page are for various amino acids, the building blocks of proteins.

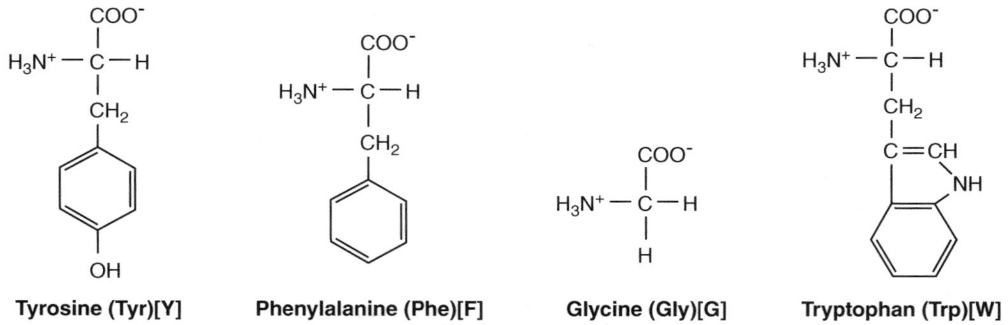

**Figure 2-3.**

### G. Chemical Reactions—The Making and Breaking of Bonds between Atoms, Ions, or Molecules

All of the chemical reactions going on in the body are called the body's *metabolism.* These chemical reactions can be classified as follows.

- **Synthesis reactions** – an example of a synthesis reaction is when amino acids are joined together with covalent bonds to form a protein.

- **Dissociation** or **decomposition reactions** – an example of a dissociation or decomposition reaction is when a molecule of glycogen is broken down into its individual glucose molecules. A decomposition reaction that involves water, and many of them do, is referred to as a *hydrolysis*.

- **Exchange reactions** – (AB + CD → AD + CB)

- **Reversible reactions** – it is to our advantage that most of the reactions in the body can be reversed. For example, *carbon dioxide* combines with water in the blood flowing through active muscles to form *carbonic acid* ($H_2CO_3$). In the lungs, this reaction is reversed, and carbonic acid breaks down into water and carbon dioxide, which is breathed out. More later.

**Rate** (= speed) of a reaction usually depends on **temperature**, **concentration** of reactants, *pH* and other factors. Reactions usually speed up as the temperature rises (they stop, of course, if the temperature rises so high that the substances in the reaction are destroyed).

**Enzymes** – the rate of a reaction may be accelerated by the presence of small amounts of certain substances called *catalysts*. A catalyst is defined as a substance that can alter the rate of a reaction without itself being consumed by the reaction. The catalytic converter in your exhaust system contains a catalyst that helps to ensure the complete combustion of your exhaust gases. *Enzymes are examples of catalysts. Enzymes are proteins, and they are very important in all the chemical reactions that take place in the body.*

## H. Acids, Bases, Salts, and Electrolytes

### 1.  Acids

*Acids* release hydrogen ions ($H^+$) when dissolved in water.

One example is *hydrochloric acid*, HCl. When dissolved in water it dissociates into one negatively charged chloride ion ($Cl^-$) and one positively charged hydrogen ion ($H^+$, this is really a proton, isn't it?).

$$HCl \rightarrow Cl^- + H^+ \qquad \textbf{ACID!}$$

Another example is carbonic acid, $H_2CO_3$. In water, it dissociates into one hydrogen ion ($H^+$) and one negatively charged *bicarbonate* ion ($HCO_3^-$).

$$H_2CO_3 \rightarrow HCO_3^- + H^+ \qquad \textbf{ACID!}$$

In the case of hydrochloric acid dissolved in water, there is complete dissociation of the hydrogen and chloride ions. Hydrochloric acid is therefore called a **strong** acid.

In the case of $H_2CO_3$, the dissociation is usually partial, and $H_2CO_3$ is regarded as a **weak** acid.

We will come back to this question next semester, when we talk about how the body maintains its acid–base balance, which is essentially a system to avoid large changes in the acidity or alkalinity of the body's fluids.

### 2.  Bases

31

*Bases* combine with hydrogen ions (protons, $H^+$) in solution. An example is sodium hydroxide (NaOH), which in solution dissociates into a sodium ion ($Na^+$) and a *hydroxyl ion* ($OH^-$).

$$NaOH \rightarrow Na^+ + OH^- \qquad \textbf{BASE!}$$

The hydroxyl ions can combine with hydrogen ions to form water.

$$H^+ + OH^- \rightarrow H_2O$$

### 3.  Salts

When an acid such as HCl reacts with NaOH, the result is NaCl and water. The NaCl is called a *salt*. Other examples of salts are potassium sulfate (formed from sulfuric acid and potassium hydroxide), calcium phosphate (formed from phosphoric acid and calcium hydroxide), magnesium chloride (formed from hydrochloric acid and magnesium hydroxide), etc.

In the case of sodium chloride, the reaction goes as follows.

First, the base (sodium hydroxide) and the acid (hydrochloric acid) dissociate into $Na^+$ and $OH^-$, and $H^+$ and $Cl^-$. The $OH^-$ then combines with the $H^+$ to form $H_2O$, leaving the two ions $Na^+$ and $Cl^-$. If we were to evaporate off the water, the Na ions and Cl ions would combine together to form electrovalent bonds, and we would be left with crystals of solid NaCl.

**4. Electrolytes**

In general, substances that are bonded together by electrovalent bonds dissociate into their constituent ions when dissolved in water. One example is sodium chloride, which gives a solution containing equal numbers of sodium and chloride ions when dissolved in water (if the water is evaporated off, then we return to solid NaCl).

These ions will conduct electricity—a solution of sodium chloride is a very good conductor of electricity, while pure water is a poor conductor of electricity because it dissociates only very weakly.

Substances such as sodium chloride that dissociate into ions when dissolved in water are therefore called *electrolytes*.

## I. Osmotic Pressure: Hyper- , Iso-, and Hypotonicity

If a cell is placed in a fluid where the concentration of solute (e.g. electrolyte) is higher than found in the cell, the fluid is said to be hypertonic. Water will leave the cell resulting in shrinkage.

If the cell is placed in a fluid where the concentration of solute is lower than found in the cell, the fluid is said to be hypotonic. Water will enter the cell, resulting in swelling and possibly bursting.

If the cell is placed in a fluid where the concentration of solute is the same as found in the cell, the fluid is said to be isotonic. Water will enter and leave the cell at the same rate, and the cell will retain its shape and remain intact.

In the figure below, we see the effect of placing red blood cells in hypertonic, isotonic, and hypotonic solutions of sodium chloride.

The pressure that causes water to flow from a region of low solute concentration (i.e. high water concentration) to a region of high solute concentration (i.e. low water concentration) is called osmotic pressure.

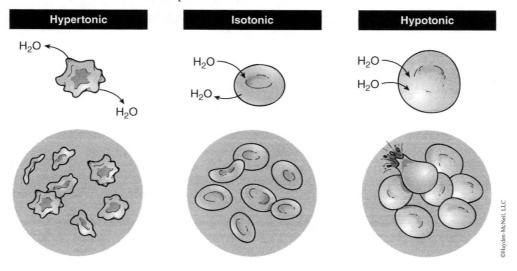

**Figure 2-4.**

### J. The Concept of pH—A Measure of Acidity or Alkalinity

pH is a vitally important measure of the acidity or alkalinity of a solution.

The acidity of a solution is defined by the concentration of $H^+$ in it. It is customary to use the negative logarithm of the $H^+$ concentration rather than the $H^+$ concentration itself. This is called pH. The reason for using pH is that it gives a very convenient scale ranging from 0 (high concentration of $H^+$, very acid) to 14 (low concentration of $H^+$, very alkaline).

Water dissociates weakly, giving equal numbers of $H^+$ and $OH^-$ ions. The concentration of $H^+$ in pure water is 0.0000001 grams per liter, or $10^{-7}$ grams per liter (1 gram of $H^+$ per liter is approximately molar). The logarithm of $10^{-7}$ is $-7$, and the negative of $-7$ is 7. The pH of water is therefore 7. Since water yields equal numbers of $H^+$ (acid) and $OH^-$ (base), it is said to be neutral. A pH of 7 is therefore neutral. That is, it is neither acid nor alkaline. As we shall see later, however, the hydrogen ions in water play a very important role in cellular metabolism, particularly in the utilization of food molecules such as glucose.

**Acid** solutions have pH values **below 7.0**.

**Alkaline** solutions have pH values **above 7.0**.

**Neutral** solutions have a pH of **7.0**.

Vinegar has a pH of about 2.4, and is therefore acid. Household ammonia has a pH of 11.5 and is therefore alkaline. Blood has a pH of 7.4, and is therefore slightly alkaline. Water, as we have said, has a pH of 7.0, and is therefore neutral.

33

## III. Chemical Composition of Cells

Cells contain *inorganic* and *organic* substances. Organic substances always contain carbon and hydrogen, and are the "stuff" of which all living things on this planet are made. All other substances are inorganic, even though many of them occur in living tissue.

At one time it was believed that there was something mysterious and distinctive about organic compounds. It was thought they had something called "vital spirit," and that they could only be manufactured by living organisms. However, between 1828 and 1850 a number of organic compounds were synthesized. The first was urea, a constituent of urine, by Friedrich Wohler in 1828.

The mythology of "vitalism" still persists, unfortunately. For example, there are those who hold that "natural" vitamin C is somehow better than "synthetic" vitamin C, even though the two are identical in every respect.

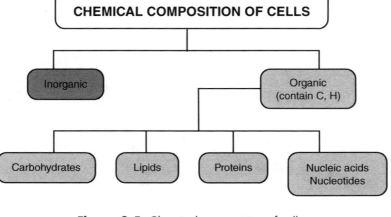

**Figure 2-5.** Chemical composition of cells.

## A. Inorganic Substances

Examples of inorganic substances are water ($H_2O$), oxygen ($O_2$), carbon dioxide ($CO_2$) and inorganic salts such as sodium chloride (NaCl), potassium chloride (KCl), magnesium chloride ($MgCl_2$), calcium chloride ($CaCl_2$), sodium phosphate ($NaH_2PO_4$), sodium carbonate ($Na_2CO_3$), sodium bicarbonate or sodium hydrogen carbonate ($NaHCO_3$), magnesium sulfate ($MgSO_4$). All the salts dissociate in water to yield the respective ions.

Which ions are produced when you dissolve potassium hydroxide in water?

What ions are found in a solution consisting of a mixture of sodium phosphate, magnesium sulfate, and magnesium chloride?

Solutions of all the above salts are found in cells, and play a very important role in maintaining proper cell function. These compounds must not only be present for cells to function, but must also be at the appropriate concentrations both inside and outside the cells.

One important inorganic compound is the gas carbon dioxide. It contains carbon, but not hydrogen. It is produced when living cells burn foods such as *carbohydrates* and *fatty acids*. Although carbon dioxide itself is a gas, it dissolves in water to form carbonic acid, according to the following reaction.

$$CO_2 + H_2O \rightarrow H_2CO_3$$

As we noted before, this reaction is reversible, and carbonic acid can form water and carbon dioxide again.

Carbonic acid is a **weak** acid. It dissociates into hydrogen ions and bicarbonate ions, but (unlike hydrochloric acid) only **partially**.

$$H_2CO_3 \xrightarrow{\text{partially}} H^+ + HCO_3$$

## B. Organic Substances in Cells

Organic compounds always contain carbon and hydrogen. Frequently oxygen is present as well, and sometimes nitrogen, phosphorus and sulfur.

Important groups of organic compounds are as follows.

**Carbohydrates**
- *monosaccharides*
- *disaccharides*
- *polysaccharides*

**Lipids**
- *triglycerides* (fats)
- *phospholipids*
- *steroids*

**Proteins**

**Nucleic** acids (*DNA, RNA*) and nucleotides

We will now consider each of these groups in more detail.

1.  **Carbohydrates**

    Carbohydrates always contain carbon, hydrogen and oxygen. A few may have other elements such as nitrogen.

    Carbohydrates include compounds called sugars, which are burned by the cells of the body to produce energy.

35

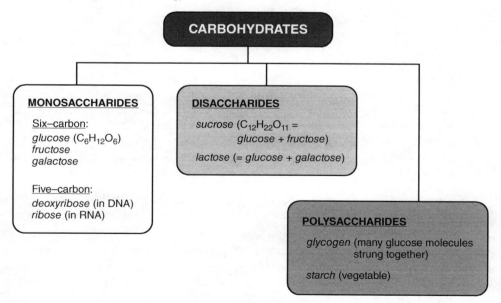

**Figure 2-6.** Carbohydrates.

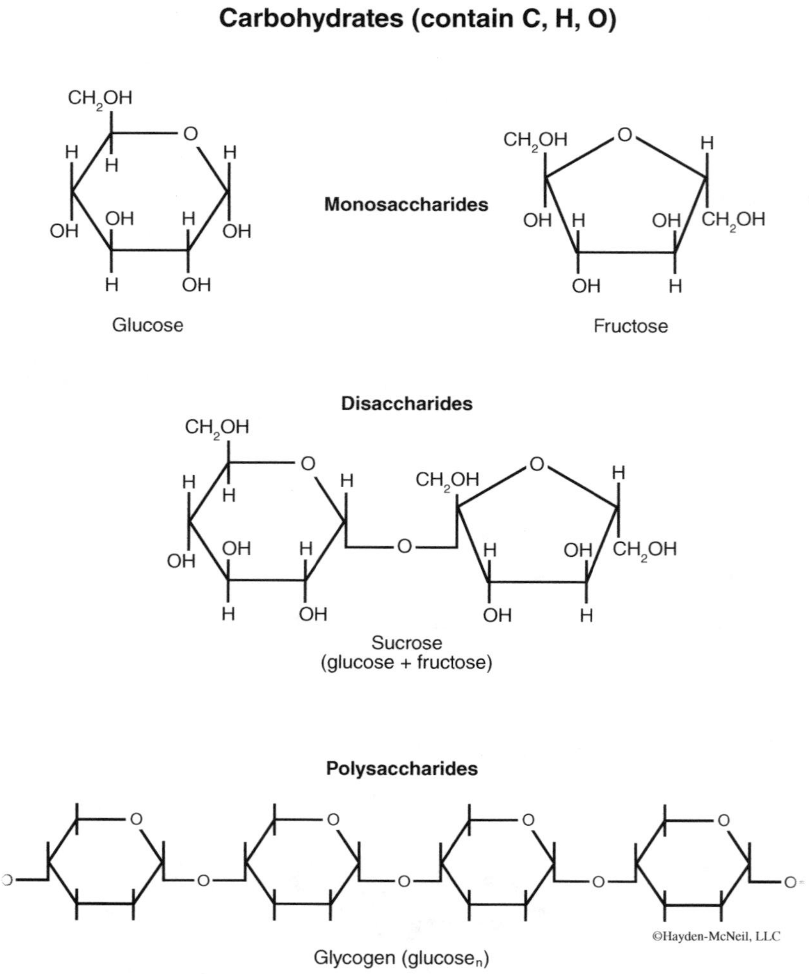

**Carbohydrates (contain C, H, O)**

**Figure 2-7.**

- **Monosaccharides** – *glucose* ($C_6H_{12}O_6$) belongs to the group of simple sugars called monosaccharides. Other monosaccharides are *fructose* and *galactose*. These simple sugars, and others we have not mentioned, are the building blocks for more complex carbohydrate molecules.

- **Disaccharides** – *sucrose* ($C_{12}H_{22}O_{11}$: ordinary table sugar) belongs to the disaccharides, each of which is made up of two molecules of simple sugars covalently bonded together. It is obtained commercially from sugar cane or sugar beet. In sucrose, the two simple sugars are glucose and fructose. When sucrose is digested, it is hydrolyzed into glucose and fructose and absorbed in the small intestine. Later, the fructose is converted into glucose in the liver (see BIOL 204, next semester). *Lactose* is another disaccharide. It is found in milk. The two simple sugars that are joined together to make this disaccharide are *glucose* and *galactose*.

36

- Some adults have problems drinking milk and eating dairy products. This is because they are deficient in the enzyme (*lactase*) that splits lactose into glucose and galactose during digestion, and so lactose accumulates in the small intestine, causing abdominal distention, nausea, cramping, pain and a watery diarrhoea. The condition is referred to as *lactose intolerance*.

- **Polysaccharides** – *glycogen* or "animal starch" consists of a large number of glucose molecules strung together in branched chains. Glycogen is the storage form of glucose, and exists as little granules in many cells of the body. Glycogen belongs to the group of carbohydrates called polysaccharides. Ordinary *starch* (of plant origin) also belongs to this group.

2. **Lipids**

   Lipids are not soluble in water. However, they dissolve in organic solvents (such as chloroform and methanol). There are many kinds of lipids—the only thing they have in common sometimes is their ability to dissolve in chloroform and methanol. Examples include the following.

   - **Triglycerides** – also known as fats, which can be mobilized and burned by the cell to produce energy. A fat molecule consists of **one** molecule of *glycerol* covalently bound to **three fatty acid** molecules. Three examples of fatty acids are *palmitic* acid, *stearic* acid and *oleic* acid. In a molecule of fat, the fatty acids may be **saturated** or **unsaturated**. *Unsaturated fatty acids* contain one or more double covalent bonds between their carbon atoms.

37

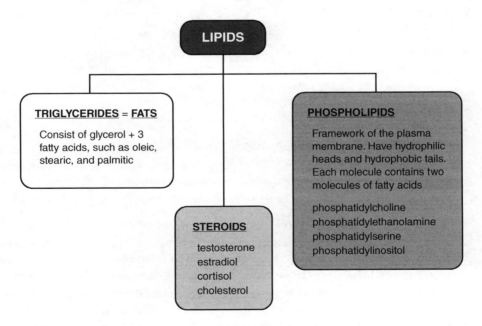

**Figure 2-8.** Lipids.

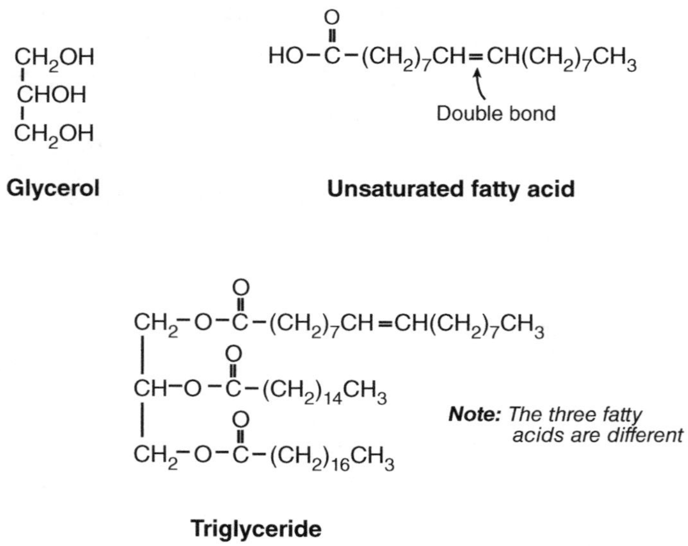

$$CH_2OH$$
$$CHOH$$
$$CH_2OH$$

**Glycerol**

$$HO-\overset{\overset{O}{\|}}{C}-(CH_2)_7CH=CH(CH_2)_7CH_3$$

↑ Double bond

**Unsaturated fatty acid**

$$CH_2-O-\overset{\overset{O}{\|}}{C}-(CH_2)_7CH=CH(CH_2)_7CH_3$$
$$CH-O-\overset{\overset{O}{\|}}{C}-(CH_2)_{14}CH_3$$
$$CH_2-O-\overset{\overset{O}{\|}}{C}-(CH_2)_{16}CH_3$$

*Note:* The three fatty acids are different

**Triglyceride**

**Figure 2-9.**

- **Phospholipids** – vitally important components of the plasma membrane of the cell. Typically they consist of one molecule of glycerol covalently bound to two fatty acid molecules and one phosphate group. The phosphate group in turn is covalently bound to one molecule of *ethanolamine, choline,* or *serine.* The corresponding phospholipids are called *phosphatidylethanolamine, phosphatidylcholine* and *phosphatidylserine.*

- **Steroids** – include the *sex hormones* and *cholesterol.* Cholesterol is widely distributed throughout the body and is an important component of cell membranes, where it has a role in regulating the fluidity of the membrane. All steroids have a common, multiple-ring structure.

3. **Proteins**

Proteins make up more than half of the dry weight of the cells in your body. They are vitally important in the cell's structure, in its metabolism, and in many other functions of the cell. *Albumin, hemoglobin, collagen, amylase* and 99% of all *enzymes* are proteins.

Proteins are linear assemblies (chains) of *amino acids.* An amino acid has an $-NH_2$ group *(amino group)* at one end, and a $-COOH$ group *(carboxyl group)* at the other. In proteins, the amino acids are joined via covalent bonds between the amino and carboxyl groups. These bonds are called *peptide* bonds. There are about 20 common amino acids found in various sequences in different proteins. *Leucine, alanine, glycine, phenylalanine, serine, cysteine, histidine, arginine, methionine, lysine, tryptophan* and *tyrosine* are examples of amino acids.

38

**Phosphatidylcholine**

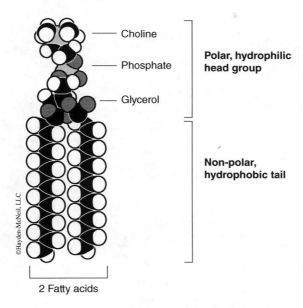

Choline

Phosphate — **Polar, hydrophilic head group**

Glycerol

**Non-polar, hydrophobic tail**

2 Fatty acids

**Phosphatidylcholine**

**Triglyceride**

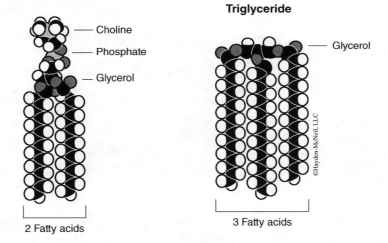

Choline

Phosphate

Glycerol

Glycerol

2 Fatty acids

3 Fatty acids

**Figure 2-10.** Molecular structures of phosphatidylcholine and a triglyceride.

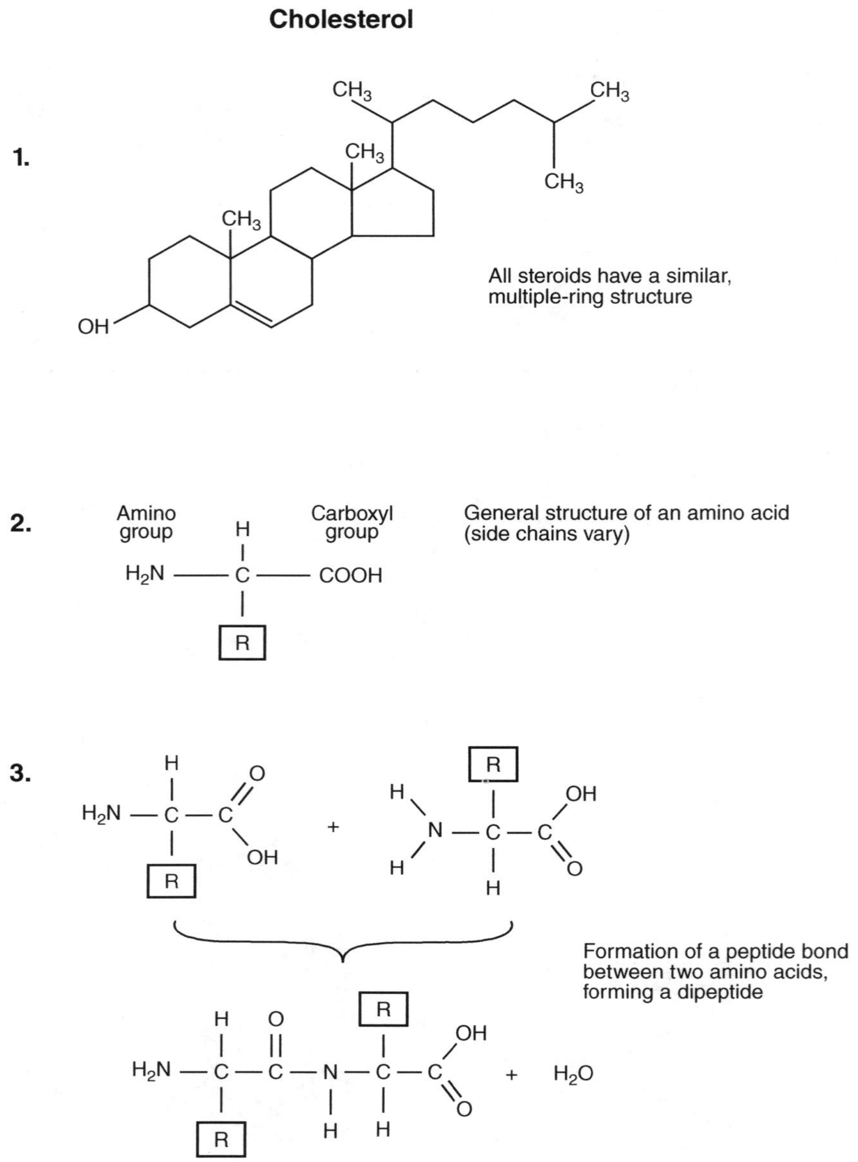

**Cholesterol**

**1.**

All steroids have a similar, multiple-ring structure

**2.**

General structure of an amino acid (side chains vary)

**3.**

Formation of a peptide bond between two amino acids, forming a dipeptide

**Figure 2-11.** Molecular structures of cholesterol and an amino acid (1 and 2), formation of a peptide bond (3). R = side chain.

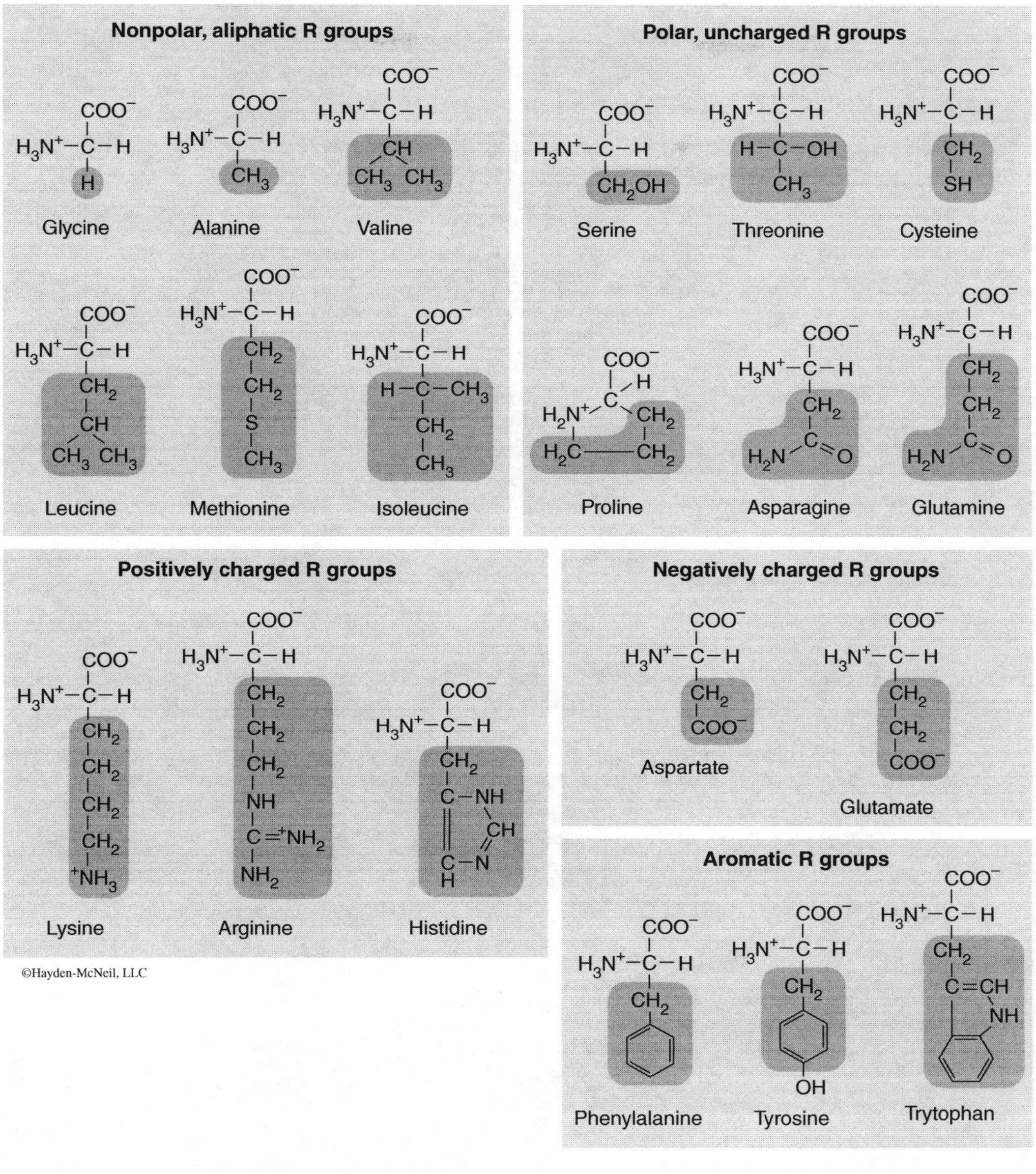

**Figure 2-12.** Structures of the 20 amino acids used to construct all the proteins in the human body.

The *amino acid sequence* of a protein is unique to that protein (although large families of proteins with similar functions are sometimes found to have similar sequences, or even regions with identical sequences). The amino acid sequence is important in determining the properties of the protein and how it folds to achieve its final shape (e.g. globular, ellipsoidal). The amino acid sequence also determines the occurrence of various *structural domains* within the protein (e.g. alpha helix, pleated sheets, random coil).

Hydrogen bonds between hydrogen and oxygen or nitrogen atoms are a major factor in maintaining the shapes of proteins. Individually, these bonds are very weak (much, much weaker than proper covalent bonds), but if there are a lot of them their combined effect can be quite important.

**Denaturation** – heat will break hydrogen bonds, causing disorganization of the protein structure and loss of its unique properties. If the protein is an enzyme, it will cease to function. When hydrogen bonds are broken, the process is called denaturation, and the protein is said to be denatured. Proteins are also denatured at abnormally high and low values of pH, which is why the pH of body fluids must be tightly controlled.

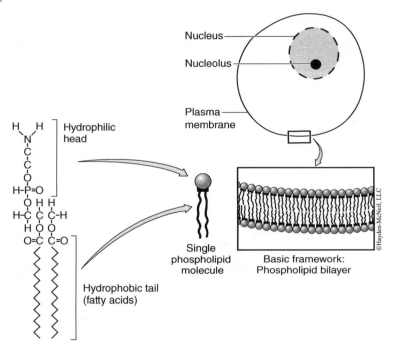

42

**Figure 2-13.** Phospholipids. The plasma membrane of the cell is built up around a framework consisting of a phospholipid *bilayer*. *Proteins* (not shown here) are then attached or inserted into this bilayer.

Proteins may consist of chains ranging from fewer than 100 amino acids to more than 50,000 amino acids. When the chain is short (e.g. 10 amino acids), the protein is usually referred to as a *peptide*.

**Genetic diseases often seem to involve a change (mutation) in one amino acid in an important protein (such as an enzyme or structural protein). The consequences can be disastrous and tragic.**

Let's illustrate this point. The normal protein might have the following partial sequence (Leu stands for leucine, Phe for phenylalanine, and so on).

——Leu-Phe-Gly-Ala-Leu-Leu-His-Arg-Gly-Ser-Gly——

The **mutant** protein may have the following sequence.

——Leu-Phe-Gly-Ala-Leu-**Ala**-His-Arg-Gly-Ser-Gly——

You will notice that an **alanine** has been substituted for one of the leucines.

4.  **Nucleic Acids and Nucleotides**

*Nucleic acids* include the very large molecules **DNA** (*deoxyribonucleic acid*) and **RNA** (*ribonucleic acid*).

DNA and RNA are made up of chains of *nucleotides* joined together by covalent bonds. A nucleotide consists of the following three components.

*   *A nitrogen-containing base*

    *   *adenine* (A), present in DNA and RNA
    *   *guanine* (G), present in DNA and RNA
    *   *cytosine* (C), present in DNA and RNA
    *   *thymine* (T), present in DNA
    *   *uracil* (U), found instead of thymine in RNA

*   *A 5-carbon sugar (pentose)*

    *   ribose (in RNA, ribonucleic acid)
    *   2-deoxyribose (in DNA, deoxyribonucleic acid)

*   *One or more phosphate groups*

    *   the nucleotides of DNA and RNA have **one** phosphate group,
    *   ATP has **three phosphate** groups

Nucleotides have many functions in addition to being building blocks for DNA and RNA. A really important nucleotide is **ATP** (*adenosine triphosphate*), which consists of the nitrogen-containing base adenine, the 5-carbon sugar ribose, and three phosphates.

We will come back to DNA, RNA, and ATP later. They are all very important molecules in the functioning of the cell.

43

44

# CHAPTER 3

## BIOLOGY OF THE CELL I
Structure and Properties

### CHAPTER OUTLINE

I.   Structure of cells
   A.   The plasma membrane (cell membrane)
   B.   The cytoplasm
   C.   The nucleus

### DESCRIPTION AND INTRODUCTION

The organs and tissues of the body are made up of **cells** and their **products**. These products include fluids and fibers made of various proteins such as *collagen* and *elastin*.

The human body is made up of more than ten trillion cells ($1 \times 10^{13}$ cells). In a typical day, however, between 60 and 70 billion cells may die and be replaced. Many of those that die will do so by a process called *apoptosis*.

Cells vary in **shape**. Some are elongated, some are spherical, some are flattened, some (such as white blood cells) vary their shape from time to time. Cells also vary in **function**. For example:

- muscle cells can contract
- nerve cells (*neurons*) transmit and process information
- *osteoblasts* manufacture bone
- white blood cells combat invading bacteria

Cells do not necessarily sit in one place all the time. Some of them (certain white blood cells, for example) can move around. Some cells do not routinely multiply (e.g. nerve cells in most parts of the brain), but others do (e.g. cells in the *stratum germinativum* of the skin), so providing new cells for growth, development, and the replacement of worn-out or injured tissue.

The goal of this chapter is to provide you with a knowledge of the structure of cells.

## OBJECTIVES

After listening to the lecture and reading this chapter, you should be able to:

1. Describe the ways in which cells differ from each other (see Description and Introduction).
2. **Draw a cell** and label the plasma membrane, nucleus, nucleolus, endoplasmic reticulum (rough and smooth), Golgi apparatus, and mitochondria.
3. Describe the molecular architecture of the **plasma (cell) membrane** and relate it to function.
4. List and describe the function of each of the **organelles** and other structures found in the cell cytoplasm or associated with the cell surface (there are eleven listed in these notes).
5. Name and describe the three types of **junction** found between certain cells.
6. Describe the structure of the **nucleus** and what it contains.
7. Explain what is meant by **chromatin**, and describe a chromosome.

CELLS AND THEIR STRUCTURE

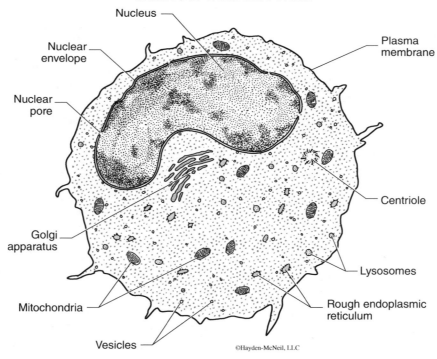

**Figure 3-1.** Monocyte.

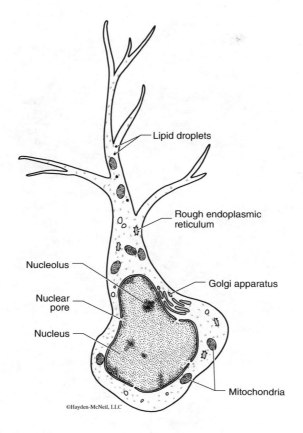

Lipid droplets

Rough endoplasmic reticulum

Nucleolus

Nuclear pore

Nucleus

Golgi apparatus

Mitochondria

©Hayden-McNeil, LLC

**Figure 3-2.** Dendritic cell.

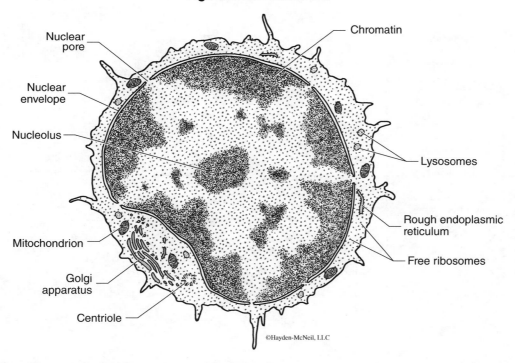

Nuclear pore

Nuclear envelope

Nucleolus

Mitochondrion

Golgi apparatus

Centriole

Chromatin

Lysosomes

Rough endoplasmic reticulum

Free ribosomes

©Hayden-McNeil, LLC

**Figure 3-3.** Resting lymphocyte.

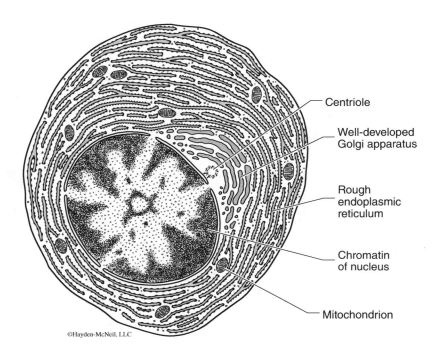

Centriole

Well-developed
Golgi apparatus

Rough
endoplasmic
reticulum

Chromatin
of nucleus

Mitochondrion

©Hayden-McNeil, LLC

**Figure 3-4.** Activated B-lymphocyte synthesizing and secreting antibodies.

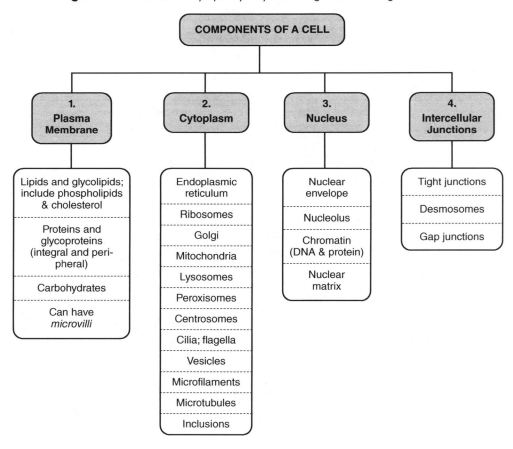

**COMPONENTS OF A CELL**

| 1. Plasma Membrane | 2. Cytoplasm | 3. Nucleus | 4. Intercellular Junctions |
|---|---|---|---|
| Lipids and glycolipids; include phospholipids & cholesterol | Endoplasmic reticulum | Nuclear envelope | Tight junctions |
| Proteins and glycoproteins (integral and peripheral) | Ribosomes | Nucleolus | Desmosomes |
| Carbohydrates | Golgi | Chromatin (DNA & protein) | Gap junctions |
| Can have *microvilli* | Mitochondria | Nuclear matrix | |
| | Lysosomes | | |
| | Peroxisomes | | |
| | Centrosomes | | |
| | Cilia; flagella | | |
| | Vesicles | | |
| | Microfilaments | | |
| | Microtubules | | |
| | Inclusions | | |

**Figure 3-5.**

## I. Structure of Cells

As I mentioned in my introductory comments, cells vary in shape and function. They also vary in their ability to multiply and move around. However, the following description of cell structure applies to all cells.

**What is a cell?**

A cell consists of a nucleus surrounded by a jelly-like *cytoplasm* consisting of a fluid (*cytosol*) containing a variety of organelles (e.g. *mitochondria*), all enveloped in the *plasma membrane* (cell membrane, cytoplasmic membrane). We will deal with these components in turn.

## A. The Plasma Membrane (Cell Membrane)

The plasma membrane is rather like the skin of a sausage. It encloses the cell, and prevents the contents from escaping. All substances entering or leaving the cell must pass through the plasma membrane. In many cases, there is selective control of which substances are allowed to pass through the membrane and which substances are barred from passage. These substances include ions such as potassium and sodium, which have special *ion-selective channels* in the membrane. As the course proceeds, we will discover much more about the plasma membrane and the highly specialized molecules found in it.

*Microvilli* – in some cases, we see fingerlike, hollow, tubular extensions of the cell membrane that serve to increase its surface area (e.g. for absorption in places such as the cells that line the small intestine). These structures are called microvilli.

49

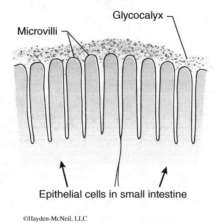

Glycocalyx

Microvilli

Epithelial cells in small intestine

©Hayden-McNeil, LLC

**Figure 3-6.** Microvilli on the apical surface of an epithelial cell in the small intestine.

1.  **Molecular architecture of the plasma membrane.**

    a.  **Lipids** – the basic framework of the plasma membrane is a *bilayer of **phospholipid*** molecules. They include phosphatidylcholine, phosphatidylserine, phosphatidylinositol and phosphatidylethanolamine. Most of the phosphatidylcholine is in the outer half of the membrane, and most of the phosphatidylserine and phosphatidylethanolamine is in the inner half. Sphingolipid, another type of lipid, is also found in the outer half of the membrane.

The lipid bilayer is freely permeable to lipid-soluble substances such as oxygen and carbon dioxide. In contrast, the lipid bilayer is impermeable to water-soluble substances such as sugars, amino acids, ions, etc. These can only pass through the plasma membrane via water-filled pores or special carriers. These are made up of membrane proteins, as will be discussed below.

*The plasma membrane is fluid, and this fluidity is partly controlled by the fatty acids* in the "hydrophobic tails" of the phospholipid molecules. Unsaturated fatty acids make for a more fluid membrane and saturated fatty acids make the membrane more rigid. Cholesterol content is also a factor (see below).

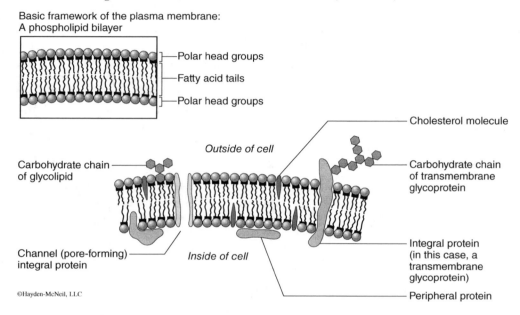

Basic framework of the plasma membrane:
A phospholipid bilayer

— Polar head groups
— Fatty acid tails
— Polar head groups

Outside of cell

Carbohydrate chain
of glycolipid

Channel (pore-forming)
integral protein

Inside of cell

Cholesterol molecule

Carbohydrate chain
of transmembrane
glycoprotein

Integral protein
(in this case, a
transmembrane
glycoprotein)

Peripheral protein

©Hayden-McNeil, LLC

**Figure 3-7.** The plasma membrane is made up of a phospholipid bilayer into which are incorporated protein molecules and cholesterol.

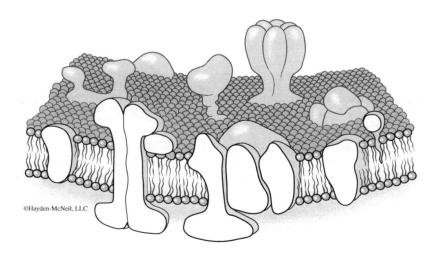

©Hayden-McNeil, LLC

**Figure 3-8.**

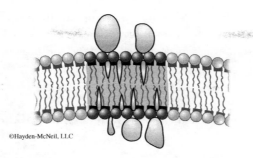

©Hayden-McNeil, LLC

**Figure 3-9.** The proteins are sometimes clustered on "lipid rafts."

©Hayden-McNeil, LLC

**Figure 3-10.** Three-dimensional illustration of two protein molecules on a lipid raft in the plasma membrane.

*Cholesterol is a lipid that is the second determinant of membrane fluidity, and that is also important in stabilizing the membrane.* Certain mutant animal cell lines that cannot synthesize cholesterol rapidly break open unless cholesterol is added to the fluid in which they are grown. There is variation in the amount of plasma membrane cholesterol between cells in different tissues. In some cases there may even be as many cholesterol molecules in a membrane as there are phospholipid molecules.

*Glycolipids* are found in the outer half of the bilayer. They contain monosaccharide sugars, which point outward from the cell surface.

b.  **Proteins** – the basic structure of the plasma membrane is provided by the lipid bilayer, but most of its specific functions are carried out by proteins. The properties of the *phospholipid bilayer* are altered by attaching proteins to it, or by inserting proteins into it. It is now realized that the membrane is much more patchy than the classical pictures suggest, and that its thickness varies from place to place. Sometimes these proteins float about on the membrane on special rafts made up of sphingolipid and cholesterol, but at other times they may be confined to special regions.

These proteins carry out specific functions within and across the membrane. They may be *receptors* for drugs, hormones, etc.; they may be *enzymes*; and they may be involved in *transporting* substances (e.g. sodium ions, glucose) across the membrane.

Proteins may be associated with the membrane in two ways.

- *Integral proteins* are embedded in the membrane. If they span it, they are called **transmembrane proteins**. Among their many functions, integral proteins may be *enzymes,* **carrier** *proteins* that transport specific molecules across the membrane (e.g. glucose, carried by glucose transporters, some of which are sensitive to the hormone insulin, which can affect glucose uptake by cells), **channel proteins**, that form water-filled pores permitting ions to cross the membrane, **transporter** *proteins* for neurotransmitters, or they may be **receptor proteins**.

  You will hear a lot about *receptor proteins* throughout this course, so you should understand what is meant by them. There are many receptor proteins, each of them tailored to bind a particular substance that the cell may be exposed to. There are special receptor proteins for ions (such as calcium), for hormones (such as insulin), and for neurotransmitters (such as acetylcholine). You will learn that many of these receptors are not found in every cell of the body. They are only present in cells that need to respond to certain substances. Further, the numbers of receptors determine the cell's sensitivity to a hormone, and in many cases we find that these numbers can be "up-regulated" or "down-regulated."

- *Peripheral proteins* are bound to the surface of the membrane. Many (but not all) of these proteins are associated with the interior surface of the membrane.

  Some proteins contain carbohydrates, and are called **glycoproteins** (see below).

c. **Carbohydrates** – carbohydrates are found attached to lipids or proteins in glycolipids and glycoproteins. The polysaccharide chains of these carbohydrates are composed of different monosaccharides such as mannose, fucose, glucose and N-acetylglucosamine. The polysaccharide chains project outward from the exterior surface of the plasma membrane. They may play a role in cell–cell interactions and cell recognition.

2. **Junctions between cells.**

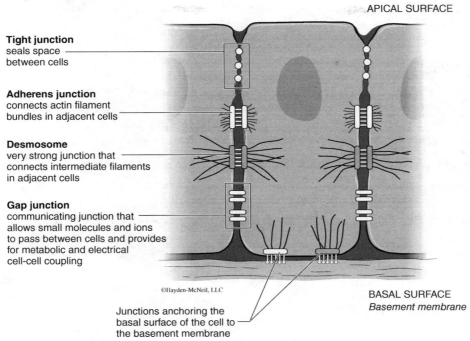

**Tight junction**
seals space
between cells

**Adherens junction**
connects actin filament
bundles in adjacent cells

**Desmosome**
very strong junction that
connects intermediate filaments
in adjacent cells

**Gap junction**
communicating junction that
allows small molecules and ions
to pass between cells and provides
for metabolic and electrical
cell-cell coupling

APICAL SURFACE

©Hayden-McNeil, LLC

Junctions anchoring the
basal surface of the cell to
the basement membrane

BASAL SURFACE
*Basement membrane*

**Figure 3-11.**

Some cells are connected by intercellular junctions. The following is a brief summary of the four major types of intercellular junctions.

a. **Tight junctions** – often between cells in an epithelial sheet (e.g. in the lining of the intestine). Tight junctions close the spaces between cells by fusing neighboring membranes. They also segregate proteins in the apical surface of an epithelium from those in the basal surface.

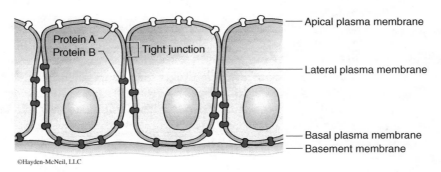

Protein A
Protein B
Tight junction

Apical plasma membrane

Lateral plasma membrane

Basal plasma membrane
Basement membrane

©Hayden-McNeil, LLC

**Figure 3-12.**

b. **Desmosomes** – very strong spot-welds between adjacent cells that reinforce the tissue. They connect intermediate filaments of adjacent cells. Found between cells in the skin. In the disease *pemphigus* individuals make antibodies against the desmosomes in the skin, disrupting them and causing severe blistering as a result of the leakage of extracellular fluid into the loosened epithelium.

c.  **Gap junctions** – couple cells electrically and metabolically by allowing passage of small molecules and ions between cells. Important in cardiac muscle.

d.  **Adherens junctions** – connect actin filament bundles in adjacent cells.

## B. The Cytoplasm

The cytoplasm is the site of all the major metabolic reactions of the cell. It is divided up into functionally distinct, membrane-bounded compartments. Each compartment is known as an *organelle*. There are also organelles that are not made up of membranes, but have specific cellular functions—the ribosomes are an example.

1.  **Endoplasmic reticulum (*smooth* and *rough* *endoplasmic reticulum; SER and RER*).**

    Complex network of interconnected membranes (very like the plasma membrane in composition) that form flattened sacs, elongated canals and vesicles. The ER is important in the synthesis of proteins and lipids. Rough ER has ribosomes attached to it, smooth ER is not associated with ribosomes (see below).

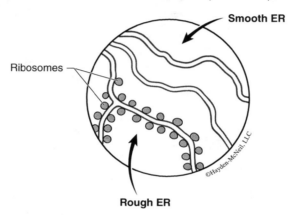

**Figure 3-13.**

2.  **Ribosomes.**

    May be attached to endoplasmic reticulum (making it *rough endoplasmic reticulum*), or they may be free in the cytoplasm. Ribosomes are actually particles composed of *ribosomal RNA (rRNA)* and about 80 different *ribosomal proteins*. They play a vital role in protein synthesis, and are responsible for joining the individual amino acids together during this process. Ribosomes are assembled in the *nucleolus* of the *nucleus* (see next section). They then move to the cell cytoplasm, where protein synthesis occurs.

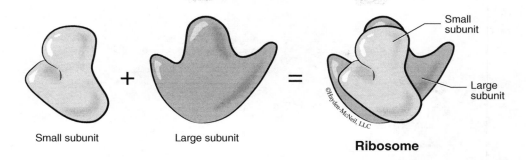

**Figure 3-14.** Ribosome.

3.  **Golgi apparatus.**

A stack of flattened membranes formed from the endoplasmic reticulum. It is located near the nucleus, often close to the centrosome.

The Golgi apparatus is named after *Camillo Golgi* (1843–1926), an Italian professor of histology and general pathology at the University of Pavia. He first reported his observations on this organelle on April 19, 1898, over 100 years ago. He used a technique called "silver staining," which he had invented in 1873, to make the transparent, invisible stack of membranes look black, and therefore visible under the microscope. He first identified the Golgi apparatus in a neuron from the brain of a barn owl.

55

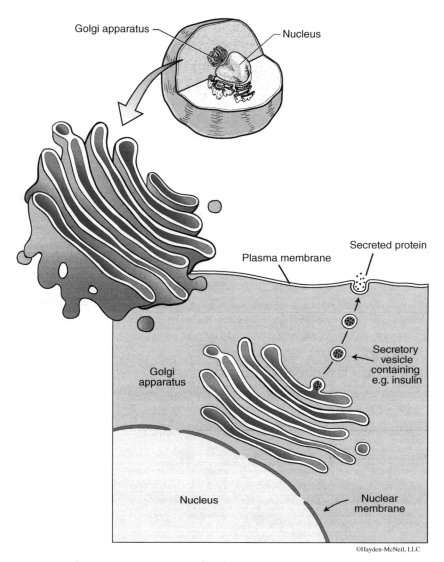

**Figure 3-15.** Function of Golgi apparatus in protein secretion by exocytosis.

The Golgi is a dynamic structure that consists of stacks of flattened membranes surrounded by swarms of *vesicles* that cluster around it. The Golgi *chemically modifies, sorts and packages newly-synthesized proteins* (some of them glycoproteins). Some of these proteins will be secreted by the cell (e.g. hormones, blood proteins, antibodies), but others remain and function within various parts of the cell.

The way it works is as follows. Proteins are first assembled in the endoplasmic reticulum, transported to the Golgi, and those that are destined for secretion are moved from there to the cell surface. As we might expect, therefore, the Golgi apparatus is prominent in cells that specialize in secreting proteins. An example is an active B-lymphocyte, which secretes large amounts of antibodies into the blood. Compared with dormant, non-secreting B-lymphocytes, active B-lymphocytes have a highly developed Golgi.

4. **Mitochondria (singular = *mitochondrion*) contain all the enzymes needed to produce most of the energy required by a cell. They are sometimes called the "powerhouses" of the cell.**

They use *oxygen* (from the lungs via the blood circulation) to oxidise glucose and fatty acids. The energy released by this process is locked up in *adenosine triphosphate (ATP)*, which is rapidly pumped out of the mitochondrion into the surrounding cytosol, where it is utilized as an energy source for the cell's activities.

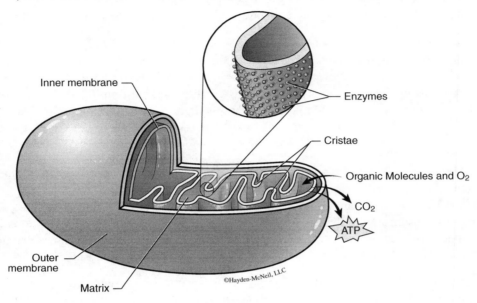

**Figure 3-16.** Mitochondrion.

It has been suggested that mitochondria play a role in apoptosis (*Science 292*, 624, 2001).

It is believed that 1–2 billion years ago mitochondria were free-living bacteria that became permanently engulfed and developed a beneficial relationship with the cells of eukaryotes at a time when the oxygen content of the atmosphere was increasing [Gray et al. (1999). *Science 283*, 1476]. Like the bacteria from which they evolved, mitochondria carry their own genetic information in the form of a circular piece of ***mitochondrial DNA (mtDNA)***. Mitochondrial DNA is small, only 16,569 nucleotides long. It carries the genetic code for 22 transfer RNAs, 2 ribosomal RNAs, and 13 proteins concerned with oxidative phosphorylation. We find mtDNA has many sequence similarities with present-day alpha-proteobacteria.

*Nearly all of our mitochondrial DNA is inherited from our mothers.* This is because sperm contribute only 0.1% of mitochondrial DNA to the oocyte (egg). Mutations may accumulate in mitochondrial DNA throughout our lifetime, and because mitochondria pass randomly to the daughter cells during cell division, they must divide. Hence "bad" mitochondria can accumulate in cells over a period of time, and could lead to disease or dysfunction as a person ages. In addition to dividing, mitochondria fuse together to maintain their size. Fusion therefore balances division to prevent the mitochondria becoming smaller. Mitochondria can also be transferred

57

from one cell to another, a phenomenon that is particularly prominent when the receiving cell has been stressed. This seems to be facilitated by intercellular connections called "tunneling nanotubes."

*Mitochondrial DNA and human evolution* – an analysis of mitochondrial DNA was carried out on the rib of an infant *Neanderthal* from the Caucasus region of Russia. The fossil was dated to less than 30,000 years ago. The analysis showed that Neanderthals and humans *evolved* from a common ancestor between 365,000 and 853,000 years ago. The method used in this study was called the polymerase chain reaction.

5. **Lysosomes.**

Membrane-bounded organelles that contain powerful enzymes that are specialized for digestion, and can break down proteins, carbohydrates and nucleic acids. These enzymes digest foreign particles such as bacteria. The optimum pH for these enzymes is very low, around 5. This acid pH is maintained by a special pump (powered by ATP) that pumps hydrogen ions into the lysosome interior.

6. **Peroxisomes.**

Membrane-bound organelles present in nearly all cells, particularly abundant in liver and kidney. ***Peroxisomes are basically bags of enzymes***—they contain more than 40. These enzymes break down fatty acids, synthesize cholesterol, and make parts of the myelin sheath that surrounds many nerve axons. Some of these reactions are oxidative, and produce hydrogen peroxide, a potentially dangerous substance that is broken down into water and oxygen by a peroxisomal enzyme called *catalase.*

*Peroxisome diseases* – there are several genetic diseases where there is failure to form peroxisomes properly, or where there are losses of a particular enzyme within the peroxisome. The fatal *X-linked adrenoleukodystrophy* (ALD) is an example, where there seems to be loss of the peroxisomal enzyme that oxidizes very long chain fatty acids. The abnormal accumulation of these fatty acids cause loss of myelin in the central nervous system and problems with the adrenal glands. The neurological degeneration often results in death in childhood (some years ago, a movie called *Lorenzo's Oil* was made about this disease). The gene for ALD has been cloned.

7. **Centrosome.**

The centrosome, also called the "microtubule organizing center," is an area in the cell where microtubules are produced. Within an animal cell centrosome there is a pair of small organelles, the centrioles, each made up of a ring of nine groups of microtubules. There are three fused microtubules in each group. The two centrioles are arranged such that one is perpendicular to the other.

During animal cell division, the centrosome divides and the centrioles replicate (make new copies). The result is two centrosomes, each with its own pair of centrioles. The two centrosomes move to opposite ends of the nucleus, and from each centrosome, microtubules grow into a "spindle," which is responsible for separating replicated chromosomes into the two daughter cells.

8. **Cilia and flagella.**

   Cilia and flagella are hair-like projections from the cell surface. They are not present in all cells. They contain microtubules and can move back and forth. They are therefore motile. Cilia are present in large numbers on the surfaces of some cells (e.g. those lining the inner surface of the respiratory tubes). Flagella are much longer than cilia, and there is usually only one per cell. The tail of a sperm cell is really a flagellum.

   You must be able to distinguish cilia and flagella from *microvilli* (see section on the plasma membrane). Microvilli are non-motile fingerlike, hollow, tubular extensions of the cell membrane that serve to increase its surface area.

9. **Vesicles.**

   Assorted vesicles are present in cells around the Golgi and are involved in *endocytosis* and *exocytosis*. These phenomena will be discussed later. Vesicles are like very tiny balloons, where the rubber is replaced by a membrane very similar to the plasma membrane in composition. They may contain a variety of substances, such as hormones or neurotransmitters.

10. **Cytoskeleton.**

    The cytoskeleton is a network of fibers. It includes microtubules made up of tubulin, microfilaments made up of actin, and intermediate filaments composed of a variety of different proteins. Microfilaments seem to be involved in cellular *movements*. Microtubules are hollow rods that are about 25 nm in diameter and are involved in moving organelles around the cell interior. Microtubules also seem to be involved in determining cell shape, some types of cell movement, and in the process of separating chromosomes during cell division.

    Intermediate filaments are not directly involved in this type of movement. They provide mechanical strength to cells and tissues.

11. **Inclusions.**

    Cells also contain inclusions, such as *lipid droplets, glycogen granules* and *melanin granules*.

## C. The Nucleus

The nucleus is usually located near the center of the cell, and contains nearly all of the DNA found in the cell (except the mitochondrial DNA). The nucleus consists of the following.

1. **Nuclear envelope** – the double-walled **nuclear envelope** is punctured by *nuclear pores* that permit RNA to move out of the nucleus into the cytoplasm, and proteins to move out of the cytoplasm (where they are manufactured) into the nucleus.

2. **Nucleolus** – where ribosomes are assembled.

3. **Chromatin** – consists of *DNA* and associated *proteins* (mainly *histones*). The DNA consists of enormously long molecules, each of which is packaged in a separate *chromosome*. These chromosomes become highly condensed and visible structures when the cell is preparing to divide. This condensation permits chromosomes to be separated into two sets during cell division, without breaking them or entangling them.

59

The condensed chromosomes appear as doubled structures consisting of twinned *chromatids*, which are really two duplicated chromosomes joined at the centromeres. In humans there are 24 different chromosomes—2 *sex* chromosomes (X and Y) and 22 non-sex chromosomes known as *autosomes*. Each nucleus contains two copies of each autosome and two sex chromosomes (XX in females and XY in males). Thus, there is a total of 46 chromosomes in each nucleus. Condensed chromosomes are rod-like structures, consisting of two arms that meet at a central structure called the *centromere*. The two ends of a chromosome are capped by structures called *telomeres* (see figure).

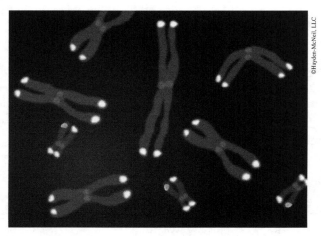

©Hayden-McNeil, LLC

**Figure 3-17.** Metaphase chromosomes stained with a special fluorescent stain that shows up the telomeres. Note that each metaphase chromosome is a double structure consisting of twinned chromatids.

4. **Nuclear matrix** – consists of a variety of soluble molecules that may play a role in *gene expression*.

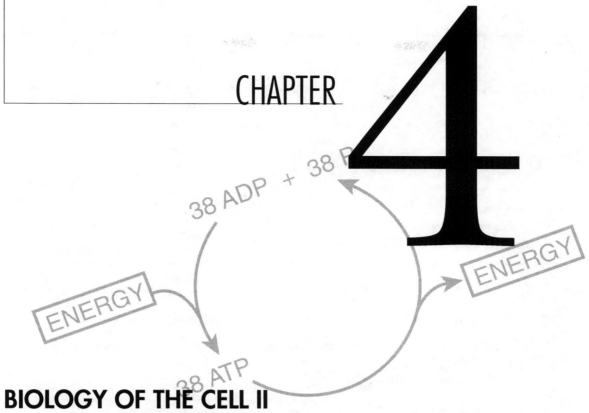

# CHAPTER 4

# BIOLOGY OF THE CELL II
Transport Across the Plasma Membrane, Life Cycle, Control of Cell Division, Apoptosis

## CHAPTER OUTLINE

## DESCRIPTION AND INTRODUCTION

The previous chapter dealt with the structure of the cell and its various components. In the present chapter we will focus on cell physiology, with particular emphasis on the following topics:

- how substances move across cell membranes
- the process of cell *division*
- how cells *differentiate*
- the *control* of cell division
- the process of *apoptosis*, where cells are induced to commit suicide
- how nuclear transfer *cloning* is carried out

## OBJECTIVES

After listening to the lecture and reading this chapter, you should be able to:

1. List the three ways in which **substances can pass across the plasma membrane** without the need for energy expenditure by the cell.
2. List three types of **endocytosis**.
3. **Draw a circular diagram** to illustrate the life cycle of a cell.
4. Describe the four stages of **mitosis**.
5. Explain the importance of having **cell cycle checkpoints**.
6. Define what is meant by cell **differentiation**, and what this means in terms of **gene expression**.
7. Describe the difference between a **tumor suppressor gene** and a **proto-oncogene**.
8. Describe the consequences of **inactivation** of a tumor suppressor gene or **activation** of a proto-oncogene.
9. Describe **metastasis**, and why it occurs.
10. Define **apoptosis**, and give one example.
11. Describe how **necrosis** differs from apoptosis.
12. Briefly describe the principle of **nuclear transfer cloning**, and why we might need to clone animals.

## I. Movement of Substances through Cell Membranes

In the living cell, there is continuous trafficking of substances across the cell membrane. Substances entering the cell include oxygen and glucose. Substances leaving the cell include carbon dioxide, waste products and secretions such as hormones.

### A. Physical Processes that Do Not Require Energy from the Cell

In all of these processes, movement is *passive*. That is, substances pass down their concentration gradients from high to low concentrations.

1. **Diffusion.**

   Oxygen and carbon dioxide diffuse passively in and out of the cell. Both these gases are soluble in the lipid bilayer. Ions (e.g. potassium) can pass in and out of the cell by simple diffusion as well, but because they are insoluble in the lipid bilayer, they must pass through special channels formed by membrane-spanning proteins.

2. **Facilitated diffusion.**

Substances that are insoluble in lipids are sometimes helped across the cell membrane by a process of facilitated diffusion, which involves special carrier proteins. For that reason, the process is sometimes called carrier-mediated facilitated diffusion. A glucose carrier protein is very important in the brain, which depends on glucose as its primary energy source.

3. **Osmosis.**

A special case of diffusion, involving *water*. How does water enter the cell, if it cannot cross the lipid bilayer? It does so via a set of glycoproteins called *aquaporins* that form water channels. A cell placed in a *hypotonic* solution swells and may burst due to excessive passage of water through these channels into its interior. A cell shrinks when placed in a *hypertonic* solution.

Water and salts pass across the walls of blood capillaries by *pressure filtration.*

## B. Physiological Processes that Need Energy to Be Provided by the Cell

1. **Active transport.**

In the processes discussed above, substances pass from regions of high concentration to lower concentration. That is, they diffuse down a concentration gradient. Living cells, however, have the capacity to move certain substances against a concentration gradient, that is, from a low concentration to a region of higher concentration. Sodium ions, for example, are pumped out of the cell, even though their concentration is much higher outside the cell than inside. This process is called active transport. Because substances are forced to move against their concentration gradients, active transport consumes a lot of energy (think of pushing a cart uphill compared with pushing it downhill). Like facilitated diffusion, special carrier proteins are involved, but they are coupled to a source of energy that is usually adenosine triphosphate (ATP).

2. **Endocytosis.**

Molecules or large particles such as bacteria that are too large to enter the cell by diffusion or active transport enter the cell by a process that involves pinching in a portion of the cell membrane to form an intracellular vesicle. Endocytosis can involve the following different processes.

a. *Phagocytosis* – engulfing of particles such as bacteria. During this process of internalization, the phagocytic cell (often a *macrophage* or a white blood cell called a *neutrophil*: see BIOL 204 next semester) will often release a burst of "*superoxide*" that kills the bacterium. Superoxide is an oxygen molecule that has one extra electron attached to it ($O_2^-$)—it is pretty lethal stuff! After internalization, the vesicle may fuse with lysosomes to form phagolysosomes, which then digest the contents.

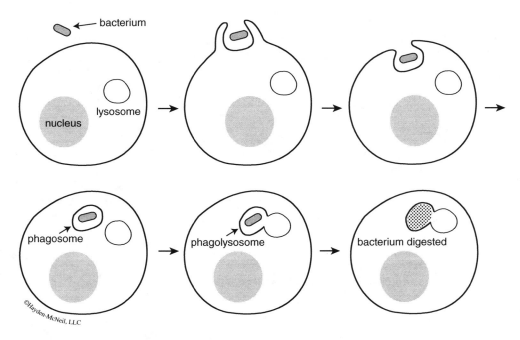

**Figure 4-1.** Phagocytosis (= cell eating).

b.   *Pinocytosis* – internalization of fluids in the form of tiny droplets.

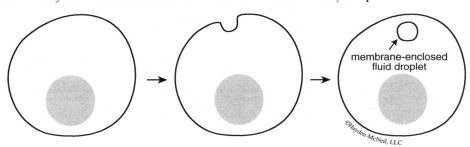

**Figure 4-2.** Pinocytosis (= cell drinking).

c.   *Receptor-mediated endocytosis* – a very specific way in which certain molecules are taken into cells. The cell membrane contains proteins that act as receptors for certain extracellular molecules (examples of such extracellular molecules include low-density lipoprotein, which carries cholesterol in the bloodstream). These extracellular molecules bind to their receptors on the cell membrane, which then pinches inward to form an intracellular vesicle containing the extracellular molecules.

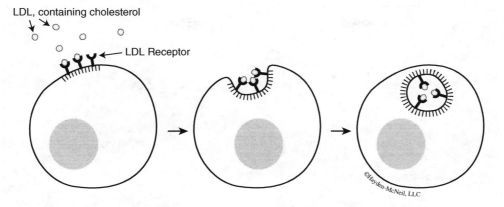

**Figure 4-3.** Receptor mediated endocytosis (specific for certain molecules).
See figure on next page for a diagram of the whole process of receptor-mediated endocytosis.

3.  **Exocytosis.**

This is the opposite of endocytosis. For example, insulin-secreting cells package the insulin in special secretory vesicles. The vesicles then fuse with the plasma membrane and open to the extracellular space, releasing their contents. Neurotransmitter release by neurons is also an example of exocytosis.

The process of membrane fusion is not fully understood. It is known to be complex, however, and involves an array of special proteins in the vesicles and plasma membrane.

65

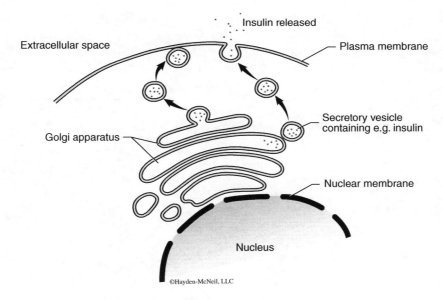

**Figure 4-4.** Secretion by exocytosis.

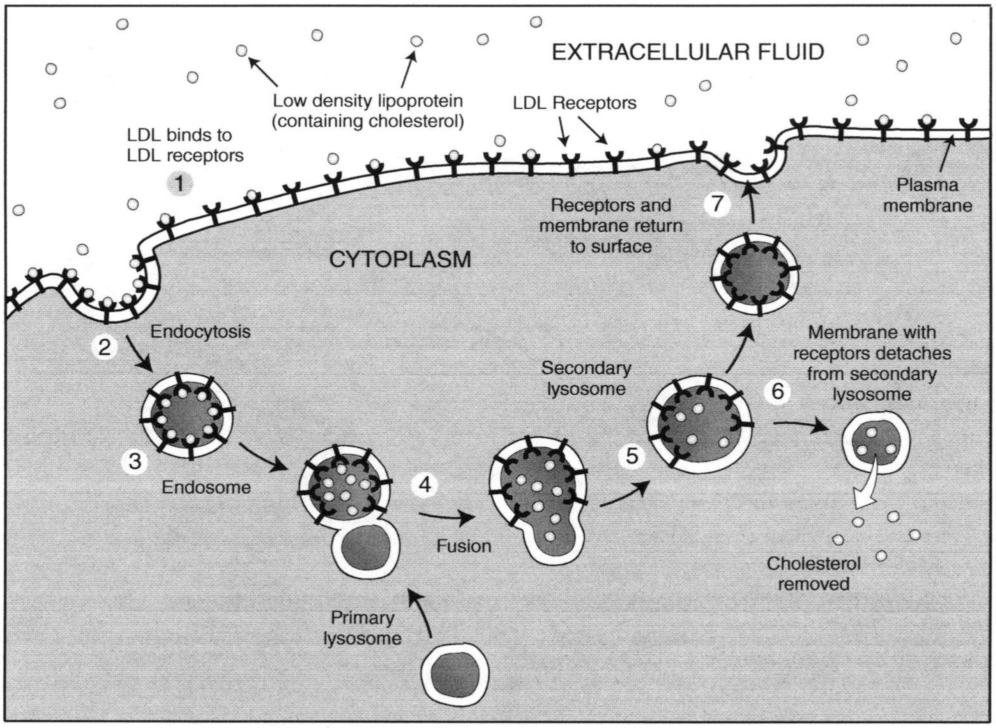

**Figure 4-5.** Receptor-mediated endocytosis of low-density lipoprotein (one of the lipoproteins that carries cholesterol in the blood).

The 2001 Nobel Prize for Physiology or Medicine was awarded to three biologists for their contributions to our understanding of the cell cycle. They were: Leland Hartwell, Fred Hutchinson Cancer Research Center, Seattle; Sir Paul Nurse, Imperial Cancer Research Fund, London; Tim Hunt, Imperial Cancer Research Fund, London.

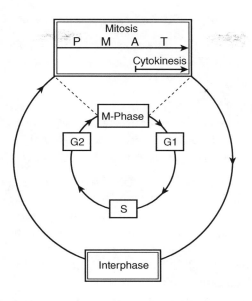

**Figure 4-6.** The cell cycle.

- G1, G2 (gap 1 and gap 2) are growth phases.

- S-phase is a time when DNA synthesis occurs and chromosomes are replicated.

- M-phase consists of **mitosis** (*prophase, metaphase, anaphase, telophase*) and **cytoki-nesis**. Cytokinesis starts during anaphase and ends at the end of telophase.

## II. Life Cycle of a Cell

Different types of cells have different life cycles. It is particularly important to note that **not all cells divide once they have differentiated.**

1. **Skeletal** and **cardiac muscle** cells do not divide. These cells are sometimes called "permanent non-dividing cells." They may be considered to have "withdrawn from the cell cycle," and to have become arrested in interphase.

   Differentiated **neurons** are also in this category, but we now know that *new* neurons are being produced from stem cells in the olfactory bulb and the hippocampus of the brain. Since they have enormous relevance to the treatment of degenerative brain disorders (e.g. *Alzheimer's disease*), these findings have attracted much attention recently.

2. Other cells continuously divide. One example is the cells that form *stratified squamous epithelium* (e.g. in the skin).

3. Yet other cells can be regarded as *quiescent*—that is, they have opted out of the cell cycle after mitosis (when they are regarded as being in the *G0 phase*), but retain the capacity to re-enter the *G1 phase* under suitable circumstances. Liver cells are a particularly interesting example. Normally, liver cells do not go on dividing after adulthood has been reached. However, if it is damaged in any way, the liver is unique in that the hepatocytes start to divide. They continue to do so until the mass of the liver is restored.

Cells that divide pass through several phases in their life cycle.

**M-phase** occurs when the cell is dividing. It consists of *mitosis* followed by *cytokinesis*. **The purpose of mitosis is to ensure that each "daughter" cell receives a complete set of chromosomes.**

The total length of DNA in a cell is 2 meters. In the cell's life cycle this DNA is duplicated, and during mitosis the two copies are separated into two new cells. To make the process easier, the DNA is divided up among 46 chromosomes, and these are compacted into visible structures at the start of mitosis (*prophase*).

In mitosis, therefore, the chromatin (DNA + proteins) of the nucleus condenses to form 46 visible chromosomes. This condensation process permits the easy separation of the chromosomes into two sets that are allocated to each of the two daughter cells. At this stage of mitosis, the chromosomes are actually double structures, consisting of twinned "sister *chromatids*" (some people call them sister chromosomes). The nuclear envelope then breaks down, and the sister chromatids are pulled apart. After they have been pulled apart, the chromatids are referred to as *chromosomes*. Two new nuclei are formed, completing mitosis. Starting in the middle of *anaphase* and finishing at the end of *telophase*, the cell cytoplasm splits into two daughter cells, each receiving one of the two sets of chromosomes. This phase where the cytoplasm actually starts to divide is called *cytokinesis*.

**Interphase** – a much longer time then elapses before each daughter cell divides again. During interphase, the cell grows and duplicates its DNA so that each chromosome consists of a pair of twinned chromatids (twinned chromosomes) again.

Interphase consists of **G1**, **S**, and **G2**.

## A. M-Phase—Mitosis (Nuclear Division)

*Mitosis* is *nuclear* division. In its latter stages, it is accompanied by division of the cell *cytoplasm (cytokinesis)*.

**The M-phase is divided into the four stages of mitosis (P, M, A, T), and cytokinesis, which starts in the middle of anaphase and is complete at the end of telophase.**

1. **Prophase (P).**

   Each of the 46 chromosomes is visible as a pair of *chromatids*, which are actually duplicated chromosomes joined at the *centromere*. The *centrosomes* have replicated before prophase, and now move to opposite poles of the nucleus. A *mitotic spindle* of *microtubules* is assembled, attached at each end to the two poles formed by the centrosomes. This mitotic spindle is very important, since it controls all subsequent movements of the chromosomes. The nuclear envelope disappears.

2. **Metaphase (M).**

   The chromosomes line up at the equator, and *spindle* fibers become attached to their centromeres.

3. **Anaphase (A).**

   The spindle fibers tug the sister chromatids apart, and each sister is pulled toward opposite poles. Once it has been pulled away from its sister, the separated *chromatid* is referred to as a *chromosome* (some people even speak of the sister chromatids as sister chromosomes). In the middle of this phase, cytoplasmic division (cytokinesis) commences.

4. **Telophase (T).**

   Chromosomes complete their journey toward the centrioles, nuclear membranes start to appear around each set of chromosomes. Cytoplasmic division (cytokinesis) is complete at the end of telophase (see Figure 4-7).

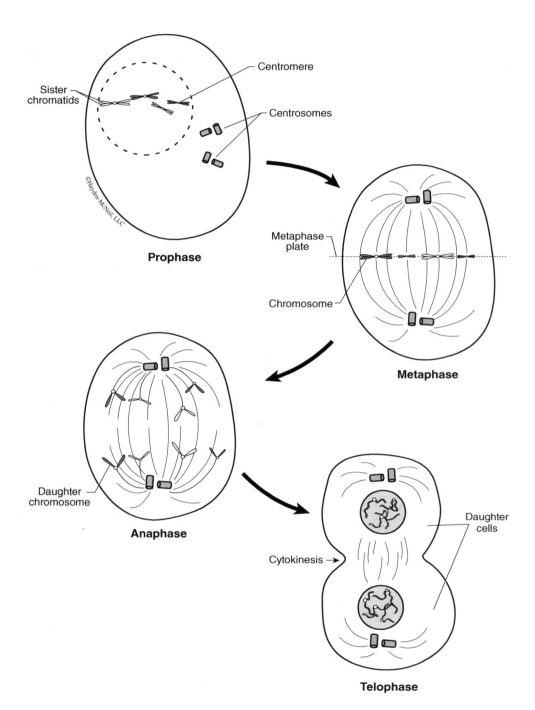

**Figure 4-7.** Phases of mitosis.

## B. M-Phase—Cytoplasmic Division (Cytokinesis; Cell Division)

The last part of the M-phase involves the contraction of a ring of actin *microfilaments* that progressively squeezes the cell into two halves, separating the two daughter nuclei into two smaller, but identical cells. This process is called cytokinesis. It starts in the middle of anaphase and finishes at the end of telophase.

## C. Interphase

During the first part of interphase, known as G1 or gap 1, the chromosomes *decondense*, and there is a large increase in the biosynthetic activity of the cell, which was virtually shut down during the M-phase. The next part of the interphase, known as S, involves DNA synthesis (*replication*) and continues until all the 46 chromosomes have been duplicated. During the next cell division, each duplicated chromosome will be seen as a twinned structure consisting of the two "sister" chromatids, which are really two conjoined chromosomes, or sister chromosomes. After S phase, the cell passes to the G2 (gap 2) phase, where it prepares for the onset of a new M-phase and another round of division.

## D. Cell Cycle Checkpoints Provide Time for DNA Repair and DNA Editing, and Help to Prevent Cancer

It is very important for the cells in our bodies to protect the integrity of their DNA. Cancer is one consequence if damage is allowed to accumulate, as we shall see later. Therefore, throughout the interphase of the cell cycle, complicated enzyme mechanisms come into operation to *repair* damaged DNA, both before and after replication, and also to *"proofread"* newly-replicated DNA and *correct ("edit")* any mistakes that may have occurred during the replication process.

It is therefore important that checkpoints are placed in the cell cycle to provide the time necessary for these mechanisms to come into operation and ensure that a faithful copy of DNA will be transmitted to the daughter cells arising from the next mitosis. Cell cycle checkpoints are mainly at G1 (Start), G2, and M. The G1 checkpoint is where a decision is made as to whether DNA will be replicated during S phase. At this point, the cell can choose to leave the cell cycle, and become quiescent, a phase that is called G0. The G2 and M checkpoints ensure that DNA replication has been completed and that the chromosomes are properly lined up on the *spindle* before being divided between the daughter cells. Some of these checkpoints involve the *tumor suppressor gene* p53, which will be discussed later.

## E. Stem Cells, Genes, and Cell Differentiation

All the cells of your body originated from a single fertilized egg cell. During development, this cell has divided many times. At some point, the daughter cells start to look different from one another. Some become skin cells, others become bone cells, still others become nerve cells and so on. This process is called *differentiation*. During this process, some cells *withdraw* from the cell cycle (i.e. they cease to divide and enter the G0 phase), while others continue to divide throughout life.

The embryo and even the adult body contain "master" cells called **stem cells** that have the ability to multiply and differentiate into many different cell types.

The term *stem cells* applies to those cells in the embryo, fetus, or adult human that have not yet become terminally differentiated and still have the capacity to divide and differentiate.

During progressive specialization the differentiation potential of cells decreases gradually. A complete human being can develop from a **totipotent** fertilized *oocyte* and also from *totipotent* embryonic cells up to the 8-cell stage. In later stages of embryonic development **pluripotent** stem cells can give rise to the various types of body tissues. The organ-specific stem cells found in the fetus and in adult humans have a much more restricted differentiation potential. These **pluripotent** stem cells are found in the bone marrow, the digestive tract, the skin and the central nervous system, where they may be important in regeneration.

Therapeutically, it is obvious that stem cells offer the opportunity to replace damaged and lost tissue in diseases such as *Alzheimer's* and *Parkinson's, diabetes, myocardial infarction, stroke* and *spinal cord injuries.* Those obtained from embryos have the greatest viability and potential.

Embryonic stem cells had been obtained from surplus embryos created for couples having difficulties in conceiving. Typically, a number of eggs are fertilized in this procedure. Only one embryo is implanted in the uterus, and any unused embryos can then be donated for use as a source of stem cells.

In July 2001, researchers at the Jones Institute for Reproductive Medicine in Norfolk, Virginia, obtained stem cells from human embryos that had been produced from the eggs and sperm of volunteers who made the donations *specifically* for this purpose.

There have been many divergent views expressed on the ethics of these techniques.

**72**

***Genes and cell differentiation* – it is important for you to understand that each and every cell of the adult body contains exactly the same genetic information encoded in the DNA of its nucleus.** This DNA was present in the fertilized egg (*zygote*). Since a liver cell has exactly the same genes as a skin cell or a nerve cell, how is it that they have become very different in their structure and function? *The answer is that in different cells some genes are turned on and others are turned off.* The cell-specific mechanisms that turn genes on and off are under intensive investigation in many laboratories around the world. Already there have been some impressive advances in our understanding of what controls *gene expression* in a cell-specific way.

### Epigenetics (See Chapter 6)

One aspect of epigenetics involves DNA methylation ($-CH_3$). DNA methylation causes transcriptional silencing.

Epigenetics explains differences between genetically identical human twins.

## III. Control of Cell Reproduction (Division)

In the body, cells can:

- Differentiate
- Grow and divide (proliferate)
- Not grow, not divide, but stay alive and functioning
- Die by a process called *apoptosis* (see next section)

Some cells reproduce themselves continually throughout life—for example, skin cells, blood-forming cells, and cells that line the intestine. In humans, a cell can divide roughly 50–100 times. Next semester (BIOL 204), we shall see that the structure that caps the ends of chromosomes—the *telomere*—may play a role in determining just how many times a cell can divide. An enzyme called telomerase is responsible for maintaining the integrity of telomeres. Increased longevity has been observed in mice that have undergone gene therapy to increase their cells' levels of telomerase. Further, this has occurred without increased prevalence of age-related disease such as osteoporosis and insulin resistance.

There are other cells, such as those of the liver, that divide until a certain number of cells is present, then stop. If, however, the number of liver cells is reduced by injury, the remaining cells are stimulated to divide again.

Yet other cells, such as muscle cells and most nerve cells, lose their ability to divide once they have become differentiated.

Cell division depends on complex controls, some stimulatory and some inhibitory. Genetically, some of these controls have been identified with *tumor suppressor genes* and with other genes called *proto-oncogenes*. They produce proteins that work side by side to regulate cell division by acting at various cell cycle checkpoints during interphase. These controls act on the timing of events in the cell cycle, such as the beginning of mitosis and the beginning of the S phase. The S phase is when DNA replication occurs.

The timing of events during the cell cycle is very important, because cells need to monitor DNA replication, to edit out any errors that may have occurred during this process, and to generally control other factors such as growth, replication of cell organelles, etc.

In *cancer* cells, the checks and balances that govern the division of normal cells are lost. These cells continually divide. Such uncontrolled division can be due to changes in the DNA of the chromosomes in the nucleus, sometimes associated with inherited predisposing mutations.

A further problem with cancer cells is that, unlike normal cells, they do not adhere to each other. Consequently, it is easy for groups of them to break away from the main *tumor* and be carried by blood or lymph to other parts of the body. There they become established as *secondary tumors*. This phenomenon is called *metastasis*.

Two major types of gene may be involved in the production of cancer.

1. **Tumor suppressor genes.**

    **Inactivation** (or loss) of a tumor suppressor gene causes cancer (e.g. *retinoblastoma*). Note that cells that have one copy of an inactivated tumor suppressor gene may be normal. These cells only become cancerous if the second copy on the other chromosome becomes inactivated.

2. **Proto-oncogenes.**

    **Activation** of a proto-oncogene causes cancer (e.g. *acute T-cell leukemias*).

The causes of activation or inactivation are varied. There may be mutations in the gene, or even rearrangements of pieces of DNA in the chromosome on which the gene is found.

**Viruses** may be involved. The incorporation of foreign, *viral DNA* into the DNA of a chromosome may sometimes activate a proto-oncogene. This is more common in animal cancers. In humans, viral DNA can bind to, and inactivate, the protein products of tumor suppressor genes.

## IV. Tumor Suppressor Genes, the Cell Cycle, Cell Cycle Checkpoint Determinants, DNA Repair and Editing, and Cancer

All of the phenomena we have discussed previously upset the control of cell division.

Tumor suppressor genes produce proteins that are called ***cell cycle checkpoint determinants.*** These proteins act to arrest cell division, often in the G1 phase of the cell cycle. This allows the cell time to repair damaged DNA. In certain cases, if the DNA is irreparably damaged, the cell may be induced to self-destruct (see next section). Other cell cycle checkpoint determinants appear to be important in allowing the cell time to correct ("edit") any errors that have occurred during *DNA replication* at S phase.

- One important example of a tumor suppressor gene is the ***retinoblastoma tumor suppressor gene.*** Retinoblastoma is a childhood tumor of the *retina* of the eye. The development of this tumor can lead to loss of the eye and even death if the tumor cells have migrated up the optic nerve to the brain. The development of this *malignancy* is due to loss of the retinoblastoma tumor suppressor gene. The protein produced by this gene is called pRB, and it suppresses cell division. Cells that want to divide inactivate pRB by placing a phosphate group on it (*phosphorylation*).

- Another tumor suppressor gene is the ***p53 tumor suppressor gene*** [the p stands for "protein" and the 53 for its molecular weight of 53,000]. ***p53 is the most frequently mutated gene in human cancer.*** A second gene, Mdm2, has a negative regulatory effect on p53. The relationship is a highly complex one, and has been the subject of a large volume of research.

A number of proteins like p53 have now been found, and future research will show how many of them are implicated in human cancers.

## V. Cell Suicide, Programmed Cell Death, or Apoptosis Is a Process that Differs from Necrosis

*Apoptosis* comes from a Greek word that refers to the falling of leaves from a tree or petals from a flower.

During normal embryonic development, many "unwanted" subpopulations of cells are killed selectively. The webs of skin between the fingers and toes of the fetus are destroyed, for example. Neurons die within the developing brain and self-reactive T-lymphocytes are purged within the thymus gland.

In the adult, cell death can be observed in tissues such as the breast, which undergo reversible expansion under the influence of hormones (for example). Neutrophils (a white blood cell) that have been treated with the hormone cortisol commit suicide. So do neurons that have been exposed to excessive amounts of the neurotransmitter glutamate, as can happen if a person has a stroke.

The above cases are all examples of apoptosis (usually, but not always, pronounced "apotosis"). It is possible that some cancers may result from a failure of apoptosis, and that certain neurodegenerative disorders (Alzheimer's disease, Parkinson's disease) may result from increased, abnormal apoptosis. The killing of tumor cells and virus-infected cells by certain cells of the the immune system is achieved by inducing them to undergo apoptosis.

During apoptosis, the cells:

- shrink and may round up
- their DNA breaks up and the chromatin condenses
- the nucleus breaks up into masses of condensed chromatin
- the cell develops "blebs" on its surface, which break away into membrane-bound vesicles (apoptotic vesicles or bodies)
- these vesicles are recognized and phagocytized by surrounding macrophages in the tissue (including macrophage-like cells called *microglia* in the brain)

The detailed mechanism of apoptosis is currently under study by many researchers. An early event is the specific activation of a series of special "executioner enzymes" called *caspases*. Some researchers have suggested that the mitochondria play a central role in this activation (read *Science 292*, 624, 2001).

The caspases are *proteases* (the name is derived from *cysteine **asp**artyl prote**ases***). They break down cellular proteins and activate enzymes that break down the DNA in the nucleus. A cell that dies from this process fragments into large vesicles that are rapidly gobbled up by macrophages before they can disintegrate and before such disintegration releases dangerous substances that might cause inflammation. **The cells therefore die without triggering inflammation.**

75

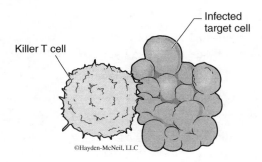

Figure 4-8.

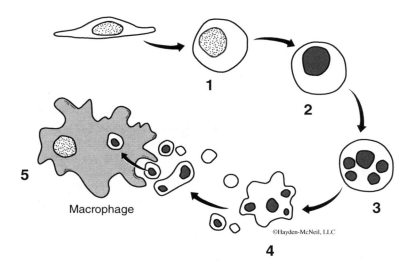

**Figure 4-9.** Apoptosis.

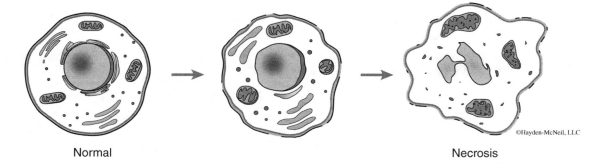

**Figure 4-10.** Necrosis.

*Necrosis* **is different from apoptosis. Necrosis can be described as accidental cell death rather than suicide.** When cells are damaged by severe and sudden injury (e.g. physical and chemical *trauma*), the following events occur.

1.  cells and mitochondria change shape, swell and lose their function
2.  membranes break down
3.  cells and organelles undergo lysis
4.  substances are released that trigger inflammation

## VI. Cloning

There has been a considerable amount of discussion recently about *cloning* of mammals. The first mammal was cloned at the Roslin Institute in Edinburgh, Scotland [Wilmut, Schnieke, McWhir, Kind, & Campbell (1997). *Nature 385*, 810–813]. It was a sheep called Dolly. The technique is called **nuclear transfer cloning**. An *oocyte* is taken and the nucleus is removed (in other words, the oocyte is *enucleated*). Using electric pulses, it is then fused with a differentiated donor cell complete with nucleus taken from an adult. In the case of Dolly, the differentiated cell was from the udder.

Wilmut's team succeeded because they made the donor cells from the udder *quiescent* before transferring the nucleus to the enucleated egg cell. For some reason, this caused the donor nucleus to be "reprogrammed" by the egg cell and start off from the beginning again, just as if it were the nucleus of a fertilized egg.

After activation, the combination starts dividing, and develops into an animal that is a clone of the adult from which the donor cell was taken.

Why clone?

- Producing herds of identical animals with high-quality genes. For example, if you have bred a cow that produces phenomenally high milk yields, you might want to clone it so that you have a whole herd of these cows.

- It is possible to engineer pigs genetically so that they have organs that will not be rejected by the human immune system. Such precious animals could be cloned to provide a supply of organs for patients on transplant waiting lists.

- Many genetic human diseases are caused by a defect in a protein—for example, hemophilia is caused by a defect in a clotting protein. Several companies are trying to make genetically engineered animals that secrete these human proteins into their milk. Cloning could create herds of these so-called "pharm" animals.

- Repair of the human body with cell and tissue grafts that are perfectly matched to the recipient. A healthy cell could be taken from the patient and the cloning process could be initiated as described for Dolly. The early stages of division could then be a source of stem cells that (in theory, at any rate) could be used to replace any of the patient's tissues.

78

# CHAPTER 5

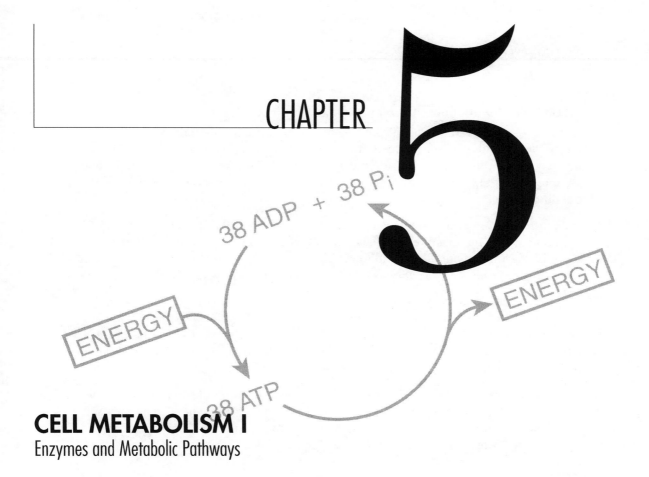

## CELL METABOLISM I
Enzymes and Metabolic Pathways

## CHAPTER OUTLINE

## DESCRIPTION AND INTRODUCTION

Our bodies cannot function without a supply of energy. This energy is provided by foods. We depend on foods in much the same way that an automobile depends on gasoline. Foods are the fuel that provide the energy to drive all the chemical reactions that are important to life. Foods provide the energy to synthesize the molecules that are the building blocks of cells.

Therefore, it is important to know how different foods are utilized as energy sources in the body, and to understand how this energy is packaged and used. We shall deal with some of the fundamentals of handling glucose and fatty acids this semester, but will continue next semester with a more detailed discussion of how various food types are utilized.

The chemical reactions that occur within cells represent the cells' *metabolism*. There are two main types of reaction. *Catabolic reactions* break down complex molecules of nutrients into simpler molecules, sometimes yielding usable energy in the process. *Anabolic reactions* are biosynthetic—that is, complex molecules are built up from simpler ones.

In a test tube, most of these reactions are so slow that they cannot be detected. In order to be useful, they must be speeded up. That is where *enzymes* come in. Enzymes are special proteins synthesized by cells. Their function is to speed up reactions. In doing so, they play vital roles in facilitating and regulating metabolic pathways.

## OBJECTIVES

After listening to the lecture and reading this chapter, you should be able to:

1.  Distinguish **anabolic** and **catabolic** metabolism.
2.  Give **three** examples of anabolic metabolism.
3.  Give **four** examples of catabolic metabolism.
4.  Explain what an **enzyme** is, and how it participates in the control of metabolic processes.
5.  Give the general **names** of enzymes that break down **lipids** and **proteins**.
6.  Describe what is meant by a **cofactor**.
7.  Name eight **metal ions** that are necessary for certain enzymes to function.
8.  Name two **coenzymes** and the vitamins they are derived from.
9.  Describe **two factors** that are important in affecting enzyme action.
10. Discuss the adaptation of enzymes to **extreme conditions**.
11. Name one **poison** that acts on an enzyme. Name the **type** of enzyme.
12. Explain what we mean by **oxidation** and **reduction**.
13. Explain the overall **strategy** for the production of energy by oxidation of the food molecule *glucose*.
14. Now describe *in detail* the four fundamental steps in the controlled "burning" of glucose.
15. Describe the general metabolic pathways for **fats** and **proteins**.
16. State which organ uses **fatty acids** as its primary source of energy.
17. Define what is meant by **deamination**.

## I. Metabolic Processes (Metabolism)

Metabolic processes (metabolism) include all the chemical reactions taking place in a cell. There are two types. One generates all the energy required by the body, the other uses this energy.

*   **Anabolic metabolism** involves *synthesis* of new molecules, a process that utilizes energy. An example is the synthesis of proteins from amino acids.

*   **Catabolic metabolism** involves *breakdown* of molecules, a process that is usually designed to generate energy. An example is the breakdown of glucose to carbon dioxide and water.

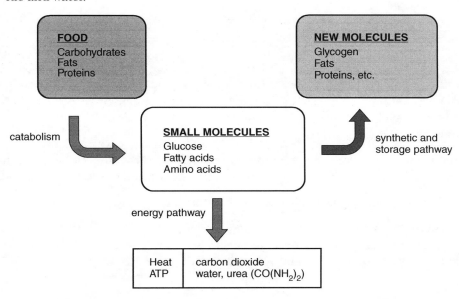

**Figure 5-1.** Metabolic processes. All of the chemical reactions in the body.

## A. Anabolic Metabolism (Anabolism)

Examples of anabolic metabolism include the synthesis of *glycogen* and *fat* for storage, and the synthesis of proteins.

1.  **Glycogen synthesis.**

    Glycogen is a **polysaccharide**, and is the storage form of carbohydrate, specifically glucose. Glycogen consists of a very long chain of molecules of the **monosaccharide glucose**. Adjacent monosaccharide molecules are strung together by elimination of a *hydroxyl group* (−OH) from one of them and a hydrogen atom (H) from the other. Since these represent the elements of water (one OH and one H combine to form $H_2O$), the process is therefore referred to as *dehydration synthesis*. The opposite of dehydration synthesis is *hydrolysis*.

2.  **Fat synthesis.**

    Fats are stored in ***adipose tissues*** in the body. Fats are ***triglycerides***. A molecule of fat consists of a *glycerol* molecule joined to three fatty acids. Fat synthesis occurs by elimination of the elements of water from one molecule of **glycerol** and three molecules of **fatty acid**. This process is therefore a dehydration synthesis.

3.  **Protein synthesis.**

    Proteins consist of chains of ***amino acids*** united by a covalent bond called a ***peptide bond***. The peptide bond is established by eliminating the elements of water from adjacent amino acids. Again, this process is a dehydration synthesis. The precise sequence of amino acids strung together to form a protein is encoded in molecules of DNA that make up the chromosomes of the nucleus.

## B. Catabolic Metabolism (Catabolism)

There are many catabolic reactions. Some simple catabolic reactions carried out by the body are the breakdown of:

1.  **polysaccharides** (e.g. glycogen) into *monosaccharides* (e.g. glucose)
2.  **proteins** into *amino acids*
3.  **fats** into *fatty acids* and *glycerol*

These processes are the opposite of dehydration synthesis, and involve breaking the bonds between the monosaccharides, amino acids, or between glycerol and fatty acids by inserting the elements of water (H and OH). The process is called **hydrolysis** and is facilitated by specific **enzymes**.

During digestion, fats are **hydrolyzed** to fatty acids and glycerol, proteins are **hydrolyzed** to their constituent amino acids, and carbohydrates are **hydrolyzed** to monosaccharides.

A fourth, more complex catabolic reaction is as follows.

82

4.  Combustion of food molecules to generate energy for the body's activities. This process (sometimes called ***cellular respiration***) effectively "burns" food molecules (e.g. glucose) by using oxygen, and generates carbon dioxide, water, heat and usable energy.

## II. Enzymes Are Involved in Metabolic Pathways

## A. Enzymes

Enzymes are proteins that act as catalysts for specific chemical reactions. They speed up reactions, but are not consumed.

Chemical reactions occur when chemical bonds between atoms are made or broken. Chemical reactions require energy before they will occur. This energy is referred to as the *activation energy* of the reaction. In the laboratory it is often provided by heating the reactants.

Although the most energetically favorable forms of carbon, hydrogen and oxygen are carbon dioxide and water, a teaspoon of sugar or glucose does not disappear in a puff of smoke. For the same reason, this piece of paper does not burst into flame spontaneously. The molecules of sugar, glucose, or paper require activation energy before they can pass into the more favorable, lower-energy states consisting of water and carbon dioxide, giving off energy in the process.

Now you can, if you wish, provide this activation energy by throwing the sugar or glucose on a lighted charcoal grill, or applying a lighted match to the paper. If you do this, the sugar, glucose, or paper will burn with the emission of heat and light energy. But this process won't help the living organism, which needs to derive usable energy during the burning process. Therefore, in the living organism combustion of foods (usually glucose or fatty acids) is achieved in a controlled fashion that releases not only heat, but energy in a form that can be used.

Because of their high activation energies, most of the chemical reactions in cells would take place at immeasurably slow rates and in an uncontrolled fashion if the cells did not contain enzymes.

Enzymes are proteins that act as catalysts. Cells manufacture many enzymes, each catalyzing a specific reaction. Enzymes function by *lowering the activation energy of the reaction*, so *increasing the rate of the reaction.*

Enzymes therefore make chemical reactions happen rapidly.

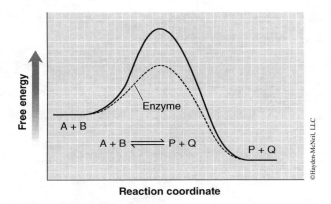

**Figure 5-2.** An enzyme reduces the activation energy of a reaction.

An enzyme lowers the activation energy of a reaction by first binding with its *substrate*, the molecule it is acting upon. Because the enzyme is very specific, it must recognize its own substrate out of the many different molecules in the cell, and combine with it to form an *enzyme–substrate complex*. Once the reaction has taken place, the enzyme is released unaltered and can be used again and again.

This recycling of enzyme molecules means that the energy of the cell is not wasted by having to continuously manufacture new enzyme molecules.

83

Shown below is an example of how an enzyme might act to promote the splitting of a substrate A.B into two components, A and B.

**enzyme + A.B → enzyme.A.B → enzyme + A + B**

If A is glucose and B is galactose, then A.B would be lactose. The enzyme in this case would be *lactase*: this reaction would represent the splitting of lactose into its monosaccharide components during digestion.

**lactase + lactose → lactase.lactose → lactase + glucose + galactose**
(enzyme)  (substrate)

Note that the enzyme lactase is not consumed in the reaction, and may be recycled for splitting more molecules of lactose.

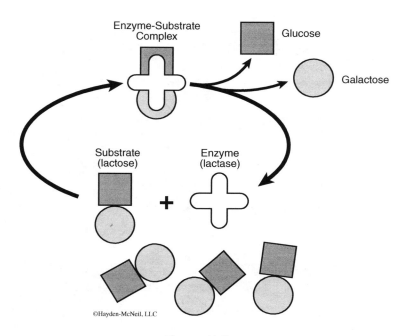

©Hayden-McNeil, LLC

**Figure 5-3.**

Another enzyme could act to promote the combination of two molecules C and D to form a new molecule, C.D.

**enzyme + C + D → enzyme.C.D → enzyme + C.D**

C might be glucose and D *fructose*. The result, C.D, is sucrose, and the reaction might represent the synthesis of sucrose in sugar cane.

Commonly, the names of enzymes are derived by adding the suffix **-ase** to the name of the substrate. An enzyme that splits lipids is called a *lipase*, one that breaks down proteins is a *protease,* etc.

Other names are derived by defining the substrate and the mechanism by which the enzyme acts. Thus, groups of enzymes are known as *hydrolases, synthetases, isomerases, dehydrogenases,* etc. An enzyme that removes hydrogen from lactate is therefore called *lactate dehydrogenase.*

## B. Cofactors—Substances Required for Some Enzymes to Function

In order to function properly, many enzymes require **cofactors**. These cofactors can either be *metal ions* or a group of small organic molecules called *coenzymes*.

1.  **Metal ions.**

    In addition to their basic protein structure, enzymes often contain components that are not amino acids. About one-third of known enzymes require metal ions in order to function. Some enzymes contain copper tightly bound within their molecules, and many other enzymes are inactive unless a specific metal ion is present. Examples of metal ions that are required by some enzymes are *iron, calcium, cobalt, copper, magnesium, manganese, molybdenum,* and *zinc*. Some of these metals are called *trace elements* because although they are essential components of our diet they are only needed in very small quantities.

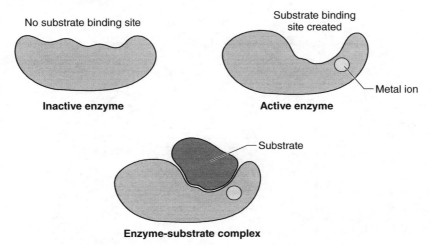

**Figure 5-4.** About one-third of known enzymes require metal ions in order to function.

2.  **Coenzymes.**

    Small organic molecules that work with enzymes. Many are derived from the vitamin B complex. Some *coenzymes* are involved in oxidation–reduction reactions. Two examples of important coenzymes involved in oxidation–reduction reactions are *nicotinamide adenine dinucleotide (NAD$^+$)* and *flavin adenine dinucleotide (FAD)*. NAD$^+$ is derived from nicotinate (*niacin*) and FAD from *riboflavin* (*vitamin B$_2$*).

85

## C. pH and Temperature—Two Factors that Affect Enzyme Function

Most enzymes work best at certain values of pH and temperature. These are called the optimum pH and temperature for the enzyme in question.

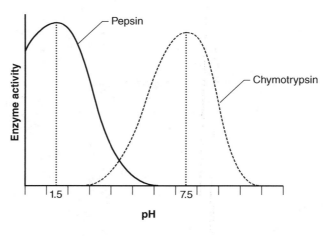

**Figure 5-5.**

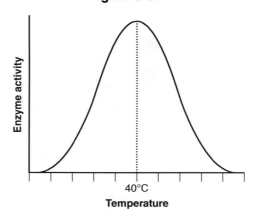

**Figure 5-6.**

For example, enzymes become less effective at pH values that are above or below certain optimal values (usually, but not always, around pH 7–8). Extremes of alkalinity and acidity will inactivate them permanently.

Most enzymes in the human body work very slowly or not at all at temperatures much below body temperature. If human body temperature rises above 45°C, most human enzymes are inactivated. Most of these enzymes are irreversibly denatured (like all proteins) if exposed to temperatures at or above 55°C. At these temperatures, weak bonds called hydrogen bonds are broken. Hydrogen bonds are responsible for maintaining the shapes of proteins, allowing them to function.

### D. Enzymes that Operate Under Environmentally Extreme Conditions

Did life ever develop on Venus, Mars and the other planets of the solar system? At the moment, we do not know. The evidence for life in a Martian meteorite reported a few years ago is now discredited, although the Mars Explorer probes have revealed strong evidence for past water on the planet. However, life can be very resilient, and there are organisms on Earth that have adapted to very harsh environments. Certain bacteria live in hot thermal springs in Yellowstone National Park, Wyoming, and in thermal vents under the oceans. The enzymes found in these bacteria are able to survive and function at about 90°C, close to the temperature of boiling water. Apparently, they have developed extremely stable structures, and cannot be unravelled (denatured) at these elevated temperatures. At the other end of the scale, some fish live in very cold Antarctic waters and have enzymes specially tailored to operate at low temperatures. Yet other organisms live in oil wells, beneath the Arctic and Antarctic ice sheets, and in salt marshes.

Some chemists have coined the word *"extremozymes"* for all these enzymes that can operate under environmentally extreme conditions.

### E. Poisons

Some poisons such as *cyanide* interfere with the respiratory enzymes in the mitochondria and kill cells by halting their ability to make ATP. These processes will be described below.

### F. Oxidation–Reduction Reactions: Enzymes and Coenzymes

In metabolism, *oxidation* refers to the *removal of hydrogen atoms* from a molecule. *Reduction* is the opposite of oxidation, and refers to the *addition of hydrogen atoms* to a molecule.

1. **Oxidation.**

    In metabolism, this usually refers to the removal of two or more hydrogen atoms from a molecule. At this point, it has nothing to do with oxygen. An example is the conversion of *lactic acid* to *pyruvic acid*.

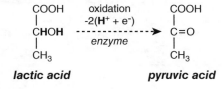

**Figure 5-7.** Oxidation of lactic acid to pyruvic acid.

Note that we have written the two hydrogen atoms as $2(H^+ + e^-)$ instead of the equivalent $2H$. This is because in the body, this oxidation is a little more complicated than the reaction above suggests. There is an enzyme called **lactate dehydrogenase** involved, and the very important coenzyme, **nicotinamide adenine dinucleotide** or **$NAD^+$**.

$$\text{lactate} + NAD^+ \xrightarrow{\text{\textit{lactate dehydrogenase}}} \text{pyruvate} + NADH + H^+$$

Note that two $H^+$ and two electrons ($= 2H$) are removed from lactate. However, although the two electrons are transferred to $NAD^+$, only one of the $H^+$ is. Thus, the positive charge of the $NAD^+$ is neutralized by the extra electron. The remaining $H^+$ goes into the solution.

In this oxidation, therefore, **NAD$^+$ acquires two electrons and one proton** (the other proton goes into solution). **The resulting *NADH* molecules therefore store electrons generated in the body's oxidation reactions.**

Ultimately, the electrons in NADH (together with hydrogen ions from the solution) will be used to interact with atmospheric oxygen to form water in the reaction:

$$4\,e^- + 4\,H^+ + O_2 \rightarrow 2\,H_2O$$

2.  **Reduction.**

    Is the opposite of oxidation. It refers to the addition of hydrogen atoms (electrons and hydrogen ions) to a molecule. If we reverse the above reaction, we get reduction instead of oxidation (note that the enzyme is still lactate dehydrogenase).

$$\textit{pyruvate} + NADH + H^+ \xrightarrow{\text{lactate dehydrogenase}} \textit{lactate} + NAD^+$$

When it is converted to lactate, pyruvate gains two H$^+$ and two e$^-$, the one H$^+$ and the two electrons having come from NADH itself (NADH is an electron repository), and one of the H$^+$ from the solution.

Oxidation and reduction reactions are always coupled: whenever a substance is oxidized, another is reduced. *Oxidation–reduction reactions* play important roles in carbohydrate, lipid and protein metabolism.

## III. How We Get the Energy to Sustain Life

We need energy for many activities. Energy is needed to:

-   Synthesize molecules (anabolic metabolism).
-   Generate force and movement (in muscles).
-   Carry out active transport across membranes (e.g. pumping sodium ions out of cells).

---

The energy to sustain these life processes is generated by **oxidation–reduction** reactions—that's why we spent some time talking about them in the previous section.

---

Cells obtain energy by oxidation of food molecules (glucose or fatty acids, for example) to carbon dioxide and water. The breakdown and oxidation of food molecules occurs in sequences of enzyme-catalyzed reactions. The success of cells is due to their ability to make enzymes of many different types to perform specific tasks in the cell. These enzymes can speed up reactions by as much as 1014 times.

---

Energy generated by oxidation–reduction reactions is packaged for transfer around the cell—these energy-containing packages are molecules of **adenosine triphosphate (ATP).**

---

Part of the energy released by "burning" glucose is coupled to the formation of a very important compound called *adenosine triphosphate*, or *ATP*. ATP is a store of energy that can diffuse around the cell, and can be used to drive many different reactions.

The coupling of glucose catabolic metabolism to ATP formation is achieved mainly through NADH, and to a lesser extent through *flavin adenine dinucleotide*, FADH$_2$. Both these compounds store electrons, which are ultimately passed to oxygen (see the section on oxidation–reduction reactions, above).

When ATP is "cashed in" for energy, it is hydrolyzed to *adenosine diphosphate (ADP)* and a phosphate ion *(inorganic phosphate, or P$_i$)*. More ATP is then generated from ADP and P$_i$ during oxidation of more food molecules.

## A. The Four Steps in Carbohydrate Metabolism

During digestion, polysaccharides (e.g. starch from vegetables, glycogen from food of animal origin), and disaccharides (sucrose, lactose) are hydrolyzed (split by enzymes and water) to monosaccharides—glucose, fructose and galactose. After absorption by the small intestine they are carried to the liver, where fructose and galactose are converted to glucose (next semester).

**Glucose is the monosaccharide that is burned to produce energy in the body.** Any glucose that is not used for immediate energy production is stored in the liver and skeletal muscle cells in the form of granules of the polysaccharide glycogen. Glycogen consists of many glucose molecules strung together. If the glycogen storage areas are filled up, the liver cells transform glucose to fat, which is stored in adipose tissue.

89

In the body, glucose is burned to produce carbon dioxide, water and *energy*. Part of the energy generated by this process appears as heat, and serves to keep our bodies warm. The remainder is used to generate ATP.

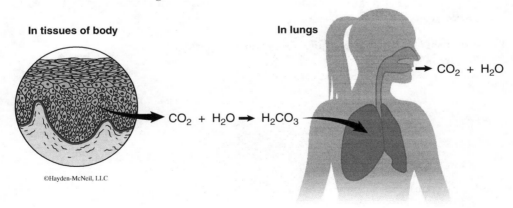

**Figure 5-8.**

**The purpose of the catabolic metabolism of glucose is to generate ATP.**

$$C_6H_{12}O_6 + 6\,O_2 + 38\,ADP + 38\,P_i \rightarrow 38\,ATP + 6\,CO_2 + 6\,H_2O + heat$$

Note: two of the ATPs are actually *GTP, guanosine triphosphate,* which in some ways is equivalent to ATP.

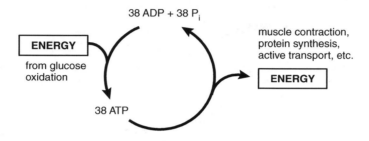

**ATP molecules are energy packages
that release their energy when ATP
is hydrolyzed to ADP and P**

**Figure 5-9.** Overall strategy.

The controlled burning of glucose to produce useful energy (in the currency of ATP) takes place in four sequential steps:

1. *glycolysis*

2. **formation of *acetyl coenzyme A***

3. **addition of the acetyl two-carbon fragment to oxaloacetic acid to form citric acid in the *Krebs cycle***

4. ***oxidative phosphorylation,* or the *electron transport chain***

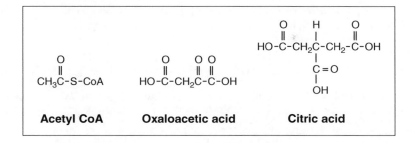

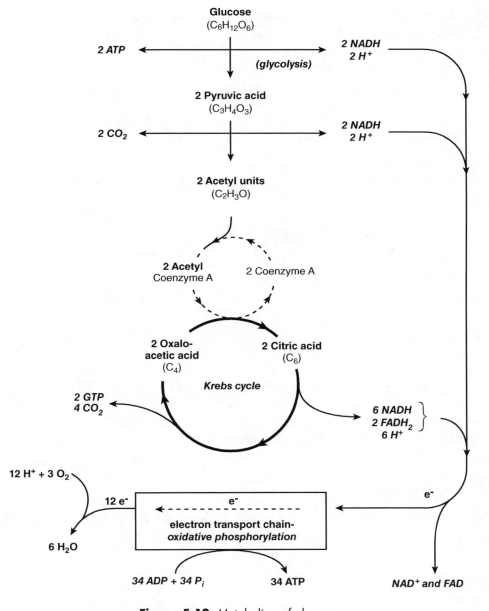

**Figure 5-10.** Metabolism of glucose.

Overall, glycolysis converts one 6-carbon molecule of glucose to two 3-carbon molecules of pyruvate, in the process generating two molecules of ATP and two molecules of NADH.

$$C_6H_{12}O_6 + 2\ ADP + 2\ P_i + 2\ NAD^+ \rightarrow 2\ \text{pyruvate} + 2\ ATP + 2\ NADH + 2\ H_2O$$

The process is complex, and actually involves 10 reactions, each with its own specific enzyme. Two molecules of ATP are consumed during these reactions, but since four molecules of ATP are produced, there is a net production of 2 molecules of ATP, as shown in the above equation.

1.  **The fate of pyruvate depends on the availability of oxygen.**

    Under *anaerobic* conditions, such as occur in a skeletal muscle during strenuous exercise, pyruvate is converted into lactic acid.

    $$\text{pyruvate} + NADH + H^+ \xrightarrow{\text{lactate dehydrogenase}} \text{lactate} + NAD^+$$

    The process is reversible, and some lactate is converted back to pyruvate when oxygen becomes available again.

    When adequate oxygen is available under normal, *aerobic* conditions, however, the 3-carbon pyruvate is prepared for the next stage of catabolic metabolism (the Krebs or citric acid cycle) by passing it into the mitochondria.

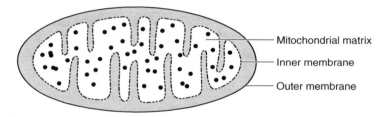

**Figure 5-11.** Simplified diagram of a mitochondrian.

2.  **Formation of acetyl coenzyme A (in the mitochondrial matrix).**

    In the matrix of the mitochondria, pyruvate is converted into one molecule of $CO_2$ and one molecule of a 2-carbon "acetyl" that is then attached to a carrier called *coenzyme A*. The combination is called *acetyl CoA*.

    $$\text{pyruvate} + NAD^+ + \text{coenzyme A} \rightarrow \text{acetyl CoA} + CO_2 + NADH + H^+$$

    This process generates one molecule of NADH.

3.  **The citric acid cycle or Krebs cycle (in the mitochondrial matrix).**

    The next step is the processing of the two carbon acetyl fragment in a cycle of reactions called the **Krebs** or **citric acid cycle**.

Sir Hans Krebs obtained important data that led to the discovery of the citric acid cycle at the University of Sheffield in England in the late 1930s. Most of laboratory work was actually done by a PhD student of his called William Arthur Johnson. The work was first submitted to the prestigious scientific journal *Nature*, which rejected it, allegedly because of lack of space! The paper was finally accepted in the journal *Enzymologia*. Sir Hans received the 1953 Nobel Prize for Physiology and Medicine as a result of these studies, which have played a central role in our understanding of cell metabolism. In a speech made in Dallas in 1980, Johnson was reported to have said that biochemistry had given him "at an early and impressionable age, the opportunity of working with one of the world's finest minds…"

The oxidative reactions of the Krebs *(citric acid)* cycle generate electrons that are "stored" in **NADH** (and to some extent in **FADH$_2$** as well). The citric acid cycle is the final common pathway for oxidation of food molecules, including not only *carbohydrates* but also *fats* and *proteins*.

In the Krebs cycle, the 2-carbon acetyl unit of acetyl CoA is oxidized to $CO_2$, generating GTP. We will talk about GTP in a future chapter. At present, let us think of it as equivalent to ATP. More importantly, however, the process generates NADH and FADH$_2$. The overall reaction is as follows:

$$\text{acetyl CoA} + 3\ NAD^+ + FAD + GDP + P_i + 2\ H_2O \rightarrow 2\ CO_2 + 3\ NADH + FADH_2 + GTP + 2\ H^+ + CoA$$

The Krebs cycle has many steps, however. We will not deal with them all.

The Krebs cycle starts by the addition of the 2-carbon acetyl group of acetyl CoA to a 4-carbon "carrier" called **oxaloacetic acid**, a process that generates the 6-carbon molecule of **citric acid** (hence the alternative name for the Krebs cycle, the citric acid cycle).

The 2 carbon atoms donated to oxaloacetic acid by the acetyl group of acetyl CoA result in the formation of citric acid. These two carbons are then lost in the form of carbon dioxide through a complex series of reactions involving seven intermediates and ending up with oxaloacetic acid again.

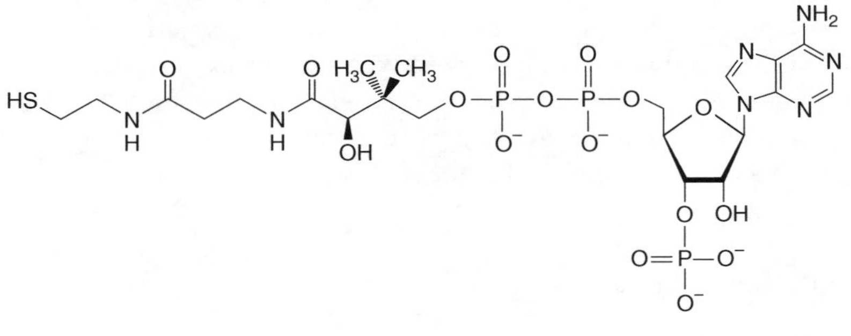

93

**Figure 5-12.** Coenzyme A.

In the cycle, oxaloacetic acid is regenerated, and is used again. Oxaloacetic acid, therefore, is a carrier for 2-carbon acetyl groups, and is not used up. This is important. If oxaloacetic acid were used up, we would need to obtain a kilogram of it from somewhere every day!

**Beri-beri is caused by lack of vitamin B$_1$, which is part of two important enzymes in the Krebs cycle.** *Beri-beri* is a disease that was first recognized in Asia and the Far East. It is due to eating "polished" white rice. The polishing process removes the husk, which contains *vitamin B$_1$ (thiamine)*. The symptoms are pain, muscle weakness, and cardiac problems caused by inadequate cardiac output. Vitamin B$_1$ (thiamine) is a component of two enzymes of the Krebs cycle—*pyruvate dehydrogenase* and *alpha-ketoglutarate dehydrogenase*. In beri-beri, levels of pyruvate and alpha-ketoglutarate in the blood are much higher than normal. Another affected enzyme is transketolase.

4. **The electron-transport chain, oxidative phosphorylation (in the inner membrane of the mitochondria).**

   The reactions of the Krebs cycle occur in the *matrix* of the mitochondria, oxidative phosphorylation occurs in the *inner membrane* of the mitochondria.

   ---

   In oxidative phosphorylation the electrons transferred to NADH and FADH$_2$ by glycolysis and the Krebs cycle are used to generate large numbers of ATP molecules.

   ---

During oxidative phosphorylation, electrons flow from NADH (and FADH$_2$) to *oxygen*. This is coupled to the pumping of H$^+$ ions out of the mitochondrial matrix. When the H$^+$ ions flow back into the mitochondrial matrix, large numbers of ADP molecules are phosphorylated with the aid of a rotary enzyme called ATP synthase, so generating large numbers of ATP molecules and water.

$$ADP + P_i + 4e^- + 4\,H^+ + O_2 \rightarrow 2\,H_2O + ATP$$

Oxidative phosphorylation involves a chain of molecules embedded in the inner membrane of the mitochondria that allow electrons to flow from NADH and FADH$_2$ to oxygen, the result being water. Three stationary enzyme complexes are linked together by two mobile electron carriers. When electrons are transferred from each of these complexes to the next, there is a release of free energy. This free energy is used to pump hydrogen ions across the inner membrane of the mitochondrion into the space between the inner and outer membranes.

These are:

1. NADH-dehydrogenase complex

2. Ubiquinone

3. Cytochrome b-c1 complex

4. Cytochrome

5. Cytochrome oxidase complex

The flow of electrons is as follows (see figures):

a.   at the start of the chain, NADH is reduced to $NAD^+$, its electrons being picked up by the NADH-dehydrogenase complex.

b.   the mobile carrier ubiquinone (coenzyme Q) transfers these electrons to the cytochrome b-c1 complex.

c.   the mobile carrier cytochrome transfers these electrons to the cytochrome oxidase complex.

d.   the cytochrome oxidase complex transfers these electrons to molecular oxygen — throw in some hydrogen ions and you get water.

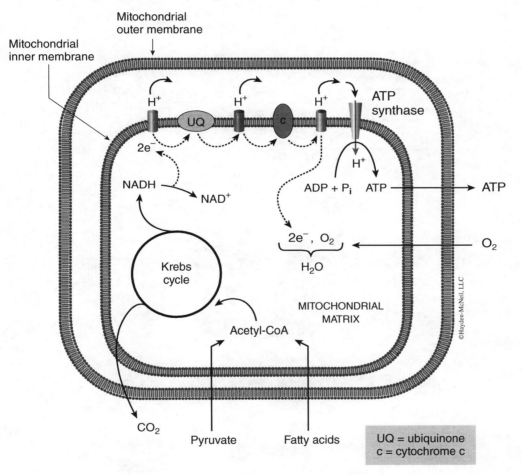

**Figure 5-13.**

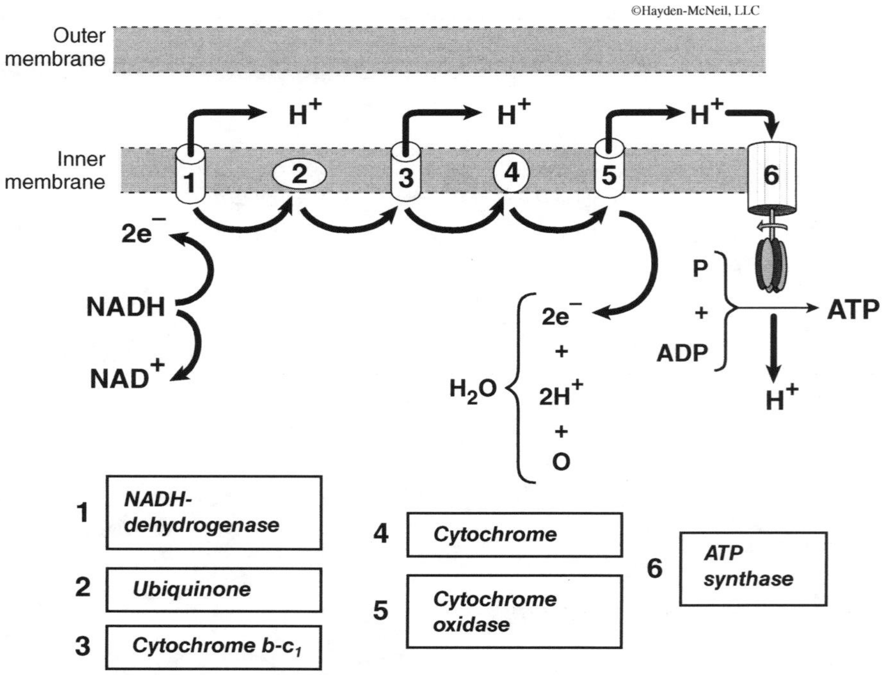

©Hayden-McNeil, LLC

Outer membrane

Inner membrane

H$^+$   H$^+$   H$^+$   H$^+$

1   2   3   4   5   6

2e$^-$

NADH

NAD$^+$

2e$^-$
+
2H$^+$
+
O

H$_2$O

P
+
ADP

ATP

H$^+$

| 1 | NADH-dehydrogenase |
|---|---|
| 2 | Ubiquinone |
| 3 | Cytochrome b-c$_1$ |

| 4 | Cytochrome |
|---|---|
| 5 | Cytochrome oxidase |

| 6 | ATP synthase |
|---|---|

**Figure 5-14.**

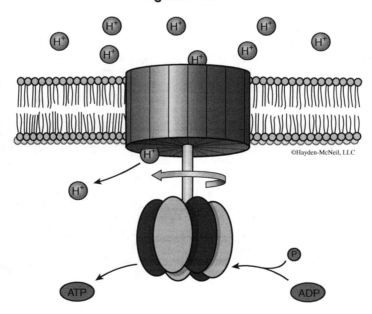

**Model of the rotary enzyme ATP synthase.**
*In 1997 the Nobel Prize in chemistry was awarded to Professor Paul D. Boyer, University of California, Los Angeles, USA, and Dr. John E. Walker, Medical Research Council Laboratory of Molecular Biology, Cambridge, United Kingdom, for their elucidation of the mechanism of ATP synthase.*

**Figure 5-15.**

**5.** **An uncoupling protein is found in brown fat.**

An **uncoupling protein** (thermogenin) occurs in brown adipose tissue. Brown fat is found in newborn babies, and also in adults. The uncoupling protein is in the inner mitochondrial membrane, and it blocks development of the $H^+$ electrochemical gradient. ATP synthesis cannot take place, and the energy appears as heat. This phenomenon is known as "**non-shivering thermogenesis**," and it is valuable as a source of extra heat in infants where the shivering reflex has not developed.

**6.** **Summary of NADH, FADH$_2$, and ATP produced during controlled catabolic "burning" of one glucose molecule.**

| Process | NADH or FADH$_2$ | ATP |
|---|---|---|
| 1. Glycolysis | 2 NADH + 2 H$^+$ | 2 ATP |
| 2. Formation of acetyl CoA | 2 NADH + 2 H$^+$ | |
| 3. Krebs cycle | 6 NADH + 6 H$^+$, 2 FADH$_2$ | 2 GTP |
| 4. Oxidative phosphorylation | uses NADH and FADH$_2$ | 34 ATP |

**7.** **Dependence of different tissues on oxidative phosphorylation.**

The *central nervous system* is the tissue that is most dependent on oxidative phosphorylation. **Even though the *brain* represents only 2% of the body's weight, it consumes 20% of the available oxygen.**

The following is a list of tissues that are very dependent on oxidative phosphorylation. As mentioned above, the central nervous system heads the list.

- central nervous system
- skeletal and cardiac muscle
- *kidney*
- *liver*

The efficiency of oxidative phosphorylation declines as a person ages, possibly because there is an accumulation of harmful mutations in mitochondrial DNA.

**8.** **Comparing glucose metabolism to gasoline burning in an automobile.**

*The fuel is burned with oxygen to provide energy* – the glucose and the carbon fragments, electrons and hydrogen ions it produces can all be compared to the gasoline fuel used by an automobile engine. Note that gasoline is also a carbon fuel.

*The engine components control the burning process, but are not consumed* – the enzymes, coenzyme A, NAD$^+$, FAD$^+$, oxaloacetic acid, components of the electron transport chain are all used to run the system. Unlike the fuel (glucose, etc.), these substances are not consumed and can be used again and again to process the fuel.

97

## B. Triglycerides Are Also an Important Energy Source

**Fats** (= **triglycerides**) are an important source of energy. Except for the brain, most tissues can use triglycerides as well as glucose for energy production. The heart is unusual in that cardiac muscle uses fats (actually **fatty acids**) as a primary source of energy.

Triglycerides originate in food or can be synthesized from excess glucose or amino acids. When fats, specifically triglycerides, are not needed immediately, they are stored in adipose tissue (fat depots). About half of the fat stored in the body is deposited in subcutaneous tissue.

Fat catabolic metabolism first involves hydrolyzing the triglycerides into glycerol and fatty acids. *When hydrolyzed,* **one molecule of a triglyceride yields one molecule of glycerol and three molecules of assorted fatty acids.**

The fatty acids may contain 16 or more carbon atoms, so three of them would contain at least 48 carbons. They are converted into *two-carbon fragments* by a process called **beta-oxidation**. These two-carbon fragments are then added to *coenzyme A*, forming *acetyl CoA*. Acetyl CoA then "injects" these two-carbon fragments into the Krebs cycle. Some acetyl CoA may be converted to substances called *ketone bodies* or *ketoacids*, but that is a topic for next semester.

The glycerol molecules (each contains only three carbons) formed by the hydrolysis of fats either enter the Krebs cycle after conversion to acetyl CoA or they can be used to synthesize glucose.

## C. Proteins

When dietary proteins are digested in the gastrointestinal tract, the resulting **amino acids** are absorbed and often joined together in new combinations to make new protein molecules for use as enzymes and cell parts.

When amino acids are not being used as building blocks for human proteins they may be processed for energy production. The first step in this processing is *deamination*. That is, removal of the nitrogen-containing portion.

During deamination, the nitrogen-containing $NH_2$ groups are removed, combined with carbon dioxide, and converted into the waste substance ***urea***, $CO(NH_2)_2$, which is then excreted *via* the urine (next semester).

What is left after deamination is a molecule that contains all the carbon atoms of the original amino acid, but which has lost its nitrogen. If energy is needed, the deaminated portion of the amino acid is further processed and enters the Krebs cycle either as acetyl CoA or as one of the other substances in the Krebs cycle.

If energy is not needed, the deaminated portion of the amino acid may be converted to glucose or fat molecules.

Glucose, together with certain nitrogen-containing molecules, can be changed into some amino acids. However, about eight amino acids cannot be synthesized in human cells by this route, and must be provided in the diet. These amino acids are called *essential amino acids* (next semester).

## IV. Regulation of Metabolic Pathways

Rates of enzyme-controlled reactions often depend on the concentrations of substrate and enzyme molecules. However, in many metabolic pathways, the first enzyme in the pathway is often inhibited by the final metabolic product of that pathway. This is a *negative-feedback* mechanism.

Negative-feedback serves to control the rate at which the product is generated. If the product *accumulates* (perhaps because it is not needed at the moment), then it *inhibits* the first enzyme of the pathway and its rate of production is reduced. If the product is *depleted* (perhaps because it is being used very rapidly), the first enzyme of the pathway is *disinhibited* and the rate of production is increased.

# CHAPTER 6

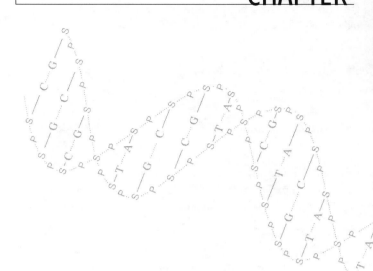

# CELL METABOLISM II
Protein Synthesis, DNA, RNA, DNA Mutations and Genetic Diseases,
DNA Profiling and PCR

101

## CHAPTER OUTLINE

## DESCRIPTION AND INTRODUCTION

**Proteins** play a central role in the functioning of the cell. There are vast numbers of proteins in the human body. Here are some examples that you need to know.

- nearly all **enzymes** are proteins
- **structural components of the cell** such as *collagen* and *elastin*
- *ion channels* in the plasma membrane
- **receptors** for hormones and neurotransmitters
- **contractile elements** of muscle such as *actin* and *myosin*
- *antibodies*

We cannot manufacture proteins without the assembly information carried in *DNA* and *RNA*. DNA and RNA are very large molecules concerned with protein synthesis. However, DNA and RNA are not proteins themselves: they are made up of strings of *nucleotides*.

Outside of *mitochondrial DNA*, all of the DNA in a cell is found in the nucleus, each molecule of DNA making up one *chromosome*. DNA stores genetic information that carries the codes for synthesizing each and every protein found in the body. RNA transmits this information from the nucleus to the cell cytoplasm. The genetic information in DNA is transmitted with high fidelity down through the generations.

## OBJECTIVES

After listening to the lecture and reading this chapter, you should be able to:

1. Describe the importance of **proteins** in cell function and structure.
2. Name five proteins.
3. Describe the structure of a **DNA** molecule, name the three components of the molecule, and explain how it stores genetic information.
4. Define a **gene**, and name its components.
5. Describe how the genetic information stored in the DNA molecule is used to synthesize specific proteins in the cell.
6. Explain the difference between DNA and **RNA**.
7. Name and describe the functions of the three types of RNA in the cell.
8. Distinguish **transcription** and **translation**: define the difference between a molecule of **mRNA** and a molecule of a **protein**.
9. Name the five components necessary for translation.
10. Explain the function of **nuclear pores**.
11. Describe how the cell maintains quality control of its proteins and removes misfolded, damaged and aggregated proteins by two separate pathways. What structures are responsible for ensuring that newly synthesized proteins are folded correctly?
12. Describe how and why a DNA molecule is **replicated**.
13. Explain why at metaphase a chromosome appears as a **doubled** structure consisting of two **chromatids**.
14. Describe and analyze the consequences of **mutations** in the DNA molecule.
15. Define a **genetic disease**.

16. Explain what we mean by **gene therapy**, and list two methods for introducing DNA into cells.

17. Explain what is meant by DNA **profiling** and **PCR**.

18. Explain the evolutionary origins of **mitochondrial DNA** (mtDNA).

19. Explain what is meant by RNA interference.

20. What is DNA methylation and how might it affect gene expression?

## I. Protein Synthesis—DNA and RNA, the Molecules of Heredity

### A. Proteins

Proteins are the basis of cellular function. Some examples:

- Components of cell structure (structural proteins: *collagen*, *elastin*, *tubulin*, etc.)

- Enzymes (**lactate dehydrogenase**, **cytochrome oxidase**, etc.)

- **Antibodies**, blood proteins (**serum** *albumin*), carrier proteins for vitamins A, E, etc.

- Many functions in the plasma membrane of different cells (for example, **ion channels**, **hormone receptors**, **transport molecules**)

The molecular constitution of the human body therefore depends on cells being able to synthesize proteins.

Proteins are made up of a string of amino acids joined together by means of peptide bonds. The sequence in which these amino acids are joined together characterizes the protein, which is said to have a specific amino acid sequence. Each protein must be very accurately assembled from its constituent amino acids.

103

---

The amino acids that compose the peptide backbone must be assembled in the correct order, without any wrong amino acids, and without any additions or deletions of amino acids.

---

### B. DNA and Genes

To make a protein, a cell assembles its amino acids according to a set of instructions in a "master" sequence in the DNA of its nucleus. This master sequence is the *gene* for that protein, and the gene is handed down from generation to generation of human beings.

The gene for each protein consists of a sequence of **nucleotides** in the DNA of the nucleus. It is speculated that there are about 30,000–40,000 genes in the *human genome*.

A gene consists of:

- The *coding region* – a DNA nucleotide sequence coding for the amino acid sequence of the protein.

- *Regulatory regions* – DNA nucleotide sequences (often close to the coding region but not always) that are concerned with the regulation of *expression* of the gene. That is, whether the gene is turned on or turned off. If the gene is turned on, these regulatory regions may determine how strongly it is turned on.

Interestingly, the protein-coding portions of genes account for only 3% of the DNA in the human genome.

It is now known that parts of the non-coding DNA (which was once called "junk-DNA") is involved in gene regulation and in maintaining chromosome structural stability.

Genes therefore constitute the genetic information without which it would be impossible for us to survive and perpetuate our species. Many *genetic diseases* are caused by changes in this genetic information (***mutations*** of DNA), leading to the synthesis of abnormal, often non-functioning proteins.

## C. Chimpanzees and Humans—What Makes Them Different?

During primate *evolution*, it is believed that humans and *chimpanzees* split from a common ancestor between 6 million and 9 million years ago. That is a fairly short time in evolutionary history, and in consequence we find that humans and chimpanzees share at least 98% of their DNA. However, there are regions of the genome where we see significant differences.

## D. The Molecule of DNA

Most of the DNA in a cell is found in the ***chromosomes*** of the nucleus. In a chromosome, the DNA is wound tightly around special proteins called histones. There are also small, circular pieces of DNA in the ***mitochondria***, relics of the time in evolution when these organelles were believed to be free-living *bacteria*. This is mitochondrial DNA, or *mtDNA*.

Each chromosome in the nucleus is composed of just one molecule of DNA. The DNA molecule is made up of a string of **nucleotides**. Each nucleotide has three parts:

1.  One ***nitrogenous base***, which may be ***guanine*** (G), ***adenine*** (A), ***thymine*** (T), or ***cytosine*** (C)

2.  A **pentose** (5-carbon) **sugar** called ***deoxyribose***

3.  ***Phosphate*** groups

The following is a table of the chemical nomenclature.

| Nitrogenous Base | Nucleoside (base + sugar) | Nucleotide (base + sugar + phosphate) |
|---|---|---|
| adenine | adenosine | *adenylic* acid |
| guanine | guanosine | *guanylic* acid |
| cytosine | cytidine | *cytidylic* acid |
| thymine | thymidine | *thymidylic* acid |
| uracil | uridine | *uridylic* acid |

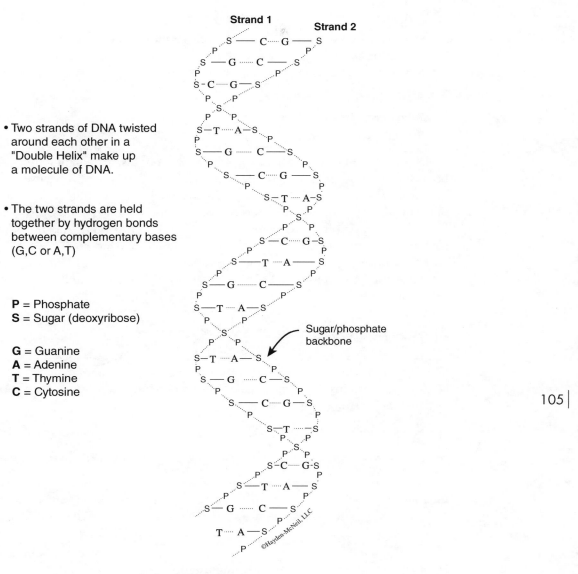

- Two strands of DNA twisted around each other in a "Double Helix" make up a molecule of DNA.

- The two strands are held together by hydrogen bonds between complementary bases (G,C or A,T)

**P** = Phosphate
**S** = Sugar (deoxyribose)

**G** = Guanine
**A** = Adenine
**T** = Thymine
**C** = Cytosine

Sugar/phosphate backbone

**Figure 6-1.** DNA.

The DNA molecule consists of two **strands**. The strands twist around each other to form a twisted ladder called a *double helix*.

The uprights of the ladder consist of alternating sugar (**deoxyribose**) and phosphate groups.

The crossbars or rungs of the ladder consist of paired nitrogenous bases, one from each strand. The paired nitrogenous bases are held together by hydrogen bonds. The rule for pairing is that adenine (A) always pairs with thymine (T) and guanine (G) always pairs with cytosine (C).

For example:

| | |
|---|---|
| Strand 1 | A G G T G G C A T A T C C G G A A |
| Strand 2 ("complementary") | T C C A C C G T A T A G G C C T T |

### E. RNA

**RNA** differs somewhat from DNA. It is single-stranded, and the pentose sugar is **ribose**. RNA contains G, A, and C. However, it has *uracil* (**U**) instead of T. There are three different kinds of RNA in cells.

1.   **Messenger** RNA or *mRNA*
2.   **Ribosomal** RNA or *rRNA*
3.   **Transfer** RNA or *tRNA*

Molecules of RNA may have been the *first life forms* on this planet. For reasons that would be too involved to go into here, there are many researchers who believe that the first life forms to evolve on this planet were based on RNA. It is postulated that the earth was once an "RNA world." Catalysis was performed not by proteins but by RNA itself. One important catalyst (enzyme) would have been an "*RNA replicase*," capable of replicating itself by performing two distinct functions. It could have achieved this by folding to form an *RNA polymerase* that used the unfolded RNA as a template for replication. In this view (which is not yet established), DNA and proteins descended from RNA during the early evolution of life forms.

## II. How a Small Protein Is Synthesized

Proteins are synthesized one amino acid at a time, always starting with the sulfur-containing amino acid **methionine**. Let's consider a very small protein that has only *six* amino acids (most proteins have many, many more amino acids than this). Let's suppose that its amino acid sequence is as follows:

Met-Gly-Ser-Ala-Gly-Phe

*(Met = methionine; Gly = glycine; Ser = serine; Ala = alanine; Phe = phenylalanine).*

The DNA strand containing the *coding sequence* of the *gene* for this protein would have the following nucleotide sequence, which we represent only by the **nitrogenous bases G, A, T, C**, because the sugar and phosphate of each nucleotide is always the same.

TAC CCG AGG CGT CCG AAA

Four things about this sequence are important.

1.   The sequence is part of an enormously long strand of DNA that makes up a *chromosome*. There will be many other genes on this chromosome.

2.   A molecule of DNA consists of **two** *complementary strands*. The cell uses only one strand for protein synthesis. This strand is the anti-sense strand, which is complementary to the sense strand, which is the one shown above.

3.   I have shown the bases for the coding or sense strand in groups of three. The reason for this is that each group of three represents a specific amino acid—this group of three is referred to as a **codon**.

4.   In the following sequence, I have indicated the amino acid corresponding to each codon.

ATG    GGC    TCC    GCA    GGC    TTT
*(Met)   (Gly)   (Ser)   (Ala)   (Gly)   (Phe)*

DNA is found in the chromatin of the *nucleus*, but our protein is synthesized by the ribosomes in the *cytoplasm*. Therefore, a copy of this nucleotide sequence is made and moved from the nucleus into the cytoplasm where it is used by the ribosomes to synthesize our protein. This copy is a single strand of nucleotides called **messenger RNA (mRNA).** The copying process is called *transcription.*

## How we build a house and how the cell synthesizes a protein

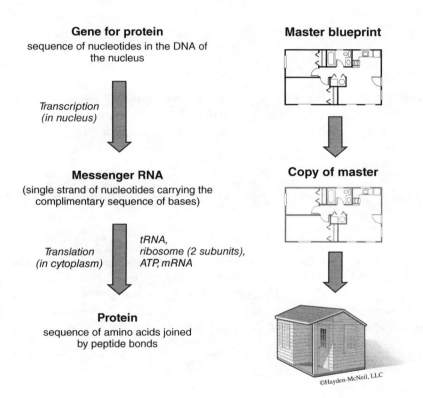

**Gene for protein**
sequence of nucleotides in the DNA of the nucleus

**Master blueprint**

*Transcription*
*(in nucleus)*

**Messenger RNA**
(single strand of nucleotides carrying the complimentary sequence of bases)

**Copy of master**

*Translation*
*(in cytoplasm)*

*tRNA,*
*ribosome (2 subunits),*
*ATP, mRNA*

**Protein**
sequence of amino acids joined by peptide bonds

©Hayden-McNeil, LLC

**Figure 6-2.**

107

## A. Transcription

The double helix of DNA is first unwound, and an enzyme called RNA polymerase binds to a region on the anti-sense strand of the DNA called a *promoter element*. RNA polymerase then tracks along the DNA strand, reading off the nucleotide sequence, and running off a complementary strand of mRNA.

---

Remember how the bases are paired:

| T in DNA or U in RNA | $\rightarrow$ | A |
|---|---|---|
| A | $\rightarrow$ | T in DNA or U in RNA |
| G | $\rightarrow$ | C |
| C | $\rightarrow$ | G |

In RNA, **uracil** nucleotides (U) are always used instead of **thymine** nucleotides. Therefore, the adenine (A) on the DNA strand corresponds to uracil (U) on the complementary strand of mRNA, not thymine (T).

---

DNA  (5'–3')   ATG  GGC  TCC  GCA  GGC  TTT  (coding, sense strand)

DNA  (3'–5')   TAC  CCG  AGG  CGT  CCG  AAA  (template, anti-sense strand)

mRNA (5'–3')   AUG  GGC  UCC  GCA  GGC  UUU  (mRNA made from template strand)

  (*Met*) (*Gly*) (*Ser*) (*Ala*) (*Gly*) (*Phe*)

The amino acid sequence for the protein is now coded in the newly-synthesized strand of mRNA. Like DNA, each group of three nucleotides codes for *one* amino acid, and is called a **codon**. If you look at the mRNA sequence for our little protein above, you will see that I have written down the amino acid that corresponds to each codon. For example, AUG stands for methionine (Met), GGC stands for glycine (Gly), and so on.

Once formed, the mRNA molecules move out of the nucleus through the pores in the nuclear envelope. When they arrive in the cytoplasm, the mRNA molecules become associated with **ribosomes**, which are dense balls consisting of about 80 **ribosomal proteins** tightly wound together with several lengths of **ribosomal RNA (rRNA)**. Ribosomes are assembled in the *nucleolus*, a structure found in the nucleus.

The ribosome–mRNA complex is now ready to start protein synthesis. This process is called **translation**, because it involves **translating** the nucleotide code carried in the mRNA into a sequence of real amino acids joined by peptide bonds.

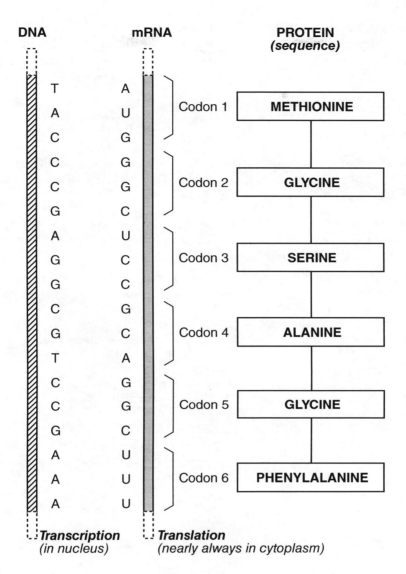

**Figure 6-3.**

## B. Translation

The ribosome consists of two parts, or subunits. To start translation, one of these subunits binds to the codon, **AUG**, which represents the amino acid *methionine*. AUG also doubles as the **start codon**. At this point, we have to find a *real* molecule of methionine, the first amino acid of our little protein. How is this done? The methionine molecule is transported into the mRNA–ribosome complex by a third type of RNA called **transfer RNA** (**tRNA**; the other two types were messenger RNA and ribosomal RNA). The second ribosome subunit then binds to the mRNA.

109

We use about 20 different amino acids to make all the proteins in our bodies, and there are correspondingly 20 transfer RNAs, a different one for each amino acid. One end of *transfer RNA* molecule binds to a real amino acid, the other end contains a sequence of nucleotides called an **anticodon** that binds to the mRNA codon for that amino acid.

- Let's take an example. Methionine tRNA would bind a molecule of **methionine** at one end, and have a **UAC** anticodon at the other. This UAC anticodon would bind to the mRNA strand at the AUG codon for methionine.

- Let's take another example. Glycine tRNA would bind a molecule of **glycine** at one end, and have a **CCG** anticodon at the other. This CCG anticodon would bind to the mRNA strand at the GGC codon for glycine.

- Yet a third example – serine tRNA would bind a molecule of **serine** at one end, and have an **AGG** anticodon at the other. This AGG anticodon would bind to the mRNA strand at the UCC codon for serine.

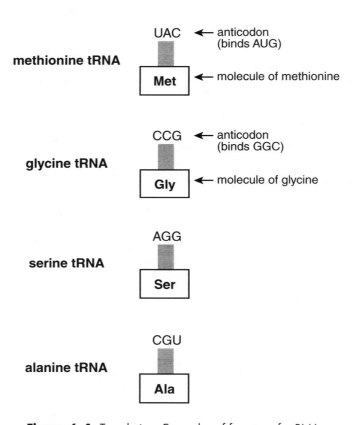

**Figure 6-4.** Translation: Examples of four transfer RNAs.

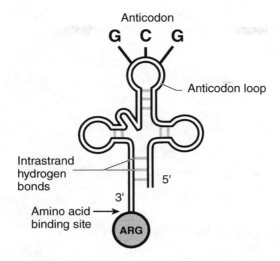

**Figure 6-5.** Structure of arginine tRNA.

The ribosome consists of ribosomal RNA and a variety of proteins, and is composed of two subunits.

When translation is initiated, one subunit of the ribosome binds to the **AUG codon.** This codon is present at the start of the coding region of all genes. AUG signals **START**, and also codes for the amino acid **methionine**. The UAC **anticodon** of methionine transfer RNA then binds to AUG. Finally, the second subunit of the ribosome binds to this complex, as shown below.

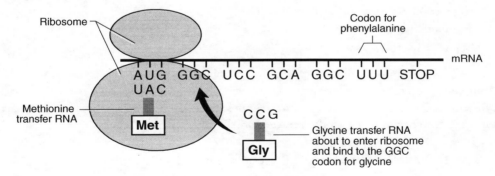

**Figure 6-6.** Translation of mRNA.

Glycine transfer RNA then enters the ribosome, and its CCG anticodon binds to the GGC codon on the mRNA. Methionine and glycine are now in position side by side, and they are then linked together by a peptide bond to form a Met-Gly *dipeptide*.

Next, the ribosome tracks along the mRNA strand for a short distance, and serine tRNA moves in, binding to the UCC codon for serine. The ribosome then joins the serine molecule to the Met-Gly dipeptide, producing a Met-Gly-Ser *tripeptide*.

The remaining amino acids are added one at a time by the same process, until we have completely assembled our little six amino acid protein:

| | | |
|---|---|---|
| start with methionine | Met | |
| add glycine | Met-Gly | *dipeptide* |
| add serine | Met-Gly-Ser | *tripeptide* |
| add alanine | Met-Gly-Ser-Ala | |
| add another glycine | Met-Gly-Ser-Ala-Gly | |
| add phenylalanine | Met-Gly-Ser-Ala-Gly-Phe | |

The ribosome tracks along the mRNA until it encounters the STOP signal at the end (actually, a UGA codon), when it drops off, leaving the peptide chain free in the cell cytoplasm. Meantime, another ribosome may have attached itself to the start of the mRNA strand, and the whole process is repeated. In this way, the single strand of mRNA may be involved in the synthesis of many molecules of our little protein.

**ATP** is used in the process of translation. A complete protein molecule may consist of several hundreds of amino acids, and its synthesis may consume the energy packaged in three ATP molecules. Consequently, a large proportion of the cell's energy supply is required for protein synthesis, particularly if the cell is young and growing.

Translation therefore requires:

1. Messenger RNA
2. Ribosomes (ribosomal RNA, ribosomal proteins)
3. Transfer RNAs (one for each amino acid)
4. Amino acids (of course)
5. ATP to drive the process

Some of the proteins manufactured in the cytoplasm are needed in the nucleus. One example is the enzyme RNA polymerase, which is involved in the process of transcription. Other proteins may serve to activate genes, and switch them on. Such proteins are imported into the nucleus via the **nuclear pore** system.

## C. Quality Control—Chaperones, Proteasomes, and Autophagy

The *shapes* of proteins are very important in their functioning in the cell, so the newly formed peptide chain must be folded. To ensure that it is folded correctly, it interacts with a group of special proteins called **chaperones**. Their functioning is illustrated in the figure.

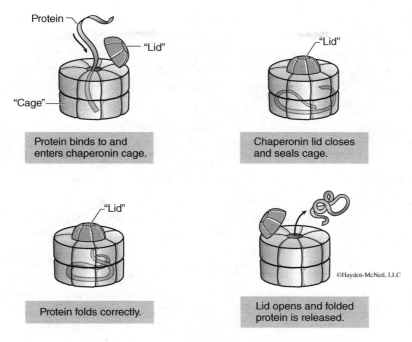

**Figure 6-7.** Chaperonin protein.

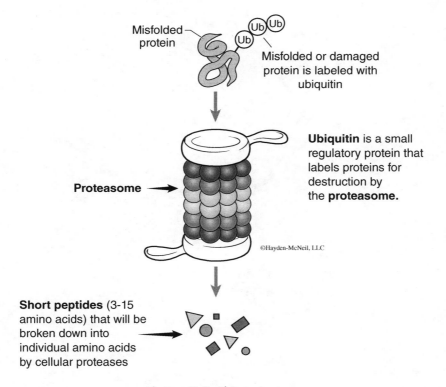

**Figure 6-8.** The proteasome.

The cell has an efficient way of disposing of proteins that are not needed, damaged, or misfolded. These proteins are first tagged with a small molecule called ubiquitin. The ubiquitinylated proteins are then recognized by the proteasome, the structure of which is very similar to that of the chaperones. The proteasome consists of a barrel-like complex of subunits enclosing an interior "death chamber" where the tagged protein is destroyed.

The cell has a second way of destroying damaged proteins, particularly those that have formed aggregates, as well as damaged mitochondria and other organelles. The process is called autophagy. It can be quite complex, and involves the cell's lysosomes.

## D. Gene Regulation by DNA Methylation and by Histone Methylation or Acetylation

When cytosine is immediately adjacent to a guanine in the DNA sequence, an enzyme called DNA methyltransferase can attach a methyl group to the cytosine, creating 5-methylcytosine. If this occurs in the promoter, the result is to alter gene expression, frequently resulting in gene silencing.

This phenomenon can be important during early development, and may even be dependent on environmental factors and experiences. DNA methylation can account for some of the differences between identical twins, even though they have identical genomes. Gene expression can also be affected by methylation and acetylation of the histones around which the DNA is wound.

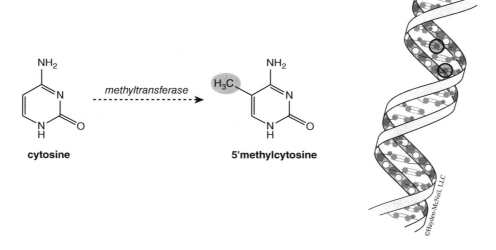

**Figure 6-9.**

## III. DNA Replication

The human **genome** contains 2800 million ($2.8 \times 10^9$) base-pairs of DNA packaged into 23 different **chromosomes**. Determining the base sequence has been a major endeavor sponsored by the publicly-funded Human Genome Project in the U.S. and Britain and by the private company Celera in the U.S. In news conferences in Washington and London, it was announced on June 26, 2000, that a rough draft of 97% of the DNA from two unidentified persons had been completed. In February 2001, draft versions of the full sequence were revealed, and in May 2003 98% of the regions that actually contain genes had been completed. The last date is significant, because it is exactly 50 years since Watson and Crick published their double helix structure for the molecule of DNA, one of the key scientific achievements of the 20th century. James Watson, Francis Crick, and Maurice Wilkins, the X-ray crystallographer, shared the 1962 Nobel Prize in Physiology or Medicine.

Of the chromosomes themselves, most have now been sequenced.

A major job will be to identify, characterize, and understand the thousands of proteins represented by the genes found in this DNA sequence. This work will open up the field to medicine to:

- New medical treatments, including *gene therapy* and the design of new drugs and their appropriateness for people with different genetic makeup.
- New understanding of the human organism.
- Novel ways to diagnose disease before birth.
- More controversially, the ability to manipulate traits such as looks, intelligence and life span.

Except for our *gametes* (sperm cells and oocytes), all the cells of our body *(somatic cells)* have two sets of chromosomes, one from our mother and one from our father. Somatic cells are therefore said to be *diploid,* with 6000 million base-pairs of DNA.

During the interphase of the cell's life, the DNA it inherited from the parent cell must be replicated so that when the cell divides again, a faithful copy can be passed on to each of the two daughter cells. An array of enzymes (helicase, primase, *DNA polymerase*) is involved. The DNA double helix is first unwound into two separate strands. Two new, complementary strands of DNA are then assembled using the old strands as templates. The result is two double-stranded DNA double helices, each with one newly-synthesized strand wound around one old strand.

For example:

    Old strand    5′   ATTGCCCAATGTG 3′

    New strand   3′   TAACGGGTTACAC 5′

---

    Note on direction of strands: the old strand reads from 5′ to 3′, while the new strand reads from 3′ to 5′.

---

Because DNA is replicated at interphase, each chromosome appears as a doubled structure consisting of two "chromatids" during late prophase and metaphase. These chromatids are pulled apart at anaphase, after which they are called chromosomes again.

## IV. Mutations of the DNA Molecule, Genetic Diseases, and Gene Therapy

### A. Mutations of the DNA Molecule

A **mutation** in a gene may result in the production of a **defective protein** by the cells of our bodies. The result is often a **genetic disease**.

Some mutations in DNA occur as a result of errors during the replication process, others because of exposure to chemicals and ultraviolet radiation. One important function in the cell that is receiving much attention these days is the process whereby the DNA is repaired, so preventing many harmful effects such as cancer. Unfortunately, the DNA repair system (which itself relies on special DNA repair genes) may fail, and mutations may survive to be passed on to daughter cells, or to the next generation.

Mutations in DNA can be of various types:

1. Incorrect pairing of bases during DNA replication.

2. Insertions of extra bases or deletion of a base or bases during replication.

3. Expansion in the numbers of "triplet or trinucleotide repeats" in a gene sequence. These triplet repeats consist of strings of repeated three-base combinations (e.g. AGC, CAG, CCG, or CGG). *Trinucleotide repeat expansion* causes a number of genetic diseases, including *Huntington's disease.*

   The gene involved may be normal if the number of trinucleotide repeats in the string is, say, 30, but may become abnormal if the number increases to, say, 70. The severity and age of onset is correlated with the length of the triplet repeat. This can happen from one generation to the next, and may lead to increasing severity and earlier onset of a disease over the generations. The mechanism of trinucleotide repeat expansion has not yet been worked out. An error of this nature occurs in several diseases. They include "*fragile X syndrome*" (mental retardation, facial alterations, enlarged testicles), spinal and bulbar muscular atrophy, myotonic dystrophy and recently in Huntington's disease.

4. Whole sections of DNA may be deleted, transposed to other parts of the DNA molecule, inverted (reversed), or even inserted into other chromosomes. Such events are more usually called "*chromosomal translocations.*"

   **Cancers and Genetic Effects (See Chapter 4)**

   Additionally, as we have seen, cancers are caused by certain genetic defects, either incurred during the patient's lifetime (perhaps because of smoking or irradiation), or as a result of a genetic predisposition. The phenomena described in item 4 above often cause inactivation or loss of tumor suppressor genes, or activation of proto-oncogenes.

There are at least 4000 human disorders attributed to genetic causes, and mutations of the type listed above are likely to be important factors in many of these genetic diseases.

116

For example, think of the consequences of a mutation occurring in that part of a gene that codes for a protein. Also, what would be the consequences if the mutation occurred in a regulatory sequence of the gene?

New therapeutic techniques for dealing with genetic diseases involve **gene therapy,** where DNA carrying the normal gene is incorporated into the patient's cells (see page 118).

## B. Genetic Diseases

In many genetic diseases, a codon may be altered, resulting in a disrupting substitution of one amino acid for another in the peptide backbone of an important protein. In one form of **Alzheimer's disease**, an *isoleucine* amino acid has replaced the "normal" *valine* amino acid in an important brain protein known as *beta-amyloid protein precursor.* The cause of this substitution of a "wrong" amino acid is the occurrence of a "mutation" in the master sequence encoded by the patient's DNA. If the patient has children, then the mutation will be carried in their DNA as well, and so on.

The following are some examples of defective genes associated with disease. Note that many different types of proteins are encoded by these genes. For example, some are enzymes (adenosine deaminase, ADA), some are structural proteins (dystrophin), and one is a cell-surface receptor for LDL (low-density lipoprotein).

| Disease | Defective Gene |
|---|---|
| Alzheimer's disease* | beta-amyloid protein precursor |
| Immunodeficiency | adenosine deaminase (ADA) |
| Hypercholesterolemia | LDL receptor |
| Hemophilia | factor IX and factor VIII |
| Cystic fibrosis | cystic fibrosis transmembrane regulator** |
| Duchenne's muscular dystrophy | dystrophin |
| Thalassemia | beta-globin |
| Sickle cell anemia | beta-globin |
| Retinitis pigmentosa* | rhodopsin |
| | peripherin |
| | rod cGMP phosphodiesterase |
| Huntington's disease | "huntingtin" |
| "Fragile X" syndrome | FMR1 (perhaps associated with RNA transcription and processing in the cell nucleus) |
| Dwarfism | FGFR3, a receptor for fibroblast growth factor |

\*    Certain subgroups of patients

\*\*    Active-transport chloride channel in epithelia that also controls water movement in the airways, pancreas, intestines, sweat glands and testes. Thick, dehydrated mucus and associated bacterial infections in the lungs of **cystic fibrosis** patients often lead to death.

**Mutations can cause genetic diseases**

...ACT    CCT    GAG    GAG...
Thr     Pro     Glu     Glu      hemoglobin A


...ACT    CCT    GTG    GAG...
Thr     Pro     Val     Glu      hemoglobin S

**Figure 6-10.** A point mutation changing the codon GAG (Glu) to GTG (Val) changes normal hemoglobin (A) to sickle cell hemoglobin (S).

## C. Gene Therapy

New therapeutic techniques for dealing with genetic diseases involve **gene therapy**, where DNA carrying the normal gene is incorporated into the patient's cells.

Methods of gene therapy for single-gene inherited diseases are still under development. The problem is to get enough copies of the genes into the patient's cells, and to ensure that they are expressed.

Approaches currently under investigation include the following.

- Cells or tissues from the patient are removed, cultured in tissue culture, the genes introduced into these cells, which are then returned to the patient.

- In the second method, genes are introduced directly into target tissues or organs *within* the patient.

- In the third method, the gene could be injected directly into the bloodstream. This has not been investigated as yet, but the method has potential therapeutic importance.

How might the DNA containing the gene in question be packaged, and how could it be introduced into the cell?

1.  **Engineered viruses.**

    Much recent research concerns the use of virus "*vectors*" to transfer copies of the normal gene into the patient's cells within the body, or into cells cultured outside of the patient's body. The viruses may be engineered *retroviruses* (RNA viruses), *adenoviruses* (DNA viruses) and *herpes simplex virus* (a DNA virus). Cold virus has been used to transfect copies of the normal gene for the cystic fibrosis transmembrane regulator into the airways of cystic fibrosis patients.

2.  **Liposomes.**

    One alternative to the use of an engineered virus is to incorporate the DNA into liposomes. For cystic fibrosis patients, these liposomes could be administered by way of a nasal pump spray.

Another possible technique involves artificially manufactured chromosomes that include sequences for maintaining their ends (telomeres), replication, and mitosis (centromeres). At the present time, we can say that gene therapy is a technique that has had some successes but has also encountered many setbacks.

118

## D. Regulation of Gene Expression Transcriptionally and Post-Transcriptionally — DNA Methylation, Histone Methylation or Acetylation, Small Interfering RNAs

The code contained in the DNA of the nucleus is copied to mRNA, which then directs protein synthesis. This flow of genetic information from DNA via mRNA to protein has been called the central dogma of molecular biology by Nobel Laureate Francis Crick.

The human genome consists of roughly 30,000 genes. Not all of them are expressed in any given cell of the body, however. One way in which gene expression is controlled is by the transcriptional process that copies DNA to mRNA. DNA methylation and histone methylation or acetylation are known to play a role in the process.

Gene expression is also regulated by a phenomenon called RNA interference. Hundreds of genes in our genome encode small RNA molecules called microRNAs. These microRNA molecules can form a double-stranded structure that activates the RNA interference machinery. The result is to block protein synthesis by attacking and destroying the mRNA for that protein. Genetic regulation by microRNAs plays an important role in development and in cell function.

The discovery of RNA interference has opened up new prospects in gene technology. Double-stranded RNA molecules can be designed to silence specific genes. One recent finding was the RNA silencing of a gene causing high blood cholesterol levels in mice. The technique also has potential in the treatment of virus infections, cardiovascular diseases, cancer, endocrine disorders, and many other disease conditions.

### E.  Genome Editing

Genome editing of somatic cells is a potential therapy for certain diseases. The technique is called CRISPR ("clustered regularly interspaced short palindromic repeats").

119

## V. DNA Profiling

**Forensic application.**

Samples such as blood, semen, or whatever can be examined by analyzing their DNA. The techniques used are now very powerful, and have been responsible for demonstrating that a number of people have been jailed for crimes they didn't commit. For example, Ronald Keith Williamson was freed early in 1999 after he had been in jail for 11 years on a rape conviction. Recent DNA testing of hair and semen found at the scene of the crime exonerated Williamson but implicated a former suspect in the case.

Nowadays, a *nanogram* ($10^{-9}$ grams) of DNA is enough. DNA can be obtained from the mouth area of a ski mask, cigarette butts and licked postage stamps that have been affixed to envelopes. Dead cells from tear fluid as well as saliva can also leave enough DNA on the fingers and other parts of the body.

The technique used relies on what is called *short tandem repeat* (STR) analysis. Human DNA contains specific areas that have simple repeating blocks of base pairs. The number of repeat units varies from person to person. The *polymerase chain reaction* (PCR) is used to make millions of copies of the selected STR region, and the number of times a repeat unit appears is determined by gel electrophoresis. Between 10 and 13 locations ("loci") can be examined, enough to reduce the chance of two unrelated individuals having the same DNA profile to about *one in a million billion*.

Future possibilities include examining the DNA for genes determining facial shape, hair color, and so on. So a facial description of a person and the color of their hair could be obtained from his or her DNA.

**Application to the study of human evolution.**

One powerful application of PCR has been in the study of human evolution. PCR has been used to analyze the traces of mitochondrial DNA present in the bones of a *Neanderthal*, an archaic human that roamed Europe and Western Asia between 230,000 and 30,000 years ago. The study showed that Neanderthals and the line leading to modern humans evolved independently of each other over a period of more than 500,000 years. There have also been observations on human and Neanderthal DNA that suggest there was mating between the two species.

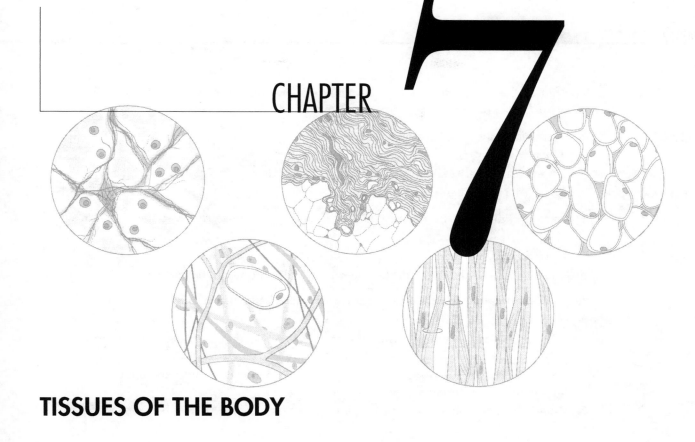

CHAPTER

7

# TISSUES OF THE BODY

## CHAPTER OUTLINE

## DESCRIPTION AND INTRODUCTION

Molecules make up the fabric of living cells, and living cells make up the fabric of **tissues**. Tissues consist of many cells held together by "sticky" molecules called *cell adhesion molecules (CAMs)*. Cell adhesion molecules such as *cadherin*, are integral parts of the cell membranes of most cells. Sometimes these adhesion molecules assist in attaching the cells of a tissue to *material that is found between cells*. This material is called the *extracellular matrix*.

The purpose of the present chapter is to give you an overview of the four basic tissue types you may expect to encounter in the human body.

- *Epithelial* tissue
- *Connective* tissue
- *Muscle* (muscular) tissue
- *Nerve* (nervous) tissue

The major emphasis in this chapter will be on *epithelial* and *connective* tissue.

## OBJECTIVES

After listening to the lecture and reading this chapter, you should be able to:

1. Describe the way cells are **held together** in tissues (cell adhesion molecules).
2. Draw and label a diagram to show the **general layout** of an epithelium.
3. List and describe the seven types of **epithelium**, and state the **organs** in which they are found.
4. Define a **gland**—describe the difference between **endocrine** and **exocrine** glands and name two examples of each.
5. Name the three physiological types of **exocrine** glands, and their subclasses where appropriate.
6. Name eight **functions** of connective tissue.
7. Name five **cell** types found in connective tissue, and describe their functions.
8. Name two varieties of **fiber** found in connective tissue (based on the major protein found in the fibers).
9. Name the special type of **protein** found in the ground substance of connective tissue.
10. Name nine **types** of **connective tissue**—describe each of them, their subclasses (if any), and where they are found.
11. Describe the difference between white and brown adipose tissue.
12. List two important characteristics of **muscle** tissue.
13. Name and distinguish the three **types** of muscle tissue.
14. Describe the two types of **cell** found in **nerve** tissue.
15. State what makes neurons different from most other cells.
16. Describe what is meant by the **basement membrane** and name three **proteins** found in it.

## I. Epithelial Tissues

### A. What Is Epithelial Tissue?

**Epithelial tissue consists of sheets of cells that cover all the surfaces in the body.** These surfaces include the outer surface of the body (*skin*), the surfaces of the body's cavities, and also the inner surfaces of hollow organs such as the stomach and the urinary bladder.

Additionally, *endocrine glands* and *exocrine glands* develop from epithelial tissue.

Epithelial cells are structurally *polarized*—that is, one end of the cell, the apical end, is a free surface that borders the outer or inner space that the epithelium lines. The opposite end of the cell, the basal end, is *anchored*, usually to underlying connective tissue, by the *basement membrane*.

The basement membrane is produced by the epithelial cells, and consists of a strong, elastic sheet that provides support for the epithelium. Its most important component is a type of **collagen** called ***collagen IV***. It also contains rather curious, carbohydrate-rich proteins called ***proteoglycans*** (proteoglycans are found in connective tissue: see later) and a protein called ***laminin***.

Mutations in the genes for collagen or proteoglycans can lead to a number of heritable disorders affecting the skeleton.

Epithelial cells are tightly packed and are attached to one another to form a sheet. More than 85% of all cancers arise from mutations in epithelial cells.

123

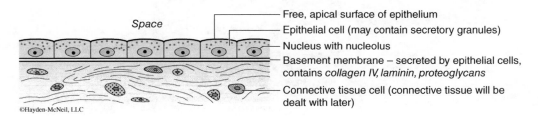

Space — Free, apical surface of epithelium
— Epithelial cell (may contain secretory granules)
— Nucleus with nucleolus
— Basement membrane – secreted by epithelial cells, contains *collagen IV, laminin, proteoglycans*
— Connective tissue cell (connective tissue will be dealt with later)

©Hayden-McNeil, LLC

**Figure 7-1.** Structure of an epithelium.

### B. Types of Epithelial Tissue

With the exception of glandular epithelium, classification is according to the *shape* and *arrangement* of the cells.

1.  ***Simple squamous*** epithelium
2.  ***Simple cuboidal*** epithelium
3.  ***Simple columnar*** epithelium
4.  ***Pseudostratified columnar*** epithelium
5.  ***Stratified squamous*** epithelium
6.  ***Transitional*** epithelium
7.  ***Glandular*** epithelium

We will now discuss each of these types in detail.

1. **Simple squamous.**

   Lines the air sacs (*alveoli*) of the *lungs*, the interiors of blood vessels (where it is called *vascular endothelium*), and membranes in the thorax and abdomen. The cells are thin and flattened, so that substances diffuse easily through them.

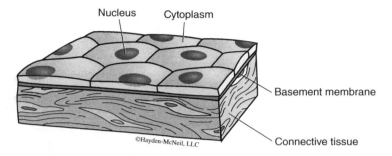

Nucleus    Cytoplasm

Basement membrane

Connective tissue

©Hayden-McNeil, LLC

**Figure 7-2.** Simple squamous.

2. **Simple cuboidal.**

   A single layer of cube-shaped cells (i.e. they are as tall as they are wide). Lines ducts of various glands, *kidney* tubules, etc. Functions in secretion and absorption.

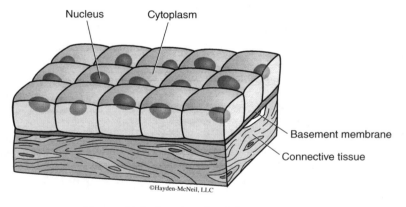

Nucleus    Cytoplasm

Basement membrane

Connective tissue

©Hayden-McNeil, LLC

**Figure 7-3.** Simple cuboidal.

3. **Simple columnar.**

   Because the cells are columnar (taller than they are wide), this epithelium is thicker than the cuboidal variety. Found lining the gut and *uterus*. Aside from providing some protection for the underlying tissues, this type of epithelium functions in secretion and absorption.

   In order to increase their surface area, columnar cells sometimes have *microvilli* (little fingers) projecting from their apical surfaces.

   A sheet of columnar epithelium often contains cells called *goblet cells* (because they look like goblets), which secrete a protective mucus coating.

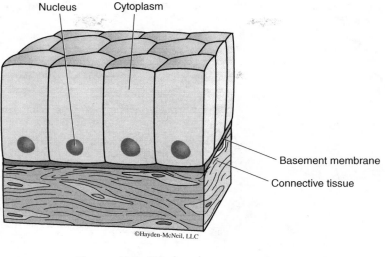

**Figure 7-4.** Simple columnar.

4. **Pseudostratified columnar.**

Because the nuclei are at different levels, this type of epithelium looks as if it is stratified (i.e. layered), but it isn't. It also has goblet cells. The cells usually have *cilia*, motile hair-like projections on their free surfaces. The mucus secreted by the goblet cells is swept along by the beating movements of the cilia.

Lines the passages of the respiratory tubes, where the *mucus* and trapped inhaled particles (including bacteria) are swept up out of the airways by the action of the cilia.

125

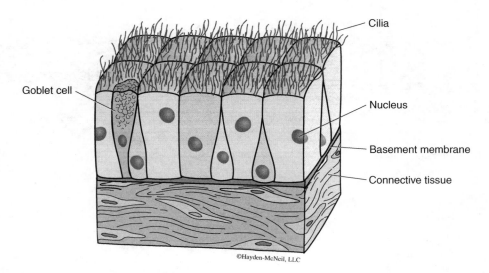

**Figure 7-5.** Pseudostratified ciliated columnar.

5. **Stratified squamous.**

Primarily protective. May be *keratinized* or *non-keratinized*. Consists of a number of layers of cells. The cells in the layer next to the basement membrane are dividing all the time. The new cells they form push the older cells toward the surface. Ultimately, the older cells slough off.

In the skin, the older cells accumulate a protein called *keratin*, become hardened, and die.

In the *mouth, throat, vagina, anal canal*, the cells are not keratinized.

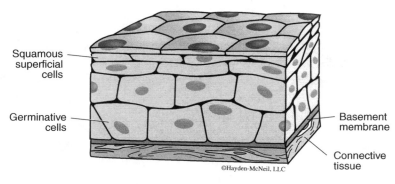

**Stratified Squamous**

**Figure 7-6.** Stratified squamous.

6. **Transitional.**

Also known as *uroepithelium* because it lines the *urinary bladder* and *urinary tract*. Its cuboidal cells provide an expandable and relatively impermeable lining to the bladder.

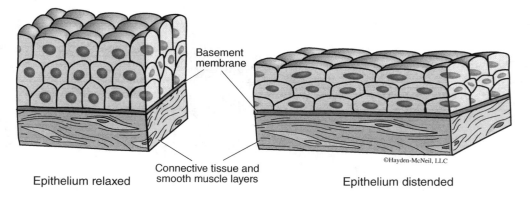

**Figure 7-7.** Transitional.

7. **Glandular.**

**What are glands**? Glands are collections of cells that *secrete* substances. There are two major types of gland.

- Glands where the secretions pass straight into the blood stream are called ***endocrine*** glands (e.g. *thyroid, pancreas, pituitary*). Endocrine glands and the products they secrete (*insulin, sex hormones, growth hormone,* etc.) will be dealt with in the second volume of this text, designed to coordinate with the spring semester.

- Glands where the cells secrete into ducts that open onto a surface are called ***exocrine*** glands (e.g. *sweat glands, salivary glands*).

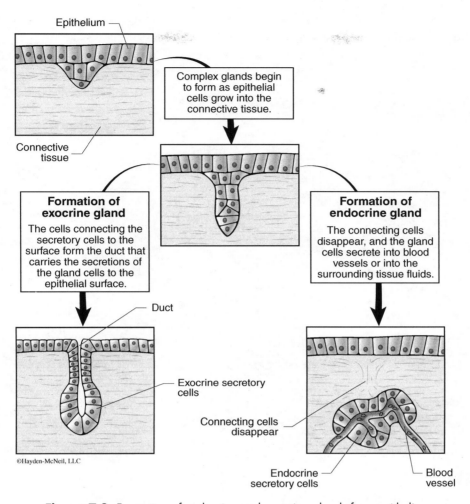

**Figure 7-8.** Formation of endocrine and exocrine glands from epithelium.

Anatomically, exocrine glands may be divided into simple types and compound types. Physiologically, and more importantly, they can be divided according to their types of secretion, as follows.

- **Merocrine glands.**
  - *Serous* merocrine glands have watery secretions (e.g. sweat glands, some salivary glands).
  - *Mucous* merocrine glands have thick secretions (e.g. glands found in the respiratory tubes, some salivary glands).

- **Holocrine glands.**
  Secrete entire cells laden with secretory cell products (e.g. *sebaceous* glands in the skin). The cells then disintegrate, releasing the secretory product.

In a third category are the apocrine glands, a specialized type of **sweat gland** found associated with hair follicles in the skin. Their secretions are odoriferous. Modified apocrine glands secrete milk. It was thought that apocrine glands secreted portions of the free ends of the cells as well as cell product. However, this is now considered to be incorrect. They secrete in the same way as merocrine glands. The only glands that may use the classical apocrine method are the mammary glands.

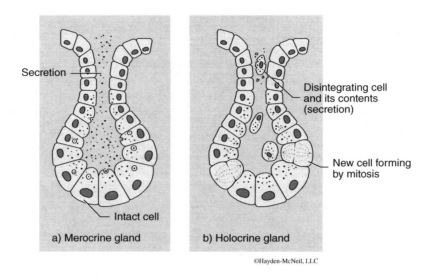

©Hayden-McNeil, LLC

**Figure 7-9.** Exocrine glands.

## II. Connective Tissues

### A. What Is Connective Tissue?

Connective tissue is abundant, and is found throughout the body. It has at least eight functions, as follows.

1. Binds structures together
2. Supports and protects
3. Serves as a framework
4. Fills up spaces
5. Stores fat
6. In some places, it generates blood cells
7. Protects against infections (we shall see next semester that connective tissue is an important site of inflammation, the body's reaction to invasion by foreign organisms)
8. Helps repair tissue damage

Connective tissue consists of *cells* embedded in a *matrix*. The matrix consists of *fibers* and *ground substance*. The fibers are of two types, depending on whether they are composed of *collagen* or *elastin*. The ground substance is an amorphous, homogeneous material in which the cells and fibers are embedded. Some types of connective tissue are flexible, while others (such as *bone*) are quite rigid.

## B. Five Types of Cells Are Found in Connective Tissue

There are five types of cell in connective tissue. You need to know them all, and their functions.

1. **Fibroblasts** – abundant cells that produce fibers.

2. **Macrophages** – derived from blood cells called monocytes. Macrophages are important cells that phagocytize cellular debris, bacteria, etc. Important in the inflammatory response.

3. **Mast cells** – the phrase "mast cells" is derived from the German "Mastzellen," which means "well-fed cells," a reference to the fact that their cytoplasm is stuffed full of granules. The granules contain *histamine, heparin,* and *proteases* (enzymes that digest proteins). The cells also produce substances (*cytokines*) that are important in signalling to other cells, and chemicals called *leukotrienes* and *prostaglandins*, which are important in inflammatory reactions (next semester). All these substances are involved in inflammation and in allergic reactions. We shall be dealing with mast cells again in BIOL 204 next semester.

4. **White blood cells** – several types of white blood cells are found in connective tissue, their numbers increasing dramatically during inflammation following infection by pathogens such as bacteria. One example is the *neutrophils*, phagocytic white cells that migrate out of the bloodstream and move into an infected area in response to chemical signals. We shall be discussing this in more detail in BIOL 204.

5. **Chondrocytes** and **osteocytes** – together with other specialized cells are found in cartilage and bone.

129

## C. The Cells of Connective Tissue Are Embedded in a Matrix

The cells of connective tissue are embedded in a matrix consisting of two types of *fibers* and *ground substance*.

1. There are two types of fiber in connective tissue.
   - *Collagenous* **fibers** – white fibers composed of *collagen*. Collagens are major body proteins, consisting of three intertwined amino acid chains ("polypeptide" chains), where every third amino acid in each chain is a glycine. The amino acids proline and hydroxyproline are also important in holding the structure of the molecule together.

     Networks of very thin collagen fibers are sometimes spoken of as being made up of *reticular* fibers.

   - *Elastic* **fibers** – yellow fibers composed mainly of the protein *elastin*, but also contain a protein called *fibrillin*.

2. *Ground substance*

   The *ground substance* of connective tissue is usually a gel-like material composed of special protein molecules to which are attached large amounts of carbohydrates. These molecules are called *proteoglycans*. They are present in all tissues and organs. They bind water, and play an important role in maintaining the *hydration* of a tissue.

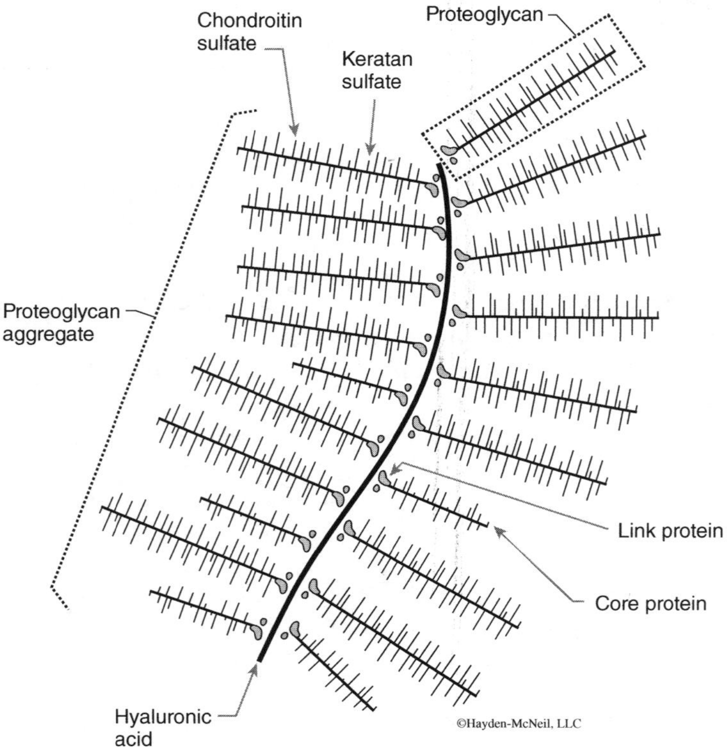

**Figure 7-10.** Structure of a proteoglycan aggregate.

## D. Types of Connective Tissue

**Connective tissue proper**

1. **Loose (areolar) connective tissue**
2. **Adipose connective tissue**
3. **Dense regular fibrous connective tissue**
4. **Dense irregular fibrous connective tissue**
5. **Elastic connective tissue**
6. **Reticular connective tissue**

**Specialized connective tissue**

1. **Cartilage**

   - *hyaline* cartilage
   - *elastic* cartilage
   - *fibrocartilage*

2. **Bone**
3. **Other types—some people include blood**

*Connective Tissue Proper*

**1.  Loose (areolar) connective tissue.**

Loose or areolar connective tissue lies in the subcutaneous tissue of skin areas where there is little adipose tissue. It is also found between muscles. The cells are mainly fibroblasts. There is a gel-like ground substance that contains collagen and elastic fibers.

Contains numerous blood vessels, and gives elasticity and some tensile strength.

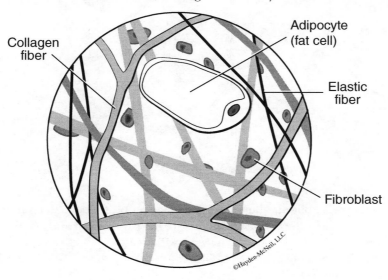

**Figure 7-11.** Loose connective tissue.

131

**2.  Adipose connective tissue.**

A type of loose connective tissue that contains fat-storing cells, or *adipocytes*. Found beneath many areas of the skin, around kidneys, and other areas. Functions to store fat, to form a protective cushion, and to act as a heat insulator. Adipocytes secrete an important hormone called *leptin*, which signals to the brain and tells it how much fat we have. We will discuss this in BIOL 204, next semester.

*Suction lipectomy* is a cosmetic procedure that involves suction of small amounts of fat from the inner and outer thigh, buttocks, area behind the knee, underside of the arms, breasts, and abdomen. The procedure can lead to serious complications, including infection and damage to internal structures.

There is **white** and **brown** adipose tissue. The function of white adipose tissue is to store energy in the form of triglycerides. Brown adipose tissue contains numerous mitochondria. In *brown adipose tissue*, oxidative phosphorylation can be uncoupled from ATP production and the energy is instead dissipated as heat. That is, brown adipose tissue is *thermogenic, and can generate heat by non-shivering thermogenesis*. It has a major function in regulating body temperature in hibernating animals and small animals such as rodents. It is also important in human infants. Although it appears to atrophy with age, brown fat is present in adult humans. This is further discussed in Chapter 8. There are many studies in progress concerning the relationship between brown fat, white fat, and even skeletal muscle cells.

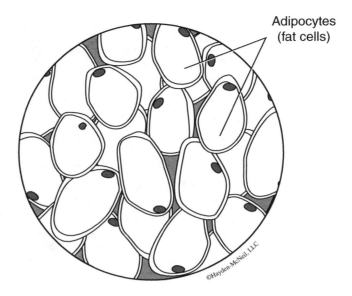

**Figure 7-12.** Adipose tissue.

3.  **Dense regular fibrous connective tissue.**

Contains few cells, but an abundance of collagenous and some elastic fibers. The matrix is predominantly *collagen fibers* that are densely packed and arranged parallel to the direction of the force they have to withstand. A few elastic fibers are interspersed among the collagen fibers. This tissue has a poor blood supply that makes the healing process very slow.

Dense regular connective tissue is located in areas of the body that encounter strong pulling forces. Therefore, dense regular connective tissue forms *tendons* (the attachments of muscle to bone), *ligaments* (the attachment of bone to bone), and *aponeuroses*, which are sheet-like tendons connecting one muscle with bone or another muscle.

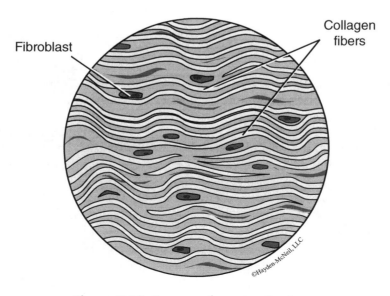

**Figure 7-13.** Dense regular connective tissue.

4. **Dense irregular fibrous connective tissue.**

In dense irregular connective tissue, the matrix is also predominantly *collagen fibers*. They are densely packed but are interwoven in three dimensions rather like a basket weave. There are also a few elastic fibers. This arrangement provides strength in *all* directions as opposed to *one* direction as in dense regular connective tissue. It is found in areas that are exposed to mechanical stress, and it also forms sheaths or capsules that protect organs. The tissue also has a limited blood supply that makes the healing process very slow.

Dense irregular connective tissue is found in the outermost layer of the *dermis* of the skin, in sheaths covering muscles, nerves, and in the adventitia of blood vessels. It also forms the capsules covering various organs and joints, the membranes covering cartilage (*perichondrium*) and bone (*periosteum*), and the *sclera* of the eye.

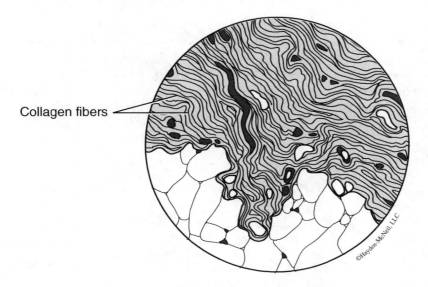

Collagen fibers

**Figure 7-14.** Dense irregular connective tissue.

133

5. **Elastic connective tissue.**

Contains mainly yellow elastic fibers arranged in parallel strands or networks. Some collagen is present. The elastic fibers contain the protein **elastin** and a small amount of a protein called **fibrillin**. Elastic connective tissue has elastic properties, and is therefore found in the walls of the heart and major blood vessels, the larger airways, and in the *ligamenta flava* ("yellow ligaments") that connect adjacent vertebrae.

**Marfan syndrome** is a disease caused by a mutation or mutations in the gene for *fibrillin 1*. It is an inherited disease named after a Paris pediatrician. It affects about one person in 10,000–20,000. Causes abnormalities of connective tissue, especially of the skeleton, eyes, and cardiovascular system. Death is often caused by cardiovascular complications such as aortic aneurysm.

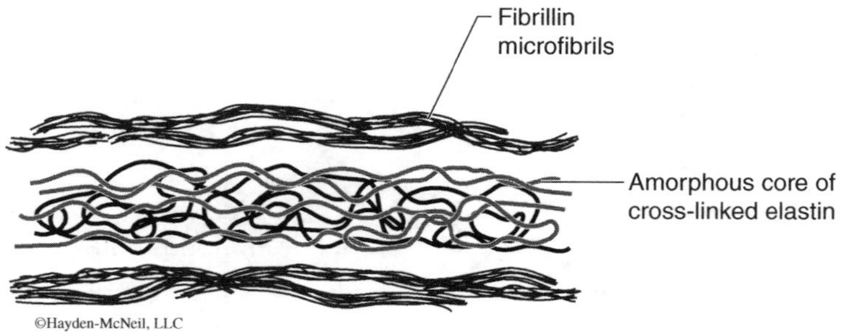

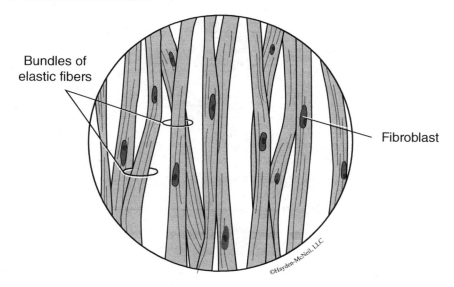

©Hayden-McNeil, LLC

**Figure 7-15.**

Fibrillin genes are found on chromosomes 5 and 15. Fibrillin is a protein normally abundant in tissues affected by *Marfan syndrome*, such as the suspensory ligament of the lens of the eye, in the aorta, and in the periosteum that covers the bones.

Flo Hyman, the U.S. volleyball player, died of Marfan syndrome. It has been suggested that Abraham Lincoln had Marfan syndrome. This has been frequently debated, even though many of his physical characteristics suggested Marfan syndrome. The Washington correspondent of the Times of London described him as a "tall, lank, lean man, considerably over 6 feet in height, with stooping shoulders, long pendulous arms terminating in hands of extraordinary dimensions, which, however, were far exceeded in proportion by his feet." This question could be solved if DNA samples were prepared from Lincoln's blood, bone, and hair. However, that is not likely to be done in the foreseeable future.

Bundles of elastic fibers

Fibroblast

©Hayden-McNeil, LLC

**Figure 7-16.** Elastic connective tissue.

6.  **Reticular connective tissue.**

    Contains many fibroblasts. Network of very thin fibers of a particular type of collagen called collagen III. Much of it is glycosylated, that is, combined with carbohydrate. Reticular connective tissue is important in forming the stroma of organs such as the *spleen, liver,* and *lymph nodes.*

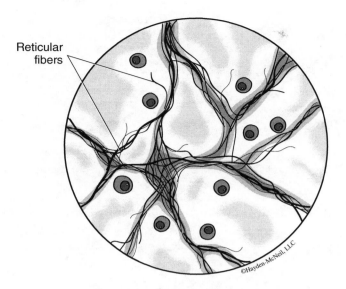

**Figure 7-17.** Reticular connective tissue.

*Specialized Connective Tissue*

**1.  Cartilage.**

A rigid material consisting of a gel-like ground substance in which are embedded varying proportions of collagenous and elastic fibers. The cells in cartilage are called *chondrocytes*, which are found in *lacunae* in the matrix. Chondrocytes can multiply, and can form more cartilage.

135

There are three types of cartilage:

- *Hyaline* – rigid: contains very fine collagenous fibers that are almost invisible. Occurs at the ends of bones and sometimes holds bones together in special joints called cartilaginous joints (e.g. the *sternum* and first *rib*). Hyaline cartilage also occurs in the soft parts of the nose and forms the supporting rings in the walls of the *trachea* and *bronchi*, preventing them from collapsing. This type of cartilage can be replaced by bone.

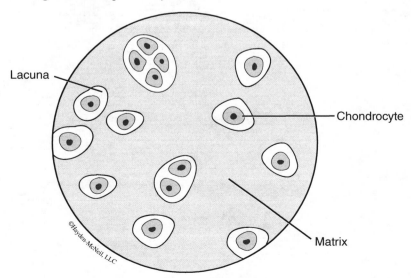

**Figure 7-18.** Hyaline cartilage.

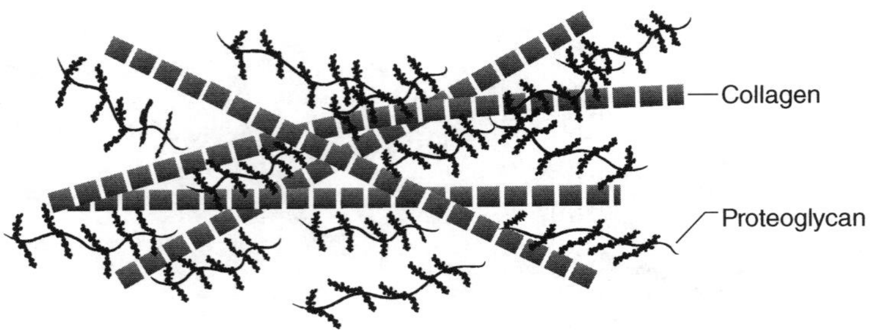

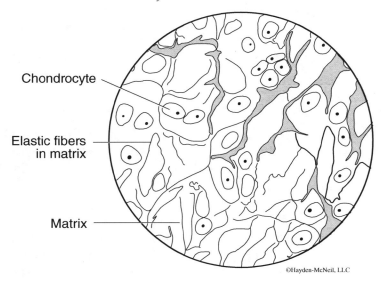

**Figure 7-19.** Collagen and proteoglycans are the principal components of the matrix in hyaline cartilage.

- *Elastic* – more flexible than hyaline. Contains many elastic fibers. Found in the external ears and *larynx.*

Chondrocyte

Elastic fibers
in matrix

Matrix

©Hayden-McNeil, LLC

**Figure 7-20.** Elastic cartilage.

- *Fibrous* (*fibrocartilage*) – tough, contains many collagenous fibers. Sometimes serves as a shock absorber between bones such as in the knee. It also forms a joint between the vertebrae and the bones that make up the *pubic symphysis.*

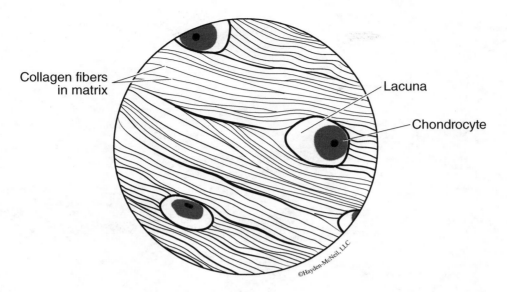

Collagen fibers
in matrix

Lacuna

Chondrocyte

©Hayden-McNeil, LLC

**Figure 7-21.** Fibrocartilage.

2. **Bone.**

Cartilage and bone make up the skeletal system. Bone is more rigid than cartilage because its intercellular matrix contains mineral salts, primarily *calcium phosphate* and *calcium carbonate*. We will be discussing bone in more detail in Chapter 9.

Bone provides support for the soft body structures, the bones of the *skull* protect the brain, and the ribs protect the *lungs* and *heart*. Bone sometimes contains *red bone marrow*, which is important for generating blood cells, and bone is also a store of calcium. Finally, bone serves as an attachment for skeletal muscles, so permitting movement.

The basic unit of compact bone is called an *osteon*. Each osteon consists of a *central* (*osteonic* or *Haversian*) *canal* containing blood vessels and nerves, surrounded by concentric rings of bone substance called *lamellae*. Bone cells or osteocytes are found in lacunae, which are evenly spaced between the lamellae. Radiating minute canals called *canaliculi* allow communication between the osteocytes.

Note that bone is vascular, whereas cartilage is not. Also, the lacunae of *osseus tissue* are interconnected whereas those of cartilage are not. Thus, in spite of its inert appearance, bone is a very active tissue compared with cartilage, and heals much more rapidly than cartilage.

137

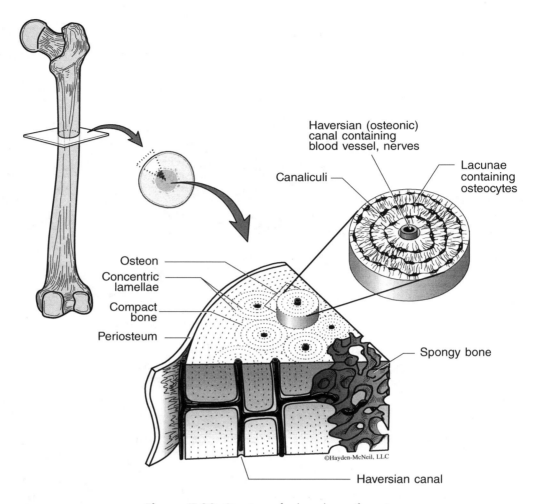

Haversian (osteonic)
canal containing
blood vessel, nerves

Canaliculi

Lacunae
containing
osteocytes

Osteon

Concentric
lamellae

Compact
bone

Periosteum

Spongy bone

©Hayden-McNeil, LLC

Haversian canal

**Figure 7-22.** Structure of a long bone (femur).

3.    **Other connective tissues.**

*Blood* – most textbooks classify blood as a connective tissue. However, blood is so unique that it will be dealt with in the second volume of this text, and is designed to coordinate with the spring lectures. Blood is composed of plasma and "formed elements" (red cells, white cells, and *platelets*).

Some textbooks also list reticuloendothelial tissue. This is an old-fashioned term used to describe macrophage-rich tissues of the body. Such tissues would include lymph nodes, the spleen, lungs, etc. Nowadays, reticuloendothelial tissue is not regarded as a type of connective tissue, and the concept of a reticuloendothelial system is no longer useful.

## III. Muscle Tissues

### A. What Is Muscle Tissue?

Muscle tissue consists of elongated cells called muscle fibers. Muscle fibers are highly specialized for contraction and the consequent generation of force. There are three types.

### B. Types of Muscle Tissue

There are three types of muscle tissue.

1. **Skeletal muscle.**

   *Skeletal muscle* is so named because it is attached to the bones of the skeleton. It is also called *striated muscle*, because its fibers are traversed with a pattern of alternating light and dark lines, or striations. Each cell, or fiber, is unbranched and has many nuclei. This muscle is voluntary, because it can be made to contract and relax by voluntary control.

©Hayden-McNeil, LLC

**Figure 7-23.** Skeletal muscle.

2. **Smooth muscle.**

   *Smooth muscle* is so named because it lacks striations. It is sometimes called nonstriated muscle for that reason. Each cell has one nucleus. Found in the walls of hollow internal structures such as blood vessels, the stomach, intestines, and urinary bladder. Smooth muscle fibers contract involuntarily.

©Hayden-McNeil, LLC

**Figure 7-24.** Smooth muscle.

3. **Cardiac muscle.**

   *Cardiac muscle* is found only in the heart. It is striated like skeletal muscle, but is involuntary and spontaneously rhythmic. That means its contractions are not under conscious control, and a heart will continue to beat even when removed from the body (provided it is given sufficient oxygen and nutrients). Cardiac muscle fibers branch to form networks in the wall of the heart. Each cell usually has one nucleus. The cells are joined end to end at specialized intercellular junctions called *intercalated discs*. These junctions are found only in cardiac muscle, and one of their functions is to facilitate the rapid spread of electrical excitation from one cell to the next.

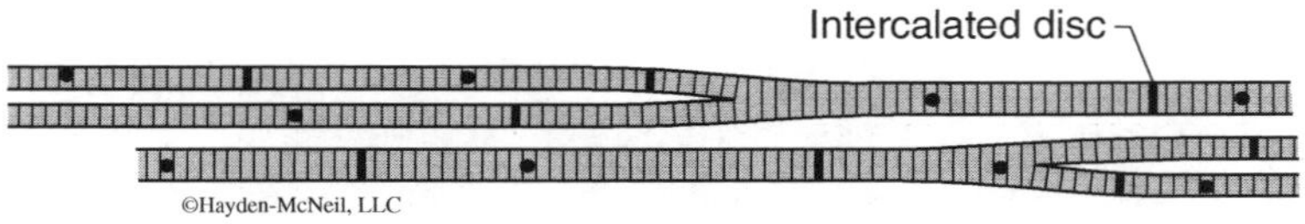

Intercalated disc

©Hayden-McNeil, LLC

**Figure 7-25.** Cardiac muscle.

## IV. Nervous Tissue

Nervous tissue makes up the brain, spinal cord, and peripheral nerves. Nervous tissue is composed of two types of cell, *neurons* and *neuroglia*.

### A. Nerve Cells, or Neurons

Neurons are varied in shape and size. Generally, a neuron consists of a cell body with processes radiating from it. These processes are called *dendrites* and *axons*. Dendrites have numerous dendritic spines projecting from their surfaces (not shown) and conduct nerve impulses toward the cell body, and axons (nerve fibers) conduct impulses away from the cell.

140

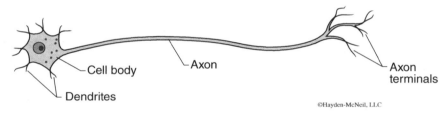

Cell body — Axon — Axon terminals

Dendrites

©Hayden-McNeil, LLC

**Figure 7-26.** Nerve cell.

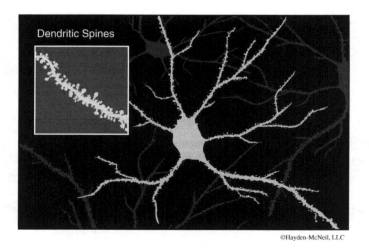

Dendritic Spines

©Hayden-McNeil, LLC

**Figure 7-27.** Dendritic spines.

Neurons are sensitive to various stimuli—chemical, mechanical, and electrical—which trigger a train of *nerve impulses*. Nerve impulses are changes in the electrical potential across the plasma membrane of the nerve cell. These changes in electrical potential are called action potentials, and will be dealt with later.

## B. Glial Cells, or Neuroglia

Many of their functions are still not known. *Glial cells* may play a role in the uptake and release of chemicals and ions, and possibly are involved in providing the neurons with certain nutrients.

# CHAPTER

**8**

# MEMBRANES FOUND IN THE BODY
The Skin, a Special Type of Membrane Involved in Regulating Heat Exchange between the Body and Its Surroundings

## CHAPTER OUTLINE

## DESCRIPTION AND INTRODUCTION

Two or more kinds of tissue grouped together and performing specialized functions constitute an **organ**. The skin is an organ. The skin and the structures associated with it (its derivatives: hair, nails, glands, and sensory receptors) make up the **integumentary** system of the body.

The skin is actually one of several types of *membrane* found in the body. We must first review these other membranes (serous, mucous, synovial), but the main thrust of this chapter is to give you an understanding of the skin, how it is structured, and how it performs one of its most important physiological functions, which is regulation of heat exchange between the body and its surroundings.

## OBJECTIVES

After listening to the lecture and reading this chapter, you should be able to:

1.  Define what is meant by a **membrane**.
2.  Describe the three major types of **epithelial** membranes, and where they are found.
3.  Name three **serous** membranes.
4.  Name a **non**-epithelial membrane.
5.  List the five important **physiological functions** of the **skin**.
6.  Describe the **structure** of the skin, including a list of its layers.
7.  List three **accessory** structures of the skin.
8.  Describe the structure of a **hair follicle**.
9.  What is **keratinization**? To what **group** of chemical substances does keratin belong?
10. Describe the **three** types of **glands** associated with the skin.
11. Explain how the skin and the rest of the body work together to regulate **body temperature**.
12. Describe how superficial epidermal **wounds heal**, and how deep wounds heal.
13. List four **causes** of **burns**.
14. List and describe the **three classes** of burn.
15. Explain what is meant by "the rule of **nines**."
16. Describe the possible **consequences** of severe burns, and the factors that can contribute to the **seriousness** of burns.
17. Describe the three forms of skin cancer and identify the most dangerous one.
18. Identify the major cause of skin cancer, and what avoidance measures can be taken.

## I. Membranes

### A. What Is a Membrane?—Epithelial and Non-Epithelial Types

An epithelial membrane is a layer of epithelium overlaying a connective tissue layer. The three epithelial membranes we will discuss are:

- **Mucous** membranes
- **Serous** membranes
- **Cutaneous** membrane (skin)

The **non**-epithelial membrane we shall discuss is called a:

- **Synovial** membrane

Synovial membranes are found in the *synovial joints* between bones.

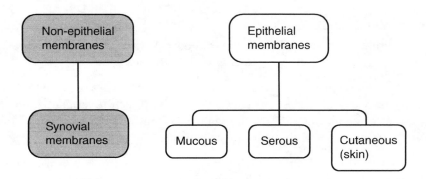

**Figure 8-1.** Membranes.

### B. Mucous Membranes

Mucous membranes line all structures that *open to the outside of your body* (i.e. to your body's exterior). These structures include the gastrointestinal, respiratory, and reproductive tracts. They consist of various types of epithelium overlying a layer of loose connective tissue. For example:

- Stratified squamous epithelium lines the oral cavity
- Pseudostratified columnar epithelium lines part of the nasal cavity
- Simple columnar epithelium lines part of the small intestine

Some mucous membranes have a layer of smooth muscle called the *muscularis mucosae.*

Some cells within the epithelium secrete mucus, which prevents the membrane from drying out. Mucus also serves to trap particles in the respiratory passages and to lubricate food so that it slides easily down the digestive tract.

### C. Serous Membranes

Serous membranes line body cavities that *do **NOT** open to the exterior.* They line the thorax and abdomen, and cover the organs within these cavities. The epithelial layer (simple squamous epithelium) secretes a watery lubricating fluid, serous fluid, that allows the organs to slip or glide easily against one another or against the walls of the cavities.

The serous membranes associated with some organs are:

**Pleura**      thoracic cavity and lungs (inflammation of this membrane is called *pleuritis*)

**Pericardium**   heart cavity and heart (inflammation of this membrane is called *pericarditis*)

**Peritoneum**   a very complex membrane that lines the abdominal cavity, and covers the abdominal organs and some pelvic organs (inflammation of this membrane is called *peritonitis*)

## D. Cutaneous Membrane—Skin

The cutaneous membrane, or skin, is an organ of the integumentary system and is discussed in Section II.

## E. Synovial Membranes

Synovial membranes line the joint cavities of the freely moveable joints of the skeleton. Examples of these *synovial joints* are the *knee*, *elbow*, and *shoulder*.

Synovial membranes consist of a four-cell thick layer of two types of *synoviocytes*, derived from macrophage and fibroblast lineages. These cells overlie the capillaries and connective tissue that make up the joint capsule. Fibroblast and macrophage derived synoviocytes play important roles in rheumatoid arthritis.

Synoviocytes with fibroblast lineage secrete *synovial fluid*, a non-Newtonian fluid which lubricates the joint. It contains the glycoprotein lubricin and hyaluronic acid. Synovial joints will be discussed later in this course.

## II. Skin

## A. What Is Skin?

The skin (together with hair and nails) is also known as the *cutaneous* membrane (see Section I above). It constitutes most of what you see when you look at a person in a bathing suit—or with nothing on at all.

The skin is an organ because it consists of tissues structurally joined together to perform specific activities. Its surface area is large, about 2 square meters or 3000 square inches.

The skin is not just a simple covering that keeps the body together and gives it protection. It has other important functions, as we shall see on the following page.

## B. Five Physiological Functions of the Skin

1.  **Regulation of body temperature.**

    When the body temperature increases in response to high environmental temperature or heat generation during strenuous exercise, sweating helps to cool the body and reduce the temperature to normal. Changes in skin blood flow also affect the amount of heat dissipated at the surface of the skin.

2.  **Protection.**

    Protects the underlying tissues against bacterial invasion, abrasion, dehydration, and ultraviolet radiation.

3.  **Sensation.**

    Skin has specialized sensory receptors that respond to pain, touch, pressure, temperature, tickle, and itch.

4.  **Excretion (minor function).**

    Sweat assists in the excretion of certain organic compounds.

5.  **Synthesis of *vitamin D*.**

    Vitamin D is necessary for normal development of bones and teeth. Lack of vitamin D results in a condition called ***rickets***, where the bones do not calcify and they remain soft and flexible. *Vitamin D3* or *cholecalciferol* is synthesized in the skin when its precursor (*7-dehydrocholesterol*) is exposed to ultraviolet radiation. Cholecalciferol is then converted into the active substance ***calcitriol*** in the kidney and liver.

147

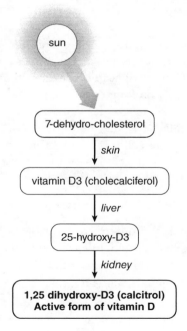

**Figure 8-2.**

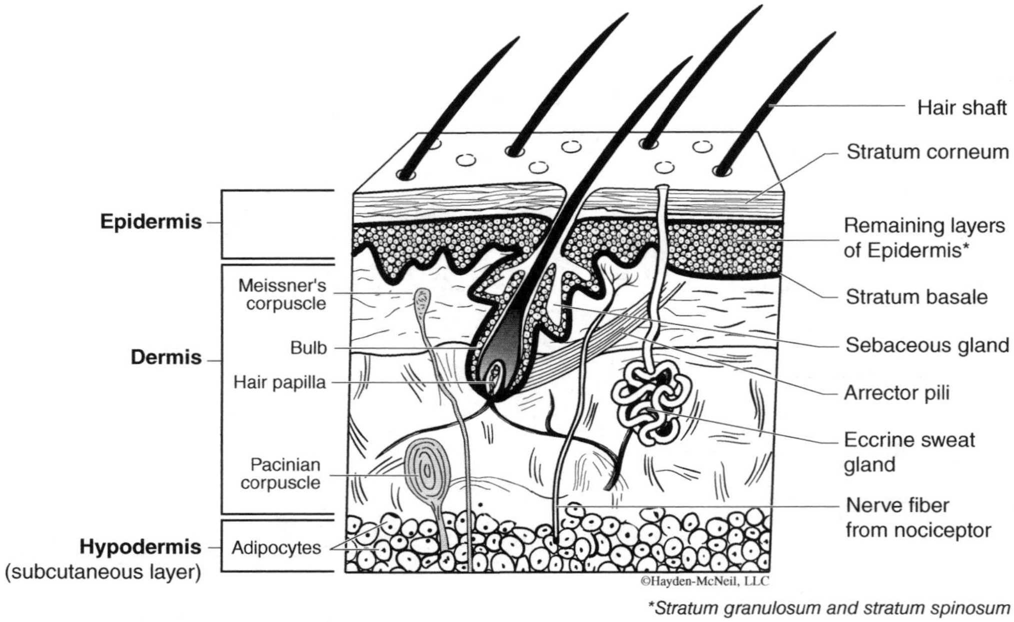

Epidermis

Dermis

Hypodermis
(subcutaneous layer)

Meissner's corpuscle

Bulb

Hair papilla

Pacinian corpuscle

Adipocytes

Hair shaft

Stratum corneum

Remaining layers of Epidermis*

Stratum basale

Sebaceous gland

Arrector pili

Eccrine sweat gland

Nerve fiber from nociceptor

©Hayden-McNeil, LLC

*Stratum granulosum and stratum spinosum*

**Figure 8-3.** Skin cross section.

## C. Structure

Skin is divided into three layers:

1. **Epidermis.**

   The outer layer is stratified squamous epithelium. It has no blood vessels. The most abundant cell is the keratinocyte. Other cells are *melanocytes*, which produce the dark pigment *melanin*. Their cytoplasm is packed with melanin granules, which are transferred to keratinocytes via long dendritic processes. Melanin protects deeper layers from the damaging effects of ultraviolet radiation. In some people, melanin tends to form patches called freckles. People who cannot synthesize melanin are called albinos. A third type of cell is the Langerhans cells and dendritic epidermal T-cells. These cells act as sentinels for the immune system, and sound the alarm if pathogens (bacteria, viruses, etc.) invade the skin or if the skin is damaged.

   The epidermis is subdivided into four layers. From the outside, they are as follows.

   a. The ***stratum corneum*** is the outermost layer of the skin. It consists of a tough layer of tightly packed, flattened, fully-keratinized dead cells (about 25–30 cells thick). These cells are continually lost by abrasion.

   b. The ***stratum granulosum*** (**granular cell layer**). The cells are joined by tight junctions.

   c. The ***stratum spinosum*** (**prickle cell layer**). Bundles of keratin filaments traverse the cells and are inserted into the *desmosome* junctions between them.

d.  ***The stratum basale*** (= ***stratum germinativum*,** **basal cell layer**) is the innermost layer. It consists of dividing cells *(keratinocytes)* that gradually push older cells nearer the outer surface where they finally form the stratum corneum. These older cells go through a process called *keratinization*, where they progressively die and become packed with a tough, fibrous, waterproof protein called ***keratin***. The melanocytes are found in this layer. They synthesize melanin and transfer it to the keratinocytes.

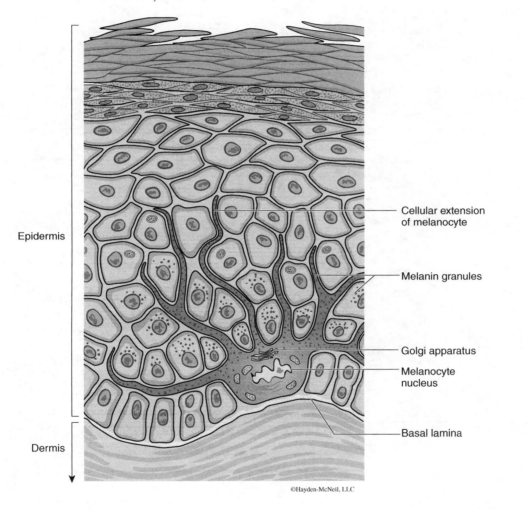

Epidermis

Dermis

Cellular extension of melanocyte

Melanin granules

Golgi apparatus

Melanocyte nucleus

Basal lamina

©Hayden-McNeil, LLC

**Figure 8-4.** Melanocyte distributing melanin granules among keratinocytes.

In healthy skin, new cells are produced in the stratum basale at roughly the rate at which they are lost from the stratum corneum. Normally, it takes 2–4 weeks for a cell from the basal layer to reach the stratum corneum and be lost by shedding.

In the condition known as *psoriasis* the rate of basal cell proliferation is accelerated, the epidermis thickens, cells do not have time to keratinize properly, and are shed within a week.

150

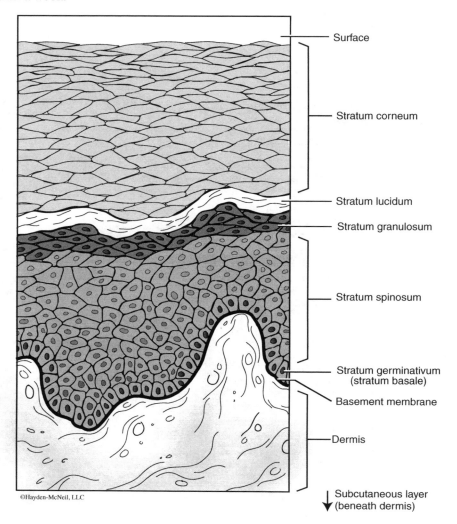

**Figure 8-5.** Layers of the skin.

Excessive *rubbing* of the skin can also overstimulate cell division in the stratum basale, causing overproduction of the stratum corneum. The result is a *callus* or *corn.*

Dandruff is a condition caused by a yeast fungus (*Malassezia*). It metabolizes sebum, causing erratic shedding of stratum corneum cells.

2.  **Dermis.**

    The dermis is relatively thick. It consists mainly of dense, irregularly arranged connective tissue containing interlacing bundles of collagenous and elastic fibers. This arrangement allows the skin to stretch (e.g. during pregnancy, or when limbs are flexed at joints such as the knee and elbow). The dermis projects up into the epidermis in little humps called *dermal papillae*.

    The dermis contains blood vessels and sometimes smooth muscle fibers (e.g. the skin enclosing the testes, the *scrotum*, and those that cause the hairs to "stand up").

    Nerve fibers course through the dermis. Some are "motor," and carry signals to the dermal muscles and glands. Others have a sensory function, and carry impulses to the central nervous system after stimulation of specialized dermal sensory receptors for pressure, touch, pain, temperature, etc. (these will be discussed later).

    *Hair follicles* and *glands* occur at various depths in the dermis, and will be discussed in the next section.

3.  **Hypodermis (subcutaneous layer).**

    Lies beneath the dermis. Fibers from the dermis anchor the skin to the subcutaneous layer, which is in turn attached to the underlying tissues and organs. The subcutaneous layer consists largely of loose connective tissue and adipose tissue. This layer also contains nerve fibers and blood vessels. The adipose tissue acts as a heat insulator.

## D. Skin Cancer

Skin cancer is the most prevalent cancer in the USA. It is estimated that one in five people will get skin cancer at some time of their lives. Over 90% of skin cancers are caused by exposure to sunlight. Skin cancer (principally melanoma) kills more women under the age of 30 than any other type of cancer. That includes breast and ovarian cancers. Avoidance measures include the use of sunscreen of at least SPF 15, tight-woven clothing, wide-brimmed hats, seeking shade when your shadow is shorter than you are tall.

There is a 75% increased risk of melanoma in those who used indoor tanning booths in their teens and twenties. The bottom line is "tan now and pay later."

*Actinic keratosis consists of scaly spots most commonly found on the face, lower arms, and back of the hands in fair-skinned people: It is not a cancer in itself, but it can develop into cancer.*

1.  Squamous cell carcinoma is the second most common form of skin cancer.

2.  Basal cell carcinoma is the most common form of cancer in the United States.

3.  Malignant melanoma is the most dangerous because of its ability to metastasize.

151

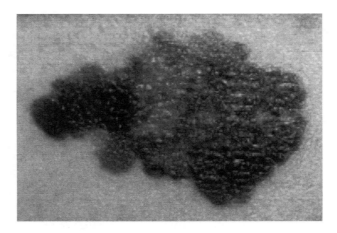

**Figure 8-6.** Melanoma.
(*Image from National Cancer Institute*)

### III. Accessory Structures of the Skin—Epidermal Derivatives

### A. Hair Follicles

*Hair follicles* are structures from which hairs arise. Hair can be an insulator, but is also protective. The eyelashes protect the eyes from flying insects, for example. Hairs in the nose and ears protect the airways and external ear canal from particles and insects. Touch receptors are associated with hair follicles, and respond if the hair is gently touched. The structure of a hair follicle is complex.

A smooth muscle, called the *arrector pili* extends from the dermis to the side of the hair follicle. When the muscle contracts under the stresses of fright, fear, cold, and emotions the hair stands on end. In humans, this contraction gives "*goosebumps*" or "gooseflesh," because the skin around each hair shaft forms an elevation. In animals such as the cat, it causes the fur to stand on end (particularly in the tail) and makes the animal look larger and more threatening.

A *sebaceous gland* or oil gland is connected to the hair follicle, and is discussed on the next page.

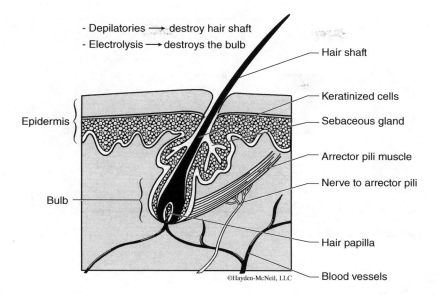

- Depilatories → destroy hair shaft
- Electrolysis → destroys the bulb

Hair shaft

Keratinized cells

Sebaceous gland

Arrector pili muscle

Nerve to arrector pili

Epidermis

Bulb

Hair papilla

Blood vessels

©Hayden-McNeil, LLC

**Figure 8-7.** Structure of a hair follicle.

153

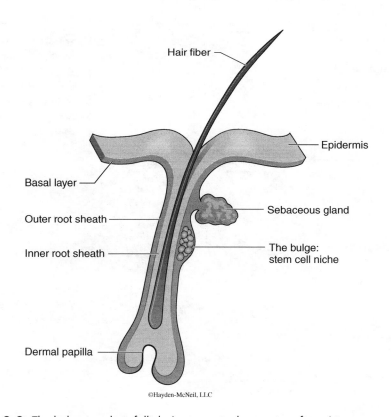

Hair fiber

Epidermis

Basal layer

Outer root sheath

Sebaceous gland

Inner root sheath

The bulge:
stem cell niche

Dermal papilla

©Hayden-McNeil, LLC

**Figure 8-8.** The bulge in a hair follicle (not seen in the previous figure) is a stem cell niche.

**MYTHS**

Hair grows back faster, thicker and darker after shaving – False

After shaving, two hairs grow back in place of one – False

Plucking a gray hair causes 10 to grow back in its place – False

Hair can turn gray overnight – False

Hair continues to grow after death – False (the skin shrinks)

**Figure 8-9.**

## B. Glands

There are three types of glands associated with the skin.

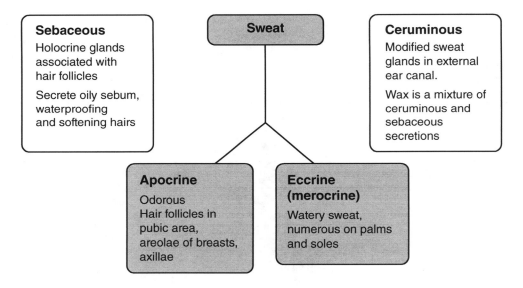

**Figure 8-10.** Skin glands.

1.  **Sebaceous glands.**

    Holocrine glands almost always associated with hair follicles. They secrete an oily material called sebum that keeps the hairs and the skin soft and pliable, forms a protective film that prevents excessive evaporation of water, and inhibits the growth of certain bacteria.

    Sometimes the sebaceous glands become enlarged because of accumulated sebum, and acne lesions called blackheads develop. Pimples or boils often develop, because sebum contains nutrients for certain bacteria. The blackhead is black because it contains melanin and oxidized oil from the sebum.

2.  **Sweat (sudoriferous) glands.**

These glands are divided into two types, apocrine sweat glands and merocrine sweat glands. In the skin, these merocrine glands have a special name—*eccrine* sweat glands. Note that we still use the term apocrine sweat glands, even though their mechanism of secretion does not consist of pinching off of the cell apices.

Apocrine sweat glands are mainly in the skin of the *axilla*, pubic region, and pigmented areas (*areolae*) of the breasts. The ducts of apocrine sweat glands open into hair follicles. Apocrine secretions are rich in fatty acids and proteins, which are broken down by naturally occurring bacteria. This leads to the development of odor. Deodorants, most of which are applied to the axillary region of the body, contain a variety of ingredients including the antibacterial agent triclosan. Antiperspirants, on the other hand, usually contain aluminum compounds that act by preventing sweating.

Eccrine sweat glands are much more common on the body surface, and their secretion is more watery than that from apocrine sweat glands. They are present everywhere except for the margins of the lips, nail beds, glans penis, glans clitoris, labia minora, and eardrums. Eccrine glands are most numerous in the skin of the palms and soles. Hence "sweaty palms" when you are under emotional stress. The sweat from eccrine sweat glands is a very dilute solution of sodium chloride (with minor proportions of other inorganic salts), lactic acid, and several nitrogen-containing compounds such as urea, ammonia, amino acids, and uric acid. Other substances that need not concern us are also present in trace amounts.

3.  **Ceruminous glands.**

Modified sweat glands found only in the external ear canal. The combined secretion of the ceruminous and sebaceous glands in the external ear canal forms the ear wax. This material acts as a sticky barrier that prevents the entrance of foreign bodies (such as the odd bug or whatever).

## C. Nails

Each nail consists of a nail *plate* (body) that overlies a surface of skin called the nail bed. The nail is produced by epithelial cells that reproduce and undergo keratinization in the half-moon (*lunula*) region of the nail. The nail junction with the skin at the tip of the finger is called the hyponychium.

## D. Skin Obtains Some Oxygen Directly from the Air

Air supplies the top 0.25–0.4 mm of the skin with oxygen. This zone includes the entire epidermis and even some of the dermis. However, this still accounts for only 0.4% of the body's oxygen needs [Stücker, M. et al. (2002). *Journal of Physiology 538*, 985–994].

## IV. Regulation of Body Temperature

Human beings, unlike amphibians and most reptiles, are warm-blooded organisms. They are able to keep their bodies at the remarkably constant temperature of about 37°C, even when the environmental temperature varies over a broad range. The body temperature varies somewhat, however, because the temperature regulatory system is not perfect.

155

Body temperature is controlled by balancing heat **production** against heat **loss**.

Heat is **produced by metabolism**. In exercise, for example, the rate of heat production by the body can increase enormously.

Heat is **lost through the skin**.

## A. What Happens When the Body Is Too Hot

When heating of the body is excessive, such as during exercise or if the environmental temperature is very high, heat-sensitive receptors in the skin and in the hypothalamus of the brain initiate a set of reactions to promote heat loss through the skin. Heat is lost via four routes.

- Conduction
- Convection
- Radiation
- Evaporation

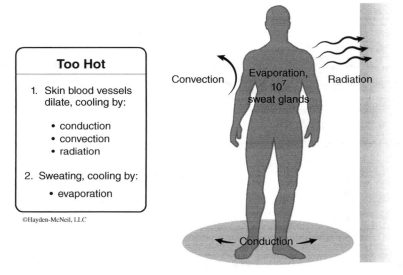

**Figure 8-11.**

1. **Skin blood vessels dilate**, making the skin flush and heating it up. This can increase heat loss as much as eight times. Cooling is achieved by:

   a. *Conduction* to the air in contact with the body
   
   b. *Convection* via air currents passing over the body
   
   c. *Radiation* to the surrounding walls, ceilings, etc. For the naked body, radiation constitutes a major route of heat loss.

2. **Sweating is initiated.**

   The sweat glands start secreting sweat, which evaporates on the surface of the skin, causing evaporative cooling.

## B. What Happens When the Body Is Too Cold

When heat loss is in excess of heat production, as might happen when the environment is very cold, cold receptors in the skin and in the hypothalamus initiate the following reactions.

1.  **Skin blood vessels constrict.**

    If a person is light-skinned, the skin turns paler. Because less warm blood flows through the skin, flow of heat from the body's "core" to the skin is reduced. Therefore, heat loss from the skin surface by conduction, convection, and radiation is diminished.

2.  **Heat production increases.**

    This is achieved by *shivering.* There is also another method, called *non-shivering thermogenesis,* where in brown fat the efficiency of oxidative phosphorylation is reduced. Instead of being packaged into ATP, the system in brown fat mitochondria is uncoupled and metabolic energy is converted directly into heat. Newborn infants can increase their rate of heat production by 100% by this method, although adults can achieve only a modest 10–15% increase. The phenomenon is a characteristic of **brown** adipose tissue, which is found in hibernating animals, small mammals such as rodents, in newborn and adult humans. See Chapter 7.

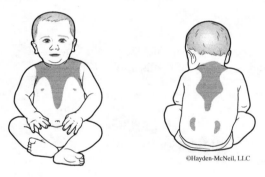

©Hayden-McNeil, LLC

**Figure 8-12.** Brown fat distribution in the neonate.

157

## V. Skin Color

Depending on the state of its blood vessels and on the presence of colored substances, skin can have a variety of colors: black, brown, yellow, pink, white, bluish. Genetics plays a major role, but other factors can also come into play (e.g. sunlight, blushing, blanching, eating large amounts of carrots which contain the yellow pigment *carotene*).

## VI. Wounds and Burns

## A. Superficial, Epidermal Wounds

This type of *wound* extends as far as the dermis, and entails loss of the stratum germinativum. Basal epithelial cells multiply and migrate laterally to fill the gap.

## B. Deep Wounds

These wounds extend into the dermis and often involve the subcutaneous layers as well. The body responds to this damage in four successive phases.

1.  **Inflammatory phase.**

    A vascular and cellular response that removes pathogens (e.g. bacteria), foreign material, and dying tissue in preparation for repair. A blood clot forms in the wound and loosely unites the wound edges. Keratinocytes adjacent to the wound activate dendric epidermal T-cells.

2.  **Migratory phase.**

    Clot begins to form a scab, epithelial cells migrate beneath scab to bridge the wound, fibroblasts begin synthesizing scar tissue and damaged blood vessels begin to regrow by a process called angiogenesis. Tissue filling the wound is called granulation tissue.

3.  **Proliferative phase.**

    Extensive growth of epithelial cells, deposition of collagen fibers by fibroblasts, continued growth of blood vessels.

4.  **Maturation phase.**

    Scab sloughs off, scar tissue remains.

## C. Burns

*Burns* are caused by heat, electrical, radioactive, or chemical agents. These agents destroy (denature) proteins in exposed cells and kill the cells.

A life-threatening consequence of extensive burning is the very large loss of body fluid that accompanies it. This fluid seeps out from the damaged capillaries and blood vessels. It is composed of water and plasma containing plasma proteins (this is the fluid that is present in a blister). If fluid loss is extensive, it causes *hypovolemia*, and a condition known as *circulatory shock* can set in. Circulatory shock can lead to kidney and heart failure.

The seriousness of a burn is related to the following factors.

1.  **Depth.**
    a.  *First-degree burns (superficial partial-thickness)* involve only surface epidermis. There is redness but no blistering.

    b.  *Second-degree burns (deep partial-thickness)* involve entire thickness of epidermis and varying portions of the dermis. There is usually blistering (accumulation of fluid between the epidermis and dermis.

    c.  *Third-degree burns (full-thickness)* involve destruction of the epidermis, dermis, and the epidermal derivatives.

2.  **Percentage of skin surface area affected.**

    The percentage of skin surface area affected is important in determining the seriousness of a burn situation, and whether there is a threat to life. For example, if more than 70% of the skin surface is subjected to a third-degree burn, then the chances of survival may be worse than 50/50.

The "*rule of nines*" is a quick way of estimating what percentage of the skin surface has been affected. The body is divided up into sections, each of which represents 9% of its surface.

Each of the following represents nine percent (total 54%):

- anterior surface of the two arms, hands, and shoulders
- anterior surface of head and neck
- anterior surface of one leg and foot
- posterior surface of the two arms, hands, and shoulders
- posterior surface of head and neck
- posterior surface of one leg and foot

Each of the following represents eighteen percent (total 36%):

- anterior trunk
- posterior trunk

3. **Area affected.**
4. **Age.**
5. **General health.**

159

## D. Local Mechanical Stimulation of Skin

The *white* reaction is seen when the surface of the skin is stroked lightly with a blunt "pointed" instrument. It appears as a white line after 15–20 seconds, reaches maximal intensity between a half and one minute, then fades and disappears in 3–5 minutes. The reaction has no nervous component, and appears to be due to a direct effect on minute venous vessels that respond to the stimulus by constriction.

The *triple response* of Lewis is made up of the *red reaction*, the *flare*, and the *wheal*. It is caused by the blunt instrument being drawn more firmly across the skin, especially of the forearm or back. It consists of a red line instead of a white line, and reaches maximum intensity between 3 and 15 seconds. On either side of the red line is a white line. If the stimulus is stronger, the reddening of the skin is not confined to the stroke line, but spreads outwards for a variable distance depending on the intensity of the stroking action that has been used to provoke it. The flare may involve local nerve endings, but is not a true reflex. When the stimulus is more intense, the skin along the line of injury first becomes red and is surrounded by a flare, then turns edematous, and a wheal or welt is produced (this effect also occurs when the injury is inflicted with a whip lash).

The triple response can be mimicked by a subcutaneous injection of histamine, but it is not known whether histamine is the cause.

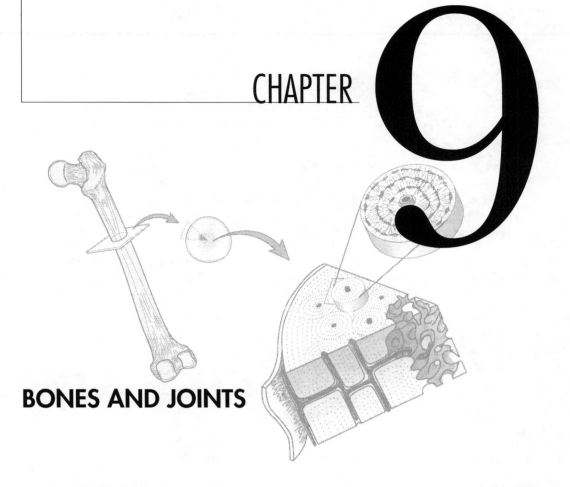

# CHAPTER 9

# BONES AND JOINTS

## CHAPTER OUTLINE

## DESCRIPTION

This chapter covers a lot of material (on which you will be examined), so you need to come to the lecture well-prepared. That means thoroughly studying this material *before the lecture* (as always).

Without the skeletal system, we would be soft, unprotected creatures without the capacity to stand erect, grasp, chew, or even to throw and hit a baseball. This chapter deals with the nature of bone, its development and growth, and its ability to heal when damaged. Although the skeleton is made up of rigid bones, joints allow whole structure to move, bend, and twist.

I have given you a list of the bones I expect you to know. *You should learn this material by studying these notes.* Useful information on the skeleton is also given in *ATLAS OF THE SKELETAL MUSCLES*, by R.J. and J.A. Stone, which I strongly recommend.

Those of you who are taking the laboratory classes (BIOL 203) will also have the opportunity to handle and identify the bones of the human skeleton. However, the bones in the laboratory are dead and dusty. In the living body, bones are living material and are constantly being remodeled. When damaged or broken, they hurt and bleed. After they have been damaged they can repair themselves. We will be discussing all of this in this chapter and in the lecture.

## OBJECTIVES

After listening to the lecture and reading this chapter, you should be able to:

1.  **Classify** bones according to their shapes and name an example from each group.
2.  Describe the **general structure** of a typical **long bone** and list the functions of the parts.
3.  Describe how bone is similar to reinforced **concrete**.
4.  Describe (with a **diagram**) the **microscopic organization** of compact bone.
5.  List and describe the **four** types of **cells** found in bone.
6.  Describe **osteoporosis**, its possible causes, and therapy (distinguish *osteoporosis* from *osteopetrosis* — what's the difference?). Describe the role of RANK Ligand and osteoprotegerin in bone remodeling and in osteoporosis.
7.  Name and describe the condition caused by lack of **vitamin D**.
8.  Distinguish **intramembranous** and **endochondral** bones and describe their development.
9.  Describe the five important factors that affect bone **development**, **repair**, and **turnover**.
10. Describe four stages of repair in a bone **fracture**.
11. Describe five major **functions** of bones.
12. Describe three major different types of **joints** and the **tissues** that hold them together. List the subtypes of these joints, where applicable.
13. Describe the four structures that make up a **synovial** joint.
14. Describe **synovial fluid** and its properties.
15. Describe three **structures** associated with synovial joints.

16. List the **seven types** of **synovial joints**, giving an example of each.

17. Distinguish between **axial** and **appendicular** skeletons, and name the major components of each.

18. Locate and identify the bones and the major features of the bones that make up the **skull**, **vertebral column**, **thoracic cage**, **pectoral girdle**, **upper limb**, **pelvic girdle**, and **lower limb**.

19. Explain how skeletal muscles produce **movements** at joints.

20. Describe the following joints and explain how their articulating parts are held together:

    **shoulder joint**

    **elbow joint**

    **hip joint**

    **knee joint**

## I. Bone Structure

### A. Shapes of Bones

Bones can be long, short, flat, or irregular.

### B. Parts of a Typical Long Bone, the Femur

1.  At the ends are the two *epiphyses*, made up of *spongy bone* (also called *trabecular bone*; it consists of branching, bony plates). The epiphyses contain *red marrow*, which is engaged in the manufacture of blood cells. The epiphyses are covered with special hyaline cartilage called *articular cartilage*.

2.  The shaft of the bone is the *diaphysis*, made up of *compact bone* (also called *cortical bone*). The diaphysis is a hollow tube containing a cavity (the *medullary cavity*) lined with squamous cells (*endosteum*), filled with *yellow marrow* and containing blood vessels. Yellow marrow is mainly adipose tissue. The blood vessels (together with nerves and lymphatics) penetrate into the medullary cavity via small channels (canals) that perforate the bone.

3.  Except at the ends, the bone is covered by a fibrous vascular layer called *periosteum*. The periosteum plays a very important role in the formation and repair of bone tissue.

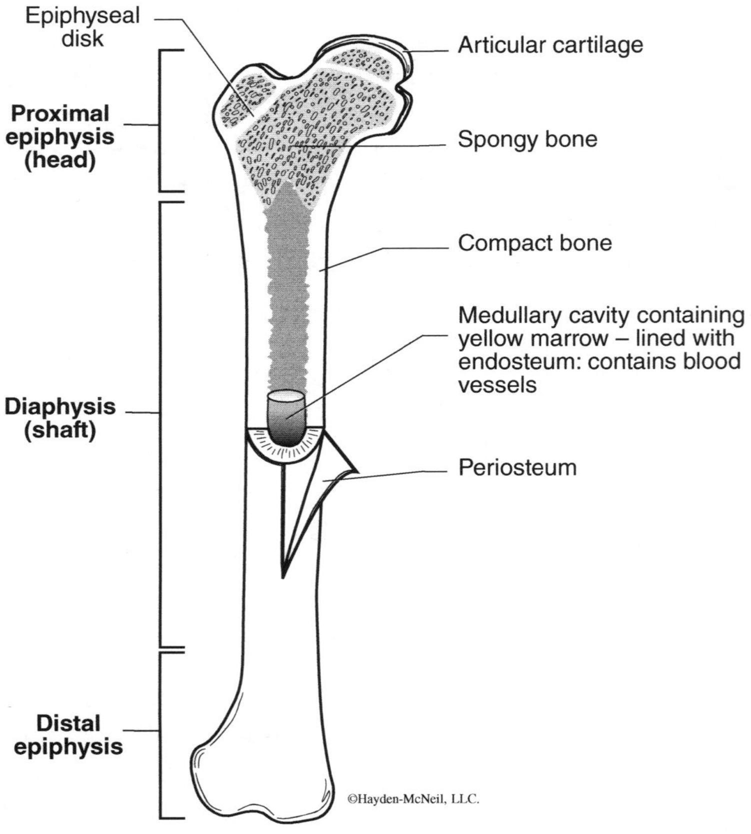

**Figure 9-1.** Structure of a long bone (femur).

## C. What Is Bone?

Contrary to what many people think, bone is a living material that is continually remodeling itself. We will discuss that in a moment.

Bone is similar to reinforced concrete, which consists of concrete (providing *compressional* strength) containing steel rods (providing *tensile* strength).

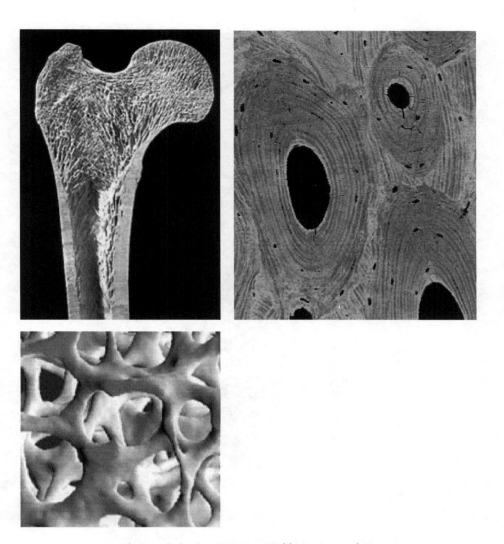

**Figure 9-2.** Compact, cortical bone (top right);
spongy, cancellous or trabecular bone (bottom).

1.  **Collagen** fibers (= steel rods) provide *tensile* strength.

2.  **Calcium phosphate**, mainly in the form of the mineral *hydroxylapatite*, $Ca_{10}(PO_4)_6(OH)_2$ (= concrete), provides *compressional* strength (some calcium carbonate and other compounds are also present—see later).

## D. Microscopic Organization of Bone

The basic unit of compact bone is called an *osteon*. Compact bone consists of osteons cemented together. Each osteon consists of a central canal (*osteonic canal* or *Haversian canal*) containing blood vessels and nerves, surrounded by concentric rings of bone called *lamellae*. Each bone cell or *osteocyte* nestles in a little cavity called a *lacuna*. Lacunae are evenly spaced between the lamellae. Radiating little canals called *canaliculi* provide numerous routes so that oxygen, nutrients, and wastes can pass to and from the osteocytes, which would otherwise be cut off by the impermeable mass of bone. Delicate osteocyte processes penetrate the network of canaliculi, and in this way the interior osteocytes can communicate with each other and also remain in contact with the surface *osteoblasts*.

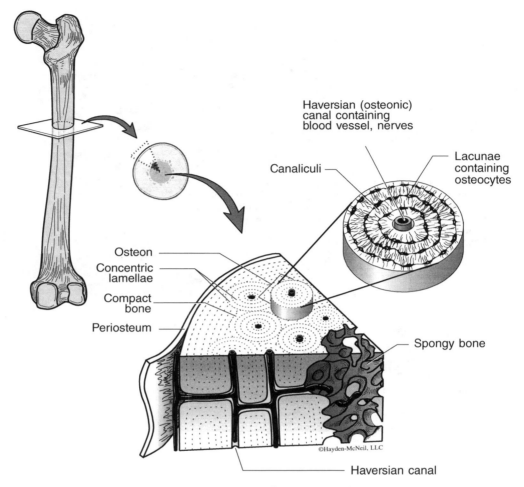

**Figure 9-3.** Structure of a long bone (femur).

There are *four* types of cells found in bone tissue. You must know them and understand their function. The first three, *osteoprogenitor cells*, *osteoblasts*, and *osteocytes*, are all related to each other.

1.  **Osteoprogenitor cells.**

    Unspecialized cells that can multiply and differentiate into **osteoblasts** (see below). They are found in the endosteum and elsewhere in the bone marrow compartment.

2.  **Osteoblasts.**

    Formed from osteoprogenitor cells. Cannot multiply, make bone by secreting collagen and possibly other proteins (the enzyme alkaline phosphatase, osteonectin, and osteocalcin) involved in bone formation. Upon completion of bone formation, a layer of "resting" osteoblasts remains on the surface of the bone, associated with the periosteum. Renewal of the osteoblast population results from the differentiation of osteoprogenitor cells residing in the bone marrow compartment.

3.  **Osteocytes.**

    Mature bone cells. Principal cells of bone tissue. Involved in daily cellular activities of bone tissue. Osteocytes are really osteoblasts that have isolated themselves in lacunae, surrounded by the bony substance they secrete but still in contact via gap junctions with the other osteocytes and surface osteoblasts via processes that permeate the canaliculi. This extensive communication network may mediate the effects of mechanical loading. This network of osteocyte processes is sometimes called the "osteocyte-lacuno-canalicular network."

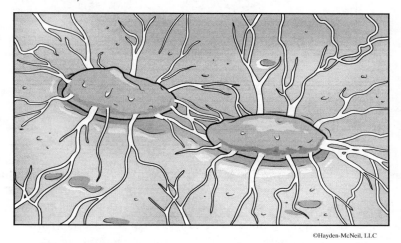

©Hayden-McNeil, LLC

**Figure 9-4.** Osteocytes showing cytoplasmic connections.

4.  **Osteoclasts.**

    Large, multinucleated cells. They have many nuclei because they are formed by fusion of a number of "stem" progenitor cells found in the bone marrow. These progenitor cells also give rise to circulating **monocytes**, a type of white blood cell that enters the tissues and develops into *macrophages* and other cells connected with the body's immune system (BIOL 204).

    Osteoclasts collect on bone surfaces. They contain large numbers of mitochondria and lysosomes. One side of an osteoclast has a plasma membrane with a "ruffled" appearance (*ruffled border*). The ruffled border abuts the bone surface, and it is surrounded by a zone that forms a tight seal against the bone surface. Here, the osteoclast secretes acid and lysosomal enzymes that dissolve the collagen and calcium phosphate that make up the bone. One enzyme is the protease *cathepsin K*. Some drugs that are used in the treatment of *osteoporosis* inhibit cathepsin K (see later).

    The dissolved bone components are endocytosed by the osteoclast. The endocytotic vesicles then move to the opposite surface of the osteoclast (*transcytosis*), where their contents are exocytosed.

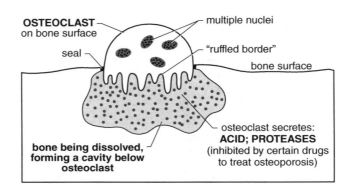

**Figure 9-5.** Osteoclast.

## II. How Bones Develop and Grow

### A. Bone Development and Remodeling

Bones start to form around the the sixth or seventh week of embryonic life. Bones form by replacement of existing connective tissues by a process called **ossification**. Ossification involves the deposition of collagen fibers by osteoblasts followed by calcium phosphate deposition on these fibers. The process requires normal plasma concentrations of calcium and phosphate, and is dependent on vitamin D. Two kinds of bone formation occur.

168

- **Intramembranous ossification.**

  Formation of bone directly on or within fibrous membranes (for example, the broad, flat bones of the skull, *mandible*, and the *clavicles*). The bones formed in this way are called *intramembranous bones*.

- **Endochondral ossification.**

  Formation of bone within a cartilaginous structure. Most bones of the body are formed this way (for example, the *femur*, *tibia*, and *humerus*). The bones so formed are called *endochondral bones*.

In intramembranous ossification, the process starts with a fibrous membrane. Osteoprogenitor cells differentiate into bone-forming osteoblasts, which start to secrete bone constituents. Because it looks a bit like a sponge, the bone formed in this case is called *spongy* bone. It doesn't *feel* like a sponge!

However, most of the bone in your body started out in embryonic life in the form of a cartilage model of your future skeleton, and bones were formed by **endochondral** ossification. In the case of a long bone, such as the tibia, there was a tightly regulated sequence of events depending on the expression of several genes. The process depends on a series of gene–protein interactions that form a "feedback loop" controlling *chondrocyte* differentiation.

1. In the beginning, the cartilaginous model tibia is ensheathed in **perichondrium**.

2. Then a **periosteal collar** forms—a *primary ossification center* develops, where bone replaces cartilage. A marrow cavity appears.

3. Nourishing blood vessels invade from the perichondrium, penetrating the marrow cavity. The cartilage model continues to grow at its ends.

4. The periosteal collar thickens and lengthens due to the activity of osteoblasts in the periosteum. *Secondary ossification centers* appear at the epiphyses, when spongy bone is laid down.

5. The cartilage remains in two places—in the **articular cartilage** and in the *epiphyseal plate* (= *epiphyseal disk*).

6. As long as the **chondrocytes** in the epiphyseal plate remain active, a long bone will continue to grow in length.

7. When the chondrocytes finally stop dividing, the cartilage in the epiphyseal plate is replaced by bone, and growth in length stops.

8. However, bones grow in *thickness* due to bone-manufacturing osteoblasts adding bone at the surface (just below the periosteum). In parallel, the marrow cavity is enlarged by the bone-dissolving osteoclasts.

9. This system is an ingenious way of starting out with a basic cartilage design, partially converting it to bone (which is needed once you have been born), but at the same time **allowing for the enormous amount of growth** that occurs during development from infancy through adolescence. For example, the long bones of an infant lengthen by 50% during the first year after birth.

## The Epiphyseal Plate

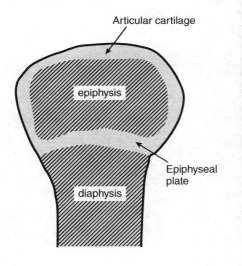

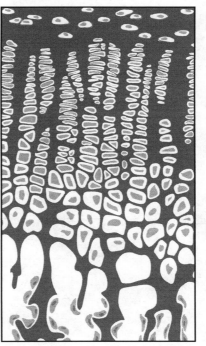

169

Quiescent chondrocytes

Proliferation

Maturation hypertrophy

Apoptosis, calcification

Ossification

©Hayden-McNeil, LLC

Osteoblasts and osteoclasts break down calcified cartilage and replace it with bone

**Figure 9-6.**

Bones undergoing ossification are continually undergoing *bone remodeling*. Remodeling is the replacement of old bone tissue with new bone tissue. Remodeling involves coupling the activities of **bone-making osteoblasts** and **bone-dissolving osteoclasts**.

Even after bones have reached their adult shapes and sizes, old bone is perpetually destroyed and new bone is formed in its place. As much as 15% of the total bone mass turns over each year. This turnover is not evenly distributed throughout the skeleton, however. The distal portion of the femur is totally replaced every four months, although the bone in certain areas of the shaft will not be replaced during one's lifetime.

### RANK Ligand

RANK Ligand is a protein expressed by osteoblasts that is essential in bone remodeling. It promotes formation of active osteoclasts. RANK Ligand activity must be regulated so that bone formation and bone resorption are balanced. Increased RANK Ligand would result in excessive osteoclast activity and bone resorption. To prevent this happening, osteoblasts produce low levels of osteoprotegerin (OPG). OPG binds RANK Ligand and takes it out of action. In osteoporosis this delicate control is lost (see Figure 9-14).

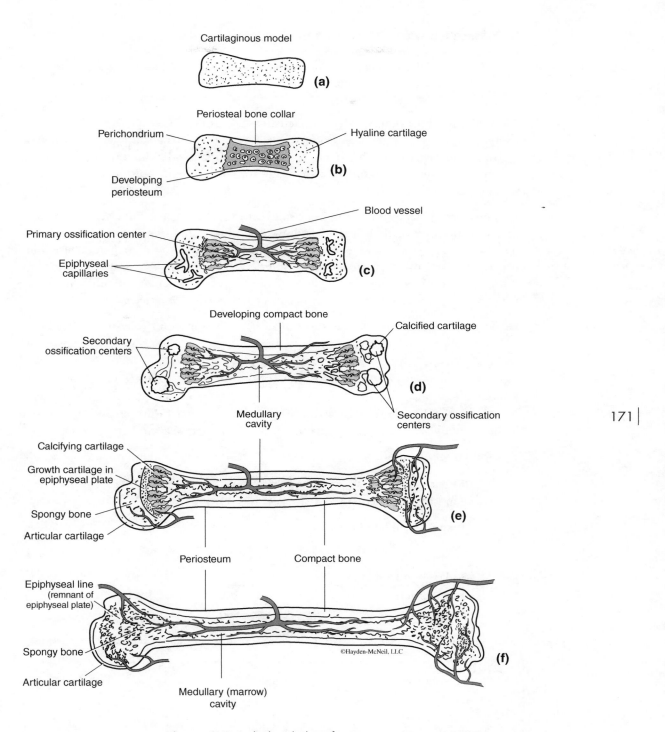

Cartilaginous model

**(a)**

Perichondrium

Periosteal bone collar

Hyaline cartilage

Developing
periosteum

**(b)**

Blood vessel

Primary ossification center

Epiphyseal
capillaries

**(c)**

Developing compact bone

Calcified cartilage

Secondary
ossification centers

Medullary
cavity

Secondary ossification
centers

**(d)**

Calcifying cartilage

Growth cartilage in
epiphyseal plate

Spongy bone

Articular cartilage

Periosteum

Compact bone

**(e)**

Epiphyseal line
(remnant of
epiphyseal plate)

Spongy bone

Articular cartilage

Medullary (marrow)
cavity

©Hayden-McNeil, LLC

**(f)**

**Figure 9-7.** Endochondral ossification.

## B. Balance between Osteoclast and Osteoblast Activity

There is a delicate balance in the activities of the bone-making osteoblasts and the bone-dissolving osteoclasts.

As we discussed previously, osteoclast activity is controlled by RANK Ligand and osteoprotegerin, both of which are produced by osteoblasts. If osteoclast activity outweighs osteoblast activity, too much bone is dissolved and not enough is manufactured to make up for it. The result is **osteoporosis**, a condition found in many postmenopausal Caucasian women and older men.

If osteoblast activity outweighs osteoclast activity, usually because the osteoclasts are depleted in number or their activity is diminished, more bone is manufactured than is dissolved. The result is a rather rare disorder called **osteopetrosis**, a congenital condition present at birth. In osteopetrosis there is increased skeletal mass and the bone marrow is replaced with solid bone. In some cases, there may be a lack of cathepsin K, the major protease of osteoclasts. Loss of bone marrow can lead to *aplastic anemia* and death.

**Healing of fractures**: osteoblasts and osteoclasts play important roles in the healing of fractured bone (see later).

## C. Factors Affecting Bone Development, Growth, and Repair

Bone development, repair, and turnover are influenced by many factors. At the *molecular* level, osteoblasts and osteoclasts are controlled by many different substances that include vitamins, *cytokines* (cell signalling molecules), *hormones*, and *growth factors*.

The following are known to be important in bone development and maintenance.

1. **Nutrition—minerals.**

   There must be adequate intake of:

   - Calcium—see table below for some foods rich in calcium.

| Source | Calcium (milligrams) |
| --- | --- |
| 1 glass of milk | 300 |
| 1 oz of cheese | 200 |
| 1 cup of yogurt | 300 |
| 1 slice of pizza | 100 |
| ¼ cup of almonds | 100 |

   - Phosphorus in the form of phosphate.

   - Other elements, including boron and manganese.

2. **Nutrition—vitamins.**

   There must be adequate supplies of:

   - Vitamin C (important for maintaining connective tissues in general).

   - Vitamin A (important in development).

- Vitamin D (*the most important*). This vitamin is uncommon in natural foods except for eggs. Milk and other dairy products, however, are nowadays fortified with vitamin D. *Vitamin D₃* (= *cholecalciferol*) is synthesized in the skin when its precursor (*7-dehydrocholesterol*) is exposed to ultraviolet radiation. Cholecalciferol is then converted into the active substance *calcitriol* in the kidney and liver. Vitamin D is important in calcium regulation and calcium absorption. Lack of vitamin D in children causes *rickets*, a condition where the bones do not calcify and they remain soft and flexible. The result is malformed bones and bowing of the legs as seen in the X-ray below.

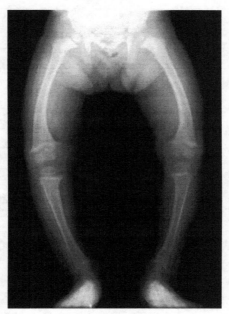

In the adult, the condition is called *osteomalacia*.

3. **Hormones.**

   The following hormones are all important in bone development and maintenance.

   a. *Growth hormone* (secreted by the pituitary gland) and *somatomedin* (secreted by the liver under the influence of growth hormone) stimulate bone formation.

   b. Sex hormones (*testosterone* and *estrogens*; see below) stimulate new bone growth but the epiphyseal disks quickly disappear in the process: it should be noted that people who take anabolic steroids experience the same effect, sometimes inducing premature obliteration of the epiphyseal plate.

   c. *Parathyroid hormone* (parathyroid glands) is very important in calcium regulation. The hormone has a complicated action. It causes osteoblasts to release a substance that stimulates osteoclasts and increases their number.

   d. *Thyroid hormone* stimulates bone resorption.

### 4. Exercise.

The bones of athletes are usually stronger and heavier than those of non-athletes. In the racquet arms of professional tennis players the humerus is 60% thicker than the unused arm. In the average person, the two arms do not usually differ by more than 5%.

Percent Increase (+) or Decrease (−) in Bone Mass Associated with the Following Sports Activities—Volleyball and Soccer Show the Highest Increases

|  | Spine | Hip | Arm | Leg |
|---|---|---|---|---|
| Volleyball | +12 | +17 | +6 | +12 |
| Speed skating | +5 | +4 | +5 | +5 |
| Swimming | +3 | −3 | +1 | −3 |
| Gymnastics | +12 | +24 | +7 | +10 |
| Cycling | 0 | −2 | −1 | +1 |
| Weight lifting | +12 | +6 | +20 | +11 |
| Running | 0 | +10 | 0 | +10 |
| Cross country skiing | 0 | +5 | +7 | +5 |
| Kayaking | 0 | 0 | +10 | 0 |
| Soccer | +7 | +20 | +14 | +16 |
| Ice hockey | +4 | +7 | +10 | +6 |

Source: ASBMR

Certain behaviors can be deduced by studying the bone thicknesses in early human fossil skeletons. From the thickness of cross-sections of the humerus it has been deduced that in the Neanderthals and Early Upper Paleolithic humans, the arm was used for spear *thrusting*. In the Late Upper Paleolithic, however, the shape of the humerus indicates that the arm was used for spear *throwing* (see *Science 268*, 364, 1995). There have also been comparisons between the skeletons of Neanderthals and early modern humans in an attempt to deduce other facets of their behavior (*Science 272*, 1586, 1996).

**Lack of exercise** (such as immobilization of a limb due to fracture, or confinement to bed as a result of illness) causes the bones to become thinner and weaker. *"If you don't use it, you lose it"* [Chris Ruff of Johns Hopkins University in a 1996 interview in *Science 272*, 1586].

**Weightlessness** – space travelers subjected to weightlessness for long periods of time may experience loss of bone mass. This can amount to between 1 and 2% per *month*, and may affect the hip and lower vertebrae.

Despite an exercise program designed to counter bone loss, astronauts on the International Space Station showed as much degradation as did their counterparts one decade ago on the Soviet space station *Mir*,[1] says a NASA-funded study.[2] "Despite the

---

[1] Vico, L. et al.(2000). Effects of long-term microgravity exposure on cancellous and cortical weight-bearing bones of cosmonauts." *The Lancet 355*, 1607–11.

[2] Lang, T. et al. Cortical and trabecular bone mineral loss from the spine and hip in long-duration space flight. *J Bone Miner Res*, E-pub ahead of print, March 8, 2004, doi:10.1359/jbmr.040307.

passage of [time], this problem has not really been ameliorated," says lead author Thomas Lang, associate professor of radiology in residence, University of California, San Francisco.

The primarily male study group lost a monthly average of about 1% of their exterior hipbone, about 2.5% of the interior or trabecular hipbone, and about 1% of the spine. Researchers used CT scans, the first time this method was used to assess bone loss in the hip and spine.

The astronauts' exercise regimen included running on a treadmill and lifting weights. "The study shows the exercises were not as effective as we hoped they would be," says Guy Fogelman, NASA's director of bioastronautics research. A new treadmill study will have astronauts wearing stress monitors while they exercise.

It is likely that for long space flights (e.g. to Mars) the spacecraft will need special artificial gravity areas (created by rotating sections). Dosing with bisphosphonates (zoledronate) is also an option.

See below for more discussion.

**Mechanical stress, exercise, weightlessness** – the bones are always mechanically stressed, and this is reflected in the arrangement of spongy bone (= trabecular bone).

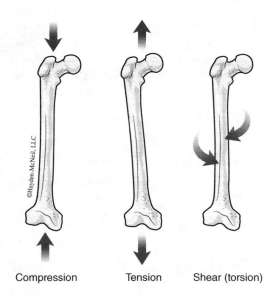

Compression          Tension          Shear (torsion)

**Figure 9-8.**

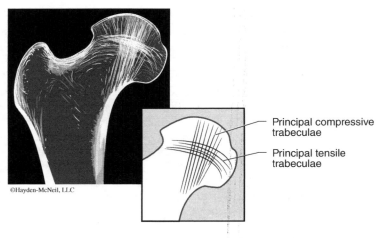

©Hayden-McNeil, LLC

Principal compressive trabeculae

Principal tensile trabeculae

This image of a femur shows the thick cortical (compact) bone, and the trabecular (spongy) bone which is arranged to withstand the stresses from usual standing and walking. Compressive stresses are those of the body weight pushing the bone down, and tensile stresses are from the muscles, pulling the bone apart.

**Figure 9-9.** Femur.

This mechanical stress seems to be important in maintaining bones in adequate condition by stimulating deposition of mineral salts and production of collagen fibers. The loss of bone mass seen in space travelers is because there is no longer mechanical stress on the bones in maintaining posture and equilibrium. Exercises that increase stress on bones (and exercise muscles) are now being developed for use by astronauts.

It is not understood how the mechanical stress operates, but it may be signalled through the osteocyte–osteoblast network.

**Hormones and exercise** – it is possible that exercise may affect the secretion of hormones that influence bone mass, but this is not established.

5. **Aging and osteoporosis.**

In men, there is an age-related loss of calcium from the skeleton, starting after 60 years of age.

In *women*, loss of calcium from the skeleton begins after age 30, and accelerates around 40–45 as estrogen levels decrease. This may lead to *osteoporosis*, a condition found mainly in women at *menopause*. About 28 million people in the United States, 80% of whom are women, are affected. A *bone density scan* can reveal how much bone mass has been lost as a person ages. Osteoporosis is characterized by decreased bone mass and increased susceptibility to bone fractures.

Osteoporosis causes 1.5 million fractures each year. The condition affects the entire skeleton, but its effects are more pronounced in the vertebral bodies, proximal femur (hip), ribs, humerus, and distal radius. About one-third of post-menopausal females experience at least one osteoporotic fracture in their lives, and 300,000 new cases of osteoporotic hip fractures are reported annually in the United States alone.

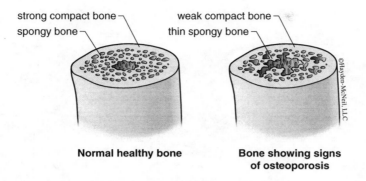

**Figure 9-10.** Normal healthy bone (left); bone showing osteoporosis (right).

The causes of osteoporosis are not fully understood. It seems to be linked to the deficiency in the female hormone 17 β-estradiol ($E_2$) that occurs at menopause. $E_2$ plays an important role in regulating the balance between bone formation by osteoblasts and bone resorption by osteoclasts. The major effect is that in a complex way existing osteoclasts are activated and new osteoclasts may be formed from osteoclast progenitor cells.

©Hayden-McNeil, LLC

**Figure 9-11.** Osteoporosis.

177

However, although all postmenopausal women are estrogen-deficient, only about 1 in 5 develop osteoporosis. So the situation must be more complicated than a simple lack of estrogen in the bloodstream. Genetic susceptibility factors may also be involved, and the sequencing of the human genome is likely to provide more information on this important question.

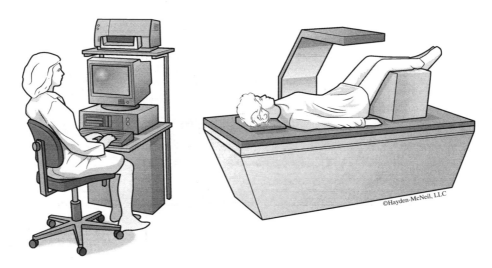

**Figure 9-12.** Bone density scanning equipment.

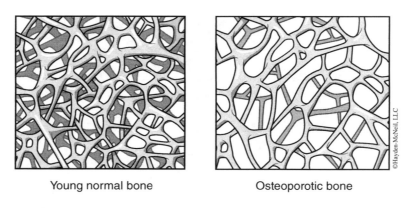

Young normal bone                    Osteoporotic bone

**Figure 9-13.** Young normal bone (left); osteoporotic bone (right).

Prevention of osteoporosis includes an emphasis on *exercise* and calcium supplements in the 20s and 30s. Current therapies attempt to slow down bone loss. They include estrogen, the hormone *calcitonin*, and *bisphosphonates*. Estrogen and estrogen-progestin replacement therapy can have certain risks and unpleasant side effects. Efficacy has not been established, either. Recently, new estrogen-like drugs have been developed. *Raloxifene* (Evista) is a selective *estrogen receptor modulator* (SERM). It increases bone mineral density by decreasing bone resorption by reducing the number and activity of osteoclasts. Calcitonin nasal spray (Miacalcin) interferes with osteoclasts and can decrease loss of bone, but does not produce a long-term increase in formation of new bone.

Bisphosphonates such as Merck's Alendronate (Fosamax™) act by inhibiting osteoclast activity and even triggering apoptosis in osteoclasts. Another bisphosphonate is Risedronate (Actonel™), which inhibits bone resorption by binding to the hydroxyapatite crystals and inhibiting the intracellular enzymes of the osteoclasts. Possible new drugs undergoing preclinical testing are those that inhibit cathepsin K of osteoclasts (Axys-Celera-Merck).

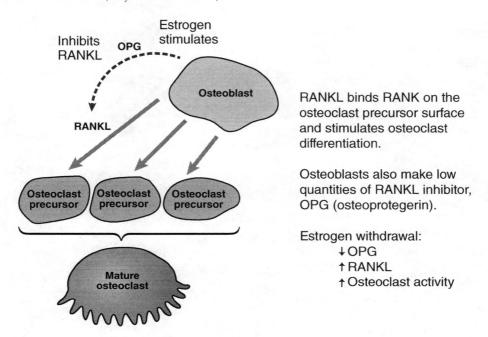

**Figure 9-14.**

The newest drug is Lilly's *Forteo*™, which is recombinant parathyroid hormone (PTH). When secreted normally, PTH keeps blood calcium levels normal. The body places a high priority on maintaining blood calcium levels. When blood calcium drops, PTH signals osteoblasts to signal osteoclasts to destroy bone, thus releasing calcium into the blood. The new PTH drugs trick the system. By giving PTH in a single blast once a day, the osteoblasts become very active (thus building more bone) but don't have time to stimulate the osteoclasts, which would tear bone down. The net result is new bone growth, something the anti-osteoclast treatments described in the previous paragraph cannot achieve.

## D. Fractures

A break due to injury is called a *traumatic fracture*. There are a number of different types of fracture.

When a bone is broken, blood vessels in the bone and periosteum are likely to be ruptured and the periosteum itself torn. Blood escaping from the broken vessels forms a ***fracture hematoma***. The stages in repair are as follows.

1. **Fracture hematoma** formation.

2. **Fibrocartilaginous callus** formation.

   Within days or weeks, the region originally occupied by the hematoma is invaded by new blood vessels and by large numbers of osteoblasts originating from multiplying osteoprogenitor cells in the periosteum and fibroblasts. Masses of fibrocartilage formed by fibroblasts replace part of the blood clot, particularly in regions more distant from intact or developing blood vessels.

3. **Bony callus** formation.

   A bony callus in the form of trabeculae of spongy bone is produced by the osteoblasts. Spongy bone tends to form in regions close to developing blood vessels. Finally, however, all of the fibrocartilage is replaced by spongy bone. Phagocytic cells clear away the blood clot and debris.

4. **Remodeling.**

   Osteoblasts and osteoclasts work together to replace the spongy bone with compact bone. The amount of bone produced in the callus is usually more than needed, and the excess is removed by the osteoclasts. In this way, osteoblasts and osteoclasts remodel and refashion the healed fracture so that it looks much like the original. Sometimes healing is so complete that the fracture line cannot be detected even with X-rays.

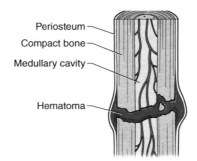

1. **Fracture hematoma**
   (Blood escapes from ruptured blood vessels)

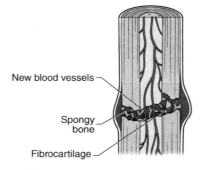

2. **Fibrocartilaginous callus**
   (Spongy bone forms in areas surrounding new blood vessels, fibrocartilage forms in more distant areas.)

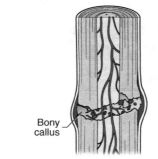

3. **Bony callus**
   (Bone replaces fibrocartilage)

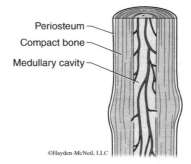

4. **Remodeling**
   (Osteoclasts and osteoblasts remodel and refashion the fracture)

©Hayden-McNeil, LLC

**Figure 9-15.** Repair of bone fracture.

## III. What Is the Function of Bones in Humans?

Bones have at least five functions.

- **support** and **protection**
- **lever** arms for the **muscles** to act upon
- **blood cells** are produced in the red marrow
- **storage depots for Ca⁺⁺**, and important in *calcium homeostasis*; bones release Ca⁺⁺ on demand, when osteoclast activity is increased
- **energy** can be provided by the fat stored in the yellow marrow

### A. Support and Protection

Think about this—it is fairly self-evident.

### B. Bones Are Levers that Muscles Can Act Upon

The body movements generated by most skeletal muscles are accomplished through a system of levers. Bones are an important part of this lever system, and we will discuss this topic in great detail when we discuss muscles.

### C. Blood Cell Formation by Red Bone Marrow

Red marrow is capable of producing blood cells (*erythrocytes, leukocytes, thrombocytes*), a process called *hematopoiesis*. Red marrow consists of blood cells in immature stages, adipocytes, and macrophages. Red marrow is found in all the bones of infants, but in adults red bone marrow is restricted to the skull bones, vertebrae, ribs, sternum, clavicles, pelvic bones, and epiphyses of long bones. Blood cell formation will be discussed in the spring semester of this course (BIOL 202/204).

181

### D. Bones and Calcium Homeostasis

It should be realized that bone is an important calcium storage depot. Calcium is needed for the proper functioning of many tissues of the body (for example, cardiac muscle). Activation of osteoclasts (by parathyroid hormone, for example) permits this calcium reserve to be mobilized when plasma calcium levels fall.

Bone tissue also has smaller amounts of magnesium, sodium, potassium and carbonate ions. Dietary elements such as lead, radium, and strontium may also accumulate in bone.

### E. Yellow Marrow of Bones Is a Source of Energy

Triglycerides stored in the adipocytes of the yellow marrow are an important source of energy.

## IV. Joints—Where Two (Or More) Bones Meet

Bone is rigid. To permit movement, many of the bones in the skeleton are attached to their neighbors by *joints* (= junctions, articulations). A joint is formed where two or more bones meet.

The following is a brief summary of their **structural** classification.

---

You will sometimes see joints classified according to the degree of **movement** they allow.
- Immovable – *synarthrosis*
- Slightly movable – *amphiarthrosis*
- Freely movable – *diarthrosis*

---

## A. Tight, or Fibrous, Joints

*Fibrous joints* fasten bones tightly together. They allow little or no movement. Examples are between the distal ends of the tibia and fibula, between the bones of the skull, and a special type uniting a tooth to the bone of the jaw.

1.  **Syndesmosis.**

    Permits slight movement – bones bound by *interosseus ligaments,* the tibia and fibula held together by this joint.

2.  **Suture.**

    Not movable – occurs between flat bones of the skull.

3.  **Gomphosis.**

    Teeth fastened to maxillae and mandible by *periodontal ligament.*

## B. Bones Held Together by Cartilage—Cartilaginous Joints

*Cartilaginous joints* sometimes permit restricted movement. The articulating bones are united by a plate of hyaline cartilage or a fibrocartilaginous disk.

1.  **Synchondrosis.**

    Bones united by bands of hyaline cartilage—*sternum* and first rib are united by the *costal cartilage.*

2.  **Symphysis.**

    The articular surfaces of the bones are covered by a layer of hyaline cartilage, which in turn is attached to a pad of fibrocartilage. Limited movement. Occurs between vertebrae and at the *symphysis pubis* in the pelvic girdle.

## C. The Most Complex Type of Joints—Synovial Joints

Most joints of the skeletal system are *synovial joints.* These joints are complex structures with built-in lubrication that allows smooth and efficient movements under variable conditions of loading. Normally, synovial joints act without jamming, except under disease conditions.

As I said, these joints are freely moveable. The articulating bones move freely over smooth, lubricated articular cartilage, all enclosed within a flexible articular capsule. Of the synovial joints, the knee is the most complex.

This joint is composed of:

1.  The **articular surface**, or **articular cartilage**: a special variety of hyaline cartilage which covers the ends of the bones in the joint. The articular cartilage is wear-resistant, has low friction, and is able to absorb the high forces of compression and shear that can occur when the joint moves. The articular cartilage has no nerves or blood vessels.

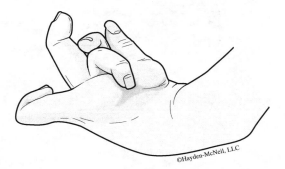

©Hayden-McNeil, LLC

This deformity of the hand is due to rheumatoid arthritis (RA). This autoimmune disease leads to synovial proliferation and joint destruction, typically in a symmetrical pattern involving small joints of hands and feet, followed by wrists, ankles, elbows, and knees.

**Figure 9-16.** Rheumatoid arthritis.

2.  The **joint capsule** (= *fibrous capsule*) and associated **ligaments**, which hold the bones together and prevent excessive or abnormal movement of the joint.

3.  The **synovial membrane**, a vascular lining that forms the inner layer of the joint capsule and covers exposed bony surfaces.

4.  The **synovial cavity**, or **joint cavity**, filled with *synovial fluid* both secreted and absorbed by the synovial membrane. The consistency and appearance of synovial fluid is a little like egg white. Synovial fluid is essentially a dialysate of plasma containing mucin (hyaluronate) secreted by synoviocytes, cells that make up the innermost layer of the synovial membrane. Synovial fluid is a lubricant solution with non-Newtonian properties and consisting of the carbohydrate polymer *hyaluronate*, and the glycoprotein *lubricin*. Lubricin reduces friction and prevents wear and tear of the articular cartilage. A genetic deficiency of lubricin causes early joint failure. It is highly viscous if the joint is stationary or moving slowly. During rapid movements, however, its viscosity drops sharply.

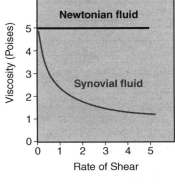

**Figure 9-17.** Non-Newtonian properties of synovial fluid.

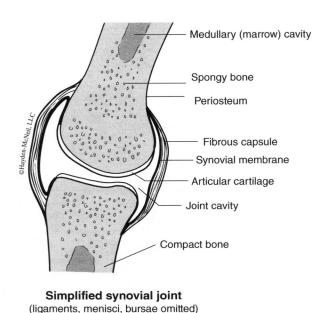

**Simplified synovial joint**
(ligaments, menisci, bursae omitted)

**Figure 9-18.** Simplified synovial joint.

184

Other structures associated with synovial joints include the following.

- **Ligaments.**

    Can be part of the joint capsule or in the form of accessory ligaments located outside or inside the capsule.

    In the knee joint, the *fibular collateral ligament* is an *extracapsular* ligament, while the *cruciate ligaments* are *intracapsular ligaments* (note that the cruciate ligaments are NOT inside the synovial cavity).

    In the shoulder joint, stability depends not only on its ligaments, but on a set of muscles called the *rotator cuff* (*supraspinatus, infraspinatus, teres minor, subscapularis*), which nearly completely circle the joint. A *rotator cuff tear* (sometimes seen in baseball pitchers) involves one or more of these muscles and/or their associated tendons.

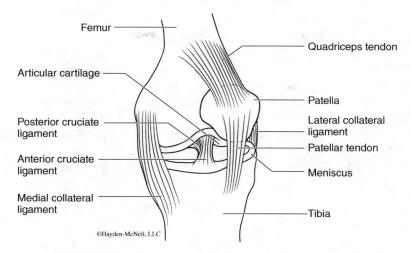

Femur

Quadriceps tendon

Articular cartilage

Patella

Posterior cruciate
ligament

Lateral collateral
ligament

Patellar tendon

Anterior cruciate
ligament

Meniscus

Medial collateral
ligament

Tibia

©Hayden-McNeil, LLC

**Figure 9-19.** Ligaments and other structures associated with the knee joint.

- **Menisci.**

  Some synovial joints are partially or completely divided into two compartments by pads of fibrocartilage called menisci (sometimes called articular disks) situated between the articular surfaces. The menisci are attached to the fibrous layer of the joint capsule.

- **Bursae.**

  Some synovial joints have synovial fluid-filled sacs or bursae associated with them. A *bursa* has an inner lining of synovial membrane, which may be continuous with the synovial membrane of the joint. The bursae lie between the skin and the underlying bony prominence. They cushion movements between skin and bone, tendons and bone, muscles and bone, or ligaments and bone.

  *Bursitis* is caused by inflammation of the bursa. Tennis elbow is a form of bursitis involving the bursa lying between the olecranon process and the skin.

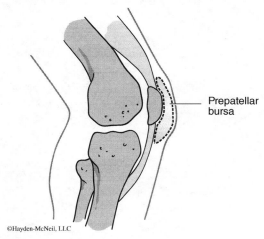

Prepatellar
bursa

©Hayden-McNeil, LLC

**Figure 9-20.** Prepatellar bursa.

## D. Types of Synovial Joints

The seven major types of synovial joints are as follows.

1. **Ball and socket.**

   Hip and shoulder. Permits the maximum variety of movements: flexion/extension, abduction/adduction, rotation, circumduction. Their surfaces are not strictly spherical, but very slightly ovoid.

2. **Condyloid** (= ellipsoid).

   *Radius* and *carpals*. Permits movement in all planes, but no rotation.

3. **Gliding.**

   Various joints in *wrist* and *ankle*. One surface slides over the other without any angular or rotary motion.

4. **Hinge.**

   Elbow, for example. Permits flexion and extension. Note that the elbow joint is complex. It consists of two articulations—the humero-ulnar and the humero-radial.

5. **Pivot.**

   In the neck, between *atlas* and *axis*; proximal ends of radius and ulna. Permits rotation.

6. **Saddle.**

   *Carpal* and *metacarpal* of thumb. Permits flexion/extension, abduction/adduction, circumduction.

7. **Bicondylar.**

   Knee. Like a hinge joint but with a small degree of rotation as it bends.

You should be familiar with the structures of the knee, hip, elbow, and shoulder joints (BIOL 203 students—you will have a chance to see models of the knee and shoulder joints in the laboratory). Be aware that there are different types of *joint movements*.

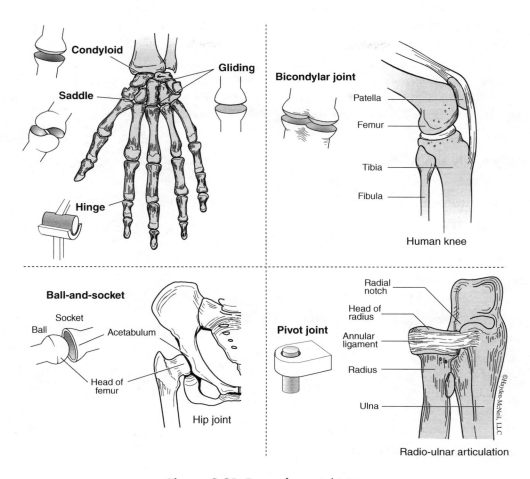

**Figure 9-21.** Types of synovial joints.

## V. List of Bones You Should Know

You should know the *number of bones* in the human skeleton, and how they are distributed throughout the skeleton.

---

Total = 206
*Skull* = 22 (made up of 8 *cranial bones*, 14 *facial bones* including the *mandible*)
*Vertebral column* = 26 (7 *cervical vertebrae*, 12 *thoracic vertebrae*, 5 *lumbar vertebrae*,
  1 *sacral vertebra*, 1 *coccygeal vertebra*)
Ribs = 24 (the *thoracic cage* includes the sternum, and therefore has 25 bones)
*Pectoral girdle* = 4
Arms and hands (upper limbs) = 60 (same as legs and feet)
Pelvic girdle = 2
Legs and feet (lower limbs) = 60 (same as arms and hands)

---

Note that the *sacrum* is a structure formed by fusion of five vertebrae that become fused between the eighteenth and thirtieth year of age.

The *coccyx* (tailbone) is usually composed of four vertebrae fused together by the twenty-fifth year of age.

---

In addition to the above list, and the sacrum and coccyx, you should know the following bones and their associated structures and parts (examples of associated structures and parts are intervertebral discs, symphysis pubis, etc.).

---

## A. Axial Skeleton

1. **Skull.**

   - skull sutures (*coronal suture, sagittal suture, lambdoidal suture, squamosal suture*)

2. **Cranial bones of skull.**

   - *occipital* (1)
   - *parietal* (2)
   - *frontal* (1)
   - *temporal* (2)
   - *sphenoid* (1)
   - *ethmoid* (1)

3. **Facial bones of skull.**

   - *maxillary bones* (2)
   - *mandible* (1)
   - *zygomatic* (2)
   - *nasal* (2)

4. **Associated bones of skull.**

   - *hyoid*
   - *malleus*
   - *incus*
   - *stapes*

5. **Vertebral column.**

   Know the parts of a vertebra: the vertebral body, spinous and transverse processes; know that they are separated by intervertebral discs of fibrocartilage; know that they are connected by ligaments; know that the spinal cord passes through the vertebral canal that is formed by openings in the vertebrae; know the divisions of the vertebral column and the number of vertebrae in each division—cervical, thoracic, lumbar, sacral, coccygeal; know the sacrum and coccyx.

   - atlas
   - axis

6. **Thoracic cage.**

   Ribs (true ribs, costal cartilage composed of hyaline cartilage, false ribs, floating ribs) breastbone or sternum (composed of the upper *manubrium*, the middle *body*, and the lower *xiphoid process*).

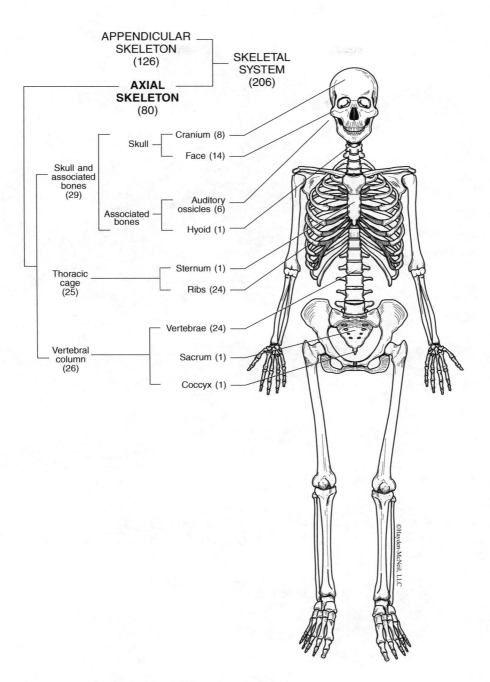

APPENDICULAR
SKELETON
(126)

SKELETAL
SYSTEM
(206)

**AXIAL
SKELETON**
(80)

Skull — Cranium (8)

Face (14)

Skull and
associated
bones
(29)

Associated
bones

Auditory
ossicles (6)

Hyoid (1)

Thoracic
cage
(25)

Sternum (1)

Ribs (24)

Vertebrae (24)

Vertebral
column
(26)

Sacrum (1)

Coccyx (1)

©Hayden-McNeil, LLC

**Figure 9-22.** Axial skeleton—anterior view.

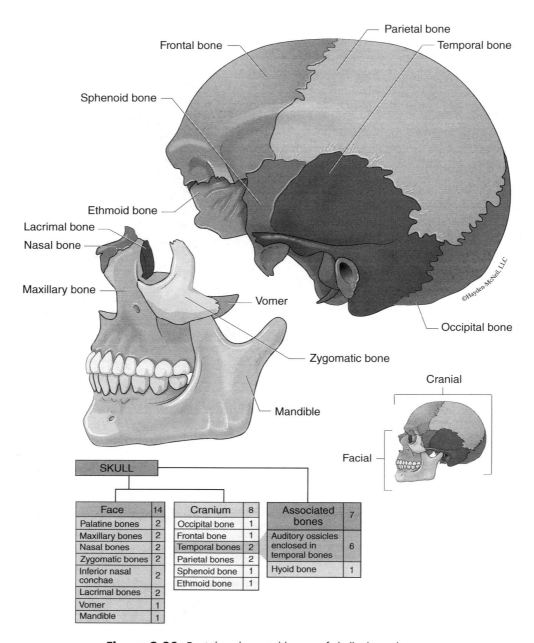

**Figure 9-23.** Facial and cranial bones of skull—lateral view.

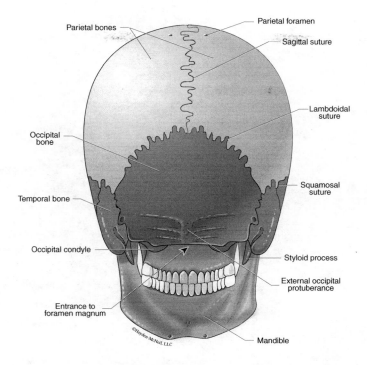

**Figure 9-24.** Posterior view of skull.

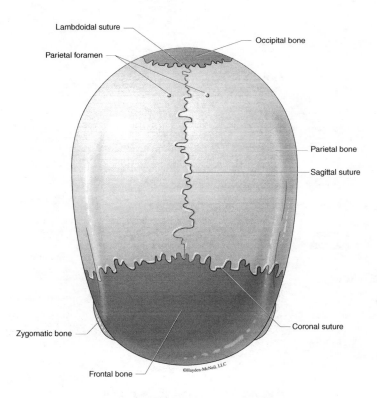

**Figure 9-25.** Superior view of skull.

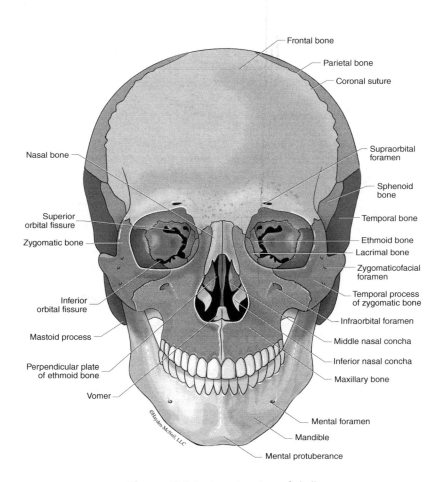

**Figure 9-26.** Anterior view of skull.

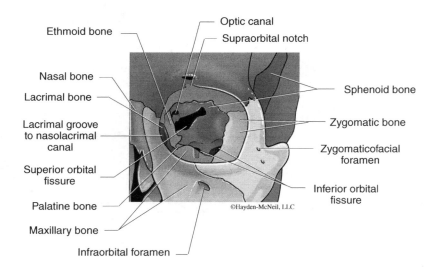

**Figure 9-27.** Orbit bones of skull.

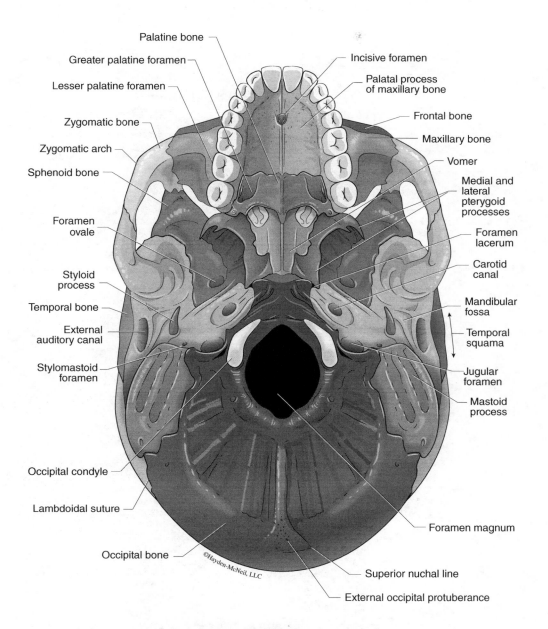

Palatine bone
Greater palatine foramen
Lesser palatine foramen
Zygomatic bone
Zygomatic arch
Sphenoid bone
Foramen ovale
Styloid process
Temporal bone
External auditory canal
Stylomastoid foramen
Occipital condyle
Lambdoidal suture
Occipital bone

Incisive foramen
Palatal process of maxillary bone
Frontal bone
Maxillary bone
Vomer
Medial and lateral pterygoid processes
Foramen lacerum
Carotid canal
Mandibular fossa
Temporal squama
Jugular foramen
Mastoid process
Foramen magnum
Superior nuchal line
External occipital protuberance

©Hayden-McNeil, LLC

**Figure 9-28.** Inferior view of skull.

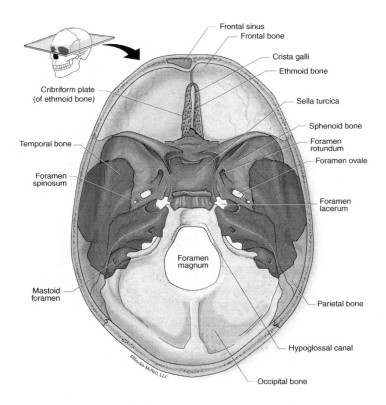

**Figure 9-29.** Horizontal view of skull.

194

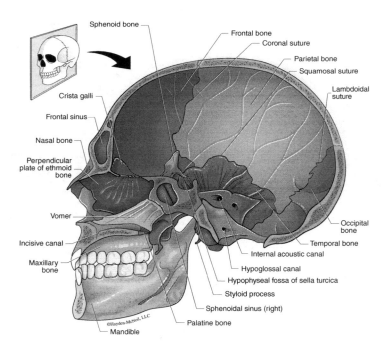

**Figure 9-30.** Sagittal view of skull.

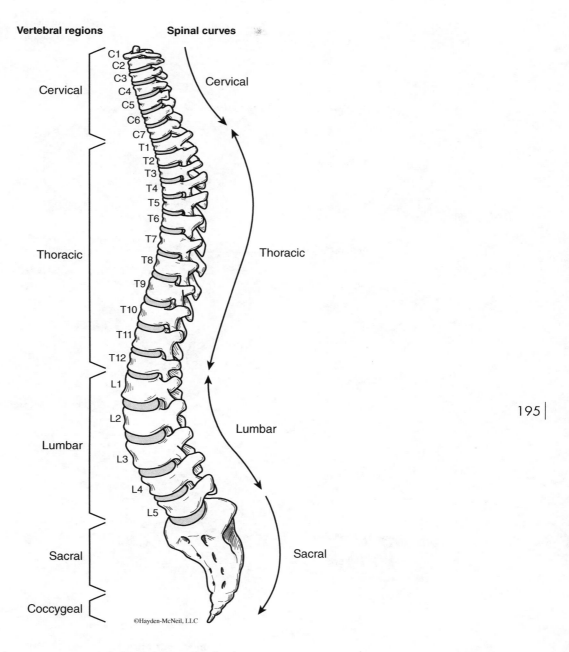

**Vertebral regions**    **Spinal curves**

Cervical

C1
C2
C3
C4
C5
C6
C7

Cervical

Thoracic

T1
T2
T3
T4
T5
T6
T7
T8
T9
T10
T11
T12

Thoracic

Lumbar

L1
L2
L3
L4
L5

Lumbar

Sacral

Sacral

Coccygeal

©Hayden-McNeil, LLC

**Figure 9-31.** Vertebral column.

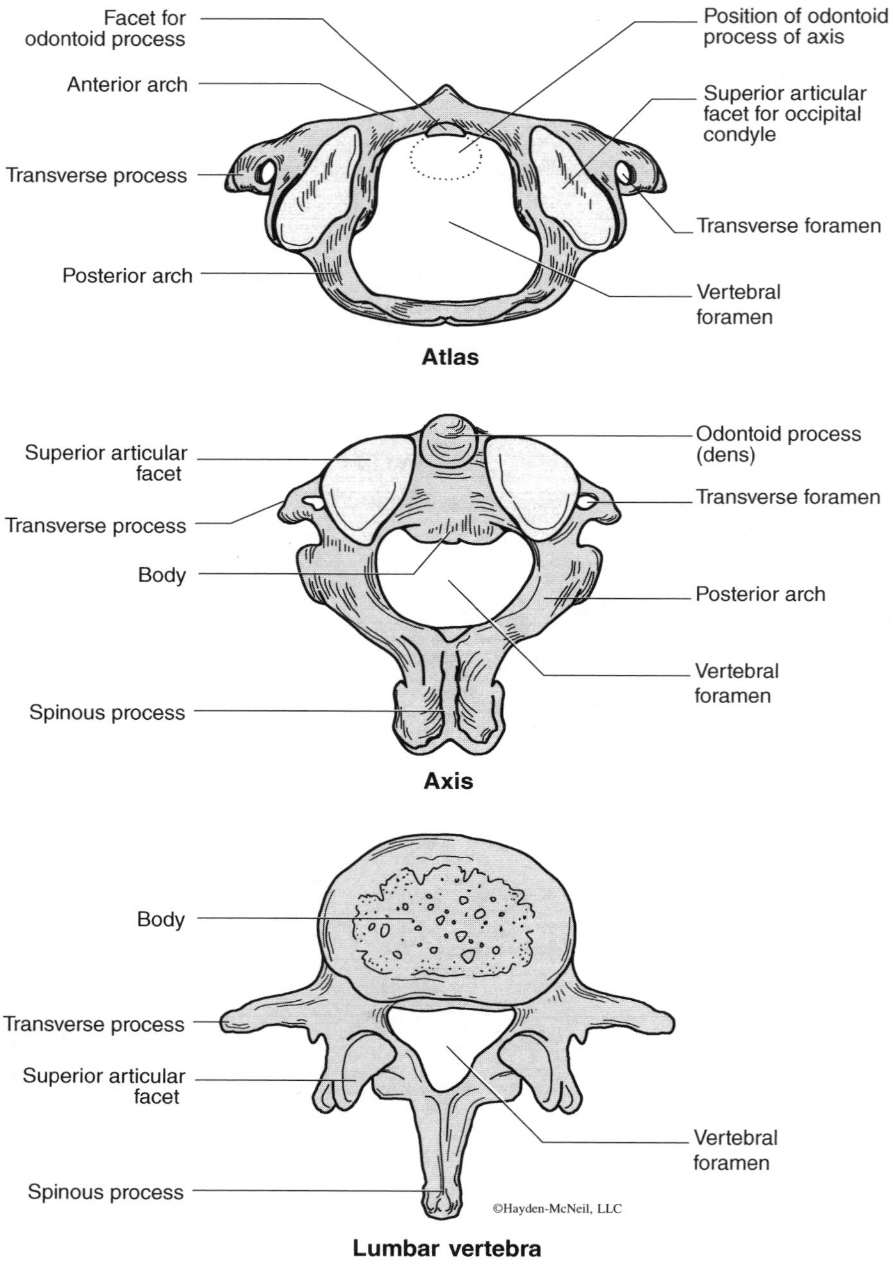

Facet for
odontoid process

Anterior arch

Transverse process

Posterior arch

Position of odontoid
process of axis

Superior articular
facet for occipital
condyle

Transverse foramen

Vertebral
foramen

**Atlas**

Superior articular
facet

Transverse process

Body

Spinous process

Odontoid process
(dens)

Transverse foramen

Posterior arch

Vertebral
foramen

**Axis**

196

Body

Transverse process

Superior articular
facet

Spinous process

Vertebral
foramen

©Hayden-McNeil, LLC

**Lumbar vertebra**

**Figure 9-32.** Anatomy of atlas, axis, and lumbar vertebra.

## B. Appendicular Skeleton

1.  **Shoulder girdle or pectoral girdle.**
    - *scapula*
    - *clavicle*

2.  **Upper extremity.**
    - *humerus*
    - *radius*
    - *ulna*
    - *carpals*
    - *metacarpals*
    - *phalanges* (the name is used for the toes as well as the fingers)

3.  **Pelvic girdle.**
    - each *coxa* (hip) is formed by the fusion of three bones:
        - *ilium*
        - *ischium*
        - *pubis*
    - (also know the meaning of the *acetabulum* and *pubic symphysis*)

4.  **Pelvis.**

    The pelvis is made up of the two coxae (each consisting of an ilium, ischium, and pubis), the *sacrum*, and the *coccyx*

5.  **Lower extremity.**
    - *femur*
    - *patella*
    - *tibia*
    - *fibula*
    - *tarsals*
    - *calcaneus* (one of the tarsals = heel bone)
    - *metatarsals*
    - *phalanges* (this term is used both for the toes and the fingers)

197

198

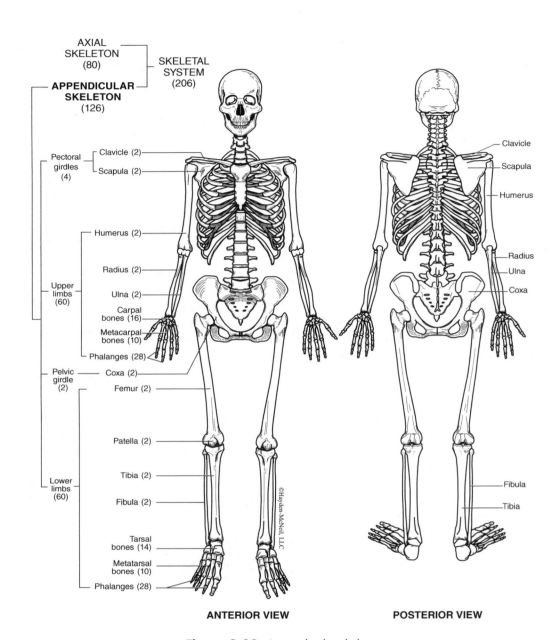

AXIAL
SKELETON
(80)

SKELETAL
SYSTEM
(206)

**APPENDICULAR
SKELETON**
(126)

Pectoral
girdles
(4)
— Clavicle (2)
— Scapula (2)

Upper
limbs
(60)
— Humerus (2)
— Radius (2)
— Ulna (2)
— Carpal
bones (16)
— Metacarpal
bones (10)
— Phalanges (28)

Pelvic
girdle
(2)
— Coxa (2)

Lower
limbs
(60)
— Femur (2)
— Patella (2)
— Tibia (2)
— Fibula (2)
— Tarsal
bones (14)
— Metatarsal
bones (10)
— Phalanges (28)

Clavicle
Scapula
Humerus
Radius
Ulna
Coxa
Fibula
Tibia

©Hayden-McNeil, LLC

**ANTERIOR VIEW**          **POSTERIOR VIEW**

**Figure 9-33.** Appendicular skeleton.

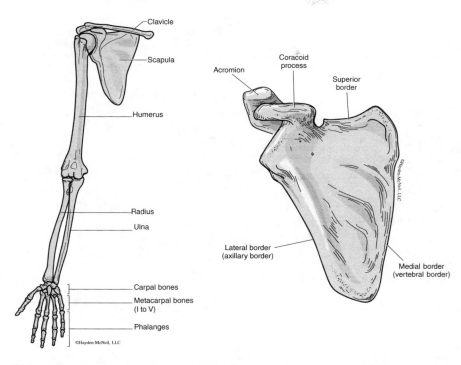

**Figure 9-34.** Pectoral girdle and limb (left); anterior view of scapula (right).

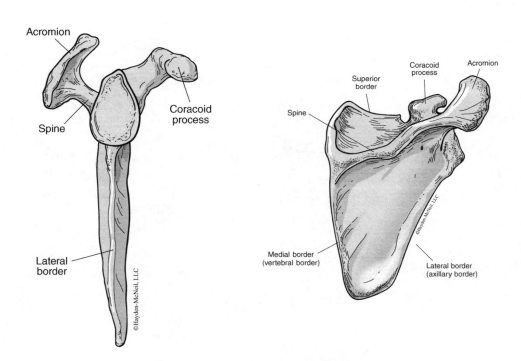

**Figure 9-35.** Lateral view of scapula (left); posterior view of scapula (right).

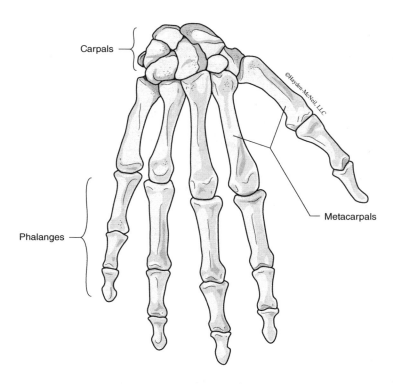

**Figure 9-36.** Bones of the hand.

200

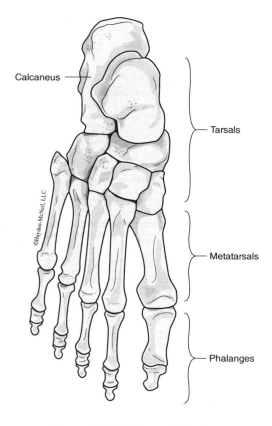

**Figure 9-37.** Bones of the foot.

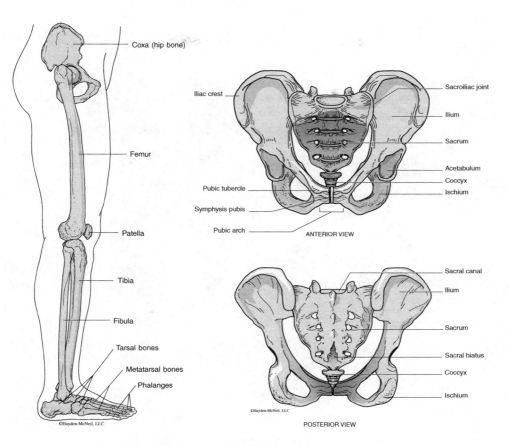

**Figure 9-38.** Pelvic girdle and lower limb (left); pelvic girdle (right).

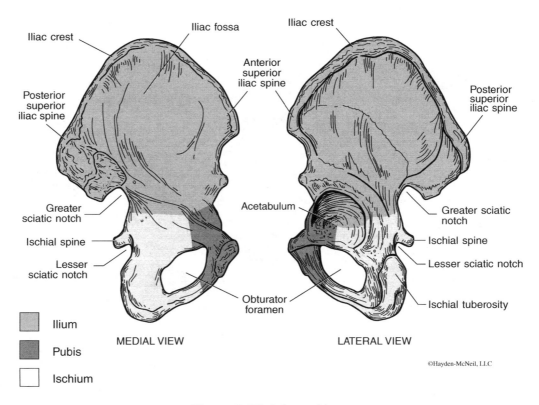

**Figure 9-39.** Left coxal bone.

# CHAPTER 10

## MUSCLE I
### Skeletal Muscle

## CHAPTER OUTLINE

## DESCRIPTION AND INTRODUCTION

Muscles make up 40–50% of the total body weight. Muscles are elongated cells that can contract and generate force. They are important in the following.

- **Movement** – muscles are the basis for all movements made by the body and its components. Movement refers not only to the limbs, facial muscles, etc., but also to the beating heart, to contraction of the bladder during urination, to contraction and relaxation of the intestines during peristalsis, and to constriction and relaxation of various blood vessels of the body.

204

- **Posture** – muscles are also responsible for maintaining posture. When postural muscle tone is lost (for example, during fainting), the body collapses and becomes limp.

Three different types of muscles are used for these different functions.

1.  **Skeletal** (striated, voluntary) primarily (but not always) for limb movements
2.  **Cardiac** (striated, involuntary) for heart movements
3.  **Smooth** (nonstriated, involuntary) for movements of hollow organs such as the bladder, blood vessels, intestines, etc.

Muscle cells are elongated and contain organized arrays of proteins that are specialized to cause the cells to contract. Muscle contraction is powered by ATP derived from the metabolism of foodstuffs. A major source of energy for skeletal muscle is *glucose*, but *fatty acids* derived from triglycerides are also an important fuel for exercising skeletal muscle, and may even become a major energy source for moderate sustained exercise.

## OBJECTIVES

After listening to the lecture and reading this chapter, you should be able to:

1.  Describe the **functions** of the various types of muscle (see Description and Introduction).
2.  Describe the involvement of **connective tissue** in a skeletal muscle.
3.  Name the **components** of a skeletal muscle fiber and describe their functions.
4.  Sketch a **myofibril**.
5.  Describe the **neuromuscular junction**.
6.  Name the **neurotransmitter** used at the neuromuscular junction.
7.  Draw a **diagram** showing how the thin and thick filaments are organized in the sarcomere, and list the five steps involved in the contraction of a muscle fiber.
8.  Define what is meant by **excitation–contraction coupling**, and describe how it works.
9.  Describe how excitation–contraction coupling in **cardiac** muscle is slightly different.
10. Describe muscle **relaxation**.
11. Explain **rigor mortis**.
12. List the processes and substances that provide **energy** for contracting muscle.
13. Explain why an athlete might take a **creatine** dietary supplement and how this relates to the **phosphagen** system.
14. Describe the **sources of oxygen** for contracting muscles. Describe the function of the proteins hemoglobin and myoglobin and know the name of a related protein recently found in the brain.
15. Draw a diagram summarizing muscle **metabolism**: show how the blood supply, aerobic and anaerobic processes, and the phosphagen system all interact.
16. Explain what is meant by **oxygen debt**.
17. List the **energy systems** used in various sports (e.g. 100-meter dash, 200-meter dash, 800-meter run, marathon).
18. Distinguish between **fast** and **slow** muscle fibers, and indicate their proportions in the gastrocnemius and soleus muscles. Give an explanation for the difference in the ratio of fast and slow muscle fibers in these two muscles. Indicate the difference in the proportions of fast and slow muscle fibers in the quadriceps femoris muscle group of a marathoner and a sprinter.
19. Summarize the cause of **heat stroke** in athletes.

205

20. List the **30 muscles** you are expected to know. List their origins and insertions, and the movements associated with them. Identify them on a diagram of the body's musculature.
21. Name at least **ten proteins** found in skeletal muscle.
22. Describe the **functions** of each of these ten proteins.
23. Explain the actions of the **poison** *curare* and the snake venom *α-bungarotoxin*.
24. Explain how **botulinum** toxin acts.
25. Explain **myasthenia gravis**.

## I. Skeletal Muscle: Structure

A skeletal muscle is made up of elongated cells called muscle fibers or myofibers. These cells can:

- **contract** and generate force
- **stretch** when an opposing muscle contracts
- return to their original length after stretching—that is, they are **elastic**
- **contract** when **stimulated** by a motor neuron.

A skeletal muscle (e.g. the biceps brachii of the upper arm) contains:

- nerves
- blood vessels
- connective tissue
- muscle cells (= *myofibers*).

We can say the following about muscle cells (= *myofibers*).

- Muscle cells are bundled into *fascicles*.
- Muscle cells are packed with *myofibrils*.
- Myofibrils contain thick and thin *myofilaments* (filaments).
- Myofilaments consist of a number of different *proteins* involved in the process of contraction.

## A. Connective Tissue in Muscle

The different muscle components are ensheathed in connective tissue.

1. **Endomysium.**

   Delicate networks of connective tissue that surround and fill the spaces between individual muscle fibers (myofibers = cells).

2. **Perimysium.**

   Stronger connective tissue that ensheaths the fascicles, which are bundles of muscle fibers (myofibers = cells).

3. **Epimysium.**

   Ensheaths the whole muscle. It is continuous with the perimysium and also with connective tissue layers in the body called *fascia*, a loose term that describes collections of connective tissue large enough to be observed with the naked eye.

The various connective tissue sheaths listed above contain blood vessels, lymphatic vessels, and nerves.

Epimysium, perimysium, and endomysium may be extended beyond the muscle fibers as a *tendon*—a cord of dense regular fibrous connective tissue that attaches a muscle to the periosteum of a bone.

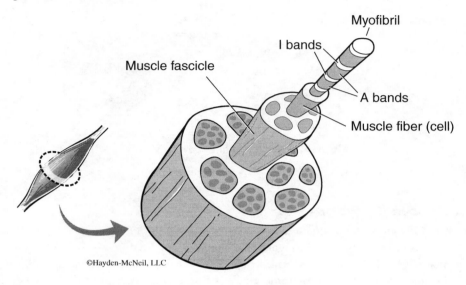

©Hayden-McNeil, LLC

**Figure 10-1.** Cross section of skeletal muscle.

207

When the connective tissue elements extend as a broad flat layer, the tendon is called an *aponeurosis*. This structure may attach to the coverings of a bone, another muscle, or skin. The *galea aponeurotica* is a large aponeurosis that caps the skull and is connected to the occipital and frontal belly of the *epicranius muscle* and also to the *temporoparietalis muscle* (these muscles draw back or tighten the scalp, raise the eyebrows, wrinkle the forehead, raise the ears).

Certain tendons, especially those of the wrists and ankles, are enclosed by tubes of fibrous connective tissue called *tendon* or *synovial sheaths*. They are similar in structure to bursae. They contain synovial fluid. Tendon sheaths permit tendons to slide back and forth more easily.

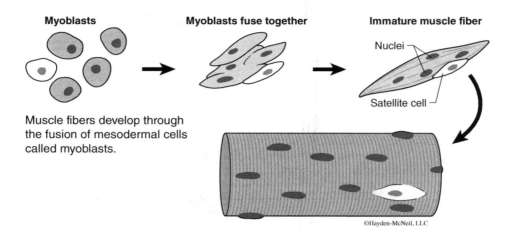

**Figure 10-2.** Muscle fiber development.

## B. Muscle Fibers (Myofibers)

Because muscle cells are elongated, they are called muscle fibers or *myofibers*. The skeletal muscle fiber is not only an elongated cell, but it is unusual in that it contains many nuclei, instead of just one. Its cytoplasm is called *sarcoplasm*. Its plasma membrane is called the *sarcolemma*—the sarcolemma extends inward into the sarcoplasm as a series of *transverse tubules* or *T-tubules*. As we shall see, these T-tubules are very important in the process that triggers muscle contraction.

The sarcoplasm is packed with:

1.  **Mitochondria**, to provide ATP.

2.  **Sarcoplasmic reticulum.**

    A network of membranous channels equivalent to the endoplasmic reticulum in other cells. Together with the **T-tubules**, with which it is closely associated, the *sarcoplasmic reticulum* plays an important role in *excitation-contraction coupling*.

3.  **Myofibrils.**

    *   A myofibril is the contracting element of skeletal and cardiac muscle. Myofibrils consist of repeating assemblies of protein *myofilaments.*

    *   The thick filaments are composed mainly of *myosin*, an elongated molecule with two globular heads that can hydrolyze **ATP** and bind to *actin* (see below).

    *   The thin filaments are composed mainly of actin. One end of an actin molecule is attached to a *Z-line*, that extends across the muscle fiber. The segment of myofibril lying between two Z-lines is called a *sarcomere.*

    *   Contraction occurs when the thick and thin filaments slide past one another, pulling the Z-lines together and shortening the sarcomere.

    *   *The myofilaments themselves do not shorten during contraction.*

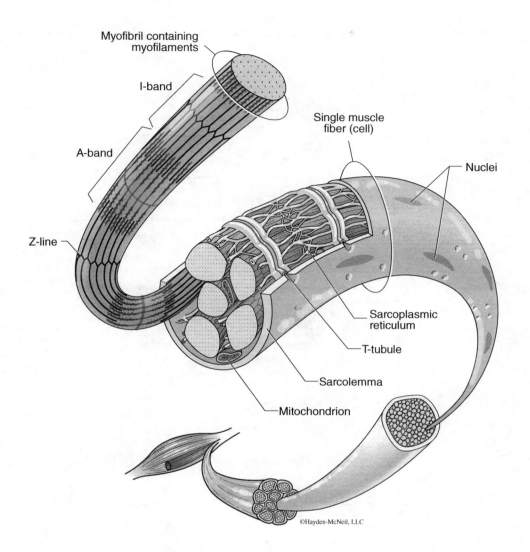

Myofibril containing myofilaments

I-band

A-band

Z-line

Single muscle fiber (cell)

Nuclei

Sarcoplasmic reticulum

T-tubule

Sarcolemma

Mitochondrion

©Hayden-McNeil, LLC

**Figure 10-3.** Muscle cross section.

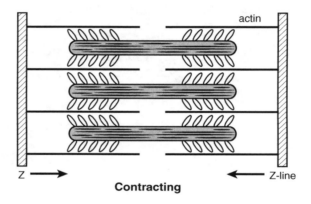

Sarcomere

**Relaxed**

**Contracting**

thin filaments – actin
thick filaments – myosin

**Figure 10-4.** Sarcomere.

### C. How Nerves Are Connected to Skeletal Muscles: The Neuromuscular Junction

Each skeletal muscle fiber is connected to the axon of a *motor neuron*, the body of which is located in the spinal cord or a nucleus in the brain. Note that one muscle fiber receives commands from only **one** motor neuron, but that one motor neuron may connect with (and send commands to) **many** muscle fibers.

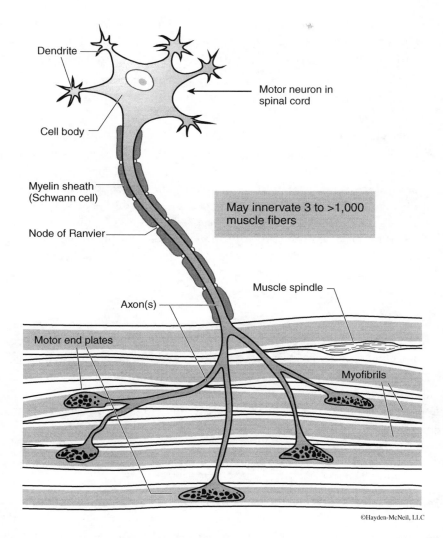

Dendrite

Motor neuron in spinal cord

Cell body

Myelin sheath (Schwann cell)

Node of Ranvier

May innervate 3 to >1,000 muscle fibers

Muscle spindle

Axon(s)

Motor end plates

Myofibrils

©Hayden-McNeil, LLC

**Figure 10-5.** Motor neurons connect to muscle fibers via neuromuscular junctions.

A motor neuron together with all the muscle fibers it innervates (= is connected to) is called a **MOTOR UNIT** (there will be more discussion of *motor units* in the next chapter).

The junction of an axon with a muscle fiber is a specialized structure called the ***neuromuscular junction***. At this point, the sarcolemma is modified to form a ***motor end plate***.

When the motor neuron is excited, the following events occur.

1.  On arrival of an electrical ***action potential*** at the end of the nerve axon, a chemical transmitter called ***acetylcholine*** is released. Acetylcholine is just one example of a large class of substances called ***neurotransmitters***. We will encounter many other neurotransmitters when we discuss the nervous system.

2.  Molecules of acetylcholine diffuse across the small gap found between the nerve endings and the sarcolemma.

3.  The acetylcholine molecules then bind to specific ***acetylcholine receptor molecules*** in the sarcolemma of the motor end plate.

211

4. The result of this binding is a wave of **electrical depolarization** (= an **action potential**) that spreads over the sarcolemma and ultimately causes the muscle fiber to contract (see later).

5. The action of acetylcholine is brief because it is rapidly **hydrolyzed** by an enzyme called *cholinesterase*.

### D. Neuromuscular Transmission Can Be Blocked by Drugs and Disease

1. **Curare** is a poison that blocks neuromuscular transmission by binding to acetylcholine receptors. Acetylcholine cannot bind to the blocked receptors, resulting in paralysis. Curare is obtained from certain plants and is used to coat the tips of blow darts and arrows by natives of South America, notably in the Amazon region. The effects can often be reversed by *anticholinesterases* such as neostigmine, which increase the concentration of acetylcholine at the neuromuscular junction, so overcoming the effects of the curare. Substances related to curare are often used as muscle relaxants during surgery.

2. The snake venom **α-bungarotoxin** acts similarly to curare.

3. **Botulinum toxin** prevents the release of acetylcholine. It is one of the most potent toxins known. A half pound would kill every human on earth. However, in very small and controlled doses, it has been used clinically in the relief of muscle spasms.

---

As discussed in Chapter 18, *tetanus toxin* acts similarly on the central nervous system by preventing the release of acetylcholine and other neurotransmitters. Due to the complicated nature of the neuronal networks affected by this toxin, its effects are complicated, and lead to severe muscle spasms (tetanic seizures) and possibly death.

---

4. **Myasthenia gravis** is an uncommon autoimmune disease. Patient develops antibodies against acetylcholine receptors in the neuromuscular junction. This interferes with the transmission of impulses from the nerve to the muscle. Muscle contractions become progressively weaker, and may cease altogether.

5. **Nerve gases** (Saran, Soman, Tabun) block acetylcholinesterase—increase AcCh, causing constant stimulation of muscles and thus asphyxiation.

6. **Black widow venom** (latrotoxin)—explosive release of AcCh.

## II. How Skeletal Muscles Contract: The Conversion of Energy in Foodstuffs into Mechanical Activity

### A. Molecular Architecture of Muscle: Thick and Thin Myofilaments and Their Role in Muscle Contraction

As noted above, contraction occurs when thick filaments (mainly myosin) and thin filaments (mainly actin) slide past one another. The filaments do NOT shorten.

A myosin molecule is elongated and has two globular head regions. These heads can bind to actin under certain circumstances.

## B. ATP Hydrolysis Drives Muscle Contraction

The myosin molecule acts rather like the oar of a rower. The procedure is as follows (see diagram).

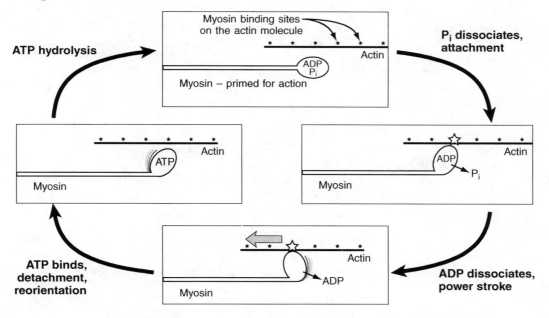

**Figure 10-6.** ATP hydrolysis drives muscle contraction.

1. **Resting** condition, the myosin is primed and ready for action.
2. **Attachment** of myosin head to actin (= dipping oar in water).
3. **Power stroke** (= rower pulling on oar).
4. **Detachment** and **reorientation** (= rower raises oar and brings it forward again).
5. **Preparation** and **priming** for next attachment step (not shown in diagram).

As you can see, this whole cycle is associated with the **hydrolysis** of **ATP** to ADP and an inorganic phosphate group ($P_i$). If you look at the diagram, you will see that ATP binds to the myosin head in the detachment and reorientation step (4). In the resting, primed condition (1), this ATP has been hydrolyzed (by the ***ATP-ase*** activity of the **myosin heads**, catalyzed by actin) and the products ADP and $P_i$ remain bound to the myosin head.

---

During this hydrolysis the energy of the ATP molecule becomes locked up in the myosin molecule, which is now primed and ready for action.

---

In the resting muscle, however, although the myosin molecule is primed and ready to go, it is prevented from attaching to actin until a nerve impulse arrives at the neuromuscular junction and causes a wave of electrical depolarization to spread over the sarcolemma. How does this event trigger muscular contraction? Read on to the following page.

### C. Excitation-Contraction Coupling: Muscle Contraction Is Initiated by a Rise in Intracellular Calcium Ions, Mediated by the Two Actin-Associated Proteins Troponin and Tropomyosin

The coupling of the nerve impulse with muscle contraction hinges around the release of *calcium* ions that are stored within the sarcoplasmic reticulum, and the effect of these calcium ions on the two actin-associated proteins called *troponin* and *tropomyosin*.

1.  The action of acetylcholine at the neuromuscular junction causes a wave of electrical depolarization to spread over the surface of the sarcolemma and penetrate into the interior of the muscle fiber via the T-tubule system.

2.  The depolarization of the T-tubule membrane causes the sarcoplasmic reticulum to release a large amount of calcium ions into the sarcoplasm. In skeletal muscle, this seems to work because of a special molecule in the T-tubule membrane that acts as a voltage sensor (this molecule may also be a calcium channel). The voltage sensor molecule triggers the release of calcium through special *calcium-release channels* in the membrane of the sarcoplasmic reticulum.

3.  **The result is a sharp rise in the concentration of calcium ions in the sarcoplasm.** This rise of sarcoplasmic calcium ion concentration enables the first phase of muscle contraction—attachment of the primed myosin heads to actin.

4.  The action of calcium is mediated by two proteins we haven't mentioned before. These two important proteins are as follows.

    a.  *Tropomyosin* – a filamentous protein that winds over the surface of the actin filament, and which obstructs the binding of myosin to actin in the resting muscle.

    b.  *Troponin* – binds to actin and to tropomyosin. It also binds calcium ions.

5.  When the calcium ion concentration in the sarcoplasm rises sharply, it binds to troponin, which then causes a change in the tropomyosin molecule so that it no longer hinders the binding of myosin to actin, and the primed myosin molecule is free to attach to actin and generate the power stroke of muscle contraction.

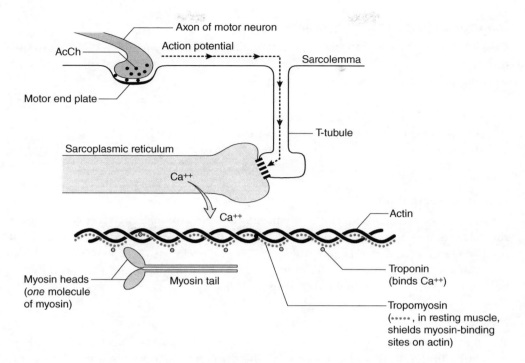

**Figure 10-7.** Muscle excitation-contraction coupling.
Based on a diagram summarizing excitation-contraction coupling prepared by
two students in BIOL 203: Rene Daniel and Erika Reichert.

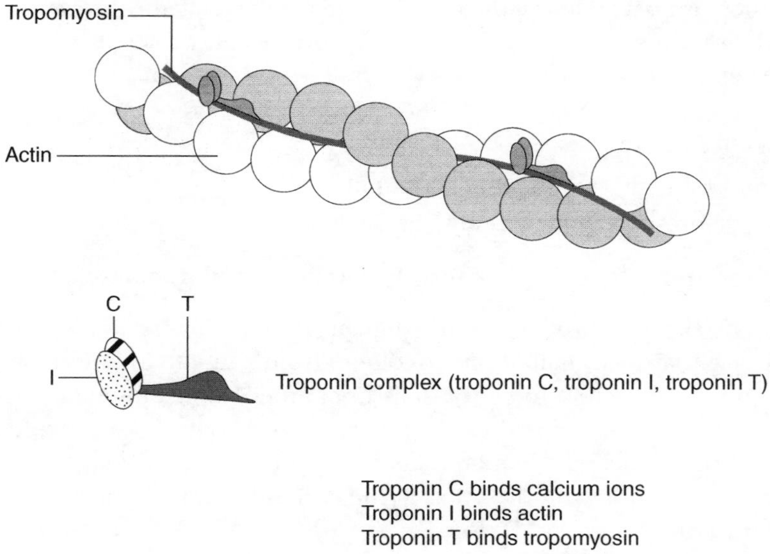

215

Tropomyosin

Actin

C    T

I

Troponin complex (troponin C, troponin I, troponin T)

Troponin C binds calcium ions
Troponin I binds actin
Troponin T binds tropomyosin

**Figure 10-8.** Interaction of actin, tropomyosin, and the troponin complex.

In resting muscle, tropomyosin blocks the myosin-binding sites on actin. During *excitation-contraction coupling*, calcium binds to troponin C. As a result, the positioning of the tropomyosin molecule changes, exposing myosin-binding sites on actin and permitting myosin heads to bind to actin during the attachment phase of the contraction process.

### D. Cardiac Muscle Is Slightly Different

In *cardiac muscle*, comparatively large amounts of calcium ions enter the muscle cells through the T-tubule membranes. This calcium then acts to trigger release of more calcium ions from the sarcoplasmic reticulum.

---

The contraction of cardiac muscle, therefore, is much more dependent on calcium ions in the external medium than the contraction of skeletal muscle. *Remember this!*

---

### E. Muscle Relaxation

An *ATP-driven calcium* pump in the membranes of the sarcoplasmic reticulum removes the calcium ions from the sarcoplasm back into the interior of the sarcoplasmic reticulum, where much of it binds to a protein called *calsequestrin*. Consequently, the calcium ion concentration in the sarcoplasm drops, and the myosin-binding sites on the actin molecule are once again shielded by tropomyosin.

### F. Rigor Mortis

When a person dies, the ability to generate ATP is lost. Calcium ions leak from the extracellular fluid into the muscle fibers, raising the concentration of calcium ions in the sarcoplasm and exposing most of the myosin-binding sites on actin. The result is that myosin binds to actin and the muscles contract. Muscle pH is also reduced as a result of lactic acid production, and this may also play a role.

The muscles cannot relax because the *detachment step involves binding ATP to the myosin head*, and there is no ATP left in the muscle. The result is called *rigor mortis* ("rigidity of death"). Rigor mortis persists until lysosomal proteases start to break down the muscle proteins, when relaxation of the muscles occurs.

### G. Proteins in Muscle

The proteins of muscle can be grouped as follows.

1.  contractile proteins: **actin** and **myosin**

2.  excitation-contraction coupling proteins: **troponin** and **tropomyosin**

3.  sarcomeric skeleton proteins: **titin** is a giant protein expressed in cardiac and skeletal muscle that spans half of the sarcomere from Z-line to M-line. Titin plays a key role in muscle assembly, force transmission at the Z-line, and maintenance of resting tension in the I-band region. It also contributes to the elastic recoil of a muscle that has been stretched. **Nebulin** is another giant muscle protein. Its molecule has one end at the Z-line and the other at the end of the thin filament. Nebulin is not found in cardiac muscle.

4.  cytoskeletal proteins: **desmin** and the microtubules, that maintain the structural order within the cell and connect the cytoplasm and all cellular organelles with the sarcolemma.

5.  <u>membrane-associated proteins</u>: such as **dystrophin**, that links the intracellular structural components with those of the extracellular matrix. A mutation in the **dystrophin gene** causes Duchenne muscular dystrophy.

By the time you have finished reading this chapter and the next, you should be able to name at least eleven proteins found in skeletal muscle.

- Actin
- Myosin
- Troponin
- Tropomyosin
- Titin
- Nebulin
- Desmin
- Dystrophin
- Myoglobin
- Creatine phosphokinase
- Calsequestrin

| Contractile | Excitation-contraction coupling | Sarcomeric skeleton | Cytoskeletal | Membrane-associated |
|---|---|---|---|---|
| Actin myosin | Troponin tropomyosin | Titin nebulin | Desmin Mictrotubule proteins | Dystrophin |

Also: *Calsequestrin, creatine phosphokinase, myoglobin*

**Figure 10-9.**

## III. Energy Sources for Contraction

The energy during exercise is derived from:

- *ATP* already in the muscle cell (enough for 3 seconds activity)
- *creatine phosphate* (also known as phosphocreatine: adds energy for another 5–7 seconds activity)
- *glycolysis* (an anaerobic process)
- *Krebs cycle*
- *oxidative phosphorylation* (aerobic)

It is not only glucose that can provide acetyl CoA for the Krebs cycle, but also **fatty acids**. This process is outlined in Chapters 5 and 6, which you should refer to before reading the next section. Consequently, while a major and rapid source of energy for skeletal muscle contraction is glucose (in the bloodstream or derived from glycogen in the muscle), fatty acids are also an important fuel for exercising skeletal muscle, and may even become a major energy source during moderate, sustained exercise.

## A. Cellular Metabolism, ATP, and Creatine Phosphate

ATP is generated in the cell by anaerobic glycolysis of glucose to pyruvate and by oxidative phosphorylation "downstream" from the Krebs (citric acid) cycle. **The largest quantities of ATP are generated by oxidative phosphorylation.**

During the start of a vigorous muscular contraction, ATP is hydrolyzed into ADP and $P_i$. The amount of ATP in a muscle is only about 5mmol/kg, and the very high demand for ATP at this time cannot always be met by metabolism. However, there is a pool of energy stored in the cell in the form of *creatine phosphate*, its amount being about 15–25mmol/kg. The enzyme **creatine phosphokinase** (**CPK** or **CK**) transfers the high-energy phosphate group of creatine phosphate to ADP, so generating more ATP for immediate use. This is known as the *phosphagen system*.

$$\textbf{creatine phosphate} + \textbf{ADP} \xrightleftharpoons{\text{creatine phosphokinase}} creatine + ATP$$

The muscle cell's store of ATP and creatine phosphate is usually good for about 8–10 seconds' activity.

After the creatine phosphate has been used up following a period of high demand for ATP, how is new creatine phosphate manufactured and the phosphagen system recharged?

You can see that the above reaction is **reversible**. Moving from right to left, creatine phosphate is formed from creatine and more ATP produced by cellular metabolism. Therefore, the store of creatine phosphate in the sarcoplasm acts like a battery. Creatine phosphate can generate ATP when demand is high during muscle contraction, and then when the muscle is resting it is recharged from new ATP that is produced by cellular metabolism.

## B. Creatine Dietary Supplementation

Over 95% of our total creatine is found in skeletal muscle, most of it in the form of creatine phosphate. Meat and fish are dietary sources of creatine, which can also be synthesized in the body from the amino acids arginine, glycine, and methionine. Some athletes use creatine as a dietary supplement (up to 20 mg daily) in the hope that it will enhance their performance by building up the amounts of creatine phosphate in their muscles. Even though some expensive urine is going to be produced, performance of high intensity, intermittent exercise appears to be enhanced by creatine supplementation [Balsom, P.D., Soderlund, K., Ekblom, B. (1994). Creatine in humans, with special reference to creatine supplementation. *Sports Medicine 18*, 268–280]. Endurance types of exercise do not benefit, however. Over the short-term, no adverse affects of creatine supplementation have been reported. However, the long-term consequences of these high doses are not known. At present, the use of creatine in amounts up to ten times the natural dietary quantities is as legal as "carbohydrate loading" (see below).

## C. Oxygen Supply

Creatine phosphate is the major source of energy during the first 8–10 seconds of a 100-meter sprint. After that time, however, the muscles become dependent on cellular metabolism as a source of energy for synthesizing more ATP.

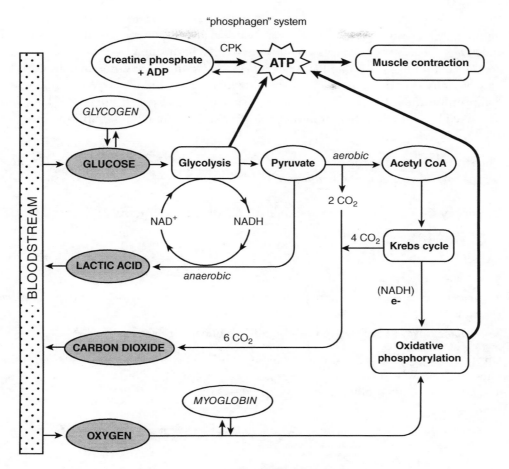

"phosphagen" system

**Muscle metabolism – IMPORTANT!**

**Figure 10-10.** Muscle metabolism.

To repeat—the controlled burning of glucose to produce usable energy in the currency of ATP consists of four steps. These four steps are:

1.  **glycolysis** (anaerobic conversion of glucose to pyruvate) – produces two molecules of ATP for each glucose molecule. This is a fast process. The remaining processes (2, 3, 4) involve oxidative phosphorylation and are comparatively slow.

2.  formation of **acetyl CoA.**

3.  the **Krebs** (citric acid) cycle, which generates NADH and $FADH_2$ that are used during the fourth step, below.

4.  **oxidative phosphorylation** – requires molecular oxygen and produces 34 molecules of ATP for each glucose molecule metabolized.

As you can see, most of the ATP (34 molecules per molecule of glucose) is produced by oxidative phosphorylation.

In most tissues, oxygen for oxidative phosphorylation is provided by *hemoglobin* in the blood. However, some skeletal muscles and cardiac muscle contain a related red protein called *myoglobin*. Myoglobin acts as a store for oxygen in the muscle (much like **glycogen** acts as a store for glucose) and also facilitates oxygen diffusion to the mitochondria. It may be utilized under conditions where the blood flow is reduced due to blood vessel compression when the muscle contracts. A similar protein called *neuroglobin* has been identified in the brain, where it probably serves the same function [see Burmester et al. (2000). *Nature 407*, 520–523].

The store of oxygen in the myoglobin of all the muscles in your body is about 0.3 liters compared with 1 liter in the **hemoglobin** of your blood.

### D. Energy Consumption During Exercise: Aerobic and Anaerobic Sources of ATP

The energy (ATP) used during strenuous exercise is derived from:

- **ATP** already in the cell.
- **creatine phosphate** already in the cell.
- *anaerobic energy* (ATP) derived from **glycolysis**—glucose is derived from *glycogen* stored in the muscle cells.
- *aerobic energy* (ATP) derived from **oxidative phosphorylation**.

During glycolysis, each glucose molecule is split into two pyruvate molecules, and the energy is released to form two ATP molecules. The process does not require oxygen, and is said to be anaerobic.

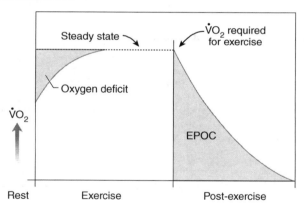

**Figure 10-11.** Oxygen deficit, exercise oxygen uptake, and excess post-exercise oxygen consumption (EPOC). $\dot{V}O_2$ signifies oxygen consumption.

Under aerobic conditions, the pyruvate enters the mitochondria of the muscle cells, is converted to acetyl CoA, and passes through the Krebs (citric acid) cycle, generating carbon dioxide, water, and the electron-storing substances NADH and $FADH_2$. Fatty acids also enter the Krebs cycle as 2-carbon fragments via acetyl CoA. NADH and $FADH_2$ then pass their electrons to oxygen, generating ATP by the process of oxidative phosphorylation. A total of 36 molecules of ATP (plus 2 of GTP) is generated by the Krebs cycle and oxidative phosphorylation combined. This is the aerobic part of the system.

Under anaerobic conditions, oxidative phosphorylation does not occur. Therefore, the only source of ATP (other than creatine phosphate) is from glycolysis. Further, as we shall discuss, there are certain muscle fibers (e.g. in the gastrocnemius muscle) that derive much of their ATP by glycolysis.

The formation of pyruvate during glycolysis generates NADH, and therefore requires a continual supply of NAD$^+$. Normally, this would be provided during oxidative phosphorylation, when the NADH molecules give up their electrons and are converted back to NAD$^+$. When oxygen is lacking, NAD$^+$ is provided by converting pyruvate to **lactate**, a process that consumes NADH and generates NAD$^+$ (see Chapter 5). This NAD$^+$ is then recycled during glycolysis, when more pyruvate and ATP are formed. Much of the lactic acid then diffuses out of the muscle cell into the blood. It is important to understand that this cannot go on indefinitely, however. The lactic acid will have to be disposed of later, as we shall discuss.

When large amounts of ATP are required for short to moderate periods of muscle contraction, this anaerobic glycolysis mechanism can be used as a rapid source of energy. It is about one half as rapid as the phosphagen system. The anaerobic system (glycogen-glucose-pyruvate-lactic acid) can provide 1.3 to 1.6 minutes of maximal muscle activity in addition to the 8–10 seconds provided by the phosphagen system.

| Phosphagen system | 8–10 seconds |
| --- | --- |
| Anaerobic system | 1.3–1.6 minutes |
| Aerobic system | unlimited time (as long as nutrients last) |

Energy systems used in various sports are as follows.

**Phosphagen system, almost entirely**
- 100-meter dash
- jumping
- weight lifting
- diving
- football dashes

**Anaerobic system, mainly**
- 400-meter dash
- 100-meter swim
- tennis

**Aerobic system**
- 10,000-meter skating
- cross-country skiing
- marathon run (26.2 miles)
- jogging

**Phosphagen and anaerobic systems**
- 200-meter dash
- baseball home run
- ice hockey dashes

**Anaerobic and aerobic systems**
- 800-meter run
- 200-meter swim
- 1500-meter skating
- boxing
- 2000-meter rowing
- 1500-meter run
- 1 mile run
- 400-meter swim

221

### E. Excess Post-Exercise Oxygen Consumption (EPOC) Pays off the Oxygen Debt Built Up during Exercise

An oxygen deficit always occurs at the start of exercise because energy use rises immediately but the aerobic systems respond more slowly.

Anaerobic production of lactic acid leads to its progressive accumulation in the body. This contributes to the so-called oxygen debt which must be repaid at the end of exercise. The amount of oxygen debt built up is equal to the amount of oxygen needed to:

* Convert the accumulated lactate back to **glucose** in the liver. The glucose is used to replenish the glycogen stores of the liver and muscle. The cycle of glucose-pyruvate-lactate-glucose is sometimes called the **Cori** cycle, named after Carl and Gerty Cori, who worked on the system in the 1930s and 1940s.
* Replenish the muscle **ATP** and **creatine phosphate** stores.
* Replenish the **oxygen** content of the muscle **myoglobin**.

This is why, after strenuous exercise, you continue to breathe hard and consume excessive amounts of oxygen for at least a few minutes and sometimes for up to an hour afterward. This phenomenon is called "excess post-exercise oxygen consumption," or EPOC.

### F. Muscle Fatigue

Muscle fatigue occurs after long periods of repeated contraction. The force the muscle exerts progressively diminishes and there is accompanying discomfort. The causes of this effect are not well understood. One factor may be depletion of muscle *glycogen*. Eating carbohydrates before a marathon race ("carbohydrate loading") may increase muscle glycogen and delay the onset of fatigue. Drinking a solution of glucose during the race may also be beneficial. Other important factors seem to be the accumulation of *lactic acid* and elevation of muscle temperature. Some runners hyperventilate before a race to raise the blood pH so that they can accommodate more lactic acid. The hyperventilation does NOT raise arterial blood oxygen, which is always saturated. However, recent evidence suggests that an important component of fatigue may be the development of leaky calcium channels in the sarcoplasmic reticulum and consequent elevation of sarcoplasmic calcium.

## IV. Fast and Slow Muscles

In humans and other primates, skeletal muscle cells are specialized into two main types.

### A. Slow, Oxidative (Red) Fibers (Type I)

Slow, *red fibers* are **endurance fibers**—they generate aerobic energy and are relatively fatigue-resistant. Red fibers look red because they contain the red protein *myoglobin*, a good supply of blood containing hemoglobin, and the red cytochromes in their many *mitochondria*. These fibers are important for utilizing fatty acids as well as glucose.

### B. Fast, Glycolytic (White) Fibers (Type II)

Fast, *white fibers* carry out **rapid, forceful** movements—they generate anaerobic energy and are susceptible to fatigue. [The "white meat" in chickens and turkeys is made up mainly of fast fibers, and the "red meat" is made up mainly of slow fibers.] There is also a type IIa that is intermediate between type I and type II. The latter is sometimes called type IIb.

## C. Fast and Slow Fibers Compared

Know this table.

|  | Slow, Oxidative (Red) Muscle Fibers Type I | Fast, Glycolytic (White) Muscle Fibers Type II |
|---|---|---|
| Fatigue | resistant | susceptible |
| Mitochondria | many | few |
| Myoglobin content | high | low |
| Levels of glycolytic enzymes | moderate | high |
| Speed of contraction | slow | fast |
| Rate of ATP hydrolysis | moderate | fast |
| Sarcoplasmic reticulum pumping rate | moderate | fast |
| ATP consumption | moderate | extremely high |
| Diameter | moderate | large |
| Capillary density | high | low |

## D. Distribution of Fast and Slow Fibers in Different Muscles and in Different Types of Athletes

All muscles in the human body have a mixture of fast and slow muscle fibers, but there is usually a predominance of one or the other. The *gastrocnemius* has a high proportion of **fast** fibers, which enable it to contract rapidly and forcefully, as when you **jump**. However, it **fatigues** rather easily. On the other hand, the *soleus* has a high proportion of **slow** fibers, and is used for more **prolonged** lower leg activity (such as maintenance of posture) where **fatigue resistance** is required.

Several experimental procedures can change the ratio of fast and slow fibers in a muscle, apparently by converting one into the other. The table on the next page shows that the distribution of fast and slow fibers in the quadriceps femoris muscle group is different in different types of athlete. One explanation might be that we are seeing the effects of training. Another explanation is that genetic factors are at work, and may play an important role in determining a person's aptitude for a particular type of sport. Probably the truth is represented by a combination of these two. It is known, however, that the skeletal muscles of marathon runners have a very high capacity for producing ATP because the production of new mitochondria is stimulated by endurance exercise. The concentrations of enzymes that promote glycogen utilization decrease, while the concentrations of enzymes that synthesize glycogen and utilize triglycerides increase. Marathon runners can therefore spare their glycogen reserves and effectively use their more abundant fat reserves for energy production.

Percentages of fast versus slow fibers in the quadriceps femoris muscle group of different types of athletes.

| Athlete | Fast Fibers (glycolytic) | Slow Fibers (oxidative) |
|---------|--------------------------|-------------------------|
| Marathoner | 18% | 82% |
| Swimmer | 26% | 74% |
| Average man | 55% | 45% |
| Weight lifter | 55% | 45% |
| Sprinter | 63% | 37% |
| Jumper | 63% | 37% |

## V. Heat Production by Contracting Muscles—Heat Stroke in Athletes

When muscles are active, large amounts of heat are produced. During endurance athletics, even under normal environmental conditions, the body temperature may rise from its normal level of 98.6°F to 102° or 103°F. With very hot and humid conditions or excess clothing, the body temperature can easily rise to as high as 106°–108°F. This can be destructive to cells, particularly brain cells. Symptoms include extreme weakness, exhaustion, headache, dizziness, nausea, profuse sweating, confusion, staggering gait, collapse, and unconsciousness. If dehydration occurs, there can be debilitating muscle cramping. **Post-exercise, painful muscle cramping (sometimes hours later) can occur in comparatively mild cases of dehydration, so it is important to drink large amounts of water after exercise even if one doesn't feel thirsty.**

The whole complex of symptoms is called *heat stroke*. Untreated, it can lead to death. Even if exercise is stopped, body temperature does not easily decrease by itself. There is a breakdown in homeostasis because the temperature regulating mechanisms often fail. Therefore, clothing must be removed, the body sprayed with cold water or even immersed in ice water containing a mush of crushed ice if available.

Although heat stroke deaths are preventable, as many as 33 football players have died from heat stroke since 1995 (25 high school, 5 college, 2 professional, and one sandlot). This illustrates that coaches must be better trained in dealing with this problem, and also that it is their responsibility to instruct athletes in the dangers of heat stroke, and to take proper precautions. One of these precautions is to provide an abundance of cold water before, during, and after practice.

## VI. Thirty Muscles You Should Know

The following is a list of 30 muscles you should know. In addition to knowing the name of the muscle and its location, you should know its origin and insertion, as well as the movement it is associated with.

1. *orbicularis oculi*
2. *orbicularis oris*
3. *masseter*
4. *sternocleidomastoid* (sternocleidomastoideus)
5. *platysma*
6. *pectoralis major*
7. *pectoralis minor*
8. *rectus abdominus*
9. *obliquus externus abdominus* (external oblique)
10. *trapezius*
11. *latissimus dorsi*
12. *deltoid* (deltoideus)
13. *biceps brachii*
14. *triceps brachii*
15. *gluteus maximus*
16. *biceps femoris*
17. *rectus femoris*
18. *gastrocnemius*
19. *diaphragm*
20. *pronator quadratus*
21. *extensor digitorum* (brevis, communis longus)
22. *flexor digitorum profundus*
23. *sartorius*
24. *soleus*
25. *supraspinatus* (one of the four muscles of the *rotator cuff*)
26. *infraspinatus* (one of the four muscles of the rotator cuff)
27. *teres minor* (one of the four muscles of the rotator cuff)
28. *subscapularis* (one of the four muscles of the rotator cuff)
29. *coracobrachialis*
30. *teres major*

225

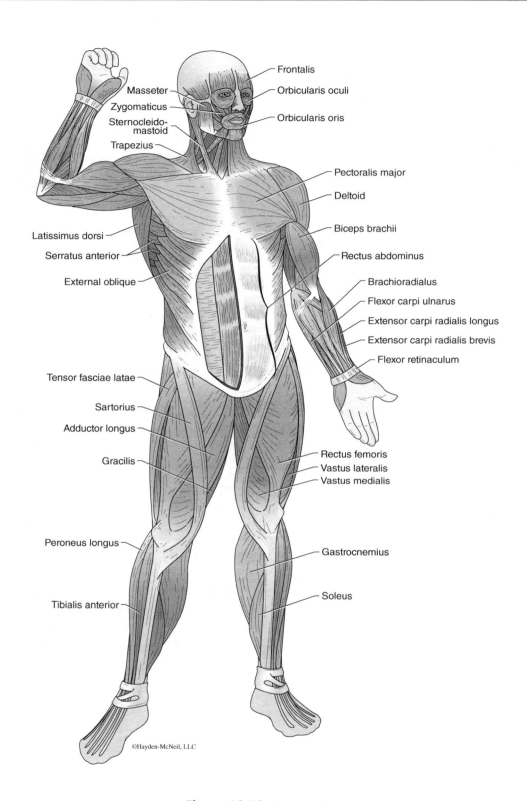

Masseter
Zygomaticus
Sternocleido-
mastoid
Trapezius

Frontalis
Orbicularis oculi
Orbicularis oris

Pectoralis major
Deltoid
Biceps brachii
Rectus abdominus
Brachioradialus
Flexor carpi ulnarus
Extensor carpi radialis longus
Extensor carpi radialis brevis
Flexor retinaculum

Latissimus dorsi
Serratus anterior
External oblique

Tensor fasciae latae
Sartorius
Adductor longus
Gracilis

Rectus femoris
Vastus lateralis
Vastus medialis

Peroneus longus

Gastrocnemius

Tibialis anterior

Soleus

©Hayden-McNeil, LLC

**Figure 10-12.** Anterior view.

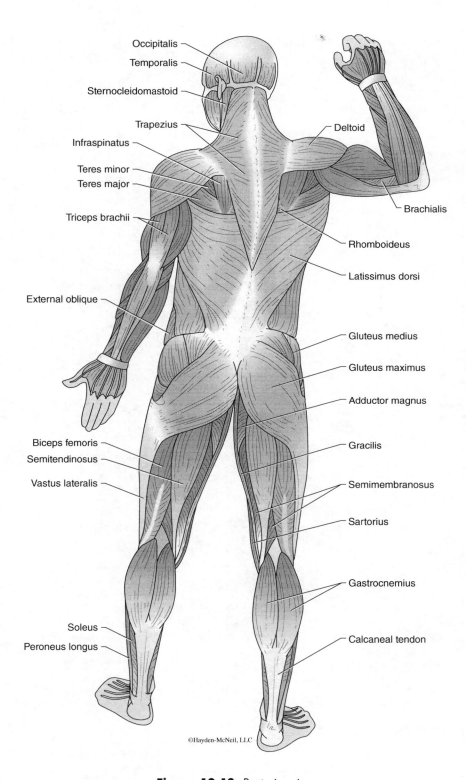

Occipitalis

Temporalis

Sternocleidomastoid

Trapezius

Infraspinatus

Teres minor

Teres major

Triceps brachii

External oblique

Biceps femoris

Semitendinosus

Vastus lateralis

Soleus

Peroneus longus

Deltoid

Brachialis

Rhomboideus

Latissimus dorsi

Gluteus medius

Gluteus maximus

Adductor magnus

Gracilis

Semimembranosus

Sartorius

Gastrocnemius

Calcaneal tendon

©Hayden-McNeil, LLC

**Figure 10-13.** Posterior view.

## Identification of Skeletal Muscles

| Muscle | Origin | Insertion | Action |
|---|---|---|---|
| orbicularis oculi | maxilla, frontal bone (orbit) | continues around orbit and returns to origin | blinking (closure) |
| orbicularis oris | maxilla, mandible | lips | closes lips, protrudes lips |
| masseter | zygomatic, maxilla | mandible | elevates mandible (closes lower jaw, clenches teeth) |
| sternocleidomastoid | sternum, clavicle | temporal, occipital (mastoid process) | flexes neck, elevates chin, rotates head, elevates sternum |
| platysma | fascia of chest | lower mandible | draws mouth downward |
| pectoralis major | clavicle, sternum, cart. of ribs | humerus | flexes, adducts, rotates humerus |
| pectoralis minor | sternal ends of upper ribs | scapula | pulls scapula forward and downward, raises ribs |
| rectus abdominus | pubic symphysis | sternum (xiphoid process), ribs | flexes vertebral column, compresses abdomen |
| external oblique | lower ribs | pelvic bones (iliac crest, linea alba) | compresses abdomen, flexes and rotates vertebral column (depresses ribs) |
| trapezius | occipital bone; spines of cervical and thoracic vert. | clavicle, scapula | elevates, retracts, depresses, or rotates scapula |
| latissimus dorsi | spinous processes of S,L,T vert.; ilium | humerus | extends, adducts arm; rotates humerus inward |
| deltoid | scapula, clavicle | humerus | abducts upper arm; extends, flexes, and rotates humerus |
| biceps brachii | scapula | radius | flexes forearm and shoulder; rotates (supinates) hand |
| triceps brachii | humerus, scapula | ulna | extends forearm, (aids in adduction) |
| gluteus maximus | sacrum, coccyx, ilium | femur; fascia | extends, abducts leg, laterally rotates thigh |

| Muscle | Origin | Insertion | Action |
|---|---|---|---|
| *biceps femoris* | ischium, femur | fibula, tibia | flexes knee, and extension and lateral rotation at hip |
| *rectus femoris* | ilium | patella (tibia) | extends leg at knee, flexes hip |
| *gastrocnemius* | femur | calcaneous | plantar flexion; flexion of leg at knee |
| *diaphragm* | sternum (xiphoid process), lower ribs, lumbar vertebrae | central tendon | pulls central tendon downward (increases volume of thoracic cavity) |
| *pronator quadratus* | distal end of ulna | distal end of radius | pronates forearm and hand |
| *extensor digitorum communis* | humerus | phalanges | extends fingers and wrist |
| *flexor digitorum profundus* | ulna | phalanges | flexes distal joints of fingers |
| *sartorius* | ilium | tibia | flexes thigh; abducts thigh, rotates leg |
| *soleus* | fibula, tibia | calcaneous | plantar flexion (adducts foot) |
| *supraspinatus* | scapula | humerus | abduction of arm, weak flexion of arm, stabilizes shoulder |
| *infraspinatus* | scapula | humerus | lateral rotation of arm; abduction of upper arm, stabilizes shoulder |
| *teres minor* | scapula | humerus | lateral rotation of arm; weak adduction of upper arm, stabilizes shoulder |
| *subscapularis* | scapula | humerus | medial rotation of arm, stabilizes shoulder |
| *coracobrachialis* | scapula | humerus | weak adduction of upper arm |
| *teres major* | scapula | humerus | medial rotates arm, adducts arm, extends arm |

229

# CHAPTER 11

## MUSCLE II
All-or-None, Motor Units, Smooth Muscle, Cardiac Muscle,
Levers, Muscle Use and Disuse

## CHAPTER OUTLINE

## DESCRIPTION AND INTRODUCTION

In Chapter 10 we concentrated on **skeletal** muscles and their mechanism of contraction. In this chapter, we continue with skeletal muscles, and discuss their responses to stimulation. Then we move on to the two other types of muscle—**smooth** muscle and **cardiac** muscle. Both types of muscle are important to the functioning of the cardiovascular system. The contraction and relaxation of cardiac muscle in the walls of the heart pumps blood around the body, and the contraction and relaxation of smooth muscle controls the diameter of blood vessels such as the arterioles.

In this chapter, we also discuss the way in which skeletal muscles and muscle groups coordinate their activities.

My discussion of levers differs markedly from some textbooks. For example, the ankle/foot is a first-class lever, not a second-class lever as stated in some textbooks.

## OBJECTIVES

After listening to the lecture and reading this chapter, you should be able to:

1. Define the **threshold** stimulus and the **all-or-none** phenomenon.
2. Define a **motor unit** and describe its properties.
3. Explain what is meant by **recruitment** of motor units.
4. Explain what is meant by muscle **tone**, and how it relates to **posture** and maintaining **balance**.
5. Explain the **staircase** effect.
6. Define **tetanic** contraction, and distinguish it from a **twitch**.
7. Distinguish between **isotonic** and **isometric** contractions, and give examples.
8. Describe the two ways in which **smooth muscle** is organized, and describe their functions.
9. Describe how the **mechanism** of smooth muscle contraction differs from that of skeletal muscle.
10. List **four factors** that influence the activity of smooth muscle contractions.
11. Summarize in a **table** the similarities and differences between **skeletal**, **smooth**, and **cardiac** muscle.
12. Explain the ways in which different groups of muscles(agonists, etc.) **interact** to produce smooth, coordinated movements.
13. Explain what happens to muscles when they are **exercised**.
14. Describe the effect of two **hormones** on skeletal muscle.
15. Explain what happens to muscles when they are **not used** or **denervated**.
16. Distinguish muscular **hyperplasia** from muscular **hypertrophy**.
17. Describe the cells involved in muscle **repair**.
18. Name and describe a **disease** affecting the neuromuscular junction.
19. Explain the point of having a **lever system** in the body. Illustrate with a **diagram** how the lever system activated by the biceps brachii muscle operates: discuss and *calculate* its advantages and disadvantages.
20. Give examples of **first**- and **third-class** levers in the body.

232

### I. How Skeletal Muscle Responds to Stimulation

### A. Definition of Threshold Stimulus and All-or-None Phenomenon

Researchers investigating muscle physiology have sometimes worked with the whole muscle, and sometimes with single muscle fibers carefully dissected out from it. These muscle fibers or whole muscles can be connected to devices that record contraction when the muscle fiber or muscle is stimulated electrically.

When a ***single muscle fiber*** is exposed to a weak electrical stimulus, it does not contract. This weak electrical stimulus is called a *subthreshold stimulus*. As the strength of the stimulus to the muscle fiber is increased, it reaches the level of a *threshold stimulus*, when the muscle fiber contracts fully. As we increase the strength of the stimulus further, so that it is described as a *suprathreshold stimulus*, the muscle still contracts fully. For a single muscle fiber, there is no such thing as a partial contraction. The muscle fiber either contracts, or it doesn't. This is called an ***all-or-none response***. The all-or-none phenomenon is an important one, and we shall come across it again when we talk about stimulating nerves.

**All-or-none phenomenon**

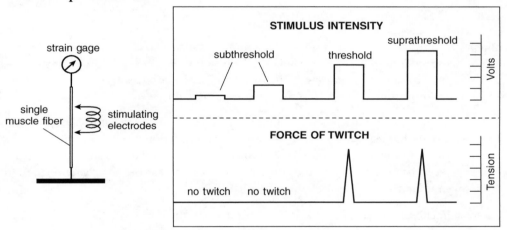

233

Single muscle fiber goes from no response to maximum response as stimulus is increased. **This is not seen if we electrically stimulate a *whole* muscle, which has *many* muscle fibers.**

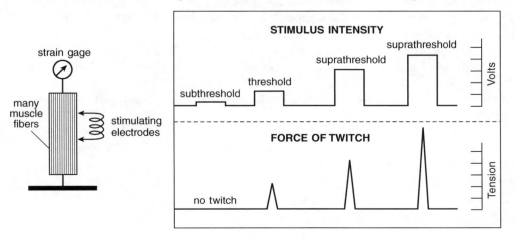

The many muscle fibers that make up the whole muscle have different thresholds, so as the intensity of the stimulus is increased, increasing numbers of muscle fibers are activated. Although *the all-or-none principle applies to each individual muscle fiber*, there is a progressive increase in the force of contraction of a whole muscle as we increase the stimulus intensity.

## B. Motor Units and Recruitment of Motor Units

Unlike a *single* muscle fiber, we can grade *whole* muscle contractions. Whole muscles are made up of many single muscle fibers (cells). It would not be convenient for us if the whole muscle acted like a single muscle fiber and contracted on an all-or-none basis. The muscles in your arms that can be used to pick up a pen can also be used to pick up a heavy suitcase, which requires more powerful contraction of the same group of muscles. In the body, therefore, the strength of a whole muscle contraction can be varied. Given that *single* muscle fibers contract on an all-or-none basis, how can this happen?

As we mentioned earlier, a single motor neuron in the spinal cord or brain can innervate a number of muscle fibers (ranging from just a few to over a thousand).

This motor neuron together with all the muscle fibers it connects to is called a *motor unit*.

One motor unit responds all-or-none, but a muscle is made up of many motor units that can be activated independently of each other. Therefore, the central nervous system can increase the strength of a muscle contraction simply by progressively activating more and more motor units. This strategy is called **motor recruitment**.

Motor units in a given muscle can contain a few to over a thousand muscle fibers. This gives an added dimension to the control of muscle contraction. Only a few muscle fibers are present in motor units of muscles that must be finely controlled, such as those that move the eyes. In muscles where the control is coarser, such as the gastrocnemius, there are many muscle fibers in a motor unit.

We find that all the muscle fibers in a motor unit are of the same type. Small motor units contain few muscle fibers, and these are type I (slow, oxidative, red). Large motor units contain a large number of muscle fibers, and these are type II (fast, glycolytic, white).

**Muscle tone, posture and maintenance of balance**—in the body, a muscle may be in a state of partial contraction even though its individual muscle fibers operate on an all-or-none basis. At any time, some fibers in such a muscle are contracted while others are relaxed. This generates what is called *muscle tone*. Muscle tone is essential for maintaining *posture* and *balance*. For example, if you faint, you lose your muscle tone and collapse.

One motor unit = a motor neuron and all the muscle fibers to which it is connected.

234

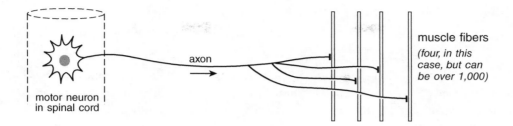

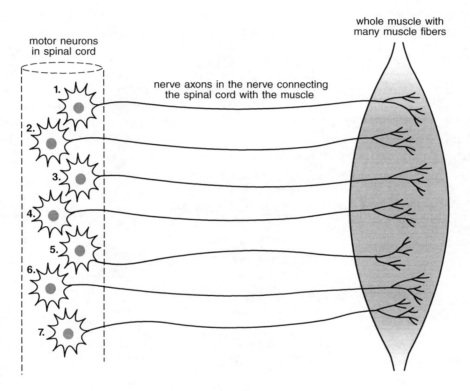

**Figure 11-1.**

Many motor units permit muscle tone during postural maintenance, and adjustment of force during voluntary muscle contraction.

*This diagram shows only seven motor units. Actually, there are many more motor units than this associated with a whole muscle.*

235

## C. Repeated Stimulation of a Muscle and the Staircase Effect

In addition to the important physiological phenomenon of motor recruitment, there is also the effect of *frequency of stimulation*.

The response of a whole muscle to a single stimulus is called a *muscle twitch*. There is a *latent period* of a few milliseconds when the muscle does not contract, but covers the time of the action potential, calcium release from the sarcoplasmic reticulum, and the molecular events preceding the power stroke of the myosin molecule after it has attached to the actin filament. There follows the period of *contraction*, which covers the time from the onset of contraction to the peak of tension development. Finally, there is the *relaxation* period.

A muscle that is stimulated repeatedly, allowing sufficient time for relaxation between stimuli, responds with a corresponding series of separate twitches. However, the strength of each twitch progressively increases up to a maximum value after a few seconds. This is called *treppe*, from the German for staircase. Hence it is sometimes called the *staircase effect*. It is caused mainly by a buildup of calcium ions in the sarcoplasm. The explanation is that not all of the calcium released from the sarcoplasmic reticulum is pumped back into the sarcoplasmic reticulum before the next stimulus arrives.

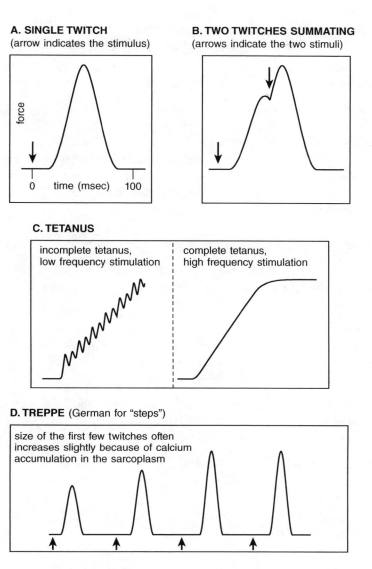

**A. SINGLE TWITCH**
(arrow indicates the stimulus)

**B. TWO TWITCHES SUMMATING**
(arrows indicate the two stimuli)

**C. TETANUS**

incomplete tetanus,
low frequency stimulation

complete tetanus,
high frequency stimulation

**D. TREPPE** (German for "steps")

size of the first few twitches often
increases slightly because of calcium
accumulation in the sarcoplasm

**Figure 11-2.** Muscle twitches.

## D. High Frequency Stimulation of a Skeletal Muscle Can Generate a Sustained Contraction or Tetanus

If a skeletal muscle is stimulated so frequently that it cannot relax after the previous twitch, the individual contractions merge together and produce a sustained contraction called *tetanus*. Short-term tetanic contractions characterize most of the contractions made by our muscles during voluntary activity, because the motor neurons controlling them typically send out rapid bursts of action potentials when activated.

Don't confuse **physiological** tetanus with the pathological condition of tetanus caused by the toxin of *Clostridium tetani*. This bacterial toxin prevents the breakdown of acetylcholine at the neuromuscular junction, and muscles therefore remain in a state of continual contraction. The condition is sometimes called **lockjaw**, because the jaw muscles are typically contracted.

### E. What Is Meant by Isotonic and Isometric Contractions

If a muscle shortens during contraction, as when you bend your arm at the elbow, the contraction is called *isotonic contraction*. During contraction, the muscle shortens and the tension remains constant.

If a muscle does not shorten during contraction, but simply develops tension, as occurs when you carry a suitcase with your arm constantly flexed, the contraction is called *isometric contraction* (constant length). During isometric contraction, the muscle length does not change but the tension developed increases sharply. Another example is when you clench your teeth—the masseter muscle exerts tension but does not shorten. Isometric contractions (or nearly isometric contractions) are very important in maintaining posture and muscle tone.

## II. Smooth Muscle

*Smooth muscle* is usually involuntary and non-striated. Smooth muscle fibers (cells) are considerably shorter than skeletal muscle fibers and each fiber has just one, centrally-located nucleus.

Like those of *skeletal muscle*, smooth muscle cells contain actin and myosin arranged in myofibrils that extend the lengths of the cells. However, they are not well organized, so that smooth muscle cells lack striations. Also, smooth muscle cells lack T-tubules and do not have the proteins troponin and tropomyosin.

238

Smooth muscle does not contract as rapidly as skeletal muscle, but there is a much greater degree of shortening and quite large movements can be produced even though it lacks the leverage of attachment to bones.

Smooth muscle cells are organized into two types of smooth muscle, called *multi-unit smooth muscle* and *visceral smooth muscle*. Visceral smooth muscle is sometimes called *single-unit smooth muscle*.

### A. Multi-Unit Smooth Muscle

In multi-unit smooth muscle the cells are not well organized, and occur as separate fibers (cells) rather than sheets. These separate fibers may contract independently of each other, but contraction is initiated by signals from the nerves of the autonomic nervous system. Examples are in the *iris* of the eye, in the walls of blood vessels, in the large passageways of the lungs, and in the arrector pili muscle.

### B. Visceral ("Single-Unit") Smooth Muscle

In visceral smooth muscle (sometimes called "single-unit") the cells are arranged in **wraparound sheets**. Visceral smooth muscle is a common type of smooth muscle found in the walls of hollow organs such as the stomach, intestine, urinary tract (including the bladder), reproductive tract (including the uterus), and small blood vessels (arterioles, for example). The individual cells are in close contact with each other, and can stimulate each other via gap junctions. Therefore, a wave of excitation (and therefore contraction) can travel along the sheet. As they pass through sheets of visceral smooth muscle, they are responsible for *peristaltic movements*, for example, which force the contents of the hollow organ in a particular direction.

Visceral smooth muscle has rhythmicity. Repeated waves of excitation can be self-initiated by *pacemaker cells*. This activity is modulated and regulated by the autonomic nervous system.

## C. Mechanism of Contraction in Smooth Muscle

Like skeletal muscle, smooth muscles have **actin** and **myosin**. **ATP** provides the energy to power the contraction process. Contraction is triggered by a rise in intracellular **calcium ions**.

However, smooth muscle does **not** have troponin and tropomyosin. Instead, excitation-contraction coupling is mediated by a calcium-binding protein called *calmodulin*.

1. When calmodulin binds calcium, the combination activates an enzyme called *myosin light-chain kinase* (MLCK).

2. The activated enzyme *phosphorylates* part of the myosin molecule.

3. The phosphorylated myosin then binds to actin.

4. Relaxation is brought about by removal of the phosphate group by another enzyme called *myosin light-chain phosphatase*.

---

Smooth muscle lacks troponin and tropomyosin.

Instead, excitation-contraction coupling is mediated by a calcium-binding protein called **calmodulin**.

---

239

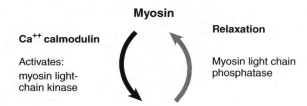

**Myosin**

**Ca$^{++}$ calmodulin**

Activates:
myosin light-
chain kinase

**Relaxation**

Myosin light chain
phosphatase

**Myosin-P + actin = Contraction**

**Figure 11-3.**

Some Comparisons between Skeletal Muscle and Smooth Muscle

| Skeletal Muscle | Smooth Muscle |
|---|---|
| striated | non-striated |
| many nuclei in muscle fiber | one nucleus per cell |
| actin | actin |
| myosin | myosin |
| ATP provides energy | ATP provides energy |
| contraction triggered by Ca$^{++}$ | contraction triggered by Ca$^{++}$ |
| troponin | calmodulin |
| tropomyosin | myosin light-chain kinase |
| | myosin light-chain phosphatase |
| under control of motor nerves | controlled by nerves, hormones, etc. (see below) |

The contraction of smooth muscle and its regulation are actually far more complicated than we have just described. Further, there are other mechanisms that regulate smooth muscle contraction that do not involve a rise of intracellular calcium. These mechanisms need not concern us in BIOL 203/204.

### D. Control of Smooth Muscle Contraction

Smooth muscle contracts or relaxes in response to the following.

1.  **Nervous input from the *autonomic nervous system*.** Smooth muscle in many parts of the body is innervated by the autonomic branch of the nervous system. The neurotransmitters released at autonomic neuromuscular junctions may be *acetylcholine* (as in skeletal muscle), or *norepinephrine*. These neurotransmitters will be discussed later in the course.

2.  **Hormones and related substances in the circulation.** Examples include the hormone *oxytocin*, which causes the smooth muscle of the uterus to contract, and *epinephrine* (secreted by the *adrenal glands*), which causes the smooth muscle in blood vessel walls to contract.

3.  **Substances produced within a metabolizing tissue can cause smooth muscle to relax.** Smooth muscle *relaxes* in response to lack of **oxygen**, the presence of excess **hydrogen ions** (as a result of lactic acid production), **carbon dioxide**, and a variety of ions that include **potassium**. These effects are particularly important in the smooth muscle found in the walls of small blood vessels.

4.  **Stretching**. Stretching of visceral smooth muscle can induce it to contract (e.g. in the intestines and in the urinary bladder).

### III. Cardiac Muscle

*Cardiac muscle* is the major constituent of the walls of the heart. It is not found elsewhere in the body. Cardiac muscle is striated but involuntary. The individual fibers have single nuclei and are connected end to end in branching networks. At the end-to-end junction of two cardiac muscle fibers (cells) is found a structure called an *intercalated disc*. Intercalated discs not only hold the ends of the fibers together, but they also contain many *gap junctions* which facilitate the spread of electrical excitation (and contraction) from one fiber to the other.

Like skeletal muscle fibers, cardiac muscle fibers are striated because they contain highly organized arrays of actin and myosin. Unlike smooth muscle, they also contain troponin and tropomyosin.

Contraction of cardiac muscle is powered by ATP. Contraction is triggered by a rise in intracellular calcium ions, mediated by the two proteins troponin and tropomyosin. Some of these calcium ions come from the sarcoplasmic reticulum, but in cardiac muscle large quantities of calcium pour into the cell from outside, via the large T-tubules. This does not apply to skeletal muscle, where all the calcium needed to trigger contraction comes from the sarcoplasmic reticulum.

240

Like smooth muscle, however, cardiac muscle has the property of rhythmicity. In the heart, specialized cardiac muscle cells display rhythmic excitatory activity and stimulate the rest of the cardiac muscle in the heart. These cells are called *pacemaker cells*. However, the rate and strength of contraction of cardiac muscle is very dependent on signals reaching it from the autonomic nervous system, as we shall discuss further when we get to the cardiovascular system.

### Some Comparisons between Skeletal Muscle and Cardiac Muscle

| Skeletal Muscle | Cardiac Muscle |
| --- | --- |
| striated | striated |
| many nuclei in muscle fiber | one nucleus per muscle fiber |
| muscle fibers not branched | muscle fibers branched |
| do not have intercalated discs | have intercalated discs |
| actin | actin |
| myosin | myosin |
| ATP provides energy | ATP provides energy |
| contraction triggered by Ca$^{++}$ (from SR) | contraction triggered by Ca$^{++}$ (from T-tubules as well as SR) |
| troponin | troponin |
| tropomyosin | tropomyosin |
| under control of motor nerves | inherently rhythmic, but can be modulated by autonomic nerves |

## IV. Actions and Interactions of the Skeletal Muscles

### A. Origins and Insertions

In considering the action of a particular muscle, one end is attached to a part of the skeleton that is moved by that muscle and the other end is attached to a fixed point on the skeleton that does not move.

The end of the muscle attached to the moving skeletal unit is called the *insertion*, and the other end, which does not move, is called the *origin*.

### B. Lever Actions and Leverage

We said previously that much of the skeleton is made up of lever systems on which the skeletal muscles act. However, not every muscle is part of a lever system (can you think of any that are not?).

The study of different types of muscles, lever systems, and their movements is called *kinesiology*.

241

There are three components to these lever systems.

- **Lever and fulcrum.**

  The rigid **lever** arm (usually a long bone) that pivots around a fixed point called the **fulcrum**.

- **Out-force.**

  The force generated by the lever. This force could be used to move the hand or a weight held in the hand, for example.

- **In-force.**

  The force the muscle applies to the lever to accomplish the desired movement.

Depending on the order in which the fulcrum, in-force and out-force are arranged, levers are divided into *first-class levers*, *second-class levers*, and *third-class levers*. Only first- and third-class levers are of importance in the human body.

1. **First class.**

   The fulcrum lies between the out-force and the in-force (like a crowbar: out-force, fulcrum, in-force).

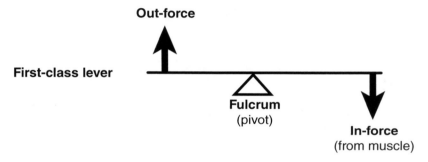

The following are three examples of first-class levers.

- *Lifting the head* – the head is lifted by the out-force, the fulcrum is the joint between the atlas and the occipital bone of the skull, the vertebral muscles inserting at the back of the head provide the necessary in-force.

- *Straightening the arm at the elbow* – the triceps brachii provides the in-force that acts on the end of the ulna which projects backward beyond the fulcrum of the elbow joint. The out-force is generated at the hand during extension of the arm.

  Contrast this forearm extension with forearm flexion, as happens when we flex the forearm at the elbow to lift a weight. This is a third-class lever (see below) where the in-force is generated by the biceps brachii muscle operating at the proximal end of the radius.

- *Movement of the foot around the fulcrum of the ankle* during walking or running (see diagram below). Most textbooks incorrectly refer to the foot as a second-class lever. The in-force is generated by the calf muscles (gastrocnemius and soleus) acting at the calcaneum. The *position* of the out-force relative to the ankle varies during walking and running, from the ball of the foot to the toes. The gear ratio of the calf muscles therefore changes. When the foot is first in contact with the ground, the gear ratio of the calf muscles is quite low (around 1), but the gear ratio increases to 3–4 as the position of contact with the ground moves toward the toes. The gear ratio is calculated from R/r, where r is the distance of the

Achilles tendon to the ankle, and R is the distance of the ankle to the point of contact of the foot with the ground [see Carrier, Heglund, and Earls. (1994). *Science 265*, 651].

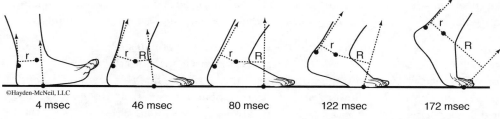

©Hayden-McNeil, LLC

| 4 msec | 46 msec | 80 msec | 122 msec | 172 msec |

*(based on Carrier et al., 1994, Science 265, 651)*

2.  **Second class.**

Like a wheelbarrow. The fulcrum is at one end, the in-force is at the other end, and the out-force is generated between the two (fulcrum, out-force, in-force).

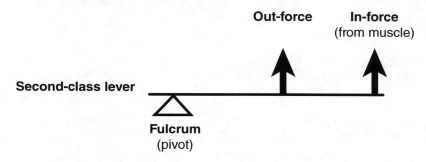

In the body, there are no really good examples of this type of lever. However, most elementary textbooks incorrectly give the foot as an example of a second-class lever. It is not. It is a first-class lever (see previous discussion of first-class levers).

3.  **Third class.**

Out-force is at one end, the in-force is in the middle, and the fulcrum is at the other end (fulcrum, in-force, out-force).

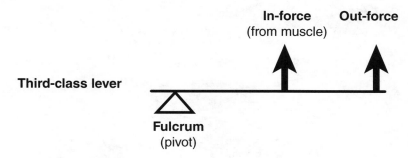

*The third-class lever is the most common lever in the body.* I give just one example below.

*   *Flexing the forearm at the elbow* to lift a weight represents a third-class lever. The weight is moved by the out-force, the in-force is generated by the biceps brachii muscle operating at the proximal end of the radius, the fulcrum is the elbow joint.

Contrast *extending* the forearm at the elbow, which is a *first-class* lever: see previous page.

243

## C. The Purpose of Levers Is to Amplify Muscle Shortening

Sarcomere lengths need to be kept close to their optimum values for best development of force. In fact, muscles do not shorten by more than a maximum of 25% of their resting lengths in most movements. Therefore, one reason for having a lever system is that **large movements of the limbs can be achieved with a small degree of muscle shortening**.

Consider the lever system that moves the forearm in a movement such as raising a weight carried in the palm of the hand. The *biceps brachii* muscle provides the *in-force*. When the forearm is at right-angles to the upper arm, the biceps brachii is attached by its tendon to the radius bone of the lower arm at a distance of about 5 cm from the *pivot* or *fulcrum* at the *elbow joint*. The *out-force* is generated at the hand, which carries the weight to be moved. The center of the hand is about 35 cm from the fulcrum at the elbow joint.

Since the above sequence is (1) *fulcrum*, (2) *in-force*, (3) *out-force*, the system is a third-class lever.

With the biceps brachii attached to the radius at **5 cm** from the elbow joint, and the distance of the center of the hand being **35 cm** from the elbow joint, *the biceps brachii has to shorten by only **1 cm** to produce a **7 cm** movement of the hand (see diagram).*

---

The lever system of the forearm therefore *amplifies* the shortening of the muscle. But there's a catch...

---

In this system, the biceps brachii muscle has a mechanical disadvantage of **1:7**. This means that in order for the hand to raise **20** kilograms, the biceps brachii must exert a force of seven times that amount, equal to **140** kilograms.

Large muscles such as the gastrocnemius are therefore called on to exert very large forces. Sometimes these forces can rupture the tendon (e.g. the Achilles tendon).

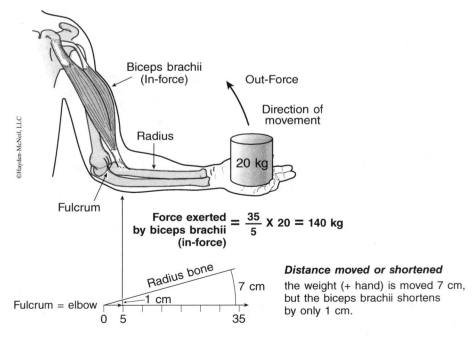

**Figure 11-4.** Third-class lever, biceps brachii.

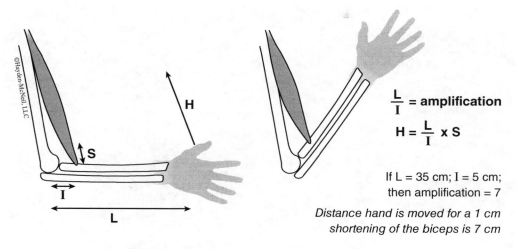

$$\frac{L}{I} = \text{amplification}$$

$$H = \frac{L}{I} \times S$$

If L = 35 cm; I = 5 cm;
then amplification = 7

*Distance hand is moved for a 1 cm
shortening of the biceps is 7 cm*

**Figure 11-5.** Long bones act as levers to amplify muscle contraction.

## D. Muscle Groups

Our brain normally visualizes the **movement** before it is carried out, not the contraction of individual muscles. Skeletal muscles usually function in groups to produce coordinated movements. Additionally, most skeletal muscles are arranged in opposing pairs at joints. That is, flexors-extensors, abductors-adductors, etc.

|  |  |
|---|---|
| **Flexor** | decreases the angle at a joint—example 1 |
| **Extensor** | increases the angle at a joint—example 2 |
| **Abductor** | moves a bone away from the midline—example 3 |
| **Adductor** | moves a bone closer to the midline—example 4 |
| **Levator** | produces an upward movement—example 5 |
| **Depressor** | produces a downward movement—example 6 |
| **Supinator** | turns the palm upward or anteriorly—example 7 |
| **Pronator** | turns the palm downward or posteriorly—example 8 |
| **Sphincter** | decreases the size of an opening—example 9 |
| **Tensor** | makes a body part more rigid—example 10 |
| **Rotator** | moves a bone around its longitudinal axis—example 11 |

245

The following examples are for your information. You do not need to memorize them, but I have given page references to Stone & Stone.

1. Flexor carpi radialis ........................................................ page 21
2. Extensor carpi ulnaris ..................................................... page 133
3. Abductor pollicis brevis.................................................. page 140
4. Adductor longus............................................................. page 176
5. Levator scapulae ............................................................ page 106
6. Depressor labii inferioris ................................................ page 41
7. Supinator ...................................................................... page 134
8. Pronator teres ............................................................... page 120
9. External anal sphincter
10. Tensor fasciae latae........................................................ page 164
11. Obturator externus ........................................................ page 159

Most movements are coordinated by several skeletal muscles acting in groups rather than individually. However, a muscle that causes a desired action and is responsible for most of the movement is called the *prime mover* or *agonist*. In the case of flexing the forearm at the elbow, the prime mover is the biceps brachii.

In the above case, while the prime mover is contracting, another muscle called the *antagonist* is relaxing. In the present example, this muscle is the *triceps brachii*.

Note that when the movement is changed so that the forearm is extended at the elbow instead of being flexed, the triceps brachii is the prime mover and the biceps brachii is the antagonist and must be relaxed.

The roles of the two muscles in the above example (which you should remember) therefore depend on which movement is being made.

When the prime mover contracts, it often acts in concert with other "helper" muscles that also contract. These muscles are called *synergists*. These muscles may smooth out the movement and help the prime mover to function more efficiently.

Synergists may also serve to stabilize the origin of a prime mover muscle. For example, the scapula is a freely movable bone that serves as the origin for several muscles that move the arm. To do this, however, the scapula must be held steady. This is accomplished by certain synergist muscles that hold the scapula firmly against the back.

In abduction of the arm, the deltoid muscle is the prime mover. It pulls on the humerus to abduct the arm. It is aided synergistically by the supraspinatus muscle. Since the origin of the supraspinatus is the scapula, and one of the origins of the deltoid muscle is also the scapula, other synergists must contract to hold the scapula steady and firm. These muscles are as follows:

• **pectoralis minor**
• *levator scapulae*
• *rhomboideus major*
• *rhomboideus minor*
• **trapezius**
• *serratus anterior*

## V. How Skeletal Muscles Are Affected by Use, Disuse, and Disease

### A. Muscle Repair, Muscular Hyperplasia, and Muscular Hypertrophy

1. **Muscle repair.**

   If you overdo it at the Co-Rec and finish up with muscles that are stiff and sore, what has happened? The answer is that some of your muscle fibers have been damaged. The repair process involves stem cells called *satellite cells* (a type of stem cell that is really a quiescent *myoblast*), which divide and form myoblasts that can fuse to form new muscle cells to replace the damaged and injured muscle fibers.

2. **Muscular hyperplasia.**

   This is an increase in the number of muscle fibers in a muscle. However, in humans, skeletal muscles have only a very limited ability to form new fibers (*hyperplasia*) by differentiation of satellite cells. Therefore, there is very little increase in the *number* of muscle fibers after birth.

3. **Muscular hypertrophy.**

   However, the *size* of the fibers may increase in response to exercise and certain hormones. Repeated forceful contractions (as occur in weight lifting) cause the muscle fibers to increase in diameter due to the production of more myofibrils, mitochondria, and sarcoplasmic reticulum.

   In addition to *exercise, testosterone* (and related *anabolic steroids*) and *growth hormone* cause an increase in the size of muscle fibers. Large changes in the circulating amounts of these hormones occur during childhood and puberty.

   Enlarged muscles are capable of carrying out more forceful contractions and of doing more work. Mathematically, the reasoning is as follows.

   • **Force** exerted by a muscle is proportional to its **cross-sectional area**.

   • **Distance shortened** during a muscle contraction is proportional to starting **length** of the muscle (in most movements, muscles do not usually contract by more than 25%).

   Since:

   **work done = force × distance shortened**

   Therefore:

   **work done ∝ cross-sectional area × length = volume of muscle**

   Muscular hypertrophy increases the cross-sectional area of the muscle, increasing its *volume*. An increase in volume therefore means that the amount of work the muscle is capable of doing also increases.

## B. Muscular Atrophy

The opposite of muscular hypertrophy is **muscular atrophy** (or wasting away).

1. **Disuse atrophy** – can occur in bedridden patients, astronauts, and in cases where the nerve to a muscle has been severed (the latter is called *denervation atrophy*).

   *Zero-gravity conditions* – in space flight there is reduced use of the muscles involved in maintaining posture under normal gravitational conditions. These muscles become reduced in mass and volume. They include the gluteal muscles, the extensors of the neck and back, and the trunk muscles. The exercises that astronauts and cosmonauts carry out may still not be enough to prevent these effects.

   *Myasthenia gravis* – is an uncommon disease that may lead to muscular atrophy. The disease is more common in women than in men. Myasthenia gravis is an autoimmune disease where the patient develops **antibodies** against **acetylcholine receptors** in the neuromuscular junction. This interferes with the transmission of impulses from the nerve to the muscle. Therefore, muscle contractions become progressively weaker, and may cease altogether.

   In myasthenia gravis, muscles of the eyelids, extraocular muscles, face, throat and neck initially become weak and easily fatigued. Later, the respiratory muscles may become involved, then the limbs. Chewing and swallowing become difficult. Speech muscles may be affected. The symptoms are aggravated by muscular exertion, and may vary in intensity during the course of the day. Death may result from paralysis of the diaphragm, but usually the disorder does not proceed to this stage. Before this stage is reached, some muscles may atrophy, so the result is a bit like denervation atrophy.

   *Treatment:* the strategy is to try and increase the concentration of acetylcholine in the neuromuscular junction, in an attempt to overcome the deficiency in active acetylcholine receptors. The patient is given **anticholinesterase** drugs (Neostigmine, pyridostigmine), which reduce the enzymatic breakdown of acetylcholine at the neuromuscular junction.

2. **Duchenne muscular dystrophy** also causes muscular atrophy. This hereditary disease leads to progressive degeneration of the skeletal muscles. The disease is due to a mutation in the gene for **dystrophin**. Dystrophin is localized at the sarcolemma. Although it represents only 0.002% of all the protein in muscle, it seems to be important for anchoring certain integral membrane glycoproteins which may control calcium flow into the muscle.

# CHAPTER 12

# NEUROPHYSIOLOGY I
Histology and Growth of Nerve Tissue, Resting and Action Potentials

249

## CHAPTER OUTLINE

## DESCRIPTION AND INTRODUCTION

There is a lot of material to cover in this chapter, so it is very important that you read it carefully before coming to the lecture.

The nervous system, together with the endocrine system (which we'll talk about next semester), controls and integrates the workings of the human body.

Of all the systems in the body, the nervous system is one that presents the most questions and philosophical challenges to our way of thinking about ourselves and humanity in general. As Nobel prizewinner Torsten Wiesel put it.

*"How much of our fate is in fact written in the DNA inside our cells? And how much freedom do we have to reach our full potential as human beings through our education and experiences?*

*These questions must ultimately involve the enormously complex interaction between the genetic information that flows out from DNA into developing and mature brains and the experiential information that flows in through our nervous system as we perceive and act in the world."*

[Wiesel, Torsten. *Science* (1994). *264*, 1647.]

These questions become even more relevant now that we have obtained the full sequence of the human genome.

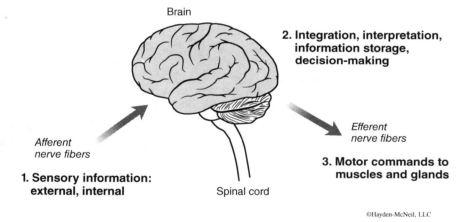

©Hayden-McNeil, LLC

**Figure 12-1.** Activity of the nervous system.

The nervous system has three types of activity.

• **Sensory** – the nervous system *detects* events and changes in existing conditions, either outside our bodies or inside our bodies. *External* stimuli originate from our surroundings or the surface of our skin. They include light, sound, warmth, cold, pressure, touch, etc. *Internal* stimuli originate from within our bodies. They include blood pressure, blood temperature, and the osmotic pressure of our body fluids. This is called **sensory activity**.

- **Integration, interpretation, information storage, decision-making** – the nervous system has the awesome capacity to integrate, interpret and store (as memories, skills) this sensory information, to decide whether action should be taken, and finally to determine what this action should be.

- **Motor** – the nervous system **sends commands** to muscles and glands, instructing them to take appropriate action: this is called **motor activity**.

The nerve cell or *neuron* is the functional cellular unit of the nervous system. Certain specialized nerve cells sense changes in the internal or external environment and transmit information about these events to the brain. This type of specialized nerve cell is called a **sensory receptor** (**NOTE**—not all sensory receptors are nerve cells: some are modified epithelial cells.).

Other nerve cells then gather and integrate this information. Still other nerve cells handle the motor responses to this information, and transmit impulses to the muscles and glands.

This activity calls for rapid transmission of information along the axons of nerve cells, as well as the ability for nerve cells to network by "talking" to other nerve cells. This goal is achieved by using electrical impulses to transmit information along axons, and chemical transmitters (*neurotransmitters*) to communicate from one nerve cell to another.

In the first of these chapters on the neurophysiology of the nervous system, we will review the organization of the nervous system, the histology of *neurons* and their associated *neuroglia*, and then discuss the electrical properties of nerve cells.

251

## OBJECTIVES

After listening to the lecture and reading this chapter, you should be able to:

1. Summarize the three basic **functions** of the nervous system.
2. Draw a diagram that shows the basic **divisions** of the nervous system.
3. In addition to **astrocytes**, name three other types of **neuroglial** cells and describe the functions that have been suggested for them.
4. Describe all the possible functions of **astrocytes**.
5. What can you say about **intracranial tumors**? What cells often give rise to them?
6. Name the three **functional types** of neurons.
7. **Draw** and **label** a neuron.
8. Describe how substances and organelles **move** up and down an **axon**. Name the terms used for this process.
9. Describe a **Schwann cell** and list its functions.
10. List the functions of the **myelin sheath**.
11. Describe the defect in **multiple sclerosis** and **Tay-Sachs disease**.
12. Describe how an injured nerve **regenerates**.
13. Define **neurotrophic factors**, which cells produce them, and what their functions may be.
14. Explain the use of the GHK equation and the Nernst equation for calculating membrane potentials. Be able to use these equations and calculate membrane potentials given various concentrations and permeabilities of ions.

15. Know the approximate value of the resting and action potential in mV.

16. List the **ion channels** that are found in the membrane of a neuron (refer to summary near the end of these notes—this summary applies to Chapters 12 and 13. It will be repeated in a little more detail in Chapter 13).

17. Explain how the **action potential** of a nerve cell is generated—draw a **diagram** of the action potential and how it relates to the number of open channels for **sodium** and **potassium** ions that exist at various times during the action potential. Superimpose curves for the changing membrane permeability to these ions during the action potential.

18. Define the **all-or-none** principle of nerve impulse transmission.

19. Discuss how nerve axon diameter is related to the thickness of the myelin sheath in mammals, and how this affects the velocity of conduction of the nerve impulse.

20. Describe our current thinking on how the nervous system is **wired up** properly during development.

## I. Divisions of the Nervous System

The nervous system is divided up as follows.

### A. Central Nervous System

The central nervous system has two components.
- *Brain* (has further subdivisions to be discussed later)
- *Spinal cord*

### B. Peripheral Nervous System

The nerves that connect the brain and spinal cord with the sensory receptors, muscles and glands make up the peripheral nervous system. The peripheral nervous system is divided up depending on whether nerve impulses travel from the periphery to the central nervous system (*sensory, afferent* fibers), or from the central nervous system to the periphery (*motor, efferent* fibers).

1. **Afferent (sensory) nerve fibers.**

   Convey information from the sensory receptors to the central nervous system.

2. **Efferent (motor) nerve fibers.**

   Convey instructions from the central nervous system to muscles and glands. These efferent neurons fall into two groups.

   a. *Somatic nerves* – the somatic nervous system innervates the skeletal muscles, is under voluntary, conscious control.

   b. *Autonomic nerves* – the autonomic nervous system innervates smooth muscle, the heart (cardiac muscle) and glands—it is not considered to be under true conscious control, and therefore involuntary. The autonomic nervous system has three divisions:

      - the *sympathetic* division
      - the *parasympathetic* division
      - the *enteric nervous system* (consists of neurons found in the gut, and in some ways can be regarded as an extension of the parasympathetic division).

Organs and muscles may be innervated by nerve fibers from both the sympathetic and parasympathetic divisions of the autonomic nervous system. When this happens, sympathetic stimulation often has an effect that is opposite to parasympathetic stimulation. For example, sympathetic stimulation increases heart rate, while parasympathetic stimulation decreases heart rate.

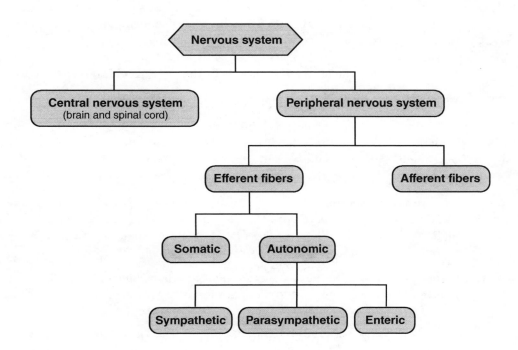

## II. Histology and Growth of Nerve Tissue

The nerve tissue of the brain and spinal cord consists of masses of nerve cells or **neurons** (the "little gray cells" that Agatha Christie's Hercule Poirot was fond of using for his deductive reasoning), in close association with non-neuronal cells called *neuroglial cells* or just **glial** cells.

### A. Neuroglia

*Neuroglia* means "nerve glue" (Greek), because at one time these cells were thought to hold the neurons of brain tissue together.

Neuroglial cells outnumber neurons by a factor of 9 to 1. Neuroglial cells make up 50% of the volume of the brain, and were once thought of as "support" cells for neurons. However, we now know that they are much more than that. Although we still do not fully understand all the functions of these cells in the nervous system, there has been an enormous increase in interest in them in recent years.

The following is a brief summary of our current knowledge of the four types of neuroglial cells found in the *central* nervous system. One of these four is the *oligodendrocyte*, which is the counterpart of the *Schwann cell* in the *peripheral nervous system*.

1. **Astrocytes.**

   Star-shaped cells found between neurons and blood vessels. Their processes cover nearly all the capillaries in the brain, and they also make contact with the surfaces of neurons. Astrocytes make up 50% in number of all the cells in the brain.

   - Astrocytes may have a nutritive function, and are important in the uptake of glucose from the capillaries supplying nervous tissue. They have special molecules in their plasma membranes that transport glucose into the interior of the astrocyte, where it produces two ATP molecules during glycolysis. The resulting pyruvate is then converted to lactate, which is passed on to neurons via the astrocyte processes. The lactate is then used by the neurons to produce energy.

   - Astrocytes are involved in the *uptake of neurotransmitters* released by neurons (e.g. *glutamate*, see later).

   - Additionally, astrocytes may act to modify the concentration of c*alcium in neurons* lying in contact with them, and so alter their excitability (responsiveness to signals).

   - Astrocytes are responsible for *homeostasis of ions* such as potassium in the surrounding medium. Astrocytes can also suck up potassium from the surrounding medium, acting to modify the firing rate of chattering neurons. By increasing the ratio of signal to noise, this increases "synaptic fidelity."

   - Astrocytes may even be involved in *signalling*, perhaps being able to listen to what neurons are saying, and to talk to other astrocytes via gap junctions and even to talk back to neurons.

   - On the darker side, astrocytes can undergo malignant transformation to form tumors called *astrocytomas* and *gliomas* (see the next page).

   - In certain regions of the brain, astrocytes may be responsible for inducing the formation of new neurons from stem cells.

2. **Oligodendrocytes.**

   Resemble astrocytes, but processes are fewer and shorter. Give support to neurons by arranging themselves in rows along nerve fibers. Produce a phospholipid *myelin sheath* around axons of neurons in the central nervous system [in the peripheral nervous system, this function is subserved by another type of glial cell, the *Schwann cell*—see later].

3. **Microglia.**

   Small cells with few processes. Like macrophages, they may originate from monocytes circulating in the blood. In fact, microglia seem to be the brain's macrophages. They phagocytize bacteria and cellular debris, and can migrate into an area of damaged nervous tissue. In this sense, they play a housekeeping role, and eat up neurons that may have been damaged or killed by disease, trauma, or whatever.

4. **Ependyma.**

   Cuboidal or columnar in shape and may have cilia. Form a continuous epithelial lining for the *ventricles* of the brain (spaces that contain the *cerebrospinal fluid*) and the *central canal* of the spinal cord.

254

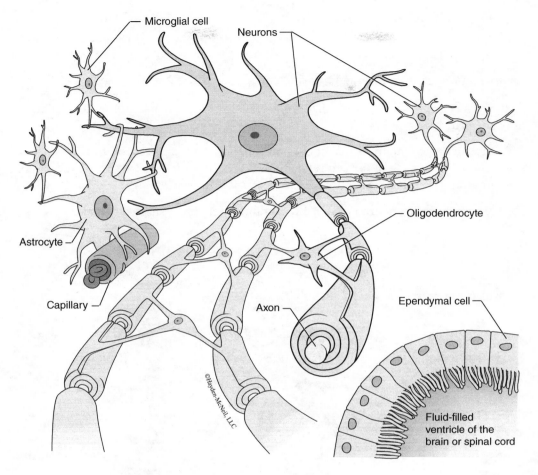

**Figure 12-2.** Neuroglial cells.

## B. Tumors Formed by Glial Cells

Glial cells can develop into tumors.

1. **Astrocytomas** develop from astrocytes. They are often low-grade tumors. Survival can be over several years and the tumors can be easily removed.

2. **Glioblastomas** (= **gliomas**) are another story. Usually, gliomas arise from malignant transformation of astrocytes. They are high-grade tumors and survival is usually less than two years. They spread easily into surrounding brain tissue, and are therefore almost impossible to remove completely by surgical means. In humans, gliomas account for more than 60% of primary intracranial neoplasms (tumors). Approximately 20,000 people are diagnosed each year in the United States.

   The cells in gliomas secrete *growth factors* (*vascular endothelial growth factor*, VEGF, is the name given to one of them) that stimulate blood vessels to proliferate, so that the tumor is well-supplied with the nutrients that promote its growth and enlargement.

3. **Oligodendrogliomas** develop from oligodendrocytes and may be operable in their early stages.

### C. Neurons—Types

On the basis of *structural* differences, neurons are divided into four types—bipolar, sensory, multipolar, and pyramidal.

More importantly, neurons can be divided into three types on the basis of *what they do*.

1. **Sensory neurons** – neurons that are involved in conveying sensory information to the central nervous system.

2. **Interneurons** – neurons that convey information from one neuron to another neuron. In some parts of the central nervous system, interneurons inhibit or stop other neurons from firing. Such interneurons are said to be inhibitory.

3. **Motor neurons** – neurons that convey motor commands, usually to skeletal muscles.

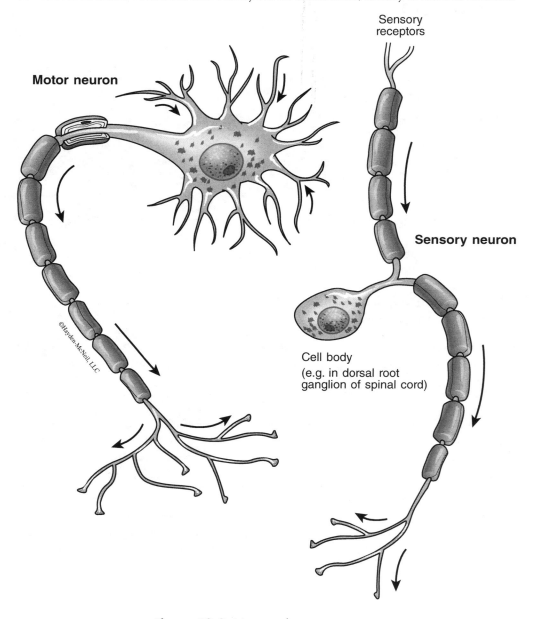

**Figure 12-3.** Motor and sensory neurons.

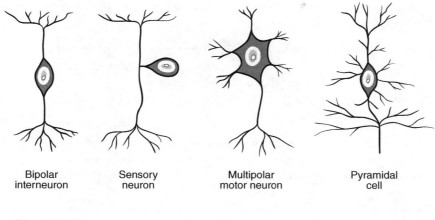

Bipolar          Sensory          Multipolar          Pyramidal
interneuron      neuron           motor neuron        cell

©Hayden-McNeil, LLC

**Figure 12-4.** Types of neurons.

## D. Neurons—Structure

Neurons have three parts.

1. **Cell body.**

   In addition to the usual items found in all cells (e.g. mitochondria), neurons contain *neurofibrils* and *Nissl bodies* or *Nissl granules*. The latter are modified rough endoplasmic reticulum, and function in protein synthesis.

2. **Dendrites.**

   Short and highly branched. Function is to conduct nerve impulses *toward* the cell body. The dendrites of many neurons are covered with dendritic spines or knobs. These are sites where synapses with other neurons occur.

3. **Axon.**

   A long thin tubular process arising from the *axon hillock* on the cell body. The axon conducts nerve impulses *away* from the cell body to another neuron or muscle or gland cells.

   Axons give off branches called *collaterals*, and their *axon terminals* have many specialized, bulb-like endings that are called *synaptic end bulbs* or *presynaptic terminals*. The presynaptic terminals are in close contact with the plasma membranes of other cells (other neurons, muscle cells or gland cells).

   The specialized structure formed at the point of close contact between the presynaptic terminal and the plasma membrane of the receiving cell is called a *synapse*. It is at this point that the neuron is able to "talk" to another neuron, a muscle or a gland, usually by means of a chemical *neurotransmitter* released by the presynaptic terminal. We'll talk more about synapses in the next chapter.

   Since the axon is a very long and narrow tube, substances cannot easily pass from the body of the neuron to the axon terminals by simple diffusion. Instead, there are special transport mechanisms.

257

- *Axoplasmic flow* – a slow process which is responsible for carrying soluble proteins synthesized in the cell body down to the axon terminals.

- *Axonal transport* – a faster, ATP-requiring process. This process is involved in the transport of organelles (such as synaptic vesicles, mitochondria) through the axon. The transport occurs on the surfaces of *microtubules*, also known as *neurotubules*. These are fine threads composed of special proteins that course inside the axon along its entire length.

- *Retrograde axonal transport* – axonal transport is not just a one-way process: it operates in both directions. Retrograde axonal transport is the opposite of *anterograde axonal transport*, and can move particles toward the neuronal cell body. Herpes, polio and rabies viruses can hitch a ride on this system, and make their way from the surface of the body via the axons of neurons into the cell bodies of the neurons themselves.

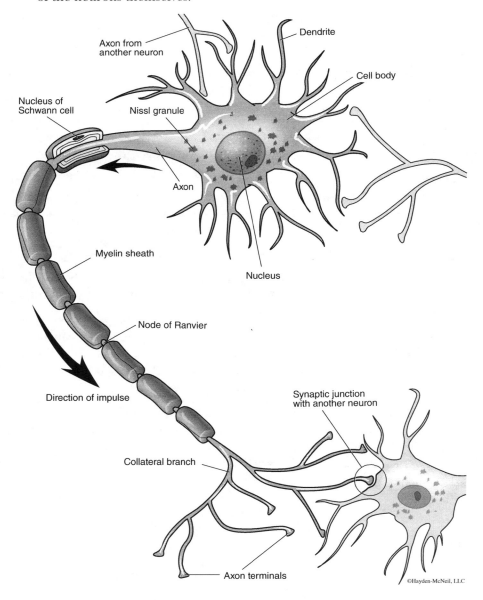

**Figure 12-5.** Structure of a neuron.

### E. Schwann Cells, the Myelin Sheath, Multiple Sclerosis, and Other Diseases Involving Myelin

Many axons, especially those outside the central nervous system, are covered by a multi-layered, white, **phospholipid**, segmented covering called a *myelin sheath*. Such axons are called *myelinated axons* (sometimes they are called *medullated* axons). The myelin sheath is an electrical insulator, and accelerates the conduction velocity of the nerve impulse by as much as ten times (see later).

The myelin sheath is formed by the Schwann cells, which are the prime target of the bacterium that causes leprosy (*Mycobacterium leprae*). The myelin sheath is also destroyed in diseases such as *multiple sclerosis*. Multiple sclerosis affects 300,000 Americans. It affects the brain and spinal cord. Like myasthenia gravis, multiple sclerosis is believed to be an *autoimmune disease* in which the body's immune system destroys the myelin sheath. Myelin speeds up the rate at which axons conduct nerve signals from one part of the nervous system to another. Damage to the myelin either slows down the nerve signals or blocks them altogether. The cause of MS is not known, although there is a theory that a viral infection (measles, mumps, herpes) acquired before the age of 15 may trigger the disease in individuals who have a genetic tendency to develop it. The phenomenon may be due to "molecular mimicry," to be discussed next semester.

Other diseases affecting myelin or storage of myelin lipids within the body of the neuron include Acute Disseminated Encephalomyelitis, leukodystrophies and neuronal lipidoses. The hereditary neurodegenerative condition known as Tay-Sachs disease belongs to the latter category.

259

Myelinated nerve fibers look white, and masses of them constitute the *white matter* of the brain and spinal cord. Unmyelinated fibers and nerve cells appear gray, and comprise the *gray matter* of the brain and spinal cord (see later).

The myelin sheath serves to speed up the nerve impulse by a factor of as much as ten times. In peripheral nerves, it is composed of the membranes of flattened glial cells called *Schwann cells*. In many ways, the Schwann cell of the peripheral nervous system is equivalent to the oligodendrocyte that is responsible for the production of myelin sheaths in the **central** nervous system. However, Schwann cells produce *neurotrophic factors*, that promote axonal regeneration, whereas oligodendrocytes seem to have proteins that inhibit axonal regeneration.

The Schwann cells wrap themselves around the axon many times, like a bandage around a finger. The outermost layer of this bandage is that part of the Schwann cell that contains the nucleus and cytoplasm, and is called the neurilemma or neurilemmal sheath.

Schwann cells have two important roles.

• They form the myelin sheath that speeds up the conduction of nervous impulses.

• They are important in the regeneration of damaged axons.

## F. Regeneration of Nerve Axons

Around six months of age, the cell bodies of most developing nerve cells lose their mitotic apparatus (centrioles and mitotic spindles) and their ability to replicate (= divide). The differentiated neuron, unlike the cells of epithelial tissue, has only limited powers of regeneration in humans (recently, however, it has been shown that the adult brain harbors stem cells that have the ability to differentiate into neurons).

Damaged **peripheral** myelinated axons, however, can often regrow if the cell body remains intact. Initially, that part of the axon severed from its cell body dies. The myelin sheath breaks down and is removed by phagocytic cells. The Schwann cells remain alive and capable of multiplying. They secrete **neurotrophic factors** (see next section) that may be important in regenerating the damaged axon.

In the early stages of this limited axonal regeneration, the proximal end of the cut axon starts to send out *axonal sprouts*. The Schwann cells then start to multiply and form rows along the course previously taken by the axon. *Growth cones* of sprouting axons are guided at the rate of 1 millimeter per day along these lines of Schwann cells and may re-innervate the muscle or other structure involved. Surgical reattachment of the ends of the completely severed nerve is beneficial in establishing a clear pathway of Schwann cells that can be easily followed by the growing axon.

In the central nervous system, however, myelin is produced by *oligodendrocytes*. When this myelin degenerates after injury, a variety of inhibitory substances prevent axonal sprouting. Some of these substances are proteoglycans. Additionally, any regenerating sprouts from the severed axon usually fail to penetrate scar tissue that is formed by astrocytes. Successful attempts to promote regeneration of axons in severed spinal cords have involved the use of peripheral nerves as bridges between the cut ends of the spinal cord. Multiple intercostal nerve grafts were used in experimental rats with complete spinal cord transections. It was found that the previously totally paralyzed hind limbs gradually recovered some function after a period of six months. This work was done in 1996 by Cheng, Cao and Olson at the Karolinska Institute in Stockholm, Sweden.

## G. Neurogenesis—Production of New Neurons

New neurons can form from stem cells in the adult brain. This has been shown to occur in the dentate gyrus (hippocampus), where they integrate into existing circuits. There are also signs of neurogenesis near the striatum, which is important for cognitive function and motor control.

## H. Neurotrophic Factors

*Neurotrophic factors* are proteins that include nerve growth factor (NGF), brain-derived neurotrophic factor (BDNF), glial cell-derived neurotrophic factor (GDNF), ciliary neurotrophic factor (CTNF) and neurotrophin-3.

Neurotrophic factors can be released by neurons, astrocytes, Schwann cells, and cells that make connections with axon terminals (e.g. skeletal muscle cells).

Neurotrophic factors are important to neurons in the following ways.

1. **Growth, differentiation and survival of neurons in the developing nervous system.**

   Neurotrophic factors are important during early development of the nervous system, when they are responsible for the growth and development of neurons, for survival of neurons, and for maintaining them in functional condition.

2. **Maintenance of neurons in the mature nervous system.**

   In the adult nervous system, neurotrophic factors are involved in the survival of neurons, and for maintaining them in functional condition. In the absence of neurotrophic factors, neurons will die.

3. **In experimental situations, neurotrophic factors can stimulate regrowth of damaged neurons.**

   Neurotrophic factors can make damaged neurons regrow their axons in experimental situations, and therefore they present opportunities for reversing the damage caused to neurons by trauma and by degenerative diseases such as *Alzheimer's disease, Huntington's disease, Parkinson's disease* and *amyotrophic lateral sclerosis (ALS; Lou Gehrig's disease)*.

Neurotrophic factors can act on the *neuron cell body* by affecting its growth, differentiation, migration during development, and also by affecting transcription and protein synthesis.

Neurotrophic factors can act on a*xons* and *dendrites* by affecting their sprouting and the transport of substances within them.

261

Neurotrophic factors can play a role in developing synapses and in the maintenance of the *target cells*, such as muscle cells.

Neurotrophic factors act on nerve cells by binding to special proteins in the plasma membrane. These proteins are called *neurotrophic factor **receptors***. These receptors are found on axon terminals or on the cell bodies of neurons. One neurotrophic factor receptor is called *trk (tyrosine kinase),* and binds *nerve growth factor* (NGF). NGF acts mainly on neurons that use the neurotransmitter acetylcholine. Another receptor is called *trk B* (*tyrosine kinase B*), which binds *brain-derived growth factor* (BDNF).

## I. How the Axons of Neurons Are Guided to Their Targets during Development of the Nervous System

For the nervous system to work properly, it must be wired up properly. During development, axons grow out from the cell bodies of neurons, and their *growth cones* are guided to the right destinations. Neurons that do not reach their targets die by the process of apoptosis. Neurons that have made inappropriate connections also die by *apoptosis*.

*Axonal or growth cone guidance*, as it is called, comes under the control of various molecules. Some are found on the surfaces of cells and act at short range. Others (the netrins and semaphorins) are soluble proteins that are secreted by cells and act over longer distances. These molecules may act as attractants or as repellants to the tip of the growing axon.

### III. Electrical Properties of Cells—The Resting Potential

### A. The Electrical Potential across a Membrane—The Resting Potential

In a resting neuron (one that is not transmitting an impulse) the inner surface of the plasma membrane is negatively charged compared with its external surface. The cell membrane is then said to be *electrically polarized*. The difference in electrical potential ("voltage") between the two sides of the membrane is referred to as the *resting potential* or *membrane potential*. Typically, the resting potential is 60–100 millivolts (a millivolt is one-thousandth of a volt, so 100 millivolts is one-tenth of a volt).

### B. The Ionic Permeability of the Membrane of a Resting Neuron

In a resting neuron, the cell membrane is very permeable to $K^+$ and $Cl^-$. It is not very permeable to $Na^+$ and is impermeable to the large, negatively charged proteins and other organic molecules in the cell interior. These negatively charged molecules may be thought of as "fixed" negative charges. An *ATP-driven pump* in the membrane pumps three sodium ions out of the cell, and two potassium ions into the cell. This is an example of *active transport, where ions are pumped against their concentration gradients.* The result is a highly unequal distribution of ions across the cell membrane, with a high concentration of sodium ions outside the cell and a high concentration of potassium ions inside the cell. The membrane potential depends on maintaining this distribution of ions on either side of the membrane. Therefore, it is essential that there is a supply of ATP to power the sodium/potassium exchange pump.

### C. Concentrations of Various Ions Inside and Outside the Neuron

Concentrations of MAJOR ions inside and outside a typical neuronal cell are as follows (Note that concentrations are given in *millimoles*. A mole is the molecular weight in grams, and contains about $10^{23}$ atoms or ions of the element in question).

| Ion | Inside Cell (millimoles/liter) | Outside Cell (millimoles/liter) | Nernst Potential (millivolts) |
|---|---|---|---|
| $Na^+$ | 7 | 144 | +81 |
| $K^+$ | 151 | 4 | −97 |
| $Cl^-$ | 4 | 114 | −90 |
| $Ca^{++}$ | $10^{-7}\,M$ | $10^{-3}\,M$ | +123 |
| Negatively charged proteins | approximately 50 | 1 | |

DON'T FORGET THAT OTHER IONS ARE ALSO PRESENT, but they do not affect our present discussion about the resting potential of the cell. Examples are $HCO_3^-$, $PO_4^{--}$, $SO_4^{--}$, $Mg^{++}$. Calcium is **very** important in muscle contraction and in the release of neurotransmitters at the axon terminal—we will talk about that in the next chapter.

## D. A Qualitative Explanation for the Resting Potential

**How do we get the resting potential?**

1.  For the resting potential, we will only consider potassium ions. This is because the resting membrane is very permeable to potassium ions but not very permeable to sodium ions. The high potassium permeability is caused by the presence in the membrane of large numbers of *potassium leak channels*.

2.  The resting membrane is impermeable to the **negatively charged proteins** and other large organic molecules inside the cell. They are too big to diffuse through the plasma membrane, and there are no pores in the membrane to allow them to pass through it.

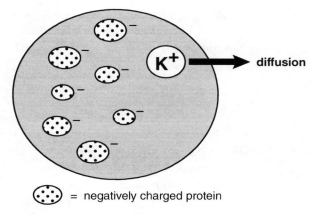

= negatively charged protein

3.  Given a high concentration of potassium ions within the cell, given that the cell membrane is permeable to potassium ions and impermeable to negatively charged proteins within the cell, how does a resting membrane potential develop? **At first, positively charged potassium ions start diffusing out of the cell through their leak channels.** They diffuse outward because their concentration is much higher inside the cell than outside (see table on previous page).

    But that cannot go on. The negatively charged proteins inside the cell cannot diffuse out. The result is that the inside of the cell becomes more and more negatively charged as positively charged potassium ions leak out.

    This negative charge creates a potential gradient that **tends to draw positively charged potassium ions back into the cell**.

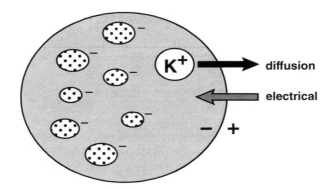

4. When the electrical forces drawing potassium ions into the cell balance the diffusion forces driving potassium ions out of the cell, there is a potential (voltage) across the membrane called the resting potential. This potential can be calculated to be about −97 millivolts (see equations in the next section).

$$E_K = 61.5 \log_{10} \frac{[K_{out}]}{[K_{in}]} = 61.5 \log_{10} \frac{4}{151} = -97 \, mV$$

5. However, there is a problem. The resting membrane is slightly permeable to sodium ions, and so sodium is continually and slowly leaking into the nerve fiber. *If this were allowed to continue, the concentrations of potassium and sodium ions inside and outside the membrane would equalize and the resting membrane potential would become zero*. This highlights the importance of the ATP-driven sodium/potassium exchange pump, which pumps out any sodium ions that leak into the cell and exchanges them for potassium. This pump therefore maintains the low concentration of sodium ions inside the cell, and keeps the concentration of potassium ions high.

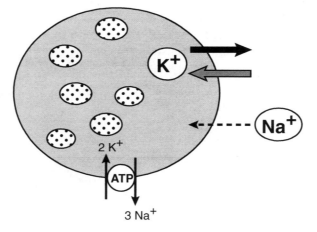

The maintenance of the resting potential therefore requires a constant supply of ATP, provided by oxidative phosphorylation. That is why nervous tissue in general and the brain in particular depend for their function on a good supply of oxygen.

### E. Calculation of Membrane Potentials: The Goldman-Hodgkin-Katz (GHK) Equation and the Nernst Equation

We can calculate membrane potential $E_m$ from the Goldman-Hodgkin-Katz equation. Only potassium, sodium and chloride are shown, but other ions can be added, inserted or subtracted.

$$E_m = \frac{RT}{F} \log_e \frac{P_{Na}[Na_{out}] + P_K[K_{out}] + P_{Cl}[Cl_{in}]}{P_{Na}[Na_{in}] + P_K[K_{in}] + P_{Cl}[Cl_{out}]}$$

*R = ideal gas constant; T = absolute temperature (degrees Kelvin); F = Faraday's constant; P = permeability of ion*

$[K_{out}]$ = concentration of potassium ions outside the cell

$[K_{in}]$ = concentration of potassium ions inside the cell

The same applies to sodium and chloride.

*At 37°C, the term before the bracket can be reduced to 61.5 $\log_{10}$*

Since the resting membrane has a very low permeability to sodium and a high permeability for potassium, and if we ignore chloride at this time, the GHK equation simplifies to the Nernst equation, where the only ion that is important in determining the membrane potential is potassium (37°C). (Walther Hermann Nernst was a German scientist who received the 1920 Nobel Prize in Chemistry for his work in thermochemistry.)

$$E_K = 61.5 \log_{10} \frac{[K_{out}]}{[K_{in}]} = 61.5 \log_{10} \frac{4}{151} = -97 \, mV$$

Where $E_K$ is the potassium Nernst potential

$[K_{out}]$ = concentration of potassium ions outside the cell

$[K_{in}]$ = concentration of potassium ions inside the cell

If the membrane were highly permeable to sodium and not permeable to potassium, then we could ignore potassium and the inner surface of the plasma membrane would be positively charged with respect to the outer surface by the amount of the sodium Nernst potential, which is +81 mV.

$$E_{Na} = 61.5 \log_{10} \frac{[Na_{out}]}{[Na_{in}]} = 61.5 \log_{10} \frac{144}{7} = +81 \, mV$$

If we are dealing with a negatively charged ion such as chloride, then the equation is written:

$$E_{Cl} = -61.5 \log_{10} \frac{[Cl^-_{out}]}{[Cl^-_{in}]} \quad \text{or} \quad E_{Cl} = 61.5 \log_{10} \frac{[Cl^-_{in}]}{[Cl^-_{out}]}$$

If the membrane were permeable to both sodium and potassium, then the membrane potential would be calculated along the lines of the GHK equation as follows:

$$E_m = 61.5 \log_{10} \frac{P_K[K_{out}] + P_{Na}[Na_{out}]}{P_K[K_{in}] + P_{Na}[Na_{in}]}$$

Where $P_K$ and $P_{Na}$ are the permeabilities of the membrane to potassium and sodium, respectively. You can see that if the membrane is not permeable to sodium ($P_{Na} = 0$), sodium drops out of the equation, $P_{Na}$ cancels out and we get the Nernst equation for potassium.

## IV. The Action Potential of a Nerve Cell

Some nerve cells are specialized as *sensory receptors*, and are excited when they (or their nerve endings) are exposed to light, heat, pressure, touch, sound, etc. Other nerve cells respond to signals coming from neurons that connect with them by special junctions called *synapses* (next chapter). These signals are often chemical agents called neurotransmitters.

Often a signal (either due to the neurotransmitter or a stimulus such as pressure, touch, sound, etc.) will act to make the inside of the cell membrane less negative with respect to the outside, in which case it is said to **depolarize** the membrane. Depolarization events can occur in graded steps.

When a depolarization event changes the membrane potential to a value called the *threshold*, an **action potential** is generated. At threshold (usually about −55mV), the membrane, which has previously been almost impermeable to sodium ions, starts to become highly permeable to them. In fact, the permeability of the membrane to sodium ions becomes much, much greater than the permeability of the membrane to potassium ions. The sudden increase in permeability to sodium is due to the opening in the cell membrane of *voltage-gated sodium channels*.

**Result?** When the membrane permeability to sodium ($P_{Na}$) increases far above potassium because of these newly-opened sodium channels, sodium now dominates the equation for the membrane potential:

$$E_m = 61.5 \log_{10} \frac{P_K[K_{out}] + P_{Na}[Na_{out}]}{P_K[K_{in}] + P_{Na}[Na_{in}]}$$

Consequently, the membrane potential swings away from the potassium resting potential of −97mV and moves toward the sodium potential of +81mV.

$$E_{Na} = 61.5 \log_{10} \frac{[Na_{out}]}{[Na_{in}]} = 61.5 \log_{10} \frac{144}{7} = +81 \, mV$$

The sudden depolarization of the membrane caused by an initial threshold depolarization event is the first phase of the **action potential**.

The action potential is an *all-or-none response*—the initial small depolarization of the membrane is either sufficient to reach threshold and trigger an action potential, or it isn't (remember we talked about the all-or-none response when we discussed muscle stimulation).

Like swing doors, the voltage-gated sodium channels remain open for only a short time, then they start to swing closed (this is simplified). Sodium permeability then drops below potassium permeability ($P_K$), so returning the membrane potential back to its resting condition, which is often close to the potassium Nernst potential.

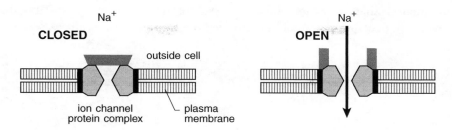

**Figure 12-6.** Simplified diagram of a closed and open voltage-gated sodium channel.

The return of the membrane potential back to its resting value is accelerated because the potassium permeability actually *rises* above its resting value for a short period of time. The transient rise of potassium permeability is due to the presence of slowly-opening *voltage-gated potassium channels* in the membrane. Since the potassium leak channels are always open, the membrane actually becomes *more* permeable to potassium than it was during the resting phase. This causes a transient hyperpolarization or overswing at the terminal phase of the action potential. Finally, the voltage-gated potassium channels close, and the membrane returns to the resting potential.

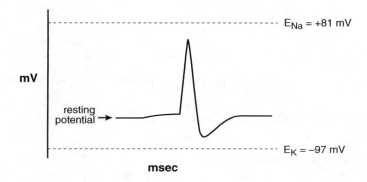

**Figure 12-7.** Action potential.

Put simply, the action potential represents a rapid swing of membrane potential from its resting potassium potential toward the sodium potential (which it never reaches) and back again.

During an action potential, the nerve will not respond to further stimuli, and is said to be in its **refractory period**.

267

The sodium ions that enter the neuron as a result of the slight "leak" at rest and during the generation of action potentials are pumped out by the *ATP-driven sodium pump*.

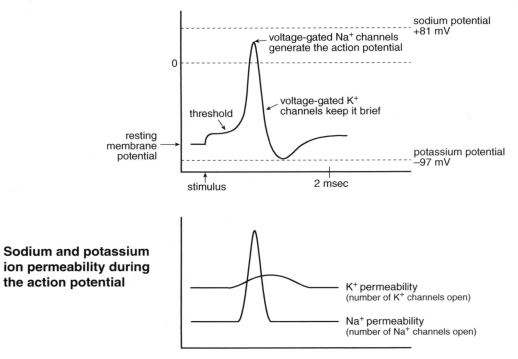

**Sodium and potassium ion permeability during the action potential**

**Figure 12-8.** Action potential and membrane permeability to sodium and potassium ions.

## V. Summary of Ion Channels You Must Know

Some of the following ion channels will be dealt with in the next chapter. Many of these channels can be classified according to whether they are just leak channels, whether they are controlled by transmembrane voltage, or whether they are controlled by neurotransmitters.

| Type | Ion |
|---|---|
| Leak channels | potassium |
| | sodium |
| Voltage-gated channels | potassium |
| | calcium |
| Transmitter-gated channels | sodium and other cations* |
| (controlled by serotonin, acetylcholine, glutamate, GABA, glycine) | chloride |

\* Cations are positively charged ions, e.g. $Na^+$ $K^+$ $Ca^{++}$
Anions are negatively charged ions, e.g. $Cl^-$

## VI. Propagation of an Action Potential Along a Nerve Fiber

When an action potential is triggered at the beginning of a nerve fiber, it causes the next region of the nerve fiber membrane to depolarize, also generating an action potential. This is repeated continuously, and the wave of depolarization (i.e. the nerve impulse) travels all the way along the fiber until it reaches the axon terminals.

Behind this wave of depolarization, the nerve fiber repolarizes again, as shown in the diagram.

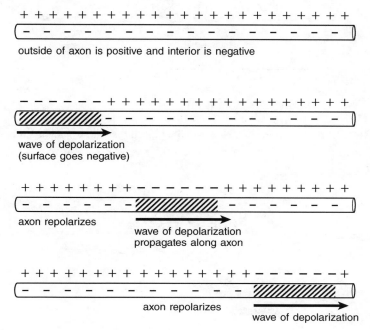

**Figure 12-9.** Propagation of action potential.

Nerve impulses travel along different nerve fibers at different speeds. The conduction velocity along a nerve fiber is determined by the diameter of the nerve fiber. Myelin is found in vertebrates. In mammals, axon diameter seems to determine the degree of myelination.

- Small diameter fibers in mammals have little or no myelin and are slow-conducting.

- Large diameter fibers in mammals have a thick myelinated sheath and are fast-conducting (some invertebrates, such as the squid, have very large diameter nerve axons: although they are not covered with myelin, their diameter is so large that conduction velocities are very high). The myelin sheath (formed by Schwann cells) is interrupted at intervals along its length by patches where the plasma membrane of the underlying nerve axon is exposed. These patches of membrane, which are very rich in voltage-gated sodium channels, are called *nodes of Ranvier*. Myelin is an electrical insulator. An action potential developed at one node of Ranvier therefore depolarizes the next node of Ranvier without having to generate action potentials in the intervening, insulated segment of nerve. The nerve impulse therefore "jumps" from one node to the next (*saltatory conduction*—see Figure 12-11).

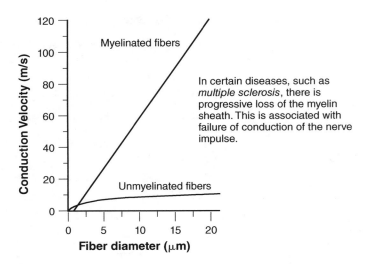

**Figure 12-10.** Conduction velocity increases with fiber diameter in myelinated and unmyelinated fibers. Conduction velocity of myelinated fibers is always greater than unmyelinated fibers.

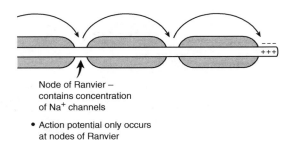

**Figure 12-11.** Saltatory conduction in a myelinated nerve fiber. The myelin sheath is interrupted at intervals by nodes of Ranvier, which have a high concentration of voltage-gated sodium channels. This permits saltatory (= jumping) conduction (curved arrows).

# 13

# NEUROPHYSIOLOGY II
The Synapse, Neurotransmitters, and Neural Networks

## CHAPTER OUTLINE

## DESCRIPTION AND INTRODUCTION

The central nervous system consists of networks containing billions of neurons. In order to function in these networks, neurons must be able to talk to each other. Additionally, motor neurons must be able to communicate with muscle and glandular epithelial cells, issuing them direct commands to contract or secrete.

Neurons talk to each other and to other cell types (muscle cells, glandular epithelium) via special junctional structures between their axon terminals and the plasma membrane of the receiving cells. These specialized structures are called *synapses* or synaptic junctions. The *neuromuscular junction* is one type of synapse that we have discussed already. The synapse is vital to the functioning of the nervous system.

Special chemical substances called *neurotransmitters* carry signals across synaptic junctions (there are electrical synapses as well, but they do not concern us here). *Acetylcholine* is the neurotransmitter at the neuromuscular junction, but it is also found in many parts of the central nervous system. In addition to acetylcholine, there are many more neurotransmitters, and we will list them in this chapter.

The **receiving** cell (= *postsynaptic cell* or *postsynaptic neuron*) typically receives input from a large number of transmitting cells (= *presynaptic cell* or *presynaptic neuron*). In some cases this input is excitatory, in others it is inhibitory.

Neurotransmitters may therefore excite the postsynaptic neuron – they give it a **GO** signal.

Alternatively, they may inhibit the postsynaptic neuron – give it a **STOP** signal.

Related molecules called *neuromodulators* serve to alter (or modulate) the activity of neurons.

Finally, we discuss how neurons are arranged in *neuronal networks*. These networks, often composed of many neurons talking to each other with different neurotransmitters through many different synapses, are important in the functioning of the central nervous system.

## OBJECTIVES

After listening to the lecture and reading this chapter, you should be able to:

1.  **Draw** a **synapse**, and label its various components.
2.  Describe what happens at the synapse when an **action potential** arrives at the presynaptic terminal and after **neurotransmitter** has been released by exocytosis from the **synaptic vesicles**.
3.  Define what is meant by "**presynaptic**" and "**postsynaptic**."
4.  What actions do different neurotransmitters have on the **ion channels** and **electrical potential** of the plasma membrane of the postsynaptic (receiving) cell?
5.  Define an **EPSP—draw a diagram** showing the change in membrane potential associated with an EPSP.
6.  Name the four major classes of **neurotransmitters**.
7.  Name the **neurotransmitters** in each class.
8.  Which ion channels are acted on by **inhibitory** neurotransmitters? **Name** the inhibitory neurotransmitters.
9.  Which ion channels are acted on by **excitatory** neurotransmitters? **Name** the excitatory neurotransmitters.
10. Use the Goldman-Hodgkin-Katz equation to explain how the channels opened by excitatory and inhibitory neurotransmitters affect the membrane potential and the excitability of a neuron.
11. Explain what is meant by an IPSP, and use the Goldman-Hodgkin-Katz equation to account for the fact that an IPSP is not always observed when a neuron is acted on by an inhibitory neurotransmitter.
12. **Draw diagrams** to explain **temporal** summation and **spatial** summation of EPSPs: explain how excitatory and inhibitory input into a neuron is integrated.

13. Describe *two* methods by which a neurotransmitter is **inactivated** after it has had its effect—give examples, naming the neurotransmitter and the method of inactivation.

14. Define what is meant by **long-term potentiation**.

15. Define a **neuromodulator**.

16. Describe all the **disorders of the nervous system** mentioned in these notes that are tied to neurons that use a particular neurotransmitter.

17. Describe four ways in which **drugs** can act at synapses, and give examples.

18. Draw diagrams explaining the meaning of **convergence** and **divergence** as these terms apply to neural networks.

19. Draw a diagram of a **negative feedback circuit** that includes an interneuron.

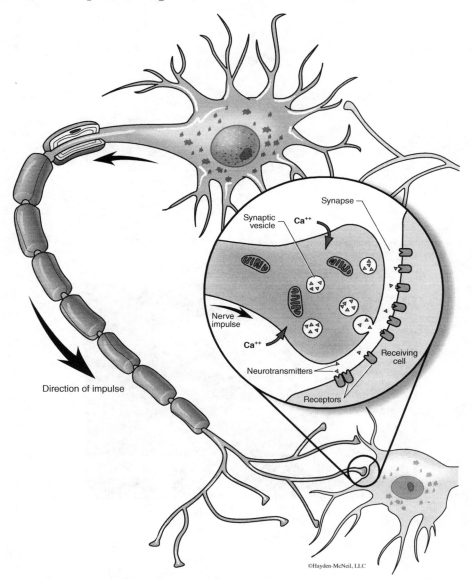

©Hayden-McNeil, LLC

**Figure 13-1.** Synaptic transmission.

## I. Synapses

Neurons in neuronal circuits talk to each other and other cell types (muscle cells, glandular epithelium cells) across special junctions between them called synapses. An example of a rather specialized synapse is the neuromuscular junction, which we have dealt with in a previous chapter.

The synapse is a particularly important structure, because it is involved in integration of signals converging on a neuron and is almost certainly important in the learning process. It is also important to note that synapses transmit impulses only in one direction—from the presynaptic (transmitting) neuron to the postsynaptic (receiving) neuron.

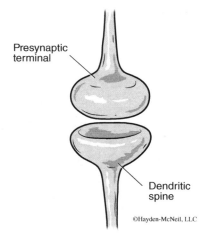

**Figure 13-2.** Synapses are often located on the dendritic spines of the receiving neuron.

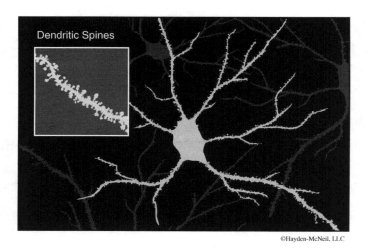

**Figure 13-3.** Dendritic spines.

Axon terminals of neurons end in bulblike structures variously called *synaptic end bulbs*, *axon end bulbs*, *synaptic knobs*, *presynaptic terminals*. The presynaptic terminals of the axon of the presynaptic neuron may synapse with dendritic spines, the cell body or *axon hillock* of the postsynaptic neuron (the axon hillock is where action potentials are first generated in the neuron). Dendritic spines are labile structures and are subject to pruning. They can also be formed and may play a role in memory.

Most of my diagrams show only a few synapses on a neuron, but you should realize that in the real world a neuron may have an enormous number of synapses making contact with it. In fact, *thousands of synapses may occur on the cell body and dendrites of a neuron, and they may cover as much as 40% of its surface. Some of these synapses excite the neuron, some inhibit it.*

The synapse is a very specialized structure. At a synaptic junction, the membranes of the pre- and postsynaptic neurons are separated by a little gap. This gap is called the *synaptic cleft.*

The presynaptic (transmitting) neuron talks to the postsynaptic (receiving) neuron across the synaptic cleft. It does so by releasing a chemical signalling agent called a neurotransmitter. The following is a list of important neurotransmitters. There are six of them, plus a large group of small proteins called **neuropeptides**.

- **acetylcholine**
- **norepinephrine** (= **noradrenalin**)
- **dopamine**
- **serotonin**
- **glutamic acid**
- **gamma-amino butyric acid** (**GABA**)
- **neuropeptides** (the **endorphins**, **dynorphin**, **enkephalin**, **substance P**, and **somatostatin**).

## SIR BERNARD KATZ (d. 2003)

275

Nobel Prize in 1970 (jointly with Ulf von Euler of Sweden and Julius Axelrod of the United States).

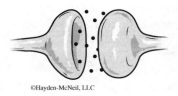

©Hayden-McNeil, LLC

© Godfrey Argent Studio

*'for their discoveries concerning the humoral transmitters in the nerve terminals and the mechanism for their storage, release and inactivation'.*

**Figure 13-4.**

A neuron normally uses only **one neurotransmitter** to talk to other neurons. If the neurotransmitter is acetylcholine, the transmitting neuron is said to be **cholinergic.** If the neurotransmitter is norepinephrine (noradrenalin), the neuron is said to be **adrenergic.** If the neurotransmitter is dopamine, the neuron is said to be **dopaminergic.** And so on....

**Neurotransmitters are packaged in synaptic vesicles.**

The presynaptic terminals enclose numerous *synaptic vesicles*, essentially little balloons of membrane that contain neurotransmitters. Some of these vesicles are attached ("docked") to the presynaptic plasma membrane in the region of the active zone. In addition to these docked, ready-to-use vesicles, there is also a large reserve of vesicles within the synaptic knob.

The docked vesicles are primed to release their neurotransmitter contents when a nerve impulse arrives at the presynaptic terminal, and the empty vesicles are recycled and refilled with neurotransmitter before being used again. The sequence of events is as follows.

1.  **Depolarization and opening of voltage-gated calcium channels.**

    The nerve impulse causes depolarization of the presynaptic membrane, and opens special *voltage-gated calcium channels* that occur in high densities near the docked, primed vesicles.

2.  **Entry of calcium ions.**

    Calcium ions enter the presynaptic terminal from the extracellular space (the concentration of calcium in the extracellular space is 10,000 times that inside most cells). The channels which permit calcium to enter are *voltage-gated calcium channels*. Therefore, the concentration of calcium ions in the interior of the presynaptic terminal increases.

3.  **Exocytosis of neurotransmitter.**

    In a complicated way that involves a variety of weirdly-named proteins (examples: synaptotagmins, synaptobrevins or VAMPs, and SNAP-25) this calcium entry causes the docked and primed vesicles to fuse with the presynaptic plasma membrane and release their neurotransmitter contents into the synaptic cleft (the process is a form of *exocytosis*). In central nervous system synapses, about 10–20 vesicles are involved.

4.  **Recycling of empty synaptic vesicle membranes.**

    The empty synaptic vesicle membranes are endocytosed and move back into the cell interior. They are rebuilt into vesicles, which take up neurotransmitter. When they have been refilled with neurotransmitter they move back to the active zone, where they dock with the plasma membrane and become primed and ready for action once again.

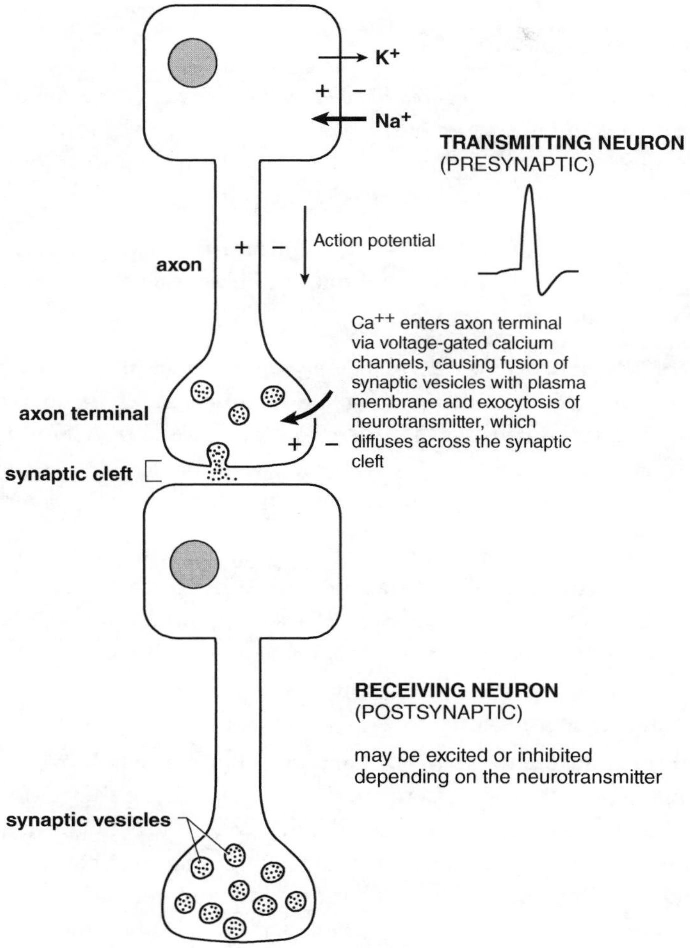

**Figure 13-5.** The action potential propagates along the axon and arrives at the axon terminal, causing release of neurotransmitter by calcium-induced exocytosis.

After its release, the neurotransmitter diffuses rapidly across the synaptic cleft, and combines with specialized membrane *receptors* on the postsynaptic membrane—that is, the membrane of the receiving neuron. The time needed for the neurotransmitter to be released, carry its message across the synaptic cleft, bind to its postsynaptic membrane receptor and cause the postsynaptic (receiving) cell to respond is about 0.5 msec. This half of one thousandth of a second is called the *synaptic delay*.

## II. Synaptic Transmission

As stated above, the neurotransmitter released by the axon terminals of the presynaptic neuron carries its message by diffusing across the synaptic cleft and combining with its receptors on the postsynaptic membrane (usually a dendrite of the receiving neuron).

Neurotransmitters usually open ion channels.

Neurotransmitters can open ion channels in the plasma membrane of the postsynaptic (receiving) cell in two major ways.

- **Directly, by opening *transmitter-gated ion channels*** – *excitatory* (GO) neurotransmitters (such as **glutamate** and **acetylcholine**) can act directly on transmitter-gated channels that pass positively-charged *sodium* ions, opening them up and causing depolarization and therefore *excitation* of the postsynaptic cell.

  One type of receptor for the excitatory neurotransmitter glutamate (called the *NMDA receptor*) is also tied to a channel that, when activated, allows calcium ions to pass into the interior of the neuron.

  *Inhibitory* (STOP) neurotransmitters (such as **gamma-amino butyric acid**, **GABA**) can act directly by opening transmitter-gated channels that pass negatively charged *chloride* ions, sometimes causing slight hyperpolarization and "clamping" the membrane potential close to the theoretical Nernst potential for chloride. This makes it more difficult to excite the postsynaptic cell, which is therefore *inhibited* (see later).

- **Indirectly** – neurotransmitters, the "first messengers," can open up ion channels indirectly by changing the concentrations in the neuron cytoplasm of substances called "second messengers." An example of a second messenger is **cyclic AMP**, which will be discussed next semester. **Norepinephrine** acts in this way.

## A. Excitatory Neurotransmission

**Excitatory neurotransmitters** (example: **glutamate**) – have a depolarizing effect on the plasma membrane of the receiving neuron. That is, they make the postsynaptic membrane more permeable to *sodium* ions. They may do this directly, by acting on transmitter-gated sodium channels (strictly speaking, these channels pass other cations in addition to sodium). Alternatively, the neurotransmitter may act indirectly by activating an enzyme that generates a second messenger called cyclic AMP, which then goes on to activate enzymes that open up the sodium channels.

**Excitatory postsynaptic potentials (EPSPs)** – generally, the release of a neurotransmitter by a single presynaptic terminal is not enough to make the postsynaptic neuron fire, i.e. develop an action potential in the postsynaptic membrane. There is usually a transient subthreshold depolarization called an *excitatory postsynaptic potential* (*EPSP*).

**Summation of EPSPs** – EPSPs last for about 15 msec. While a *single* EPSP may be insufficient to cause the postsynaptic neuron to fire, EPSPs can *sum* together, so that their combined depolarizations reach threshold, and therefore trigger an action potential at the axon hillock of the postsynaptic neuron.

- *Temporal summation of EPSPs* – when summation is the result of a train of impulses arriving one after the other at a single synapse, it is called *temporal summation*.

- *Spatial summation of EPSPs* – when the EPSPs are generated by impulses traveling down several axons arriving at several different synapses on one postsynaptic neuron, they may also sum together and cause the postsynaptic neuron to fire. This is called *spatial summation*. In this way, the postsynaptic neuron is able to integrate inputs from a number of neurons that synapse with it. We will return to this later.

## B. Inhibitory Neurotransmission

Some of the synapses on the surface of a neuron are excitatory, but others may be inhibitory. That is, they make it more difficult to excite the neuron, or they damp down its activity. Like excitatory neurotransmitters, inhibitory neurotransmitters are removed by reuptake mechanisms or enzymatically.

1. **Inhibitory neurotransmitters** (example: **gamma-amino butyric acid, GABA**) – are released at inhibitory synapses, and counteract the effect of excitatory neurotransmitters on a postsynaptic neuron.

   Inhibitory neurotransmitters usually act by opening transmitter-gated channels. The most prevalent inhibitory neurotransmitter is GABA, which increases the permeability of the membrane to **chloride** ions.

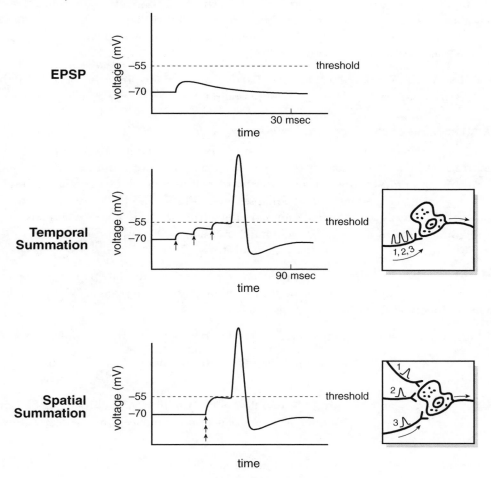

**Figure 13-6.**

A large increase in the permeability of the membrane to chloride ions "clamps" the membrane close to the Nernst chloride potential. The reason is that when a large number of chloride channels are opened, the chloride term comes to dominate the Goldman-Hodgkin-Katz equation.

$$E_m = \frac{RT}{F} \, log_e \frac{P_{Na}[Na_{out}] + P_K[K_{out}] + P_{Cl}[Cl_{in}]}{P_{Na}[Na_{in}] + P_K[K_{in}] + P_{Cl}[Cl_{out}]}$$

If you look at the table in Chapter 12, you will see that the chloride potential (−90 mV) is actually very similar to the potassium potential. This makes the neuron difficult to excite, and we say it is inhibited. We will discuss GABA and other neurotransmitters later in this book.

2. **Inhibitory postsynaptic potential (IPSP)** – The Nernst potential for chloride is at about −90 mV. If the resting membrane potential is less than this, say 65 mV, the result will be a transient hyperpolarization. This transient hyperpolarization is called an *inhibitory postsynaptic potential (IPSP)*.

   However, if the normal resting potential of the plasma membrane is very close to the Nernst potential for chloride, then we would not see an IPSP.

## C. Integration of Excitatory and Inhibitory Input

A single postsynaptic neuron receives synaptic input from THOUSANDS of presynaptic neurons. Each of these synapses releases one particular neurotransmitter, which binds to specific receptors for this neurotransmitter that cluster at the postsynaptic membrane of the receiving cell. Some of these synapses are inhibitory, while others are excitatory. We have already discussed spatial summation of excitatory postsynaptic potentials—this is the integration of many EPSPs generated by synapses that are located close to each other on the surface of the postsynaptic neuron.

The balance between these various inputs determines how the postsynaptic neuron will react. Effectively, the postsynaptic neuron is an integrator of nervous activity. It receives signals, integrates them, and responds accordingly.

If the excitatory input is greater than the inhibitory input, then the result is either:

1. A subthreshold depolarization, which **facilitates** the neuron, i.e. makes it more excitable.

2. A threshold or suprathreshold depolarization, **exciting** the neuron. The neuron generates an action potential or a train of action potentials if the depolarization is substantial.

If the inhibitory input is greater than the excitatory input, the membrane either hyperpolarizes or becomes difficult to excite. The result is inhibition of the postsynaptic neuron. No nerve impulse is generated. The greater the inhibition, the more difficult it is for excitatory synaptic activity to overcome it. The bottom line is that the neuron becomes more difficult to excite.

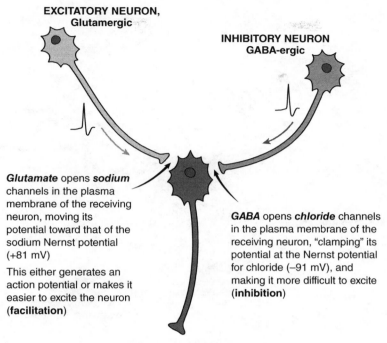

**EXCITATORY NEURON,**
**Glutamergic**

**INHIBITORY NEURON**
**GABA-ergic**

*Glutamate* opens *sodium* channels in the plasma membrane of the receiving neuron, moving its potential toward that of the sodium Nernst potential (+81 mV)

This either generates an action potential or makes it easier to excite the neuron **(facilitation)**

*GABA* opens *chloride* channels in the plasma membrane of the receiving neuron, "clamping" its potential at the Nernst potential for chloride (–91 mV), and making it more difficult to excite **(inhibition)**

**Receiving neuron –**
**response depends on the balance between**
**excitatory and inhibitory inputs**

**Figure 13-7.**

281

**Inactivation of neurotransmitter after it has had its effect** – in order to maintain proper control of what happens at a synapse, it is important that the neurotransmitter be inactivated after it has bound to its receptor site. Otherwise, it would go on stimulating the postsynaptic cell indefinitely.

1.  **Acetylcholine** is removed by an enzyme called *acetylcholinesterase* (or just *cholinesterase*), that is present in the postsynaptic membrane.

2.  **Norepinephrine (noradrenalin)** can be destroyed by the enzyme *monoamine oxidase,* but is removed mainly by *reuptake* into the PREsynaptic terminal, where it may be recycled. The neurotransmitters serotonin and dopamine are also treated the same way. Certain drugs such as *Prozac* and *cocaine* act by blocking the reuptake process (serotonin in the case of Prozac, norepinephrine, serotonin and dopamine in the case of cocaine), so increasing the concentration of neurotransmitter in the synaptic cleft.

3.  **Glutamate** (derived from L-glutamic acid) is also removed by an uptake mechanism, partly by reuptake at the presynaptic terminal, partly by glial cells called astrocytes. The astrocytes convert glutamate into **glutamine**, which is then returned to the neuron for resynthesis of glutamate.

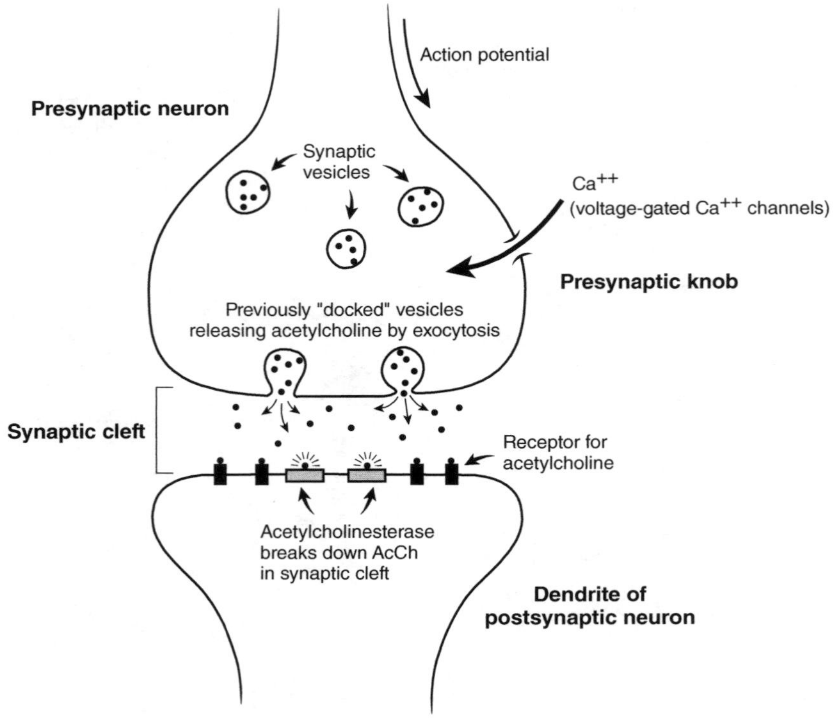

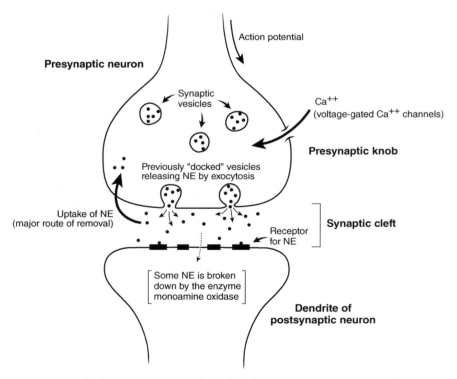

**Figure 13-8.** Removal of neurotransmitter after it has acted – enzymatic action: acetylcholine.

**Figure 13-9.** Removal of neurotransmitter after it has acted – reuptake: norepinephrine.

In summary:

**Enzymatic removal:** acetylcholine (cholinesterase) and to a lesser extent serotonin, norepinephrine, dopamine. The enzyme in these cases is monoamine oxidase.

**Reuptake:** serotonin, norepinephrine, dopamine, GABA and glutamate (which is also taken up by astrocytes).

### D. Long-Term Potentiation and Long-Term Depression at Synapses

**Long-term potentiation** is an important property of certain synapses in parts of the nervous system. Continued use of these synapses **strengthens** them, and it is thought that the process may be involved in memory formation.

When these synapses (in a region called the *hippocampus*, to be precise) are excited at high frequencies, there is a prolonged enhancement of excitability at the synapse. The synapse is "strengthened." The process is called long-term potentiation (LTP), and in the intact animal it can last for days and even weeks. It is still not clear whether LTP is the mechanism for memory, but a considerable amount of research is being carried out in this area.

LTP may result from one of the following mechanisms.

1.  Transmitting neuron releases **more** neurotransmitter for each action potential arriving at the presynaptic terminal. Entry of calcium into the dendrites of the *postsynaptic, receiving neuron* or into the *presynaptic, transmitting neuron* may be involved in this effect.

2.  Receiving neuron's **sensitivity** to neurotransmitter is increased. This increases the efficiency of the synapse.

**Long-term depression** is the opposite of LTP. LTD is a long lasting reduction in synaptic transmission, which can induced by delivering low frequency stimulation to neurons.

283

## III. Neurotransmitters and Neuromodulators

These will be discussed more fully in Chapter 18. The following is a brief summary.

*   **Acetylcholine** – the neurotransmitter at the neuromuscular junction and other synapses in the nervous system. Its action is terminated by the enzyme cholinesterase (sometimes called acetylcholinesterase).

*   The *monoamines* (also known as the *biogenic amines*) – **norepinephrine** (**NE**), **dopamine**, **serotonin** (histamine is also included in this group). Dopamine is sometimes inhibitory, while NE and serotonin appear to be excitatory. The action of these neurotransmitters is often terminated by reuptake mechanisms involving special molecules in the plasma membrane called *neurotransmitter transporters*.

    *   **Norepinephrine, epinephrine** (also known as **adrenaline**) and **dopamine** are referred to as the **catecholamines**.

- **Amino acids – gamma-amino butyric acid** (**GABA**) and **glutamate** (L-glutamic acid).

    - **GABA** is the most common *inhibitory* neurotransmitter in the brain.
    - **Glutamate**, on the other hand, is the most common *excitatory* neurotransmitter in the brain.

    [Two other amino acid transmitters are glycine and aspartate: glycine is an inhibitory neurotransmitter similar to GABA].

    The action of these neurotransmitters may be terminated by reuptake mechanisms.

- **Neuropeptides** – small peptides that include **somatostatin**, **enkephalins**, **endorphins**, **substance P**, **dynorphin**. Endorphins, dynorphin and enkephalins have morphine-like qualities, and appear to suppress transmission in pain pathways of the brain and spinal cord. Substance P, on the other hand, appears to be a neurotransmitter in the pain pathways.

    Some neuropeptides (e.g. substance P) function as true neurotransmitters, but others act as *neuromodulators* and *modulate* the response of neurons to other neurotransmitters. *Neuromodulators* may alter the responsiveness of a neuron by exciting or inhibiting the opening of ion channels, or by changing the properties of the neuron in other ways.

As well as being an energy source, ATP has now been identified as a neurotransmitter, but we will not discuss this further in this course.

284

## IV. Summary of Ion Channels

| Channel Type | Neurotransmitter | Ion Permeability |
|---|---|---|
| Leak channels | | potassium |
| Voltage-gated channels | | sodium, potassium, calcium |
| Transmitter-gated channels | acetylcholine | sodium and other cations* |
| | serotonin | sodium and other cations |
| | glutamate | sodium and other cations |
| | GABA | chloride |

\* Cations are positively charged ions, e.g. Na$^+$ K$^+$ Ca$^{++}$
  Anions are negatively charged ions, e.g. Cl$^-$

## V. How Drugs Act at Synapses

There are many disorders of the nervous system that are tied to neurons that use a particular neurotransmitter.

The treatment of these conditions often involves drugs that act at the synapse. Now you have seen how the synapse functions, you can begin to understand how many of these drugs might work. Here are four major ways.

1. **Blocking the neurotransmitter receptor.**

    This reduces the effectiveness of the neurotransmitter. *Curare* blocks acetylcholine receptors at the neuromuscular junction. Drugs that block glutamate receptors are also being investigated for their effectiveness in minimizing neuronal cell death following a cerebrovascular accident (stroke).

2. **Blocking the reuptake transporter molecules.**

   If reuptake of the neurotransmitter is blocked, then the neurotransmitter will accumulate in the synaptic cleft, and therefore its effectiveness will be enhanced. In the treatment of depression, the drug fluoxetine (Prozac) acts by blocking the serotonin transporter, and therefore blocks the reuptake of serotonin at the presynaptic terminal. Cocaine blocks the reuptake of dopamine, serotonin and norepinephrine. Methamphetamine has the same action as cocaine (see below for more discussion of methamphetamine).

3. **Increasing the amount of neurotransmitter released.**

   This may result from an increase in the amount of calcium in the presynaptic terminal. There is some evidence that nicotine acts this way. Methamphetamine acts in two ways. It increases the release of dopamine at the synapse, and also blocks the reuptake of dopamine.

4. **Inhibiting the enzymes that destroy neurotransmitters.**

   Drugs in this category include the "monoamine oxidase inhibitors" that are used in the treatment of depression.

## VI. Neural Networks

The nervous system is a network of neurons arranged in synaptically connected sequences called *neural networks* or *neuronal circuits*.

The billions of neurons in the central nervous system are not arranged haphazardly; they are organized into definite groups called *neuronal pools*. A neuron pool is a group of cell bodies and their dendrites characterized by their physiological activity. When the neurons of a pool are stimulated, they tend to act together to express a functionally defined goal. For example, a stimulated pool might produce flexing at a joint by stimulating the agonist muscles, and inhibiting the antagonists.

There are many different arrangements of neuronal circuits.

### A. Divergence and Convergence

Some neurons in the central nervous system may synapse with as many as 25,000 other neurons. When a neuron makes synaptic contacts with many other neurons, it is an example of **divergence**. In a divergent circuit, one neuron may excite or inhibit many others. An example of a divergent system is when information is conveyed by relay neurons to other neural levels by *parallel circuits* or pathways. For example, impulses from pain receptors enter the spinal cord and ascend to the brain by two parallel systems.

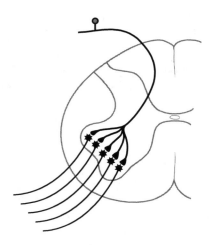

**Figure 13-10.** Divergence: one neuron inputs to five neurons

When one neuron is excited or inhibited by the synaptic input of many other neurons, this is an example of *convergence*.

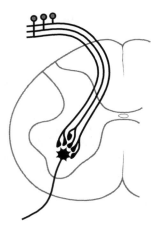

**Figure 13-11.** Convergence: three neurons input to one neuron

## B. Feedback Circuits

Feedback circuits in the nervous system are negative feedback systems, usually involving *inhibitory interneurons*. This is illustrated below.

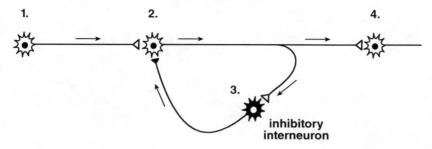

**Figure 13-12.** Inhibitory interneuron.

Neuron **2** is excited by continuous input from neuron **1**. Neuron **2** excites inhibitory neuron **3**. So after a short delay, neuron **2** is inhibited (turned off) by neuron **3**. A continuous signal from neuron **1** therefore becomes an on-off signal arriving at neuron **4**.

The circuit shown in the figure is typical of the on–off circuits found in the cerebellum.

287

288

# NEUROPHYSIOLOGY III
## Somatic Sensory Receptors

289

## CHAPTER OUTLINE

## DESCRIPTION AND INTRODUCTION

**Information** is vital to our survival. We are continually bombarded with sensory information. This information is received, processed, and acted upon by our nervous systems.

This information concerns events occurring:

- **outside** our bodies (for example – light, sound, something touching our skin, heat, cold)
- **inside** our bodies (for example – blood pressure, body temperature, joint movements and positions, muscle length and tension)

*Sensory receptors* provide this information. Specialized sensory receptors in our skin, eyes, ears, arterial walls, joints, tendons and muscles respond to various stimuli (light, sound, touch, etc.), and activate sensory neurons that notify the nervous system of changes occurring outside and inside the body.

Each type of sensory receptor responds to a particular type of stimulus. Stimuli include light, sound, acceleration, chemicals, touch, pressure, warmth, cold, tissue damage (pain), muscle length, muscle tension, arterial blood pressure, blood temperature, pH, plasma osmotic pressure, etc.

Sensory receptors can be specialized:

1. **nerve cells** – the photoreceptors of the eye and the hair cells of the ear are examples
2. **nerve endings** – these nerve endings may be "naked" (for example, pain and temperature) or they may be associated with some kind of special structure (for example, Meissner's corpuscles which respond to touch)
3. **epithelial cells** – taste cells on the tongue fall into this category

In this chapter, we shall discuss the structure, properties, and physiological function of sensory receptors. We will also discuss the sensations that are perceived when sensory receptors are stimulated. The main focus of our discussion will be on the ***somatic senses***, those senses that involve receptors located in the skin, muscles, tendons, joints and visceral organs.

The ***special senses*** (*hearing, balance, vision, taste* and *smell*) will be dealt with in a later chapter. However, you do need to know the difference between the somatic senses and the special senses. The sensory receptors for the special senses are housed in special organs in the head (hearing and balance in the **ear**, vision in the **eye**, smell in the **nose**, and taste in **taste buds** in the tongue).

The somatic senses may be classified in two ways—*where* the stimulus takes effect, or *what* the stimulus is.

### Where the Stimulus Takes Effect

1. **Exteroceptive senses** concern changes at the body *surface* or even at a distance from the body—light, touch, pressure, temperature, pain.

2. **Proprioceptive senses** provide information about body *position* and *movement*—muscle tension, muscle length, position and activity of joints, and equilibrium. Equilibrium (or balance) is largely mediated by specialized receptors found in the ear, and will be dealt with later.

3. **Visceroceptive senses** or **interoceptive senses** are associated with changes in the internal environment—receptors are found in the visceral organs and even in the brain. The stretch receptors in the walls of the aorta and carotid artery fall into this category. They provide information on blood pressure. Except for *visceral pain*, these senses will be discussed later.

*What the Stimulus Is*

- **Photoreceptors** respond to light
- **Chemoreceptors** respond to chemicals
- **Mechanoreceptors** respond when they are deformed by mechanical forces
- **Thermoreceptors** respond to either warmth or cold
- **Nociceptors** are pain receptors—they respond to impending or actual tissue damage

## OBJECTIVES

After listening to the lecture and reading this chapter, you should be able to:

1. Classify the **sensory receptors** based on **where** in the body the stimulus takes effect.
2. Classify the sensory receptors based on the **kinds of stimuli** that excite them.
3. Distinguish between **somatic** senses and **special** senses.
4. Explain what is meant by the **threshold** of a sensory receptor—**draw** a **diagram** to illustrate how a sensory receptor responds electrically to a stimulus, and what this response looks like in terms of action potentials in the sensory nerve fiber.
5. Explain how information on stimulus **intensity** and stimulus **quality** is signalled to the brain.
6. Explain what is meant by sensory **adaptation**.
7. Distinguish between nerves conducting afferent impulses at **different velocities**.
8. Describe the sensory receptors associated with the senses of **touch** and **pressure**, **temperature** and **pain**.
9. Describe the two types of **pain**.
10. Describe what is meant by the brain's **endogenous analgesic system**.
11. Name the **neurotransmitters** involved in transmitting and modifying **pain**.
12. Explain what we mean by **referred** pain (give examples), and how the phenomenon could be explained.
13. **Draw a diagram** to illustrate the distinction between the receptors that respond to muscle **stretch** and to muscle **tension**—explain their importance.
14. Describe the sensory receptors associated with **joints**, and what their function is.

## I. Types of Sensory Receptor

There are three types of sensory receptor.

1.  Specialized **nerve cells** (for example, the photoreceptors of the eye and the *olfactory cells* of the nose).

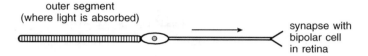

**Figure 14-1.** A rod photoreceptor (highly specialized *neuron*).

2.  **Nerve endings**. These nerve endings may be "naked" (pain, temperature) or they may be specialized, encapsulated in some kind of structure like a *Pacinian corpuscle*.

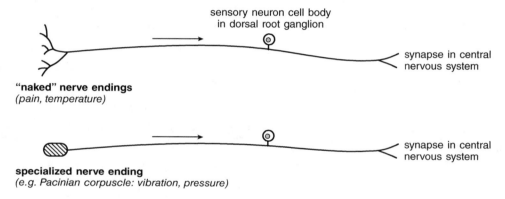

**Figure 14-2.** Nerve endings.

3.  **Non-neuronal** receptor cells. Some sensory receptors may be derived from specialized epithelial cells (taste cells on the tongue fall into this category).

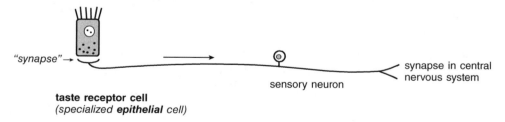

**Figure 14-3.** Non-neuronal receptor cells.

The basic task of a receptor is to respond to some aspect of its environment by converting part of the stimulus energy into an electrical signal that is meaningful to the nervous system. This process is called **transduction**.

Depending on **what stimulates them**, there are five different types of sensory receptors (we include somatic sensory receptors and the receptors associated with the special senses). They may be stimulated as follows.

- **Chemical stimuli are detected by chemoreceptors.** Changes in the concentration of *chemicals* such as hydrogen ions (pH), oxygen, carbon dioxide, glucose, salt, odoriferous agents. Substances with characteristic tastes fall into this category as well, because they stimulate the taste buds. Note that these chemoreceptors respond to many *internal* stimuli, such as pH and metabolite concentrations.

- **Tissue damage stimulates pain receptors (nociceptors).** Events that cause tissue damage give rise to pain stimuli that act in a complex way. We still do not fully understand how pain is generated. The stimuli that cause pain receptors to send pain signals to the brain are mechanical, thermal and chemical in nature (see later).

- **Warmth and and cold stimulate thermoreceptors.** Note that there are receptors for warmth and receptors for cold. Very hot stimuli will stimulate pain receptors.

- **Mechanical forces that cause physical deformation of the receptor stimulate mechanoreceptors.** Mechanical stimuli are highly varied, and include stretching or other types of physical deformation. Receptors for sound, position and acceleration (balance) in the ear fall into this category, as well as receptors for touch and pressure in the skin. These sensory receptors are called *mechanoreceptors*.

- **Light stimulates photoreceptors.** Cells in the retina of the eye called rods and cones have visual pigments that absorb light and trigger a decrease in membrane sodium ion conductance. These receptors are called *photoreceptors*.

Remember that vision, hearing, balance, smell and taste are *special senses*.

293

## II. Properties of Sensory Receptors

### A. Sensory Receptors Are Specific for Only One Stimulus Type

Sensory receptors are excited (or activated) when they detect a ***specific*** stimulus. This specific stimulus is usually unique for each receptor. This is important. Only the photoreceptors of the eye will respond to light, and generate the sensation of light, for example. Only cold receptors in the skin will respond to cold and generate the sensation of cold.

### B. The Stimulus Must Be At or Above Threshold

To activate a receptor, a stimulus must not only be appropriate for that receptor but also *intense* enough (or *adequate*) to excite it. That is to say, the stimulus must be at or above the *threshold* of that receptor.

### C. The Receptor or Generator Potential

How does a sensory receptor respond to a stimulus? There are several ways, but one of the most common is as follows.

The stimulus produces an electrical change in the receptor, usually (but not always) by opening sodium channels in the membrane.

We can detect this electrical change by inserting the end of a recording electrode through the plasma membrane into the interior of the sensory receptor.

1.  If the stimulus is a weak one (below the threshold) we observe a small depolarization of the sensory receptor membrane. This depolarization is rather similar to an EPSP, and is called a *receptor* or *generator potential.*

2.  The size of the generator potential increases as the stimulus is strengthened. When the stimulus reaches or exceeds the threshold, we find that the generator potentials are large enough to trigger trains of action potentials up the afferent sensory nerve fiber. We can record these trains of action potentials with a second electrode placed on the afferent nerve from the sensory receptor.

This leads us to the question of how the *intensity* of the stimulus is signalled to the central nervous system (see below).

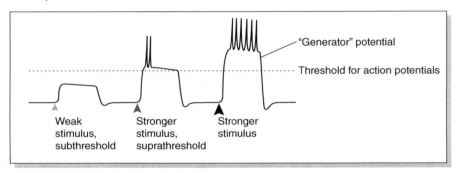

294

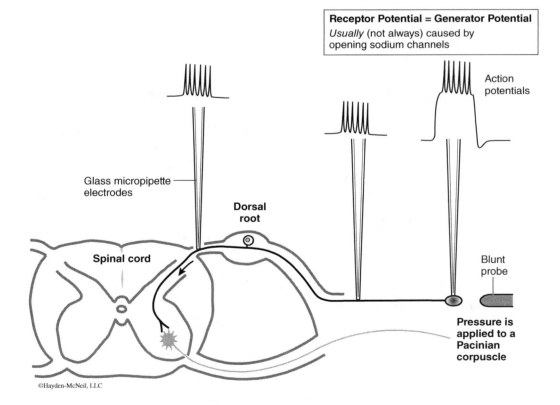

**Figure 14-4.** Sensory receptors—the generator potential.

## D. Stimulus Intensity Is Coded by the Frequency of Action Potentials

The frequency of action potentials (impulses) that pass along an afferent (sensory) nerve fiber increases as the stimulus intensity increases.

This is called the *frequency code* for stimulus intensity.

Additionally, stronger stimuli (e.g. pressure) often activate more receptors, so the stimulus intensity may also be signalled by the **number** of responding receptors.

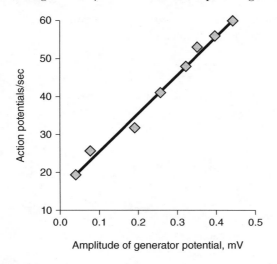

**Figure 14-5.** Relationship between frequency of action potentials in the axon of a sensory receptor and the amplitude of the generator potential.

## E. Coding of Stimulus Quality (Type)

How does the brain determine whether the stimulus is light, sound, touch, pressure, cold, etc.?

When a train of action potentials from the eye reaches the brain, it is always perceived as light, never as touch or sound. In fact, it is impossible even to imagine the sensation of sound originating in the eye.

Similarly, when a train of action potentials from specific touch receptors in the skin arrive in the brain, we perceive touch. We do not perceive light, sound or heat. You can easily close your eyes and imagine the sensation of touch in your hand, but can you imagine using your hand to perceive light? No: It is very difficult to imagine anything that is physically impossible to experience.

These examples illustrate that the *quality* of the perceived stimulus is determined by the receptor type stimulated. When a pressure receptor is stimulated, we perceive pressure. When a cold receptor is stimulated, we perceive cold. When a photoreceptor is stimulated, we perceive light, and so on.

The quality of the sensation perceived is therefore coded by the type of receptor stimulated, and in the nerve pathways that connect it to the brain.

This is called the *labelled line code*.

**Fooling the brain.**

The brain can be fooled by this system, because **how** the receptor is actually stimulated does not affect the sensation perceived. For example, pressure applied to the eyeball evokes the sensation of light, not pressure. Also, electrical stimulation of the VIII cranial nerve from the ear evokes the sensation of sound.

## F. Sensory (Receptor) Adaptation

Receptors that are continuously stimulated *adapt*. That is, the frequency of action potentials generated by them during a continuous stimulus progressively decreases. This is called *sensory adaptation*. From the point of view of sensation, the stimulus appears to be getting weaker (see section on temperature).

Receptors adapt at different rates. Pacinian corpuscles, which are sensitive to pressure and vibration, are examples of rapidly adapting sensory receptors. So are the receptors that respond to bending of hairs on the skin. The muscle stretch receptor is an example of a slowly-adapting sensory receptor.

*time*

- This recording is of action potentials from the afferent nerve of a cold receptor continually exposed to cold.

- The frequency of action potentials starts out high, then drops off.

- The brain therefore interprets the frequency code and perceives that the stimulus is getting weaker.

**Figure 14-6.** Sensory (receptor) adaptation.

## G. Rate of Nerve Impulse Conduction Varies in Different Types of Afferent Nerve Fibers

The speed at which an afferent fiber conducts action potentials is related to its diameter and whether it is myelinated or not. In mammals, large diameter fibers are myelinated, whereas small diameter fibers are not.

This has important consequences. The faster a fiber conducts action potentials, the quicker the nervous system receives information. In an average adult, the distance from the fingertips to the spinal cord is 1 meter. A large-diameter myelinated fiber (*A-∂ fiber*) can conduct impulses at the rate of 50 meters per second, and convey its information to the central nervous system in 0.02 of a second. A small-diameter, unmyelinated fiber (or *C fiber*) conducts at about 5 meters per second, and takes 0.2 seconds or more to convey information to the central nervous system.

Obviously, we cannot rely entirely on receptors connected by C fibers to tell us that our fingers have touched a hot plate—that would be equivalent to sending a message by snail mail. Severe damage could be done to the fingers during the 0.2 seconds needed to tell the central nervous system what was happening. We need to be informed prompt-ly by receptors connected to the central nervous system by the A-∂ fibers—that is equiva-lent to sending an e-mail.

## III. Somatic Senses

### A. Types

Somatic senses are divided into three broad groups, depending on *where* the stimulus takes effect. They are are also divided up according to *what* types of stimuli they respond to. On the basis of where receptors are located, we have *exteroceptors, proprioceptors* and *visceroceptors* (or *interoceptors*).

1. **Exteroceptive senses** are mediated by receptors in the skin and give rise to such sensations as touch, pressure, tickle, temperature, and pain.

2. **Proprioceptive senses** are mediated by receptors in the muscles, tendons and joints (receptors in the ear that are involved in balance and in detecting acceleration will be dealt with in the chapters covering the special senses). Proprioceptors measure physical properties, such as muscle length, tendon tension, joint angle or deep pres-sure. Proprioceptors guide body movements and (with touch) are involved in sens-ing the size, weight and shape of objects. Normally, we relegate proprioception to the realm of the subconscious.

   What happens if you lose proprioception? Ian Waterman is one of 10 people in the world who has lost proprioception. When he was 19 he had a viral infection that prevented proprioceptive information from reaching the brain but left intact his motor system. He could make movements, but because of lack of feedback he couldn't control them. He was left a helpless "rag doll," who had to be fed, washed and dressed. After some years, he found that if he used his eyes he could train him-self to carry out movements. After much work and effort, this young man finally taught himself to walk again. None of the other sufferers from this condition have been able to achieve this.

3. **Visceroceptive** or **interoceptive senses** are mediated by receptors in the viscera and in the brain. Only the visceroceptors giving rise to visceral pain will be dealt with in the present chapter.

297

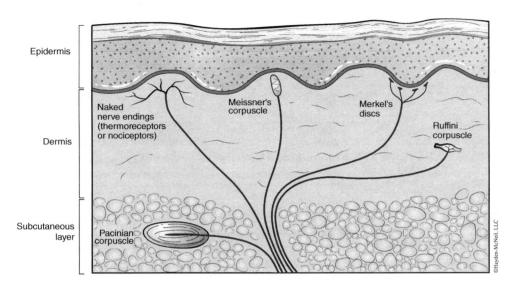

**Figure 14-7.** Skin receptors.

## B. Tactile Receptors of the Skin: Touch, Pressure, and Vibration

Tactile receptors are exteroceptors that belong to the class of mechanoreceptors, and they respond to deformation of the skin. They include the following:

1.  **Meissner's corpuscles** – elongated, encapsulated endings located in the dermal papillae of hairless skin just below the epidermis. They occur particularly in the lips, fingertips, palms, soles, external genitalia, nipples. The receptor rapidly adapts to stimuli. It is thought that Meissner's corpuscles are largely responsible for our ability to perform fine tactile discrimination, particularly with our fingertips. This would include determining textures of objects.

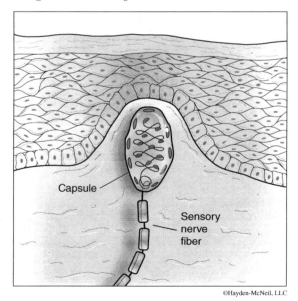

**Figure 14-8.** Meissner's corpuscle.

2. **Pacinian corpuscles** – are widespread, and commonly found in deeper subcutaneous layers of the hands, feet, external genitalia, breasts. The Pacinian corpuscle is amazingly sensitive. Because this receptor is rapidly adapting, it responds better to vibration than pressure.

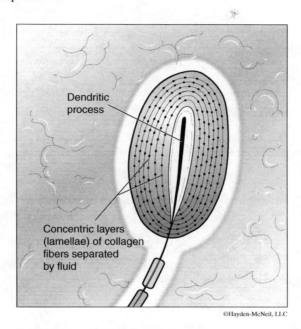

Dendritic process

Concentric layers (lamellae) of collagen fibers separated by fluid

©Hayden-McNeil, LLC

**Figure 14-9.** Pacinian corpuscle.

3. **Hair receptors** – hairy skin, which covers most of the body, has Pacinian corpuscles but lacks Meissner's corpuscles. Instead, there is the *hair receptor*. This type of receptor varies in complexity—those around cat's whiskers are quite elaborate. Those around most human body hairs consist of the spiral endings of nerve fibers wrapped around the base of each follicle. The hair receptor is a rapidly-adapting receptor, and groups of them are good at detecting movement over the skin surface.

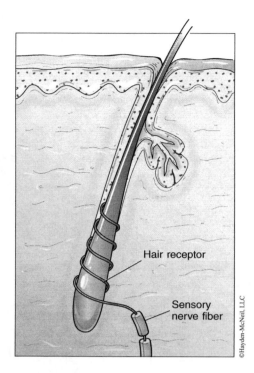

**Figure 14-10.** Hair receptor.

4.  **Merkel cells (discs)** – curious cells found in the skin at the epidermal–dermal border. They consist of modified epithelial cells that convey mechanical signals to mechanically sensitive nerve endings. They are essential for the perception of light touch, and are important in sensing texture and shape. They are particularly numerous on our fingertips and lips.

5.  **Carcinoma** – Merkel cell carcinoma is a rare tumor of the skin. It is very dangerous because it is likely to metastasize.

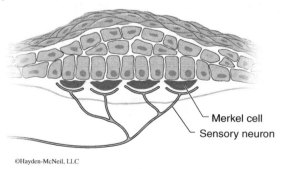

**Figure 14-11.** Merkel cells lie at the border between the dermis and the epidermis. The Figure illustrates a group of Merkel cells in a "touch dome." Branches of a sensory neuron contact the cells in this group.

6.  **Ruffini endings** – slowly adapting touch receptors found in the skin.

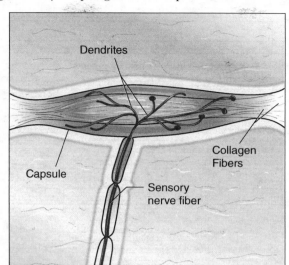

**Figure 14-12.** Ruffini ending.

## C. Temperature

Thermal sensation is mediated by one group of receptors for cold, and another group for warmth. Both groups are found in the skin, and consist of free nerve endings, without any specialized structures associated with them. These receptors are exteroceptors that belong to the class of thermoreceptors.

*Warm receptors* start responding at temperatures above 25°C (77°F), increase their rate of discharge up to 45°C (113°F), then become inactive as the temperature increases further. At higher temperatures, heat **nociceptors** are stimulated, causing heat pain. Recently it has been found that one of the receptors for noxious heat is the same as one that responds to **capsaicin**, the ingredient of red hot chili peppers.

*Cold receptors* start responding below about 30°C and continue to respond to reduced temperature down to 10°C. Some cold receptors respond to menthol, acounting for the cool sensation of **menthol**.

Warm and cold receptors adapt easily, and it is a common experience that a hot tub does not feel so hot after one has been in it for a while. Similarly, soon after the initial shock of jumping into cold water, the cold receptors adapt, and it does not feel so bad.

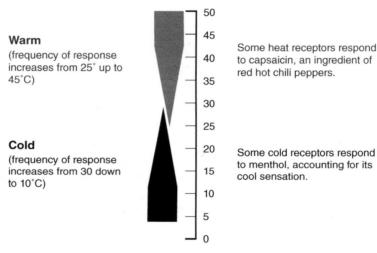

**Temperature Receptors in the Skin
(All Rapidly Adapting)**

**Figure 14-13.**

## D. Pain

Some types of pain have an important survival function, because pain receptors are stimulated whenever tissues are being stressed or damaged. The biologic function (if any) of other types of pain, such as chronic pain from cancerous conditions, is more difficult to understand, however.

**Analgesia:** refers to pain relief without loss of other sensory modalities and consciousness.

**Central anesthesia:** loss of consciousness.

Receptors for pain are both exteroceptors and visceroceptors that belong to the class of nociceptors.

Pain receptors appear to be naked nerve endings widely distributed in superficial skin layers, periosteum, arterial walls, viscera, joint surfaces, cranial vault, and cornea of the eye.

Stimuli for pain receptors include mechanical, thermal and chemical agents. When there is actual tissue damage, there may be release of two powerful peptides called ***bradykinin*** and ***substance P***. Substances called ***prostaglandins*** may also be released, which seem to act by enhancing pain (***aspirin*** acts by inhibiting the biosynthesis of prostaglandins).

Pain signals are carried to the central nervous system by A-∂ nerve fibers, which conduct at 5–30 meters per second, and by thin unmyelinated C nerve fibers, which conduct at 0.5–2 meters per second.

1.  **Two types of pain.**

•   **Fast pain** (*sharp pain, pricking pain, acute pain*) is a short-lived, well-localized sensation caused by (for example) a pinprick or a strong pinch. It is conveyed by myelinated A-∂ afferents, and is associated *only with the skin*.

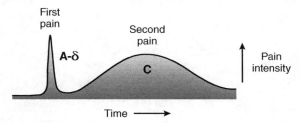

**Figure 14-14.** Double pain sensation. Two sequential pain sensations are perceived following a very brief painful stimulus. The first one is almost immediate, and is conveyed via fast-conducting A delta fibers. The second one is conveyed via slow-conducting C fibers.

303

•   **Slow pain** (*throbbing pain, burning pain, aching pain, chronic pain*) is poorly localized. It continues after removal of the stimulus. It is conveyed by unmyelinated C afferents and is associated with the *skin, joints, internal organs and muscles*.

If you quickly and sharply pinch with your fingernails the web of skin between two of your fingers, it is possible to perceive these two types of pain in the form of a double sensation—one early and brief, and the other somewhat delayed and more prolonged. Try it, but remember to make the pinch sharply and very quickly.

2.  **How the brain controls the sensation of pain.**

The perception of pain can vary enormously, depending on emotional state, mental attitude (anxiety, fear, anticipation, etc.). The conscious sensation of pain can also vary from person to person, is affected by drugs, and it may be influenced by other stimuli, such as those caused by rubbing the painful area of skin and by acupuncture.

Many aspects of pain are not understood, but it seems that impulses from neurons in special regions of the brain can control pain impulses passing up to the brain.

The special brain areas that modulate pain were first detected by placing electrodes in various parts of the brain in humans suffering from chronic pain. Stimulation of a region called the ***periaqueductal gray*** caused strong ***analgesia*** (deadening of pain sensitivity) without loss of tactile (touch) sensitivity. We now know that nuclei in the rostral ventromedial medulla are also involved.

Important substances involved in the brain's *endogenous analgesic system* and in the transmission of pain are:

- **Endogenous** *opioid peptides*, which are manufactured in many regions of the central nervous system. They include:

  - the **enkephalins** (leu- and met-enkephalin)
  - the **endorphins**
  - **dynorphin**.

The endogenous opioids cause *analgesia* and *euphoria*, and their actions may underlie some forms of complex and changeable behavior, moods, and responses to pain and stress. They are possibly involved in the good feelings one gets after exercise, and in the "withdrawal" feelings some joggers get when they miss out on their daily run.

- **Gamma-amino butyric acid (GABA)**
- **Serotonin**
- **Norepinephrine**
- **Substance P**, a non-opioid peptide that is an important excitatory neurotransmitter in the pain pathway.

The brain's **endogenous analgesic system** operates as follows. Activation of neurons in the periaqueductal gray causes excitation of neurons that use serotonin as a neurotransmitter. They stimulate inhibitory interneurons in the spinal cord. These interneurons release enkephalin, which *inhibits* the neurons that transmit pain impulses to the brain. This is somewhat simplified, because neurons in the rostral ventromedial medulla are also involved.

One excitatory neurotransmitter in the pain pathway itself is the non-opioid peptide called substance P (see diagram).

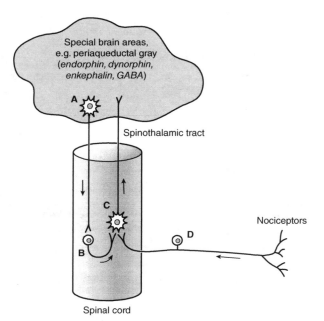

**Neuron A** is a serotonergic neuron in an area of the brain concerned with modulating pain.

**Neuron A** releases serotonin and excites neuron B in the spinal cord.

**Neuron B** is an inhibitory interneuron. It releases enkephalin, which inhibits neuron C.

**Neuron C** is in the direct pain pathway. It receives pain (nociceptive) signals via neuron D in the dorsal root ganglion. The neurontransmitter is substance P. The axon of neuron C relays these signals to the brain via the spinothalamic tract.

Special brain areas, e.g. periaqueductal gray (*endorphin, dynorphin, enkephalin, GABA*)

Spinothalamic tract

Nociceptors

Spinal cord

**Figure 14-15.** Modulation of pain by certain regions of the brain, such as the periaqueductal gray.

What is the point of having an endogenous analgesic system built into the brain's neuronal circuitry? Normally, pain induces withdrawal, escape and other types of avoidance reactions. During stress, however, it might be desirable to have one's pain perceptions dulled. Soldiers wounded in the heat of battle and athletes injured during sports events often report that they do not feel the pain. A particularly graphic account of the dulling of pain perception at a time of extreme stress comes from one of David Livingstone's books, written almost 150 years ago, where he describes being attacked by a lion that crushed his shoulder [*David Livingstone, Missionary Travels, 1857,* quoted from, *Principles of Neural Science,* Third Edition, Kandel. et al. 1991].

> *"...I heard a shout. Starting, and looking half round, I saw the lion just in the act of springing upon me. I was upon a little height, he caught my shoulder as he sprang, and we both came to the ground below together. Growling horribly close to my ear, he shook me as a terrier does a rat. The shock produced a stupor similar to that which seems to be felt by a mouse after the first shake of the cat. It caused a sort of dreaminess in which there was no sense of pain nor feeling of terror, though quite conscious of all that was happening. It was like what patients partially under the influence of chloroform describe, who see all the operation, but feel not the knife... The shake annihilated fear, and allowed no sense of horror in looking round at the beast."*

3. **Referred pain.**

   A person suffering a heart attack may feel pain resulting from lactic acid formation in the walls of the heart. However, the pain is not felt in the heart but in the left shoulder or the left arm. When pain is felt cutaneously as a result of a nociceptive stimulus to an internal organ, it is called ***referred pain***. There are characteristic skin areas to which pain is referred from different internal organs.

305

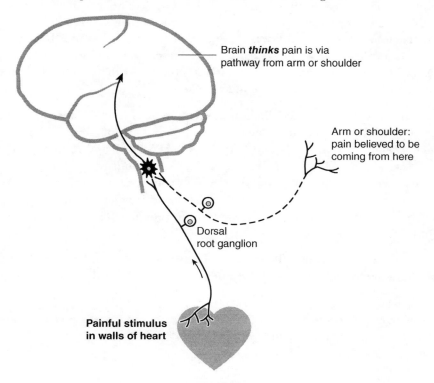

**Figure 14-16.** Referred pain.

Several suggestions have been offered to account for referred pain. They all depend on the idea that visceral and cutaneous afferent nerves converge to share a common pathway to the brain (e.g. they synapse with the same neuron in the spinal cord, or the visceral and cutaneous nerves represent branches of the same nerve fiber). The brain cannot therefore distinguish between the two possible sources of pain, and consistently misinterprets impulses in this pathway as coming from the skin, probably because most of the time this is true.

## E. Proprioception ("Sense of Self")—Sensory Receptors in Muscles, Tendons, and Joints

Provides information on limb position and movement. It also guides voluntary movement and posture.

Muscles have specialized mechanoreceptors that convey proprioceptive information to the central nervous system. These mechanoreceptors are specialized nerve endings of sensory neurons. There are two types of receptor that allow us to monitor simultaneously the length and tension of a muscle. These types are called ***muscle spindles*** and ***Golgi tendon organs***. The joints also have mechanoreceptors called joint kinesthetic receptors. They signal direction, velocity, pressure, angle and twisting of the joint.

1.  **Muscle spindles provide information on muscle length.**

    Muscle spindles are proprioceptors that provide the central nervous system with information about the ***length*** of the muscle. This type of receptor is scattered throughout virtually every skeletal muscle in the body.

    A muscle spindle is a group of thin, specialized muscle fibers called *intrafusal fibers* to distinguish them from the ordinary muscle fibers that we have discussed up till now. They have specialized nerve endings attached to them, and their center regions are enclosed in a fluid-filled, spindle-shaped (elongated) connective tissue sheath. The intrafusal muscle fibers can only contract at their ends, where they are attached to the normal, extrafusal muscle fibers.

    When the muscle is stretched, the intrafusal fibers are stretched, and the nerve endings attached to them are stimulated. There are two types of afferent fibers. As illustrated in Figure 14-17, the Group I afferents are dynamic, and respond to <u>changes</u> in muscle length. The Group II afferents are static, and respond to length only. Nerve impulses are then sent to the central nervous system via the afferent, sensory neurons with their cell bodies located in the dorsal root ganglia of the spinal cord (see following diagram: we will deal with dorsal root ganglia and the spinal cord in a future chapter).

    When the normal, extrafusal muscle fibers contract, the intrafusal fibers also contract. This keeps the muscle spindle taut and cinched up so that it is always responsive to stretch.

    Muscle stretch receptors are important in maintaining posture via the so-called *stretch reflexes*, as we shall see in Chapter 15.

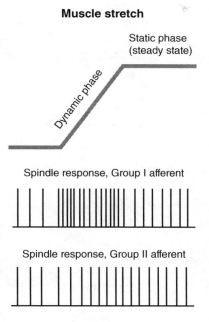

**Figure 14-17.** Action potentials in muscle spindle group I and group II afferents in response to the dynamic and static phases of stretch.

2.  **Golgi tendon organs provide information on muscle tension.**

    Golgi tendon organs are proprioceptors that provide the central nervous system with information about the ***tension*** exerted by the muscle on the tendon that attaches it to the bone.

    Golgi tendon organs are found between collagen fiber bundles close to the point where the tendon and muscle connect. They respond when the muscle contracts, because tension is exerted on the tendon. Although it was once thought that these receptors were quite insensitive, it is now known that they can respond to the contraction of just a few muscle fibers.

    One possible function of the Golgi tendon organs is protective. Some muscles can be extremely powerful and can exert enormous, even damaging tension. Under these conditions, the Golgi tendon organ response triggers a protective reflex that inhibits muscular contraction. This reflex prevents the muscle from contracting strongly and causing damage to the tendon and its insertion in the bone. As you know, damage to tendons can still occur, but presumably less often than if the protective reflex were not there.

307

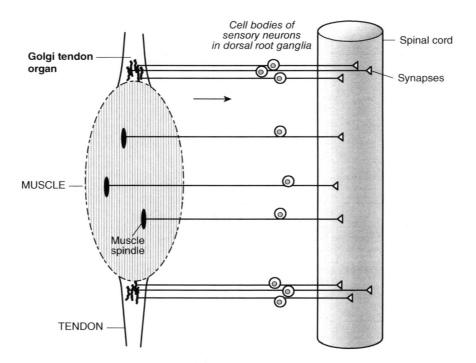

Note: These individual axons are actually bundled together in a single nerve. Nerves supplying muscles contain the axons of the sensory neurons shown here and also of the axons of *motor* neurons, which are *not* shown.

**Figure 14-18.** Muscle spindles signal muscle *length*; Golgi tendon organs signal muscle *tension*.

3.  **Joint kinesthetic receptors.**

The joints have **proprioceptors** that are specialized mechanoreceptors known as joint *kinesthetic* receptors. Some of these receptors are located within and around the joint capsules of synovial joints. Other receptors that look like Pacinian corpuscles are located in the connective tissue outside of the joint capsules. These receptors are believed to respond to acceleration and deceleration of bones forming the joint.

All these receptors are important in transmitting information about joint movement and joint position. Their importance is easily understood if you close your eyes and move your limbs about. At all times, you know what your limbs are doing and where they are. Further, if you stop all movement, you still know the angles of your limb joints, and where the limbs are in space. When your arm "goes to sleep" you lose that information because the receptors have been temporarily deprived of oxygen due to interference with the blood supply. Remember that strange disembodied feeling you get when the arm doesn't seem to belong to you any more?

# CENTRAL NERVOUS SYSTEM I
Spinal Cord, Descending and Ascending Tracts, Spinal Reflexes

309

## CHAPTER OUTLINE

## DESCRIPTION AND INTRODUCTION

The nervous system has a number of broad activities.

1.  Its sensory systems permit it to **sense** events occurring inside and outside the body.

2.  It **interprets**, **integrates** and may **store** this sensory information (in the form of memories), then it **decides** on an appropriate response, if any.

3.  It sends **commands** to muscles and glands (this is called the **motor** function of the nervous system).

4.  It can plan future actions and predict the consequences of those actions.

In Chapter 12 we saw that the nervous system is divided into the **peripheral** nervous system and the **central** nervous system. The central nervous system is made up of the **brain** and the **spinal cord**. The brain itself has many subdivisions.

In this chapter we review the major regions of the central nervous system, then we focus in on the *spinal cord*. We will consider in detail the **spinal nerves** and the **cranial nerves**, spinal cord structure, the **ascending** and **descending** nerve fiber **tracts** (**pathways**), the kinds of **neurons** found in the spinal cord, and finally the **spinal reflexes**.

## OBJECTIVES

After listening to the lecture and reading this chapter, you should be able to:

1.  List the five main **regions** of the central nervous system.
2.  List the three components of the **brain stem**.
3.  List two important structures in the **diencephalon**.
4.  List the major components of the **cerebral hemispheres**.
5.  Briefly summarize the **functions** of the main regions of the central nervous system.
6.  Summarize the **development** of the central nervous system.
7.  Describe the structure of the **spinal cord**.
8.  Summarize four principles of **organization** of the sensory and motor pathways of the brain and spinal cord.
9.  List the **segments** of the spinal cord.
10. Explain what is meant by a **dermatome**, and why dermatomes have **clinical importance**.
11. Distinguish between **ascending** and **descending** tracts (pathways) in the spinal cord.
12. Be able to identify **ascending** tracts and **descending** tracts from their names.
13. List the basic components of a **spinal reflex**.
14. Describe (with **diagrams** showing **neurons**) three examples of a **spinal reflex**: define **reciprocal inhibition**.
15. Describe what happens to spinal reflexes when the spinal cord is **cut**.
16. Distinguish **spinal** nerves from **cranial** nerves, and list the cranial and spinal nerves and the regions they innervate.
17. Distinguish **peripheral** from **central** nervous system.
18. Describe the **structure** of a peripheral nerve.

## I. Overview of the Main Regions of the Central Nervous System

The nervous system is divided into the peripheral nervous system and the central nervous system. In Chapter 12, we simply divided the central nervous system into the spinal cord and the brain. However, the brain itself is composed of a number of important regions. We have now reached the point in this course where we can go one step further and include these regions in our discussion.

The following is a *brief* summary of the major functional and anatomical divisions of the central nervous system. We will be going into them in more detail later. In addition to conventional views of brain structure, a new type of MRI called diffusion tensor imaging allows us to view the fiber tracts connecting various parts of the brain.

### A. The Spinal Cord

The spinal cord contains motor and sensory neurons, most of them connected with the limbs and trunk by means of the ***spinal nerves***. It contains ***interneurons***. It contains the large ***ascending tracts*** of nerve fibers that transmit sensory information up the spinal cord to the brain. Additionally, it contains large ***descending tracts*** of nerve fibers that transmit motor commands down the spinal cord from the brain to the muscles. It should be noted that the spinal cord is able to execute certain simple behavioral activities without involving the brain (its neural networks contain a program for *walking*, for example).

### B. The Brain Stem

Like the spinal cord, the *brain stem* has motor and sensory neurons, but most of them are related to structures in the head and neck, rather than the limbs and trunk. With the exception of the *olfactory nerves* (I), all of the ***cranial nerves*** originate in the brain stem.

Many of the neurons in the brain stem are grouped into orderly clusters (**nuclei**) with specific afferent and efferent fiber systems and reasonably well-delineated functions.

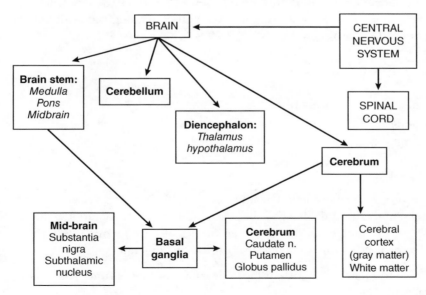

**Figure 15-1.**

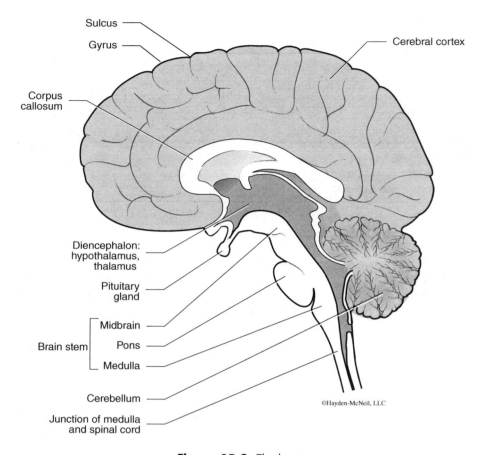

**Figure 15-2.** The brain.

The brain stem contains an important, diffusely-organized structure called the *reticular formation*, which contains neurons that have axons spreading widely in both directions up and down the brain stem.

The brain stem is composed of three units. In the inferior to superior direction, they are:

- the **medulla oblongata** – resembles the spinal cord
- the **pons**
- the **midbrain**

## C. The Cerebellum

The *cerebellum* is attached mainly to the pons, and is important in **movement** control. The cerebellum is essential for coordinated smooth movement and for posture. It regulates the rate, range, force, direction and timing of movements. It determines the sequence and pattern of muscles activated during movement.

The cerebellum may be important in the **learning of motor functions**, such as playing the piano or typing.

## D. The Diencephalon

The *diencephalon* contains two important structures.

1. The ***thalamus***, which is the major relay station for all information passing from the lower central nervous system en route for the cerebral cortex, and which also relays to the cerebral cortex important information from the *cerebellum* and *basal ganglia* (see below). There is also evidence that the thalamus may actually process information destined for the cerebral cortex.

2. The ***hypothalamus***, which is a central governor of the autonomic nervous system and the endocrine system. It has many regions (nuclei) and is involved in certain motivational drives such as feeding, drinking, fear, rage, etc.

## E. The Cerebrum or Cerebral Hemispheres

The *cerebrum* (= *cerebral hemispheres*) is a region of the brain that contains the following major structures.

1. The **basal ganglia** – In the cerebrum we have deep-lying masses of gray matter called the ***putamen, caudate nucleus*** and ***globus pallidus***. There are also two midbrain structures included in the basal ganglia. These are the ***subthalamic nucleus*** and the ***substantia nigra***.

---

Many elementary textbooks refer to the cerebral components of the basal ganglia as the "cerebral nuclei." We do not use this nomenclature here, and you will not encounter it in more advanced texts.

---

2. The **cerebral cortex** – so-called "seat of the intellect." A superficial layer of gray matter that performs the highest and most complex functions required of the central nervous system. Receives and integrates sensory information; stores and retrieves memories; thinks, conceptualizes, plans and executes movements.

## F. Nerve Fiber Connections

The various brain regions are interconnected by a complex series of nerve fibers (= axons). These nerve tracts can be visualized by a new type of MRI called "diffusion tensor imaging."

313

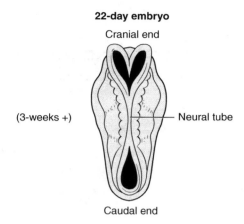

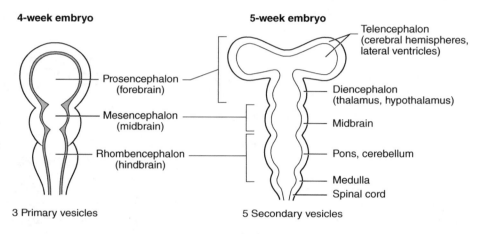

©Hayden-McNeil, LLC

**Figure 15-3.** Development of central nervous system.

## II. Development of the Central Nervous System

At 22 days, the nervous system is a simple *neural tube,* open at both ends.

In four weeks, the anterior end of the tube has progressed to three primary vesicles, which will become the brain.

1.  *Forebrain (prosencephalon)*
2.  *Midbrain (mesencephalon)*
3.  *Hindbrain (rhombencephalon)*

At five weeks, the forebrain subdivides into the telencephalon and the diencephalon, and the hindbrain subdivides into the pons (+ cerebellum) and medulla. So there are now five secondary vesicles.

1. *Telencephalon* (becomes the *cerebral hemispheres*)
2. *Diencephalon* (*thalamus, hypothalamus*) } from forebrain
3. *Midbrain*
4. *Pons, cerebellum*
5. *Medulla* } from hindbrain

## III. Some Principles of Organization of Sensory and Motor Pathways in the Brain and Spinal Cord

The following are some points to note about the organization of sensory and motor pathways of the brain and spinal cord.

- Motor pathways consist of **several distinct pathways in parallel**. There is the cortico-spinal tract, which originates in the cerebral cortex, and also tracts that originate in the brain stem. Sensory pathways also consist of several distinct pathways in parallel. There are the dorsal column tracts and also the spinothalamic tracts.

- Each pathway contains **synaptic relays**.

- Each pathway is organized **topographically**—that is, nerve fibers and neurons from particular regions of the body are grouped together. For example, nerve impulses originating from the hands all travel in groups of nerve fibers that are close to each other, and end up in discrete "hand areas" on the surface of the sensory cerebral cortex. These areas form a "map" of the body surface on the cerebral cortex. Similarly, neurons that are involved in controlling hand *movements* are grouped together in a "hand area" of the *motor cortex*.

- Sensory and motor events on one side of the body are perceived, interpreted and controlled by the cerebral hemisphere on the **opposite side of the body** (the **contralateral** side). The sensory and motor pathways (tracts) are therefore *crossed* at some point. The reason for this is not known.

## IV. The Spinal Cord Structure

The spinal cord is a slender column of nervous tissue that passes downward from the brain into the vertebral canal. The spinal cord is continuous with the brain, but is said to begin where the nervous tissue leaves the cranial cavity at the level of the foramen magnum.

### A. Nomenclature

**anterior = ventral**

**posterior = dorsal**

**Anterior** and **posterior** are basically human terms, used in reference to the upright body. **Dorsal** and **ventral** are basically terms used in animals, in reference to the body on all fours. Since most of the work on the physiology of the central nervous system has been in animals, dorsal and ventral are more often used than posterior and anterior. Sometimes these terms are mixed together. MAKE SURE YOU UNDERSTAND THIS.

## B. Peripheral Nerves—Spinal and Cranial Nerves

The nerves that emerge from the *spinal cord* are called *spinal nerves*. The nerves that emerge from the *brain* are called the *cranial nerves*. Together, these nerves make up the *peripheral nervous system*.

Know the structure of peripheral nerves.

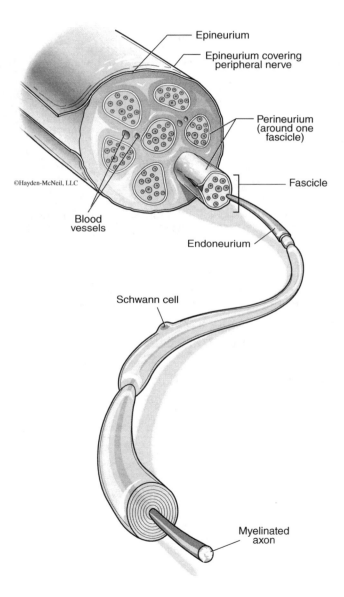

**Figure 15-4.** Peripheral nerve.

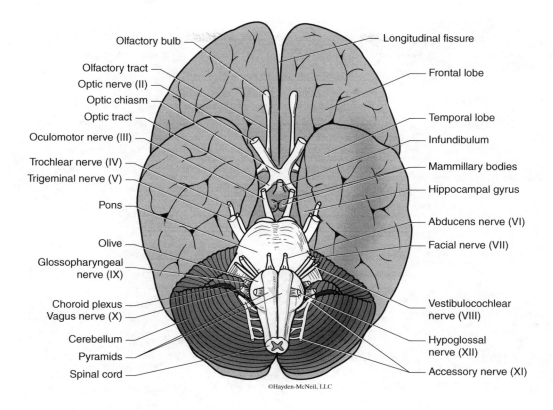

Olfactory bulb

Olfactory tract

Optic nerve (II)

Optic chiasm

Optic tract

Oculomotor nerve (III)

Trochlear nerve (IV)

Trigeminal nerve (V)

Pons

Olive

Glossopharyngeal nerve (IX)

Choroid plexus

Vagus nerve (X)

Cerebellum

Pyramids

Spinal cord

Longitudinal fissure

Frontal lobe

Temporal lobe

Infundibulum

Mammillary bodies

Hippocampal gyrus

Abducens nerve (VI)

Facial nerve (VII)

Vestibulocochlear nerve (VIII)

Hypoglossal nerve (XII)

Accessory nerve (XI)

©Hayden-McNeil, LLC

317

**Figure 15-5.** Brain—inferior aspect.

The twelve cranial nerves are numbered I through XII. Their names are as follows.

I.   **Olfactory** nerves – sensory nerve conveying information from the olfactory cells of the nose.

II.  **Optic** nerves – sensory nerve conveying information from the photoreceptor cells of the retina of the eye.

III. **Oculomotor** nerves – primarily motor, controlling the eyelids, pupil diameter, and extraocular muscles.

IV.  **Trochlear** nerves – primarily motor, controlling extraocular muscles.

V.   **Trigeminal** nerves (three divisions: ophthalmic, maxillary, mandibular) – mixed, the motor component controlling muscles of mastication and muscles in the floor of the buccal cavity.

VI.  **Abducens** nerves – primarily motor, controlling extraocular muscles.

VII. **Facial** nerves – mixed, the motor component controls muscles associated with facial expression, the lacrymal glands, and the salivary glands.

VIII. **Vestibulocochlear** nerves (two branches: vestibular, cochlear) – sensory, conveying information from the cochlea (sound) and vestibular apparatus (balance, equilibrium).

IX.  **Glossopharyngeal** nerves – mixed, the motor component controlling muscles in the pharynx involved in swallowing, salivary glands.

**X.** **Vagus** nerves – mixed, the motor component controls muscles involved in speech and swallowing, with a large autonomic group of nerve fibers that affect heart function, as well as smooth muscle and glands in the viscera of the abdomen.

**XI.** **Accessory** nerves (two branches: cranial accessory and spinal accessory) – primarily motor, controlling muscles of the soft palate, pharynx, larynx, neck and back.

**XII.** **Hypoglossal** nerves – primarily motor, controlling muscles that move the tongue.

One of the following mnemonics may help you to remember the cranial nerves.

Oh Once One Takes The Anatomy Final, Very Good Vacations Are Heavenly.

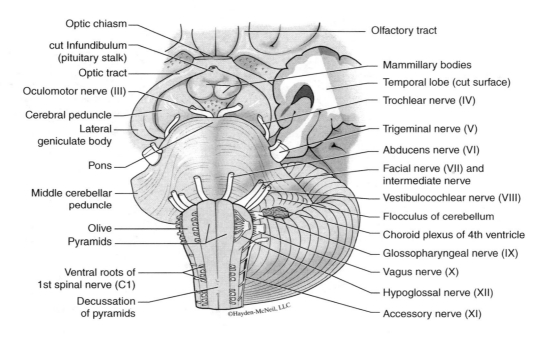

318

**Figure 15-6.** Brain stem, anterior view.

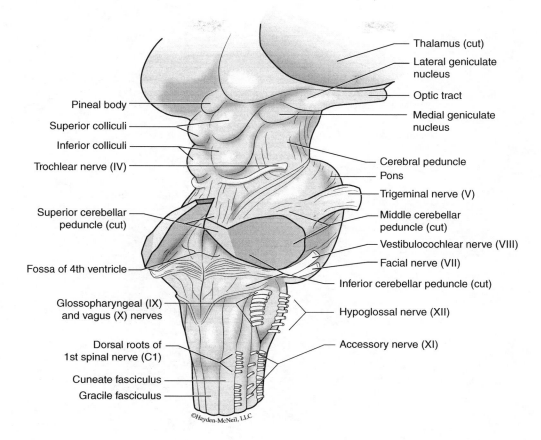

Pineal body

Superior colliculi

Inferior colliculi

Trochlear nerve (IV)

Superior cerebellar
peduncle (cut)

Fossa of 4th ventricle

Glossopharyngeal (IX)
and vagus (X) nerves

Dorsal roots of
1st spinal nerve (C1)

Cuneate fasciculus

Gracile fasciculus

Thalamus (cut)

Lateral geniculate
nucleus

Optic tract

Medial geniculate
nucleus

Cerebral peduncle

Pons

Trigeminal nerve (V)

Middle cerebellar
peduncle (cut)

Vestibulocochlear nerve (VIII)

Facial nerve (VII)

Inferior cerebellar peduncle (cut)

Hypoglossal nerve (XII)

Accessory nerve (XI)

©Hayden-McNeil, LLC

**Figure 15-7.** Brain stem, posterolateral view.

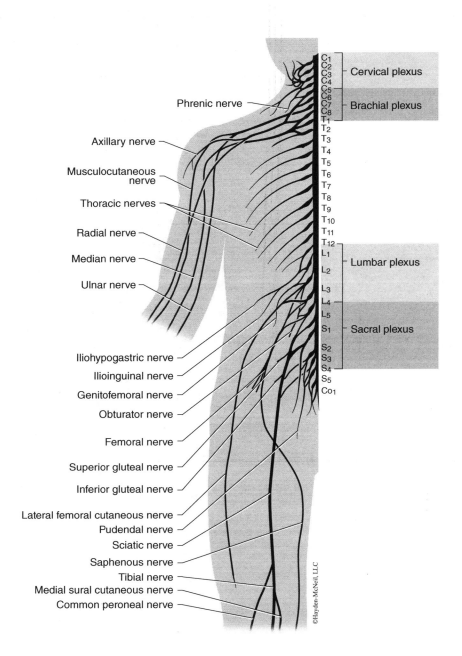

**Figure 15-8.** Peripheral nerves and nerve plexuses.

The spinal cord consists of 31 segments, each of which gives rise to a pair of spinal nerves.

- **C**ervical      8
- **T**horacic     12
- **L**umbar        5
- **S**acral        5
- **C**occygeal     1

The *cervical enlargement* gives rise to nerves for the arms, and the *lumbar enlargement* gives rise to nerves for the legs.

Each spinal nerve emerges from the spinal cord by two short branches, the *dorsal (posterior) and ventral (anterior) roots*, which are protected within the vertebral column.

The dorsal root (or sensory root) has an enlargement called the ***dorsal root ganglion***. The dorsal root ganglion contains the cell bodies of sensory neurons whose nerve endings are often specially adapted to act as sensory receptors (see Chapter 14). The axons of these sensory neurons enter the spinal cord through the dorsal root and form synapses with other neurons in the spinal cord.

The ventral root (or motor root) is actually composed of a number of *rootlets*, and carries the axons of motor neurons whose cell bodies are located in the gray matter of the spinal cord (see below).

The dorsal and ventral roots merge to form a **spinal nerve** that emerges from the vertebral canal through an ***intervertebral foramen***. After emerging from the foramen, the spinal nerve splits into an anterior and a posterior branch. The spinal nerves in the thoracic and lumbar regions also have ***rami*** (branches) that are part of the autonomic nervous system (we'll talk about the autonomic nervous system later).

The area of skin innervated by a single dorsal root is called a ***dermatome*** (see Figure 15-8). Dermatomes are important clinically, because loss of sensation in a particular dermatome indicates the level of a spinal lesion or damage to a spinal nerve root.

| Body Region Affected | Spinal Segment |
|---|---|
| Clavicle | C4 |
| Little finger | C8 |
| Nipples | T4 |
| Umbilicus | T10 |
| Inguinal area | L1 |
| Anterior thigh | L3 |
| Big toe | L5 |
| Lateral side of foot | S1 |
| Perineum | S3–S5 |

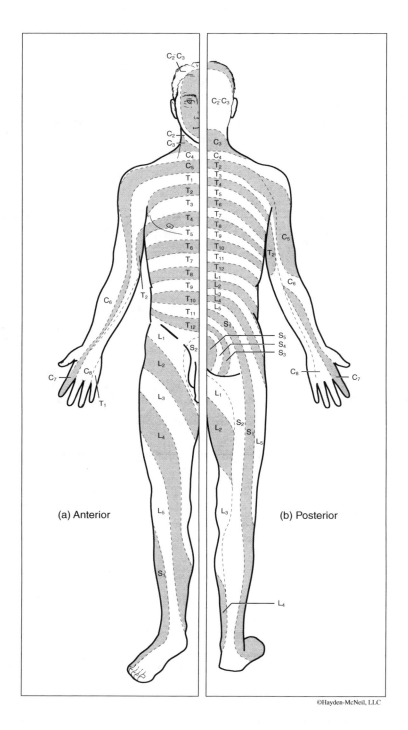

**Figure 15-9.** Dermatomes.

## C. Organization of Gray and White Matter in the Spinal Cord

The spinal cord is partially divided into right and left halves by a deep ***anterior (ventral) median fissure*** and a shallow ***posterior (dorsal) median sulcus.***

The spinal cord is composed of gray and white matter.

The gray matter, which consists of many cell bodies of different neurons with their axons and dendrites, occupies the central region of the cord, and looks like a butterfly or an H in cross-section. The two vertical bars forming the top of the H are called *posterior (dorsal) horns*, and the two vertical bars forming the bottom of the H are called the *anterior (ventral) horns*. The cross-bar of the H is the *gray commissure.*

The cell bodies of motor neurons are clustered in the ventral horn gray matter. Other neurons in the spinal cord gray matter are interneurons. Some of these interneurons send axons in the lateral and ventral columns of the white matter for distances ranging from a few to many segments up and down the spinal cord. Such neurons are called *propriospinal neurons.*

The white matter, consisting of nerve fiber tracts, is divided by the gray matter into anterior (ventral), posterior (dorsal) and lateral *funiculi.*

Points to identify in the very simplified cross section of the spinal cord below are:

* white matter and gray matter
* dorsal and ventral roots
* dorsal root ganglion containing the cell bodies of sensory neurons
* ventral horn gray matter containing the cell bodies of motor neurons

323

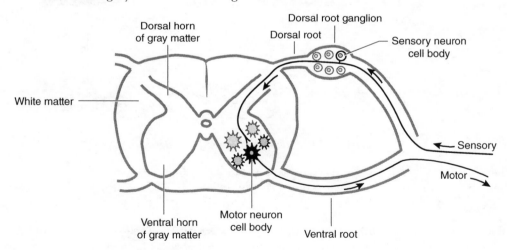

**Figure 15-10.** Simplified cross section of the spinal cord.

There are many neurons that have not been shown. Only the sensory and ventral horn motor neurons are diagrammed. The connections illustrated are for the "knee-jerk" reflex.

## V. The Spinal Cord Function—Organization of Neurons and Nerve Fiber Tracts

The major functions of the spinal cord are:

- It is the major pathway for all **information ascending** to the brain from the **sensory** systems of the body.

- It is also the major pathway for all **commands descending** from the brain to the **muscles** and other **effector** systems.

- The spinal cord is able to **execute** certain simple behavioral activities without involving the brain. These activities are referred to as *spinal reflexes* (dealt with in Section VI). Additionally (as we have mentioned in the introduction), neural networks in the spinal cord are responsible for storing the **motor program** involved in **walking**.

### A. Ascending Pathways (Tracts)

There are three major ascending systems conveying somatic sensory information to the brain. One of these systems is specifically used for carrying sensory information to the cerebellum.

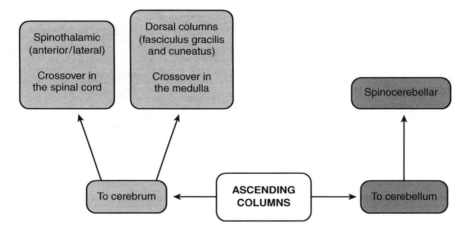

**Figure 15-11.** Summary of ascending pathways.

The first two ascending systems provide an example of the use of parallel pathways (see Section III above). Parallel pathways add subtlety and richness to the sensory experience, and also act as insurance against damage to one of them.

1.  The **dorsal column tracts** ascend in the *fasciculus gracilis* (gracile fasciculus) and *fasciculus cuneatus* (cuneate fasciculus) of the spinal cord white matter. They synapse with neurons in the **nucleus gracilis** and **nucleus cuneatus** in the medulla. The fibers from these neurons cross over to the opposite side *in the medulla*, so that signals from sensory receptors on the left side of the body are transmitted to the right side of the brain, and vice versa.

The following sensory information is carried by this system:

a.   fine, discriminatory touch

b.   vibration

c.   kinesthesia, proprioception (limb movement, position)

d.   pressure

2.   The ***anterior and lateral tracts***, which include the anterior and lateral *spinothalamic tracts*, are older on the evolutionary scale than the dorsal column tracts. The anterior and lateral spinothalamic tracts are located in the lateral and anterior funiculi of the spinal cord white matter. Most of the nerve fibers in this system cross over to the opposite side *in the spinal cord*. There is a small contingent of uncrossed fibers, however.

The following sensory information is carried by this system:

a.   crude touch (includes tickle and itch)

b.   pain

c.   temperature

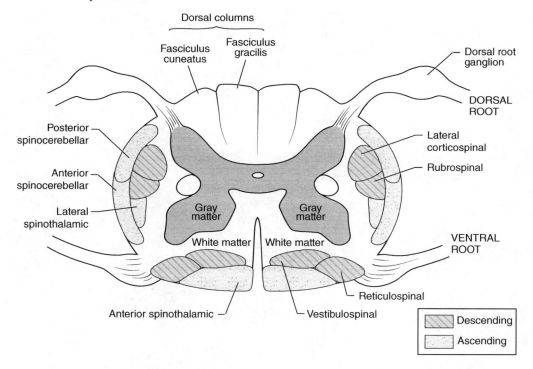

**Figure 15-12.** The spinal cord.

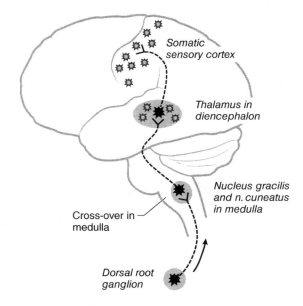

**Figure 15-13.** Dorsal column tracts (ascending).

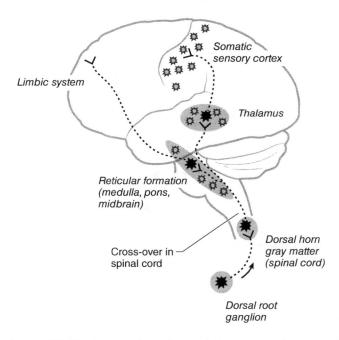

**Figure 15-14.** Anterior/lateral spinothalamic tracts (ascending).

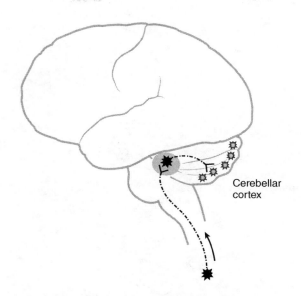

**Figure 15-15.** Spinocerebellar tracts (ascending).

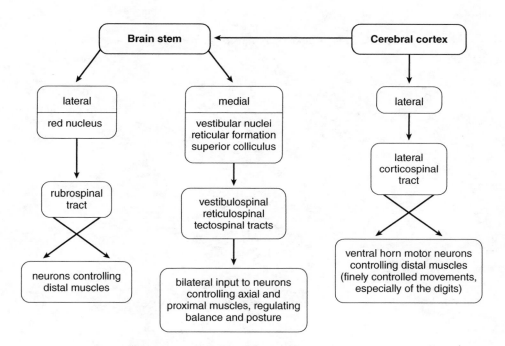

**Figure 15-16.** Summary of descending tracts.

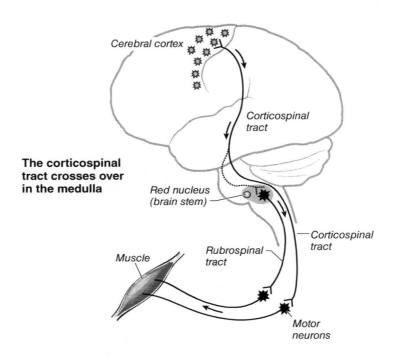

**Figure 15-17.** Corticospinal and rubrospinal tracts (lateral descending).

328

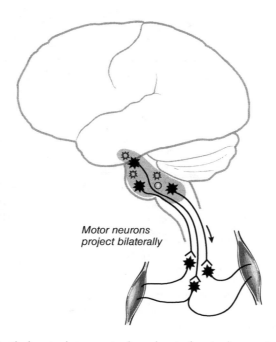

**Figure 15-18.** Vestibulospinal, tectospinal, and reticulospinal tracts (medial descending).

3.  The *spinocerebellar tracts* include the *ventral (anterior) spinocerebellar tract* and the *dorsal (posterior) spinocerebellar tract.* They are located in the lateral funiculi of the spinal cord white matter.

    The following information is carried by this system:

    a.  feedback to the cerebellum of motor signals arriving at the motor neurons in the anterior horns of the gray matter
    b.  muscle spindle discharges
    c.  Golgi tendon organ discharges
    d.  information from the joint receptors
    e.  input from certain skin tactile receptors that provide clues to joint movements and position.

    Via the spinocerebellar tracts, the cerebellum receives important feedback on the progress of ongoing movements.

## B. Descending Pathways (Tracts)

Descending tracts are involved in direct movements, maintenance of posture, modulating ascending sensory systems such as pain, and gating spinal reflex loops.

The three major descending groups of pathways in the spinal cord originate either in the *cerebral cortex* or in the *brain stem.* They include the following tracts, but note that this is not an exhaustive list!

1.  Originating in the cerebral cortex, we have the ***corticospinal*** tracts. In humans there is really only one major tract, the *lateral corticospinal* tract. It originates in the cerebral cortex, crosses over in the medulla, and descends in the lateral funiculi. It is sometimes called the *pyramidal tract.* This tract is concerned with commands for finely controlled movements, often involving the hands and digits.

    > The *anterior* corticospinal tract, mentioned in many textbooks, is a very minor tract in humans, and may not even exist at all in some individuals.

2.  Originating in the **brain stem**, we have the ***reticulospinal, vestibulospinal,*** and ***tectospinal*** tracts (see Chapter 19). The reticulospinal tract originates in the **reticular formation** of the medulla and pons and descends in the medial region of the anterior funiculi. It is not crossed, but neurons receiving input from this tract may project to both sides of the spinal cord.

    The vestibulospinal tract originates in the ***vestibular*** nuclei (of cranial nerve VIII, from the ear), and the tectospinal originates in the ***optic tectum*** (= ***superior colliculus***). The optic tectum is involved in controlling direction of gaze, often in response to new objects that appear in the visual field.

    The reticulospinal and vestibulospinal tracts are involved in the control of posture and balance.

3.  Also originating in the **brain stem**, we have the *rubrospinal tract*. The rubrospinal tract originates in the *red nucleus* (nucleus ruber) of the brain stem, crosses over immediately and descends in the lateral funiculi close to the lateral corticospinal tract. Commands passing down this tract control movements similar to those controlled by the corticospinal tract, but the movements are coarser and not so finely regulated.

### C. Lesions of the Corticospinal Tract (Pathway)

Because the corticospinal tract is a very long one, there are many locations from the cortex to the spinal cord where damage can occur.

*   **Negative** signs caused by a lesion in the corticospinal tract include **loss** of the ability to make fine movements of the digits and distal limb muscles, and **slowness** and **weakness** of voluntary movements. In this situation, most voluntary commands go through the red nucleus and descend in the rubrospinal tract.

*   **Positive** sign – the *Babinski reflex* or *Babinski sign*, described in 1896 by the French neurologist Joseph Babinski. Normally, when the sole of the foot is stroked with the end of a pencil, the foot and toes flex *downward*. When there is damage to the corticospinal tract, however, there is *upward* extension of the big toe, and the other toes fan outward. A Babinski reflex is seen in young infants up to one year, because the corticospinal tract is late to become myelinated.

**Normal plantar response**

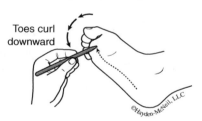

Toes curl downward

**Extensor plantar response**

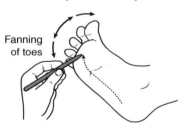

Fanning of toes

Lesion of corticospinal tract causes appearance of Babinski reflex (sign)

**Figure 15-19.** Normal and extensor plantar responses.

## VI. Spinal Reflexes

A spinal reflex is a simple motor response to a stimulus, and it activates only neurons in the spinal cord. The basic components of a spinal reflex are as follows:

*   a sensory receptor
*   a sensory neuron attached to the sensory receptor
*   sometimes an interneuron
*   a motor neuron
*   an effector, such as a gland or muscle

There are many types of reflexes. The simplest is the knee-jerk reflex, which is an example of the stretch reflex. This reflex is the only one that does not involve an interneuron.

### A. The Knee-Jerk Reflex—An Example of a Stretch Reflex

The extensor muscles in the legs are "antigravity muscles." When we are standing, they are usually partially contracted. If something happens to disturb our posture, these muscles are sometimes stretched. This is rapidly counterbalanced by stronger contraction of the antigravity muscles as a result of the so-called spinal *stretch reflexes*. The sensory receptors are the *muscle spindles*.

The contraction of the extensors called the *quadriceps femoris* muscle group in the knee-jerk reflex is the simplest of all the stretch reflexes. Only two types of neuron are involved—the **sensory** neurons in the dorsal root ganglion that receive information from the muscle spindles, and the **motor** neurons in the anterior horn of the spinal gray matter.

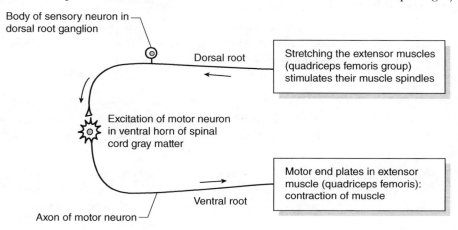

**Figure 15-20.** Neuronal pathway for the knee-jerk reflex, an example of a stretch reflex.

331

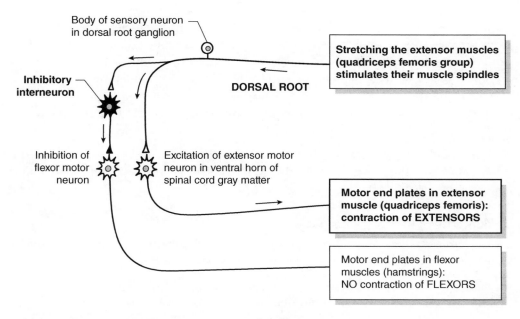

**Figure 15-21.** Knee-jerk reflex. We have added the pathway for reciprocal inhibition of the neurons controlling the flexors.

The reflex is initiated by striking the patellar ligament just below the patella (knee cap). This **stretches** the quadriceps femoris muscle group slightly and stimulates the **muscle spindles** in the muscle. The **sensory neurons** in the dorsal root ganglion synapse directly with, and excite, *motor neurons* in the anterior horn of the spinal cord gray matter. Consequently, the knee-jerk reflex is sometimes called a *monosynaptic reflex.*

Impulses from the excited motor neurons pass out along the axons in the ventral root of the spinal nerve and finally end up in motor end plates in the same muscle. The quadriceps femoris group of muscles contracts. Since these muscles are extensors, their contraction makes the leg kick upward momentarily (i.e. the leg extends).

## B. Reciprocal Inhibition of Neurons during a Movement

But things are not quite as simple as described above. When the **extensor** quadriceps femoris muscles are stimulated, there MUST be inhibition of the motor neurons controlling the **flexor** group of antagonist muscles. Otherwise, they will contract under the influence of their own stretch reflex, and movement would be impossible!

These antagonist muscles that must be inhibited constitute the *hamstring group.* The phenomenon is called *reciprocal inhibition.* This reciprocal inhibition involves an interneuron, and we will discuss this further when we talk about the withdrawal reflex below.

---

Any movement at a joint (whether the result of a conscious command or a spinal reflex) involves excitation of the neurons controlling the prime mover (agonist) and synergist muscles, and reciprocal inhibition of the neurons controlling the antagonist group of muscles.

---

## C. The Stretch Reflex Is Important in Maintaining Posture

*Let's emphasize again that stretch reflexes are not just curiosities that we play with in the lab.* The stretch reflex is prominent in extensor muscles. The extensor muscles in the legs of humans are the "antigravity" muscles and operate to maintain posture. If you are standing upright and something happens to make you sway forward, then the antigravity muscles are stretched. This causes them to contract by the stretch reflex, and posture is restored. Of course, there are other mechanisms that also operate to maintain our balance (e.g. the vestibular apparatus of the ear and the cerebellum), but the stretch reflex is a very basic one.

An important aspect of muscle spindle function is that when the muscle contracts, the *intrafusal fibers* of the muscle spindle also contract. This keeps the muscle spindle taut and cinched up so that it is always responsive to stretch.

## D. Withdrawal Reflex (Flexor Reflex)

The *withdrawal reflex* involves the withdrawal of the entire hand and arm or leg and foot away from an unpleasant, painful stimulus such as a sharp or hot object.

As the diagram shows, the sensory neuron synapses with interneurons in the spinal cord, which then relay signals to the motor neurons of the flexor muscles, causing the arm to be pulled away.

Once again, note that while the flexor muscles are stimulated, there must be inhibition of the neurons controlling the extensor, antagonist muscles. This is called **reciprocal inhibition.**

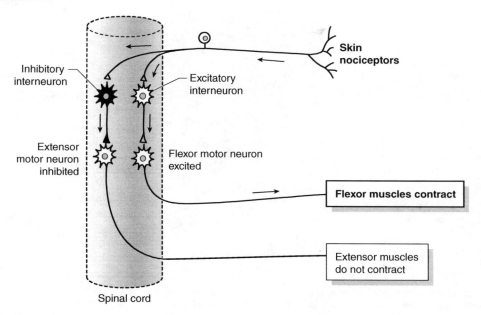

**Figure 15-22.** Simple neuronal pathway for the flexor or withdrawal reflex with reciprocal inhibition. This reflex operates if your hand or foot receives a painful stimulus.

## E. The Crossed Extensor Reflex (Leg Muscles)

It is obvious that if your left foot steps on a sharp nail and initiates the withdrawal reflex in the left leg, you will fall down unless you do something supportive with the right leg.

What happens is that although the *flexors* of the *left* (ipsilateral) leg are stimulated, the *extensors* of the *right* (contralateral) leg are also stimulated. Thus, the stimulated leg flexes and the unstimulated leg extends, straightens and becomes more rigid to support your body.

Reciprocal inhibition ensures that the antagonist muscle group on each side does not interfere with the actions of the prime movers.

This is called the *crossed extensor reflex.*

In summary, the neurons controlling the following muscle groups in the leg are excited or inhibited when the withdrawal reflex is initiated in conjunction with the crossed extensor reflex. Therefore, the neurons controlling the:

- ipsilateral flexors (hamstring group) are stimulated.
- ipsilateral extensors (quadriceps femoris group) are inhibited.
- contralateral flexors (hamstring group) are inhibited.
- contralateral extensors (quadriceps femoris group) are stimulated.

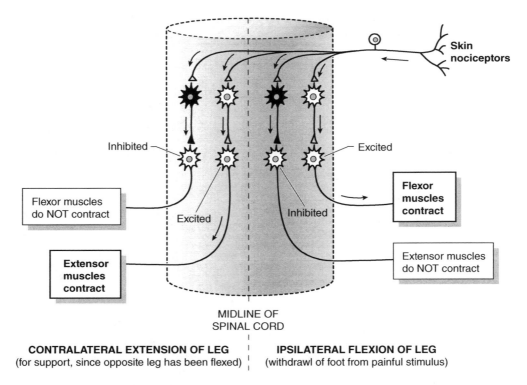

MIDLINE OF
SPINAL CORD

**CONTRALATERAL EXTENSION OF LEG**
(for support, since opposite leg has been flexed)

**IPSILATERAL FLEXION OF LEG**
(withdrawl of foot from painful stimulus)

**Figure 15-23.** Neuronal pathway for the crossed extensor reflex coupled with the flexor reflex, and reciprocal inhibition. This reflex operates if you step on a painful object.

334

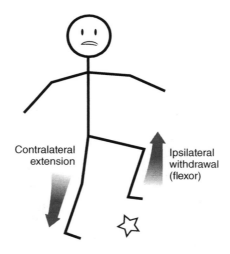

Contralateral
extension

Ipsilateral
withdrawal
(flexor)

**Figure 15-24.**

## F. Spinal Shock

When the spinal cord is cut at the level of the neck or thorax, all spinal reflexes are temporarily lost. This is called *spinal shock.*

Why should this be, when spinal reflexes involve only spinal cord neurons?

The reason is that higher brain centers normally **modulate** and **facilitate** spinal reflexes. When the spinal cord is severed, the descending nerve impulses from these higher facilitatory centers are lost. Therefore, the neurons of the spinal reflexes lose this facilitatory input, become temporarily insensitive, and fail to respond.

During recovery, the spinal reflexes return, often appearing to be exaggerated.

## VII. Spinal and Cranial Nerves You Must Know

You must know the following cranial nerves and their functions.

I.     Olfactory

II.    Optic

III.   Oculomotor

IV.    Trochlear

V.     Trigeminal (three divisions: ophthalmic, maxillary, mandibular)

VI.    Abducens

VII.   Facial

VIII.  Vestibulocochlear (two branches: vestibular, cochlear)

IX.    Glossopharyngeal

X.     Vagus

XI.    Accessory (two branches: cranial, spinal)

XII.   Hypoglossal

You must know the following spinal nerves and the regions they innervate—additionally, you need to know the *number* of pairs of spinal nerves emerging from each segment of the spinal cord (C, T, L, S, Co).

**Cervical plexus**
 phrenic

**Brachial plexus**
 musculocutaneous
 ulnar
 median
 radial
 axillary

**Lumbosacral plexus**
 obturator
 femoral
 sciatic (two divisions: tibial and common peroneal nerves)

**Intercostal nerves**

335

336

# CENTRAL NERVOUS SYSTEM II
Meninges, Ventricles, Cerebrospinal Fluid, Brain Stem, Diencephalon

337

## CHAPTER OUTLINE

I.   Meninges

II.  Ventricles

III. Cerebrospinal fluid
   A.  Formation of cerebrospinal fluid
   B.  Absorption of cerebrospinal fluid
   C.  Composition of cerebrospinal fluid
   D.  Functions of the cerebrospinal fluid

IV.  Brain stem
   A.  Medulla
   B.  Pons
   C.  Midbrain

V.   Diencephalon
   A.  Thalamus
   B.  Hypothalamus
   C.  Other parts of the diencephalon

## DESCRIPTION AND INTRODUCTION

The brain is a hollow structure, the cavities within it being called *ventricles*. The ventricles are filled with *cerebrospinal fluid*. The brain is covered with three membranes called the *meninges*. In this chapter, we will deal with the meninges, the ventricles, and the cerebrospinal fluid that not only fills the ventricles but also bathes the brain's surface.

In the previous chapter, we presented an overview of the main regions of the central nervous system. These were the spinal cord, brain stem, cerebellum, diencephalon, and cerebrum. We focused on the spinal cord and spinal reflexes. In the present chapter, we move to higher regions of the central nervous system—the brain stem and the diencephalon. We will deal with the cerebrum in Chapter 17, leaving the cerebellum for Chapter 18.

## OBJECTIVES

After listening to the lecture and reading this chapter, you should be able to:

1.  Describe the **cavities** in which the brain and spinal cord are found, and describe the **membranes** that cover the brain and spinal cord.

2.  List the **ventricles** in the brain and how they interconnect.

3.  Describe the locations where **cerebrospinal fluid** is found.

4.  Describe the **formation** and **absorption** of cerebrospinal fluid.

5.  List three **functions** of the cerebrospinal fluid.

6.  State one substance that is present in **high amounts in blood plasma** but is quite **low** in cerebrospinal fluid.

7.  Name the parts of the **brain stem** and the functions of each.

8.  Name the parts of the **diencephalon** and the functions of each.

9.  List the **cranial nerves** that are involved with each part of the brain stem.

## I. Meninges

The brain and spinal cord are well-protected against damage that could be inflicted by outside agents. The brain occupies the cranial cavity of the skull and the spinal cord occupies the vertebral canal in the spinal cord. Within these cavities, the brain and spinal cord are covered by special membranes called *meninges*.

Inflammation of the meninges is called *meningitis*. There are two major types of meningitis.

1.  *Viral* ("aseptic") meningitis is usually caused by enteroviruses.  It is contagious, serious but rarely fatal.

2.  *Bacterial* meningitis is not as common, and is usually caused by *Streptococcus pneumoniae* or *Neisseria meningitidis*. It can be very serious and result in disability or death if not treated promptly.

3.  *Fungal* meningitis is the least common of these three types.

The meninges are made up of three membranes.

*   **Dura mater** (means "tough mother") – the outermost membrane. The dura mater is composed of fibrous connective tissue containing blood vessels and nerves. The dura mater often extends between the lobes of the brain, forming partial partitions. In some areas, the dura mater is split into two layers, enclosing the *dural sinuses*, which are filled with blood (see later).

    In the spinal cord, between the dura mater and the wall of the vertebral canal, is the *epidural space*. It is filled with fat, connective tissue and blood vessels. The epidural space inferior to the second lumbar vertebra is the site for the injection of spinal anesthetics.

*   **Arachnoid mater** ("spiderlike mother") – the middle membrane. The arachnoid mater is a thin, spider's web-like membrane lacking blood vessels. Beneath it lies the *subarachnoid space* that contains *cerebrospinal fluid*. Arachnoid cysts can sometimes develop. They are CSF-filled sacs in the subarachnoid space.

*   **Pia mater** ("delicate mother") – the innermost membrane. The pia mater is thin, and contains nerves and blood vessels. It follows the contours of the brain and spinal cord quite closely.

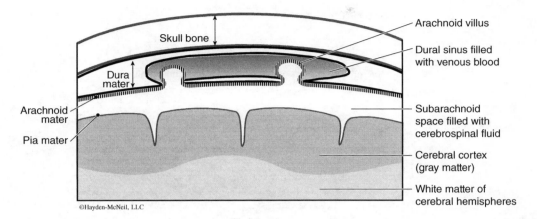

**Figure 16-1.** Arrangement of meninges (membranes) covering the brain.

Structures in order, from exterior to interior in Figure 16-1 are:

1.  skull bones
2.  dura mater – very thick, but split in parts to form the dural sinuses filled with venous blood
3.  arachnoid mater, with arachnoid villi (granulations) projecting into the dural sinuses – cerebrospinal fluid moves through these structures from the subarachnoid space into the blood filling the dural sinuses
4.  subarachnoid space – filled with cerebrospinal fluid
5.  pia mater – very thin, tightly follows contours of the surface of the brain
6.  surface of the brain – cerebral cortex (gray matter)
7.  cerebral white matter

339

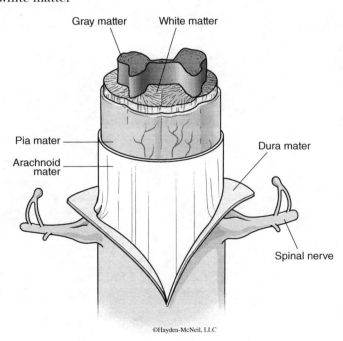

**Figure 16-2.** Posterior (dorsal) view of spinal cord and meninges.

ANTERIOR (VENTRAL) ASPECT

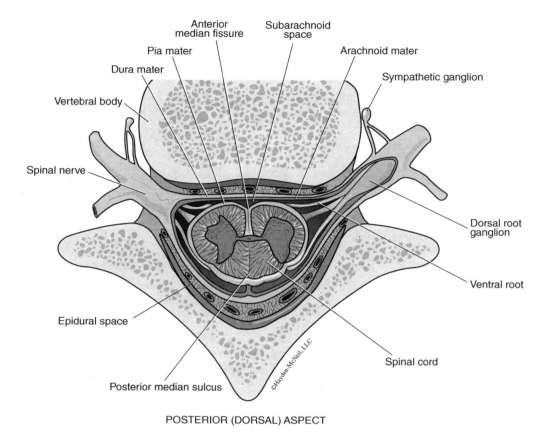

POSTERIOR (DORSAL) ASPECT

**Figure 16-3.** Transverse section of spinal cord, meninges, vertebra.

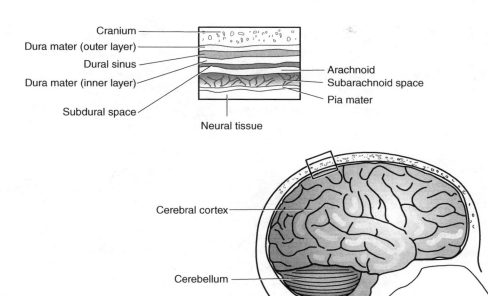

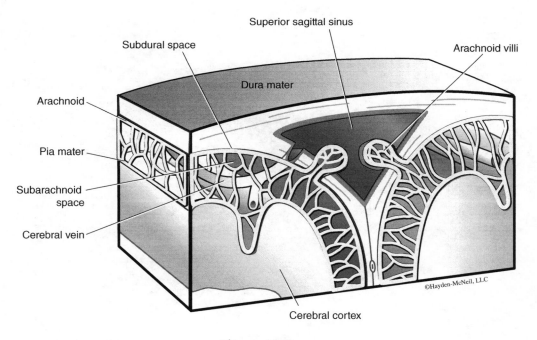

**Figure 16-4.**

## II. Ventricles

The cerebral hemispheres and brain stem are hollow, and contain four interconnected cavities called *ventricles*. The ventricles are continuous with the central canal of the spinal cord, and contain cerebrospinal fluid.

There are four ventricles. The *lateral ventricles* are the largest.

- The **right lateral** ventricle.

- The **left lateral** ventricle.

- The *third* ventricle is small. It connects with the lateral ventricles through *interventricular foramina.*

- The *fourth* ventricle is connected at its anterior end to the third ventricle via the *aqueduct of Sylvius* (cerebral aqueduct), and is continuous with the **central canal** of the spinal cord at its posterior end. The fourth ventricle has openings in its roof that permit cerebrospinal fluid to pass into the subarachnoid space.

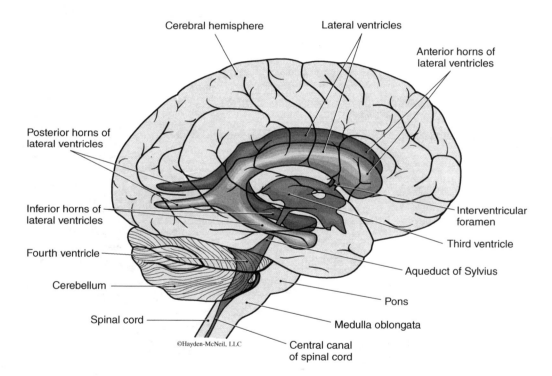

**Figure 16-5.** Ventricles, lateral view.

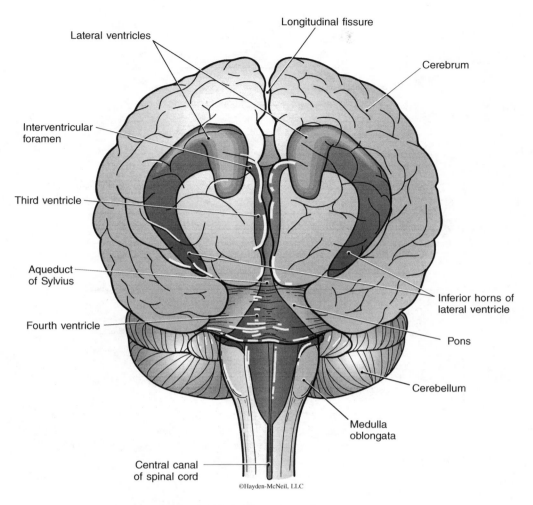

**Figure 16-6.** Ventricles, inferior view.

343

## III. Cerebrospinal Fluid

### A. Formation of Cerebrospinal Fluid

Most of the cerebrospinal fluid (about 140 mL) is found in the four ventricles, where it is formed mainly by the *choroid plexuses* at the rate of about 500–800 mL per day.

Choroid plexuses are found in all ventricles. They consist mainly of capillary networks surrounded by epithelial-like **ependymal** cells of the neuroglia.

Cerebrospinal fluid flows from the lateral ventricles through the interventricular foramina into the third ventricle. From the third ventricle it flows into the fourth ventricle through the aqueduct of Sylvius.

From the fourth ventricle, cerebrospinal fluid flows into the *central canal* of the spinal cord and also out of the fourth ventricle into the subarachnoid space. Within the subarachnoid space, cerebrospinal fluid bathes the surface of the pia mater covering the brain and spinal cord.

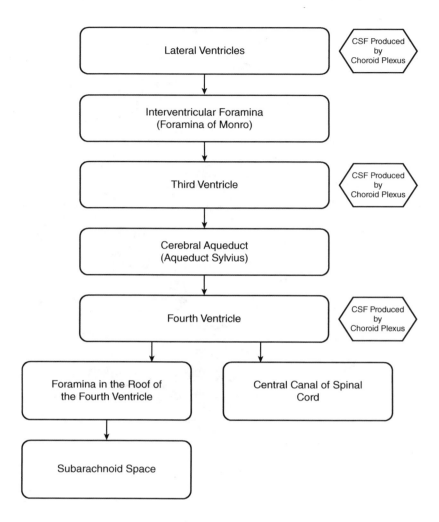

344

**Figure 16-7.**

## B. Absorption of Cerebrospinal Fluid

Cerebrospinal fluid is reabsorbed into the blood through herniations of the arachnoid membrane through the dura mater. These herniations are finger-like processes that are called **arachnoid granulations** or *arachnoid villi*. They project into the lumina of the **dural sinuses**, which are filled with venous blood that will be returned to the heart. The mechanism of reabsorption of cerebrospinal fluid is not fully understood.

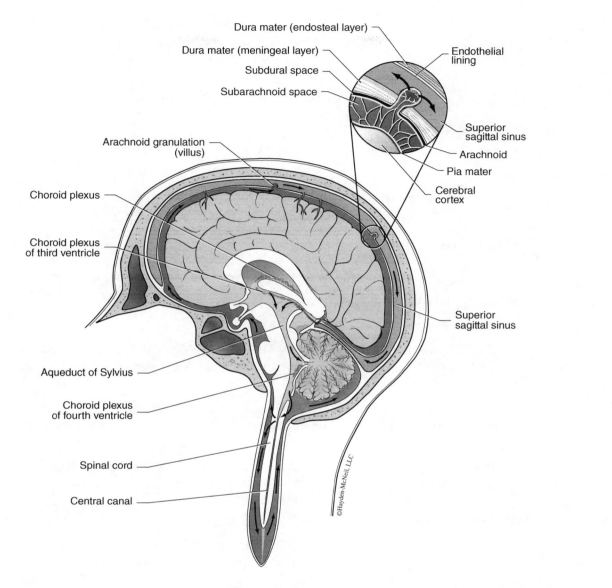

Dura mater (endosteal layer)
Dura mater (meningeal layer)
Subdural space
Subarachnoid space

Endothelial
lining

Superior
sagittal sinus

Arachnoid

Pia mater

Cerebral
cortex

Arachnoid granulation
(villus)

Choroid plexus

Choroid plexus
of third ventricle

Superior
sagittal sinus

Aqueduct of Sylvius

Choroid plexus
of fourth ventricle

Spinal cord

Central canal

©Hayden-McNeil, LLC

**Figure 16-8.**

## C. Composition of Cerebrospinal Fluid

The major difference between cerebrospinal fluid and serum is that cerebrospinal fluid has much, much less protein. There are smaller differences in most of its other components. The pH of cerebrospinal fluid is somewhat lower than that of serum. Cerebrospinal fluid can be withdrawn from a patient via a lumbar puncture.

Comparison of the Compositions of Cerebrospinal Fluid and Serum

| Component | Cerebrospinal Fluid | Serum |
|---|---|---|
| water (%) | 99 | 93 |
| **protein** (mg/dL) | **35** | **7000** |
| glucose (mg/dL) | 60 | 90 |
| sodium ions (meq/liter) | 138 | 138 |
| potassium ions (meq/liter) | 2.8 | 4.5 |
| calcium ions (meq/liter) | 2.1 | 4.8 |
| magnesium ions (meq/liter) | 2.3 | 1.7 |
| chloride ions (meq/liter) | 119 | 102 |
| pH | 7.33 | 7.41 |

## D. Functions of the Cerebrospinal Fluid

The cerebrospinal fluid has several functions.

1.  Because it is in equilibrium with the brain extracellular fluid, the cerebrospinal fluid is important in maintaining a constant **external environment** for the neurons and neuroglia of the brain.

2.  The brain effectively floats in the cerebrospinal fluid, which provides a liquid **cushion** that protects the brain from impact with the bones of the skull when the head moves.

3.  The cerebrospinal fluid serves to **remove** waste substances from the brain and transfer them to the blood, and may act to **distribute** some peptide hormones and nutrients.

## IV. Brain Stem

The *brain stem* consists of the ***medulla***, ***pons*** and ***midbrain***. It is made up of nerve fiber tracts and masses of nerve cells (gray matter) that are called *nuclei* (NOT the same as the nuclei of individual cells). The brain stem regulates many vital reflexes that control heart rate, blood pressure, respiration, swallowing, vomiting, etc. These centers are located in the lower brain stem, so a sharp blow to the base of the skull can kill a person by disrupting some of these reflexes, such as those regulating respiration.

## A. Medulla

The medulla is an enlarged continuation of the spinal cord, and resembles the spinal cord in its organization. It contains all of the ascending and descending tracts that communicate between the spinal cord and various parts of the brain. These tracts constitute the white matter of the medulla.

On the ventral side, there are two roughly triangular structures called the *pyramids*. They carry the fibers of the large motor tracts from the cerebral cortex to the spinal cord—the corticospinal tracts. Fibers in these tracts cross over to opposite sides in the *pyramidal decussation*.

The dorsal side of the medulla contains two pairs of prominent nuclei, the ***nucleus gracilis*** and ***nucleus cuneatus***, which receive sensory fibers from the fasciculus gracilis and fasciculus cuneatus.

Part of the ***reticular formation*** is found in the medulla. It is a diffusely-organized system of dispersed gray matter, nuclei and some white fibers that extends upward throughout the rest of the brain stem and up into the diencephalon. The reticular formation is important in maintenance of consciousness and in arousal from sleep. It has other functions, including the modulation of pain impulses and spinal reflexes. The term *reticular formation* is rarely used now, except when we are addressing generalities. These days we usually refer to the individual nuclei which make up the reticular formation.

The medulla contains a number of **reflex centers**. The most important are concerned with the heart (the *cardiac center*), breathing (*medullary rhythmicity center*) and the blood vessels (the *vasomotor center*). Other centers are involved in swallowing, vomiting, coughing, sneezing and hiccuping.

The medulla contains the nuclei of origin of the following cranial nerves.

1.  The cochlear and vestibular branches of VIII (hearing and balance)

2.  The glossopharyngeal nerves (IX, swallowing, salivation, taste)

3.  The vagus nerve (X, innervates many thoracic and abdominal viscera)

4.  The cranial portion of the accessory nerve (XI), which conveys nerve impulses related to head and shoulder movements (note that there is a spinal portion to this nerve, which originates in the upper five cervical segments of the spinal cord)

5.  The hypoglossal nerve (XII), conveys nerve impulses relating to tongue movements

On each lateral surface of the medulla is an oval projection called the *olive*, which contains the ***olivary nuclei*** whose cells have axons that connect with the cerebellum and probably play a role in learning of motor tasks (such as riding a bicycle).

The medulla is connected to the cerebellum by nerve fiber tracts called the ***inferior cerebellar peduncles.***

Also associated with the medulla are most of the ***vestibular nuclei***. These nuclei play a vital role in maintaining balance.

In view of the many vital functions controlled by neurons in the medulla, it is not surprising that there are often fatal consequences to a hard blow to the base of the skull (where the medulla is located).

## B. Pons

The pons contains large fiber tracts and nuclei. Large bundles of transverse fibers (***middle cerebellar peduncles***) transmit information from the cerebrum to the cerebellum.

The pons contains the nuclei for the following cranial nerves.

1.  The trigeminal (V) – a motor nerve for chewing and a sensory nerve innervating the head and face

2.  The abducens (VI) – regulates certain eyeball movements

3.  The facial (VII) – conducts impulses related to taste, salivation, facial expression

4.  The vestibular branches of the vestibulocochlear nerve (VIII) – are concerned with balance

Several nuclei in the pons relay sensory impulses from peripheral nerves to higher brain centers, and other nuclei in the reticular formation of the pons work together with nuclei in the medulla to regulate the rate and depth of breathing.

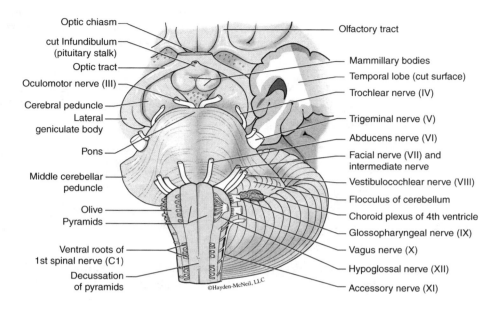

Optic chiasm
cut Infundibulum (pituitary stalk)
Optic tract
Oculomotor nerve (III)
Cerebral peduncle
Lateral geniculate body
Pons
Middle cerebellar peduncle
Olive
Pyramids
Ventral roots of 1st spinal nerve (C1)
Decussation of pyramids

Olfactory tract
Mammillary bodies
Temporal lobe (cut surface)
Trochlear nerve (IV)
Trigeminal nerve (V)
Abducens nerve (VI)
Facial nerve (VII) and intermediate nerve
Vestibulocochlear nerve (VIII)
Flocculus of cerebellum
Choroid plexus of 4th ventricle
Glossopharyngeal nerve (IX)
Vagus nerve (X)
Hypoglossal nerve (XII)
Accessory nerve (XI)

©Hayden-McNeil, LLC

**Figure 16-9.** Brain stem, anterior view.

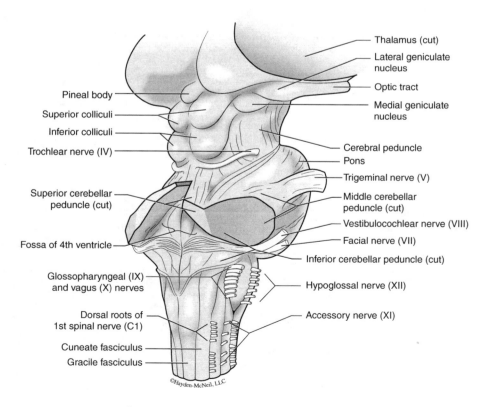

Pineal body
Superior colliculi
Inferior colliculi
Trochlear nerve (IV)
Superior cerebellar peduncle (cut)
Fossa of 4th ventricle
Glossopharyngeal (IX) and vagus (X) nerves
Dorsal roots of 1st spinal nerve (C1)
Cuneate fasciculus
Gracile fasciculus

Thalamus (cut)
Lateral geniculate nucleus
Optic tract
Medial geniculate nucleus
Cerebral peduncle
Pons
Trigeminal nerve (V)
Middle cerebellar peduncle (cut)
Vestibulocochlear nerve (VIII)
Facial nerve (VII)
Inferior cerebellar peduncle (cut)
Hypoglossal nerve (XII)
Accessory nerve (XI)

©Hayden-McNeil, LLC

**Figure 16-10.** Brain stem, posterolateral view.

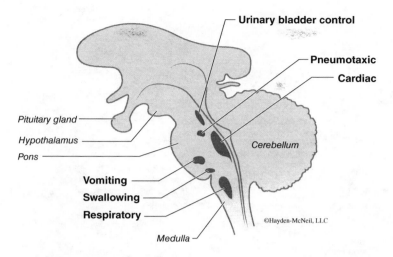

**Figure 16-11.** Regulatory centers in the brain stem.

## C. Midbrain

The cerebral aqueduct passes through the center of the midbrain. Large fiber tracts pass through the midbrain. Two prominent bundles of fibers on the underside of the midbrain comprise the *cerebral peduncles*. These include the corticospinal tracts and sensory fibers that connect with the thalamus in the diencephalon.

Two pairs of rounded eminences called the *corpora quadrigemina* on the surface of the midbrain contain four important nuclei serving as reflex centers for movements of the eyeballs and head and neck in response to visual and other stimuli (the *superior colliculi*), and movements of the head and trunk in response to auditory stimuli (the *inferior colliculi*).

Two important colored nuclei are found in the midbrain. There is the black *substantia nigra*, and the *red nucleus*. Also, there is the *subthalamic nucleus*.

The midbrain contains the nuclei for the following cranial nerves.

1.  The oculomotor nerves (III)
2.  The trochlear nerves (IV)

Both these nerves control the extraocular muscles, which produce eye movements (cranial nerve VI, the abducens, is also involved in controlling the extraocular muscles).

349

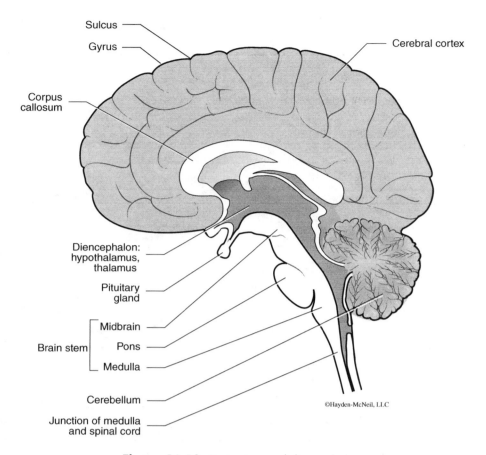

Figure labels:
Sulcus
Gyrus
Cerebral cortex
Corpus callosum
Diencephalon: hypothalamus, thalamus
Pituitary gland
Midbrain
Pons
Medulla
Brain stem
Cerebellum
Junction of medulla and spinal cord

©Hayden-McNeil, LLC

**Figure 16-12.** Brain stem and diencephalon.

## V. Diencephalon

The two major components of the diencephalon are the *thalamus* and *hypothalamus*.

### A. Thalamus

The thalamus is a massive collection of nuclei. It looks like two large eggs, one on the left side of the midline, the other on the right, each bulging into the third ventricle. In most people, there is a connection between the two (called the thalamic adhesion).

In its strategic position between the midbrain and the cerebral hemispheres, the thalamus fulfills its important function as the major **relay** and **processing** station for **all information passing to the cerebral cortex**.

Connections to the thalamus are as follows:

1.  From the *spinal cord and the sensory fibers of the cranial nerves*: sensory information from the spinal cord and the sensory fibers of the appropriate cranial nerves is relayed through neurons in the thalamus before passing on to the cerebral cortex. The fibers of the optic nerve (II) synapse with neurons in the *lateral geniculate nucleus* of the thalamus.

    One exception is smell: the fibers of cranial nerve I terminate in the *olfactory bulbs* lying below the frontal lobes of the cerebrum.

2.  From the *cerebellum*: information from the cerebellum destined for the cerebral cortex passes first through neurons in the thalamus.

3.  From the *basal ganglia*: information from the basal ganglia is relayed to the cerebral cortex through neurons in the thalamus.

4.  Not only does the thalamus convey information to the cerebral cortex, but the cerebral cortex talks back to the thalamus. We find that each part of the thalamus receives massive feedback from the part of the cerebral cortex to which it sends information. Why? We are still trying to understand these cortico–thalamic connections, but it seems that they may be important in assisting the cortex in handling and interpreting sensory information.

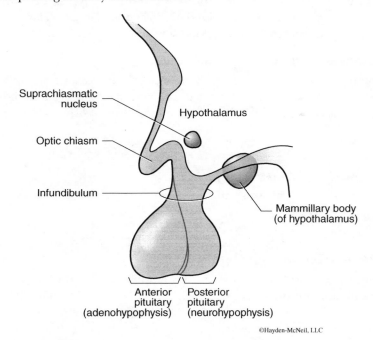

©Hayden-McNeil, LLC

**Figure 16-13.** Hypothalamus and pituitary gland.

## B. Hypothalamus

The hypothalamus is located below the thalamus, and is widely interconnected with the rest of the brain. The ***pituitary gland*** is connected to the base of the hypothalamus by the *pituitary stalk*, or *infundibulum*.

The hypothalamus contains many regions and nuclei. There are receptors in the hypothalamus that monitor salt concentration of the body fluids, blood temperature, and even certain hormone concentrations.

### Homeostatic activities

The hypothalamus plays a key role in many homeostatic activities of the body, such as regulation of heart rate and blood pressure, regulation of body temperature, regulation of electrolyte and water balance, control of hunger and body weight, control of visceral movements and glandular secretions.

351

The functions of the hypothalamus include the following. Note that functions 1 and 2 cover many activities associated with homeostasis.

1. **Control and integration of the autonomic nervous system.**

   The hypothalamus controls and integrates the autonomic nervous system, which regulates the contraction of smooth muscle, heart contractions, glandular secretions, vasomotor activity.

2. **Association with the pituitary gland.**

   The hypothalamus has a very close anatomical and physiological association with the pituitary gland, and regulates its hormonal output (these hormones are involved in control of other glands, regulate growth and influence reproductive physiology). Some hormones are actually synthesized in the hypothalamus itself and transported to the pituitary for release into the blood stream.

3. **Output pathway for the limbic system.**

   The hypothalamus is a major output pathway for the *limbic system* (to be discussed later), which is involved in many aspects of emotional behavior and motivation. In this respect it is critically involved in certain motivational drives such as:

   a. feeding and feelings of satiety
   b. drinking
   c. fear, punishment, unease
   d. feelings of reward, pleasure and well-being
   e. rage
   f. sexual drive

4. **Regulation of cyclic activities.**

   The hypothalamus contains a clock in the **suprachiasmatic nucleus** that provides a wake-up call at about the same time each morning. In addition to affecting sleep–wake cycles, the hypothalamus seems to be involved in regulating day-and-night rhythmic events (*circadian rhythms*), including temperature fluctuations keyed to day and night, feeding cycles, etc. It may do this in conjunction with the retina.

## C. Other Parts of the Diencephalon

Other parts of the diencephalon include the *optic tracts* (fibers of the optic nerve, II) and *optic chiasma* (region where the optic nerve fibers partially decussate, or cross over), the **pituitary gland** which is attached to the floor of the diencephalon, the *mammillary bodies* (part of the hypothalamus), and the *pineal gland* which projects from the roof of the diencephalon. In reptiles, amphibia and fish, the pineal may contain photoreceptor cells, and in certain species it may be regarded as a true "third eye." This function has been lost in humans, where the pinealocytes have evolved into neurosecretory cells that receive input from the retina. They secrete the hormone melatonin during the hours of darkness. The function of this hormone is not completely understood, and it will be discussed next semester.

# 17

# CENTRAL NERVOUS SYSTEM III
Cerebrum and Cerebral Cortex, Memory, Sleep, Hemisphere Dominance, Basal Ganglia

## CHAPTER OUTLINE

## DESCRIPTION AND INTRODUCTION

We have completed our discussion of the spinal cord, brain stem and diencephalon (Chapters 15 and 16). We now move to the highest level of the brain, the **cerebrum**. We include the structures of the *limbic system* in this chapter.

Additionally, we are going to talk about two important activities of the brain, both of which are poorly understood.

One of these activities is **sleeping**. *Sleep* takes up one third of our lives. Why do we need sleep, what mysterious events are occurring in the brain while we sleep, and how are they controlled? What are the causes of sleep disorders, which affect as many as 40 million Americans and cost $15 billion?

The other activity relates to the ability of our brains to store within their neuronal circuits imprints of past events and experiences—**memories**. *Memory* represents a bank of information stored within our brains that we can recall. Memory is important both in learning and in modifying our behavioral responses to external situations, many of which may contain elements that we have encountered previously. Memories color our lives, our thought processes and our perceptions. Yet although we have some promising ideas regarding the mechanism of memory, we still cannot really explain its physiological basis.

## OBJECTIVES

After listening to the lecture and reading this chapter, you should be able to:

1. Distinguish between **motor**, **sensory**, and **association** areas of the **cerebral cortex**.
2. Describe the structure of the **cerebrum**.
3. List the anatomical divisions of the **cerebral cortex**.
4. Define the location, function and structure of the **basal ganglia**.
5. Define the **limbic system**, and explain its function.
6. Describe the location and function of the **primary motor areas** of the cerebral cortex.
7. Describe the functions of **Broca's** and **Wernicke's** areas.
8. Describe the location and function of the **sensory areas** of the cerebral cortex.
9. Explain what is meant by the **association areas** of the cerebral cortex.
10. Describe the accident that happened to **Phineas Gage**, and what it tells us about the functions of the **frontal lobes**.
11. Define the three types of **memory** and the suggested role of the **hippocampus** in this brain activity.
12. Define **long-term potentiation** and describe whether it might have a role in memory formation.
13. Name the five structures that make up the **basal ganglia**, and name the parts of the brain where they are found.
14. Name two **diseases** associated with the basal ganglia.
15. Explain what is meant by **hemispheric dominance**.
16. Describe the stages that occur during a typical night's **sleep**.
17. Where is the "**master clock**" located?
18. Describe a possible function of **REM** sleep.
19. Describe the function of the **corpus callosum**, what happens when it is cut, and what this reveals about the difference between the two cerebral hemispheres.

## I. Structure of the Cerebrum

### A. What Makes Up the Cerebrum

The cerebrum, which develops from the anterior portion of the forebrain, consists of left and right masses called the *cerebral hemispheres*.

The surface layer of the cerebrum is composed of gray matter (neurons), and is called the *cerebral cortex.* The cerebral cortex contains billions of nerve cells.

Other areas of gray matter (neurons) are found in masses located deep down within the cerebral hemispheres. These masses of gray matter make up the *putamen, caudate nucleus*, and the *globus pallidus*. These three structures are part of the *basal ganglia*, which also have components in the midbrain.

Beneath the cerebral cortex is the cerebral *white matter*, composed of billions of myelinated nerve fibers that conduct nerve impulses into and out of the cerebral cortex, and also between different areas of the cerebral cortex. A huge band of these fibers connects the two cerebral hemispheres, and is called the *corpus callosum*.

During human embryonic development, the area of the cerebral cortex increases enormously, in order to accommodate the enormous number of neurons. Consequently, it becomes highly convoluted and folded. The convolutions or folds are often referred to as *gyri* (plural of gyrus). Gyri are separated from each other by grooves called *sulci* (plural of sulcus). Very deep grooves are called **fissures**.

A longitudinal fissure separates the right and left cerebral hemispheres. An extension of the dura mater called the *falx cerebri* dips down into this fissure.

355

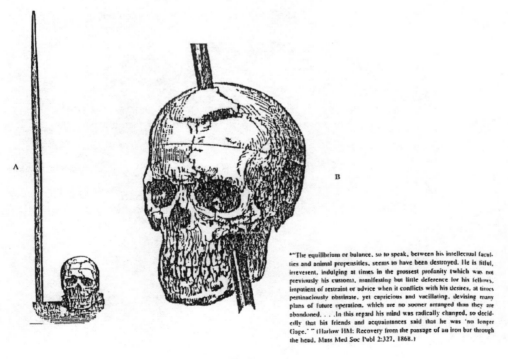

*"The equilibrium or balance, so to speak, between his intellectual faculties and animal propensities, seems to have been destroyed. He is fitful, irreverent, indulging at times in the grossest profanity (which was not previously his custom), manifesting but little deference for his fellows, impatient of restraint or advice when it conflicts with his desires, at times pertinaciously obstinate, yet capricious and vacillating, devising many plans of future operation, which are no sooner arranged than they are abandoned. . . .In this regard his mind was radically changed, so decidedly that his friends and acquaintances said that he was 'no longer Gage.'" (Harlow HM: Recovery from the passage of an iron bar through the head. Mass Med Soc Publ 2:327, 1868.)

**Figure 17-1.**

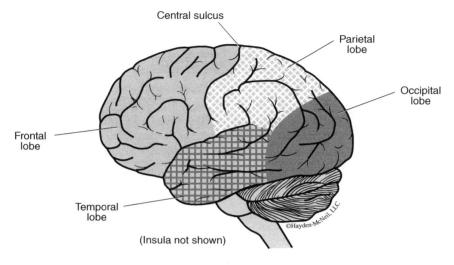

**Figure 17-2.** Lobes of cerebral cortex.

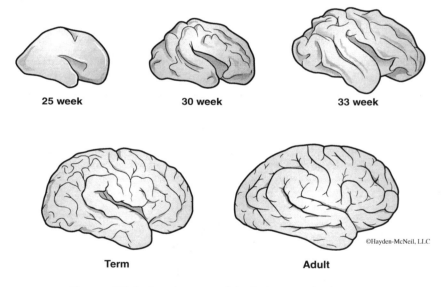

**Figure 17-3.** Development of the human cerebral cortex.

## B. Anatomical Divisions of the Cerebral Cortex

Anatomically, the cerebral cortex is divisible into five lobes, mostly named after the skull bones that overlie them.

1. **Frontal lobe** – contains an important fold or gyrus called the *precentral gyrus*, which is a landmark for the primary motor area of the cerebral cortex (see below).

2. **Parietal lobe** – separated from the frontal lobe by the central groove or sulcus. Another important gyrus called the *postcentral gyrus* is a landmark for the *somatosensory area* of the cerebral cortex (see below).

3. **Temporal lobe** – separated from the frontal lobe by the *lateral sulcus* or *lateral fissure*.

4. **Occipital lobe** – forms the posterior portion of each cerebral hemisphere, and is separated from the cerebellum by a shelf-like extension of the dura mater called the tentorium cerebelli.

5. The **insula** (Latin for "island") – lies deep within the lateral fissure under the parietal, frontal and temporal lobes. It cannot be seen in an external view of the brain unless the temporal lobe is pulled out and away from the rest of the brain. It is delineated by a *circular sulcus*. It has connections with the limbic system, specifically with the amygdala. The insula also receives certain types of sensory information.

## II. The Cerebral Cortex—Functional Areas

357

The cerebral cortex has areas that have different functions. Large regions of the cerebral cortex are committed to movement (the ***motor areas***) and sensation (the ***sensory areas***). ***Association areas*** are involved in our highest intellectual activities and often provide the link between sensation and action. The association areas integrate diverse information, often from many different forms of sensation (sensory modalities) and from other cortical areas.

Much of our knowledge stems from studies done by Penfield between 1950 and 1970. *Penfield* carried out electrical studies of the cerebral cortex in humans during neurosurgery, and was able to draw maps of the human sensory and motor areas. More recently, PET techniques (see Chapter 1) have provided important information on the areas of cerebral cortex that become active during various mental activities.

## A. Motor Areas

The motor areas contain *primary* and *higher-order* areas. Primary motor areas execute voluntary movements, while higher-order motor areas are involved in the planning of movements. The integration of movements and the tracts involved will be discussed in Chapter 19.

The major *primary motor area* is located in the precentral gyrus of the frontal lobe (Figure 17-4). Different parts of this area control movements in different parts of the body, which are roughly mapped on the surface of the cerebral cortex.

**Language and speech:** Other motor areas are involved in certain complex motor functions. One very important one is concerned with language, one of our highest cognitive functions. Language is one of the major links connecting one person with another, as well as to the historical record of civilization.

The *motor speech area*, or **Broca's area**, is in the frontal lobe (usually on the left side) just anterior to the primary motor cortex and above the lateral fissure. Broca's area controls all activities associated with speech production, including articulation and facial expression.

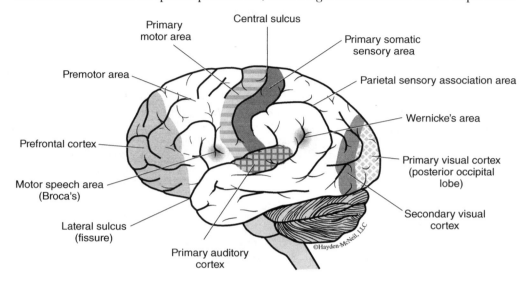

**Figure 17-4.** Functional areas of the cerebral cortex.

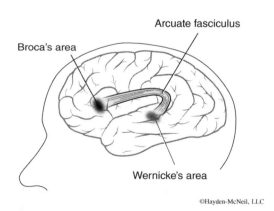

**Figure 17-5.** Broca's area and Wernicke's area.

This area coordinates the complex movements of mouth, tongue, larynx and breathing that make speech possible. A patient with a lesion in this area (known as a ***Broca's aphasia***) can comprehend speech, but cannot talk properly. In the 1860s, Broca discovered this area by noting that patients with damage to the left frontal lobe were unable to speak (i.e. they suffered from aphasia).

Another area that is intimately involved in language is found in the temporal lobe, close to the primary auditory area. This is called **Wernicke's area**. It is involved in language reception and comprehension. It processes both verbal and visual commands received by the eyes and ears. An important bundle of fibers called the *arcuate fasciculus* connects Wernicke's area with Broca's area. A lesion in Wernicke's area does not impair a patient's ability to speak, but they cannot understand. Such patients often speak fluently, but the words often convey little meaning and they cannot convey the ideas they have in their minds.

Above Broca's area is the frontal eye field area, which is involved in voluntary gaze control. Another eye field area is found in the occipital lobes, and seems to be involved in tracking movements of the eyes, as when a spectator watches the ball in a tennis match.

## B. Sensory Areas

**Primary sensory areas** receive information from sensory receptors, while **higher order** sensory areas process more complex aspects of the sensation, and analyze and integrate information that they receive from the primary sensory areas.

The primary **somatic sensory** area is located in the parietal lobe, in the **postcentral** *gyrus* (Figure 17-4). The body surface is mapped roughly on the surface of this gyrus. Damage to this area can lead to loss of fine localization of stimuli, loss of the ability to judge weights, shapes and textures.

The primary **visual** *area* is located on the medial surface of the **occipital** lobe, and the primary **auditory** *area* is located in the superior part of the **temporal** lobe near the lateral fissure. Primary areas for **taste** and **smell** are found in the **parietal** and **temporal** lobes, respectively.

## C. Association Areas

Association areas integrate diverse information, often for purposeful action. In consequence they often provide the link between sensation and action.

Association areas are found in regions of the parietal, temporal, occipital and frontal lobes. One part of the parietal lobe is known to be important in our awareness of our bodies and where all the parts are located in relation to our surroundings. People with damage to this region may fail to recognize parts of their body as belonging to them. For example, such a person might wake up startled, believing that someone had put a fake leg into bed with them. It was really their own leg they were looking at.

The region in the frontal lobe called the **prefrontal association cortex** has important functions in planning complex voluntary movements, thinking, problem-solving and other highly intellectual functions.

The prefrontal association cortex appears to play an important role in personality and emotional drive. In fact, this area is included in the *limbic system* by many authorities (see Section F).

During evolution of the mammals, this part of the cortex expanded dramatically. In human evolution, the development of a distinctively high forehead seems to be associated with the need to accommodate the increasing size of the prefrontal cortex. The

359

prefrontal cortex seems to be involved in the highest intellectual functions that include thinking and problem-solving. It appears to play an important role in personality and emotional drive: it has extensive linkages with the limbic system via the thalamus.

## D. The Story of Phineas Gage and His Horrible Accident

The brain may have a center that is associated with social behavior and morality. This center lies in the prefrontal cortex of the frontal lobe. Much has been learned about this part of the brain as a result of a strange and horrific accident that took place in 1848. *Phineas Gage*, a 25-year-old New England construction foreman for the Rutland & Burlington Railroad, was involved in laying track across Vermont. He drilled holes in rock, poured in blasting powder, laid a fuse, then filled the rest of the hole with sand. The sand was tamped down with a 13-pound, 3.5 foot long, 1.25" diameter iron rod. At the time of the accident, Gage had been momentarily distracted, and started tamping before his assistant had covered the charge with sand. The charge exploded and drove the iron just under his left cheek, up behind his left eye (which it destroyed) and out of the frontal part of his skull into the sky. The rod landed some yards away.

Incredibly, Gage seemed to be only momentarily stunned, even though much of the frontal lobe must have been destroyed. He stood up, began talking normally, and was able to walk with assistance. He was given a room at a local tavern, and had recovered physically in a matter of months! However, there was a dramatic change in personality. Gage's memory and high intelligence remained intact, but he had lost all respect for social conventions. He used profane language, lied to his friends, and could not be trusted to honor his commitments. In the words of his friends, "Gage was no longer Gage." He died in the custody of his family in San Francisco in 1861, thirteen years after his accident.

More recently, other patients with frontal lobe damage have been found to behave very similarly. They have problems in making rational decisions in personal and social affairs, and cannot process emotions. These individuals are found to be no longer trustworthy, and are impossible to employ. Persons with damage involving this region behave totally irrationally when it comes to their personal and social behavior. However, they are still smart, and perform well on intelligence tests. The reason is that there is a second (undamaged) region of the frontal lobes that is concerned with extrapersonal space, objects, language and arithmetic.

At present, we conclude that one region of the frontal lobes contains a separate circuit for decision-making within the *social* domain, with input from the *emotions*. This region has reciprocal connections with the amygdala and hypothalamus. The region also shows a high concentration of certain serotonin receptors in socially adapted monkeys, but low concentrations in aggressive, socially uncooperative animals.

## E. Modern Computer Analysis of the Brain Region Destroyed in Phineas Gage's Accident

In 1994, a century and a half later, Dr. Hanna Damasio and her associates took another look at Phineas Gage's skull, which had been preserved along with the tamping iron in the Warren Anatomical Medical Museum at Harvard. Advanced computer technology was used to reconstruct the nature and extent of the brain injury sustained by Gage. Various trajectories of the rod were investigated, and the one chosen was one that spared language and motor function, but fitted the holes in the skull. In that way, Dr. Damasio was able to identify the region destroyed much more precisely. [Damasio, H., Grabowski, T., Frank, R., Galaburda, A.M., Damasio, A.R. (1994). The return of Phineas Gage: clues about the brain from the skull of a famous patient. *Science 264*, 1102–1105].

## F. The Limbic System

The prefrontal association area that we have just been talking about is often considered part of the **limbic system**. The limbic system is a loose term for a group of gyri and associated structures (not necessarily cortical) that roughly encircles the corpus callosum and the diencephalon. In turn, the limbic system is encircled by the temporal, occipital, parietal and frontal lobes.

The limbic system will be discussed in more detail in Chapter 19.

The hypothalamus is the major output path of the limbic system, and is included in it.

Functions of the limbic system include the following.

1.  Self-preservation (feeding, fight, flight)
2.  Reproduction (mating, care of offspring)
3.  Emotions, goal-related behavior, motivation, sensations of reward, pleasure and punishment
4.  Memory
5.  The limbic system provides a link between the conscious functions of the cerebral cortex and the autonomic nervous system and endocrine system via the hypothalamus

Note that nuclei associated with many (but not all) of these functions are found in the **hypothalamus**. As noted above, much of the output of the limbic system goes to the hypothalamus.

## G. Memory

People have three kinds of *memory*:

*   procedural or "knowing how" memory
*   immediate or working memory
*   declarative or "knowing that" memory, divided into short-term (recent) memory and long-term memory

361

1.  **Procedural memory or "knowing how" memory.**

    One kind of memory is called *procedural memory*. It is concerned with the learning of motor skills. Knowing how to type, play the piano, or ride a bicycle are examples.

    Some procedural memories appear to involve the cerebellum.

2.  **Immediate or working memory.**

    Lasts a few seconds to a few minutes. Working memory is a store that holds important information in the mind for brief periods of time. It enables us to retain a piece of sensory information just long enough to plan a response. For example, the sensory information could be what someone has said, and the response would be our reply. Working memory enables us to remember a telephone number just long enough to dial it. Working memory is temporary and its capacity seems to be limited.

    *Working memory* seems to involve many brain areas, but particularly the prefrontal and posterior parietal cortex.

3.  **Declarative memory or "knowing that" memory.**

    The kind of memory that most people think of as memory holds the names of things and people, occurrences, events, and other pieces of facts for periods of time ranging from days to a lifetime. It is known as declarative memory. *Declarative memory* is divisible into two types.

    *   **Short-term** or **recent memory** – memories of events that occurred days to weeks before

    *   **Long-term memory** – memories that can last years or a lifetime

    The **hippocampus** is a region of the limbic system that seems to be involved in declarative memory. Removal of the hippocampus in humans erases memories going over the few months before surgery. Long-term memory, from many years ago, however, remains intact. Further, there is loss of the ability to form new long-term memories.

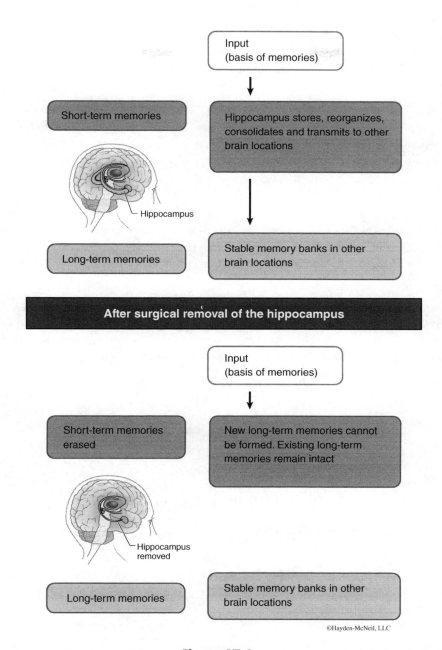

**Figure 17-6.**

Therefore, it is believed that declarative memories are first stored in the hippocampus as short-term memories. After time, there is a reshuffling and reorganization of the information and it is placed into more stable long-term memory banks in other brain locations.

How might memory (and learning) work? *There seems to be general agreement that learning and memory are associated with long-lasting, use-dependent changes in the "strength" of synapses.*

Obviously, we have to look for some long-term effect of action potentials entering a neuronal circuit. In other words, some kind of message associated with a particular memory must be imprinted on the circuit. One important property of synapses in the hippocampus is that when they are repeatedly stimulated, they are "strengthened." That is, it becomes easier to excite the postsynaptic (receiving) neurons.

In Chapter 13 we described this process as *long-term potentiation* (LTP). In the intact animal it can last for days and even weeks, and LTP may therefore be involved in memory formation.

It is also likely that growth of dendrites and new dendritic spines is important in memory formation.

One important aspect of memories (procedural and declarative) is that they seem to go through a phase of **consolidation**, during which they are reinforced. This phase may be associated with sleep, possibly *REM sleep*, although many do not accept that idea.

**Envisioning future scenarios**—work done at Washington University by Szpunar and collaborators has supported the idea that memory and thoughts about the future are highly interrelated and helps to explain why future thought may be impossible without memories. "It may just be that the reason we can recollect our past in vivid detail is that this set of processes is important for being able to envision ourselves in future scenarios," he says.

**Memory and future thought go
hand in hand**

364

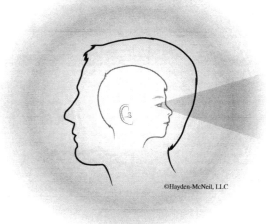

©Hayden-McNeil, LLC

**Figure 17-7.** The brain uses stored information ("memory") to imagine, simulate, plan and predict possible future events—they help us make the best decisions for the future.

## H. Difference Between Left and Right Halves of the Brain—Hemisphere Dominance and Patients with a "Split-Brain"

Both halves of the cerebral hemispheres participate in many basic functions, such as receiving and analyzing sensory information and controlling movements on the opposite side of the body.

In most people, however, one side tends to be dominant for certain other functions. If we consider language, 96% of right-handed people and 70% of left-handed or ambidextrous people primarily use the left hemisphere. In these individuals, Broca's area on one side almost completely controls the motor activities connected with speech.

The left side is also most concerned with **cognitive** *activity*.

---

*cognition* = act or process of knowing, awareness, or judgment

---

The right side is more concerned with certain aspects of music (see below), non-verbal activity, space and form perception.

According to recent reports, it is possible that the composer Ravel suffered from progressive primary aphasia, which erodes the brain's language centres, and corticobasal degeneration, which affects movement control.

The composer's loss of language would have been dealt with by the left half of the brain. However, pitch, melody, harmony and rhythm are spread throughout the brain.

Boller and his colleagues have suggested that two of Ravel's last pieces, *Boléro* and his *1930 piano concerto* for the left hand, show the early effects of the problems with the left hemisphere, with the timbre-processing right brain starting to predominate.

*Boléro* contains two themes, each repeated eight times. But it has 30 superimposed lines, and 25 different combinations of sounds. Ravel himself described it as "an orchestral fabric without music."

Mathematical analysis indicates that the *1930 piano concerto* differs from the rest of Ravel's compositions.

[Amaducci, L., Grassi, E. & Boller, F. (2002). Maurice Ravel and right-hemisphere musical creativity: influence of disease on his last musical works? *European Journal of Neurology 9,* 75–82.]

(Based on Nature News Service, Macmillan Magazines Ltd 2002)

In the normal brain, information is transferred between the two cerebral hemispheres via the great band of nerve fibers called the corpus callosum.

We can examine some aspects of hemispheric dominance in patients (usually intractable epileptics) where the corpus callosum has been surgically cut. These patients have what is called a *split-brain*. Usually such patients function quite normally, and nobody is really aware that something is wrong. However, an ingenious set of tests provides us with fascinating insights into how the two halves of the brain function after they have been separated by this procedure.

When the patient was shown an apple in the right visual field which projects to the *left hemisphere*, and questioned as to what was seen, the verbal response was—not surprisingly—"an apple." When the apple was presented in the left visual field which projects only to the *right hemisphere*, the patient was unable to respond correctly, and even made up an answer on a random basis. Yet the same person was able to feel around in a box of objects and pick out an apple to represent what he had seen.

365

The *verbal* report related what was perceived in the *left* hemisphere, while the right hemisphere was more competent in the perception of form and texture by feeling the object.

Generally speaking, the right hemisphere seems to be more competent in non-verbal functions such as music and deals with emotional processes. Recognition of people's faces is a task that seems to be carried out by the right hemisphere. The left hemisphere, on the other hand seems to be more competent in verbal functions.

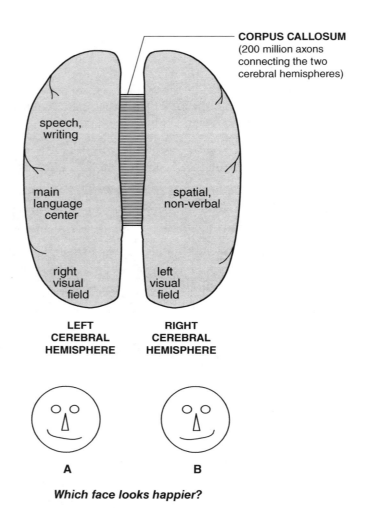

**CORPUS CALLOSUM**
(200 million axons connecting the two cerebral hemispheres)

speech, writing

main language center

right visual field

spatial, non-verbal

left visual field

**LEFT CEREBRAL HEMISPHERE**

**RIGHT CEREBRAL HEMISPHERE**

A

B

*Which face looks happier?*

**Figure 17-8.** Which face looks happier? If you picked A, then you process faces and emotion with your right brain. Based on Bourne, V. J. & Todd, B. K. (2004). When left means right: an explanation of the left cradling bias in terms of right hemisphere specializations. *Developmental Science 7,* 19–24, doi:10.1111/j.1467-7687.2004.00318.x.

## III. Sleep

### A. The Sleep–Wake Cycle—A Master Clock in the Hypothalamus

The times when we fall asleep and wake up seem to be set by a biological **master clock** located in one of the nuclei of the **hypothalamus** (the suprachiasmatic nucleus). Its activity can be affected by exposure to light and darkness, and the gene for the master clock regulator has been cloned.

Interestingly, there may be another clock located in the retina of the eye (Tosini and Menaker (1995). *Science 272*, 419; see also page 349 of the same issue of *Science*).

Nuclei in the brain stem may be involved in waking and in the various stages of sleep (see below). Neurotransmitters in these nuclei include serotonin, norepinephrine and acetylcholine (see Chapter 18 for a detailed discussion of neurotransmitters in the brain).

## B. Stages of Sleep

Sleep takes up one third of our lives. Important information on the various stages of sleep has been obtained by attaching special electrodes to volunteers, and measuring the electrical activity associated with activity of their:

1.  brains (the *electroencephalogram* or *EEG*).
2.  eyes (the *electrooculogram* or *EOG*).
3.  skeletal muscles (the *electromyogram* or *EMG*).

In 1953, these techniques led to the discovery of **rapid eye movement** (**REM**) sleep, an active period marked by intense activity within the brain accompanied by dreaming, coupled with bursts of eye movements but also a strange motor paralysis affecting the trunk and limbs.

Sleep, therefore, came to be recognized as an active process characterized by a succession of definable stages. These stages appear to be programmed in a relatively predictable sequence every night, and they appear to be controlled by different but interacting neurochemical systems.

During a typical night, a sleeper alternates between periods of REM and *slow-wave* sleep. Slow-wave sleep typically occupies a total of three-quarters of our sleeping time and has four stages (see below). The REM episodes punctuate slow-wave sleep, and occur about every 90 min. The later REM periods become longer (up to 30 minutes or more).

1.  **REM** sleep.

    REM sleep is characterized by EEGs with high-frequency oscillations (called gamma oscillations: typically 30–40 Hz). REM sleep occupies about a quarter of our total sleep time, and coincides with a time of dreaming and arousal of the sexual organs. If we are awakened from REM sleep, dreams can be easily recalled.

    REM sleep starts with a flurry of activity in the pons and neighboring midbrain regions, which send signals to the thalamus, which relays them to the cerebral cortex and creates dreams. The onset of REM sleep seems to be associated with high levels of the neurotransmitter acetylcholine in the brain. Simultaneously, signals from the pons descend the spinal cord, and shut down spinal motor neurons to cause a kind of paralysis. This paralysis does not affect the eyes, but may serve to "free" the brain to create dreams and prevent the body from jumping out of bed to act out these dreams.

367

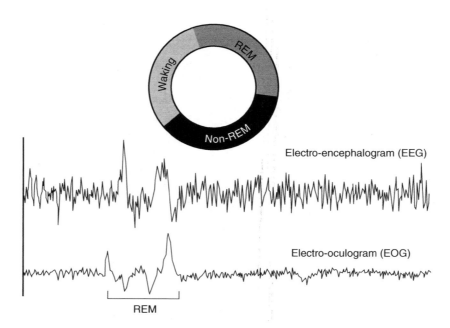

**Figure 17-9.** Comparison of EEG and EOG before, during, and after an episode of REM sleep.

2. **Slow-wave** sleep.

Slow-wave sleep (*non-REM* or *resting* sleep) is characterized by large, slow brain waves (slow-wave or resting sleep), normally comes first and is quieter than REM sleep. Blood pressure drops, heart rate and metabolism slow. Unlike REM sleep, slow-wave sleep is associated with low levels of the neurotransmitter acetylcholine in the brain.

Slow-wave sleep has four stages, each progressively deeper and each characterized by progressively slower frequencies in the EEG and higher voltage activities. At first, the brain produces steady, small electrical waves called alpha-rhythms.

*Stage 1* – the EEG displays irregular and variable waves. Occasionally we see images and may be startled awake by a *hypnic myoclonia*, a muscle contraction associated with vivid imagery (sometimes tripping or falling).

*Stage 2* – the EEG shows a pattern of larger waves with sudden bursts of activity ("sleep spindles").

*Stage 3* – the EEG has larger and slower waves.

*Stage 4* – the EEG shows very large waves, and they have a slow, jagged pattern (delta-wave sleep).

Nightmares, as opposed to normal dreams that occur in REM sleep, generally occur in Stages 3 and 4. The need for REM and Stage 4 slow-wave sleep declines during childhood and adolescence.

### C. What Is the Function of Sleep?

We are beginning to develop some ideas as to the function of REM sleep. There appears to be a specific need for REM sleep. In one experiment, volunteers who were prevented from having REM sleep for 16 days made up for its loss by having more frequent and longer REM episodes when permitted to do so.

Some researchers have suggested that REM sleep may be involved in the consolidation and reinforcement of memories, but many others do not agree with that hypothesis.

More research is needed in answering the broader question concerning the function of all stages of sleep. With more understanding and knowledge, it may become possible to improve treatments for the many sleep disorders that afflict up to 70 million Americans. These disorders include insomnia (difficulty in falling asleep and staying asleep), sleep apnea (breathing stops for extended periods), narcolepsy and night terrors. These disorders can cause behavior problems and fatigue-related accidents.

## IV. The Basal Ganglia—Structure and Broad Functions

### A. Structure of the Basal Ganglia

The basal ganglia will be further discussed in Chapter 19, when we talk about the integration of sensation and motor function.

The basal ganglia consist of three masses of gray matter in the cerebrum and two in the midbrain. The cerebral structures (sometimes called the corpus striatum) include the following.

369

- **caudate nucleus**
- **putamen**
- **globus pallidus**[*]

The midbrain components of the basal ganglia are as follows.

- **subthalamic nucleus**
- **substantia nigra**

### B. Input to the Basal Ganglia

The basal ganglia receive major input from wide areas of the cerebral cortex. Other areas also input to the basal ganglia, but need not concern us here.

### C. Output of the Basal Ganglia

Most of the output of the basal ganglia goes via the thalamus back to the cerebral cortex, much of it to areas that are involved with motor function. This makes sense, because the basal ganglia play a dominant role in **movement**.

There are also regions of the basal ganglia that plug into the limbic system. The dementias observed in Huntington's chorea and sometimes observed in Parkinson's disease (see Section E) are probably associated with these connections to the limbic system.

---

* The putamen and globus pallidus are sometimes called the "lentiform nucleus," and all three cerebral basal ganglia are sometimes called collectively the "corpus striatum." These are not terms you need to know in this course, although you may come across them in some textbooks.

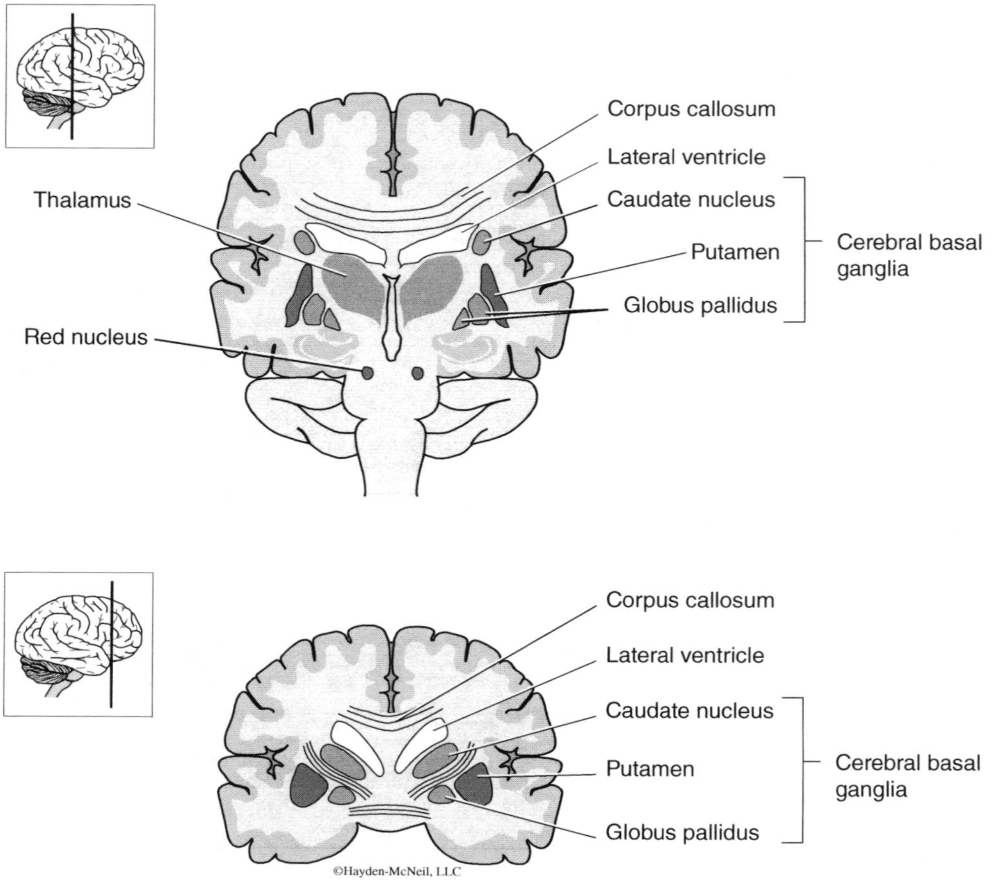

Other components of basal ganglia not illustrated:
- Substantia nigra
- Subthalamic nucleus

**Figure 17-10.** Basal ganglia.

## D. Broad Functions of the Basal Ganglia

As mentioned, parts of the basal ganglia seem to be connected with the limbic system, but here we concentrate on their role in voluntary movement. Different parts of the basal ganglia seem to **facilitate** movements, while others **suppress** them, or tone them down.

This balance between facilitation and inhibition has an important bearing on the role of the basal ganglia in **action selection**. Any increase in facilitation or inhibition could affect motor activity in the direction of either an increase or decrease in the motor output of the cerebral cortex.

The cerebral cortex often contemplates a number of different actions, some of which may be more appropriate for the occasion than others. In the above model the basal ganglia would be the arbiters of which of these potential actions actually gets executed. For example, some actions may compete with more desirable actions, and would need to be suppressed.

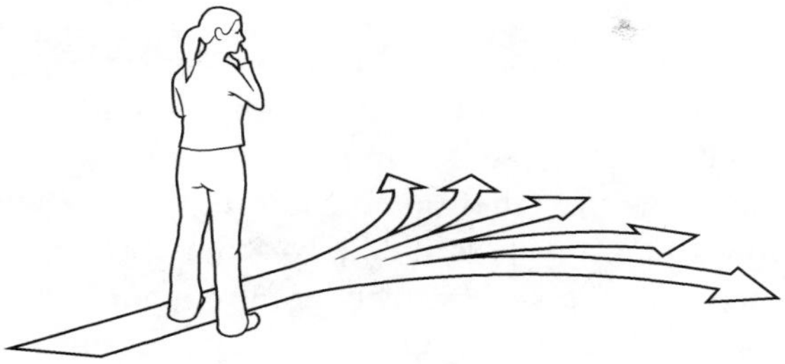

**What do I do now???**
**The basal ganglia may have the final say.**

**Figure 17-11.**

Dopaminergic neurons in the substantia nigra and neighboring parts of the brain are known to fire selectively during reward-predicting stimuli. Thus, dopaminergic input could "train" the basal ganglia to choose actions that have been rewarding in the past. In animals, these choices may be very simple, but in humans there has been an enormous increase in the sophistication of brain activities competing for motor expression.

In addition to their role in action selection, the basal ganglia seem to be involved in specific types of movement such as executing patterns of movement and making complex alternating movements (e.g. hammering a nail), timing and scaling of movements (fast, slow, extensive, limited), and complex reflexive movements, such as jumping out of the way of a car that is suddenly perceived to be bearing down on you.

371

### E. Diseases of the Basal Ganglia

As mentioned above, different regions of the basal ganglia facilitate movements, while others suppress them. This is very apparent in two well-studied disorders of the basal ganglia—*Parkinson's disease* and *Huntington's chorea* (also called *Huntington's disease*).

1. **Parkinson's disease.**

   In Parkinson's disease there may be **tremor** at rest (which disappears during voluntary movement), an increase in muscle tone (**rigidity**), **slowness** in carrying out movements, and difficulty in **starting** a movement. Additionally, there may be **poverty** of movement—the arms do not swing while walking, and facial expressions do not change while talking. There is a tendency to stooped **posture** and a shuffling **walk**. Therefore, those parts of the basal ganglia that are involved in facilitating movements seem to be damaged.

   About one third of Parkinson's patients also develop **dementia**. This can start out with memory loss and language comprehension, and can proceed to behavioral disorders and psychosis.

   We will talk more about Parkinson's disease and its relation to the neurotransmitter **dopamine** in Chapter 18.

2.  **Huntington's chorea.**

A genetic disease involving triplet (trinucleotide) repeat expansion (see Chapter 6). In Huntington's chorea (also known as Huntington's disease), the symptoms are different from Parkinson's disease. Huntington's chorea is characterized by **hyperactivity** rather than a poverty of movement. Huntington's patients have **continuous**, **uncontrollable**, **quick movements** of the limbs. Therefore, those parts of the basal ganglia that normally suppress overactivity of movement seem to have been damaged in some way. **GABA**-ergic neurons may be affected in the early stages of the disease.

There are often cognitive and personality disturbances associated with Huntington's disease, possibly because parts of the basal ganglia are connected to the limbic system.

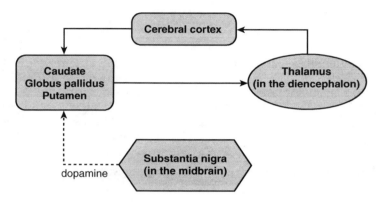

372

**Figure 17-12.** Simplified circuitry of the basal ganglia (subthalamic nucleus has been omitted).

# 18

# CENTRAL NERVOUS SYSTEM IV
Neurotransmitters of the Brain, the Cerebellum

## CHAPTER OUTLINE

## DESCRIPTION AND INTRODUCTION

In the first part of this chapter we consider the **neurotransmitters** and **neuroactive peptides** found in the brain. Some of these *neuroactive peptides* are *neurotransmitters* and some are *neuromodulators*, substances that *modulate* the response of a neuron to other neurotransmitters.

Neurotransmitters are chemical messengers that enable neurons to talk to each other. After their release at the presynaptic nerve ending, they act by binding to receptor molecules present in the postsynaptic cell membrane of the receiving neuron. Parts of these receptor molecules lie at the extracellular surface of the cell membrane and are therefore able to bind the neurotransmitters released into the extracellular space (usually, the synaptic cleft).

There are also special *transporter molecules* in the presynaptic membranes that are concerned with reuptake of the neurotransmitter into the presynaptic terminals, so terminating the action of the neurotransmitter. There are transporter molecules for *dopamine, norepinephrine, serotonin, GABA* and *glycine*. Some of these transporters are the targets of therapeutic **drugs** (including antidepressants such as *Prozac*) and also for drugs of abuse such as amphetamines, morphine, and cocaine.

Research into the **neurotransmitters** of the brain, their **receptors**, their **transporters**, and the action of **drugs** on these substances is one of the largest fields in neuroscience. Armed with this information, scientists hope to understand the neuronal circuits that may be responsible for disorders such as *Alzheimer's disease*, Parkinson's disease, clinical depression, panic attacks, anxiety and schizophrenia. Sorting out the various chemicals used in these circuits and how they function in terms of their receptors and transporters is also vital to understanding how the brain stores memories and why sex is such a powerful motivator.

The second part of this chapter concerns the *cerebellum*, a major region of the brain that is concerned with the planning, execution and smooth coordination of **movements** and **posture**. Diseases of this part of the brain cause marked impairment of motor function (compare the basal ganglia diseases). Additionally, it is believed that the cerebellum may play an important role in the learning of motor skills, such as typing and playing the violin.

## OBJECTIVES

After listening to the lecture and reading this chapter, you should be able to:

1.  Name and classify ten **neurotransmitters**.
2.  Explain how **curare, α-bungarotoxin**, and **botulinum** toxin might kill you.
3.  Explain the molecular basis of the disease **myasthenia gravis**.
4.  Explain what is meant by a **neuroactive peptide**—distinguish between **opioid** and **non**-opioid neuroactive peptides.
5.  Identify the **neurotransmitter defects** that may be involved in Parkinson's disease and Huntington's chorea, and in some forms of clinical depression, schizophrenia, clinical anxiety, and epilepsy.
6.  Describe the action of **cocaine** on the brain, and the neurotransmitters it affects.
7.  Describe the structure of the **cerebellum** and the nuclei associated with it.
8.  Describe the **functional divisions** of the cerebellum.

374

9.  Summarize the **functions** of the cerebellum.

10. Describe the effects of **lesions** to the cerebellum.

11. Describe what we mean by a **receptor** for a neurotransmitter.

12. Explain what is meant by a **transporter molecule**, as applied to neurotransmitters. Name two **drugs** that act by interfering with neurotransmitter transporter molecules.

13. Explain the importance of **excitotoxicity**—name the neurotransmitter involved and brain condition where it might be important.

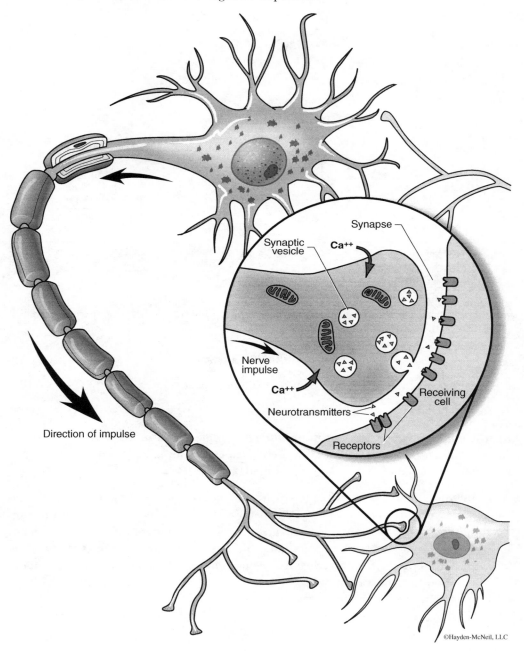

©Hayden-McNeil, LLC

**Figure 18-1.**

## I. The Chemistry of the Brain—Neurotransmitters and Neuroactive Peptides

We have already introduced the topic of neurotransmitters and neuroactive peptides in Chapter 13. The following covers some of this material in more detail, and with particular respect to the brain and to brain disorders.

There are many neurotransmitters, but the most important are as follows:

- acetylcholine
- norepinephrine
- dopamine
- serotonin
- glutamic acid

- gamma-amino butyric acid (GABA)
- endorphins
- dynorphin
- enkephalin
- substance P

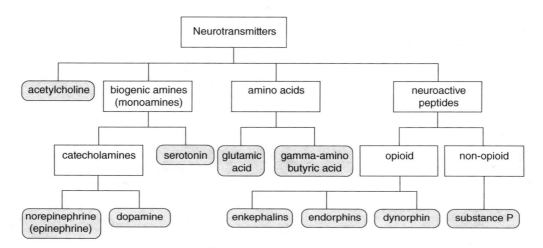

**Figure 18-2.** Neurotransmitters.

ATP is a probable neurotransmitter at certain synapses.

### A. Acetylcholine

**Acetylcholine** was the first neurotransmitter to be identified more than 60 years ago. Acetylcholine is the neurotransmitter used at the neuromuscular junction. Its action is terminated by **cholinesterase** (sometimes called **acetyl**cholinesterase).

As we mentioned previously (Chapter 10) the arrow poison used by some South American Indians contains **curare**, which causes paralysis of skeletal muscles (and death from respiratory paralysis) by competing with acetylcholine for binding the type of acetylcholine receptor found at the neuromuscular junction. The snake venom **α-bungarotoxin** has a similar action. **Myasthenia gravis** is an autoimmune disorder, where the patient develops antibodies against their own acetylcholine receptors at the neuromuscular junction, so preventing synaptic transmission.

***Botulinum toxin*** is produced by the bacterium *Clostridium botulinum*. It blocks the actual release of acetylcholine at the neuromuscular junction by preventing synaptic vesicles from fusing with the plasma membrane of the presynaptic terminal. The toxin causes fatal paralysis.

***Tetanus toxin*** (from *Clostridium tetani*) acts on the central nervous system by preventing the release of the inhibitory neurotransmitter GABA (and certain other neurotransmitters). Due to the complicated nature of the neuronal networks affected by this toxin, its effects are complicated, and lead to severe muscle spasms (tetanic seizures) and possibly death.

Acetylcholine is also used at many synapses throughout the brain. For example, acetylcholine is one of the neurotransmitters in the basal ganglia.

As mentioned in Chapter 17, there are important changes in the brain levels of acetylcholine in changing from one phase of sleep to the next. The phase of sleep known as *REM sleep* is associated with high acetylcholine levels, and *slow-wave sleep* with low acetylcholine levels in the brain [Shiromani et al. (1987). *A. Rev. Pharmacol. Toxicol. 27*, 137].

Acetylcholine is one of several neurotransmitters that are depleted in the brains of patients with Alzheimer's disease.

Neurons that use acetylcholine as a neurotransmitter are called **cholinergic**.

## B. Biogenic Amines (Monoamines)

***Biogenic amines*** have been studied extensively in the brain, particularly in the reticular formation of the brain stem.

The important biogenic amines are as follows.

1.  **Norepinephrine and dopamine (catecholamines).**

    - **Norepinephrine** (also known as *noradrenaline*) is used by neurons in a region of the reticular formation of the brain stem called the ***locus ceruleus***. These neurons may be involved in arousal, regulation of mood and dreaming. As will be discussed later, norepinephrine is also a neurotransmitter in the sympathetic nervous system, and is secreted into the bloodstream by the adrenal glands.

        A related catecholamine called ***epinephrine*** is also secreted by the adrenal glands. Another name for epinephrine is ***adrenaline***. Epinephrine has actions similar to norepinephrine. Unlike norepinephrine, epinephrine is not known to be a neurotransmitter. Rather, it should be regarded as a hormone, since it is carried round the body by the bloodstream.

        Like dopamine (see below) and many other neurotransmitters, norepinephrine is removed from the synaptic cleft by a reuptake mechanism. Both norepinephrine and epinephrine are also destroyed by the enzyme ***monoamine oxidase.***

        Norepinephrine is one of the several neurotransmitters (including acetylcholine) that are deficient in the brains of patients with Alzheimer's disease. It may also be involved in neuronal circuits concerned with learning and memory.

        Neurons that use norepinephrine as a neurotransmitter are called **adrenergic**.

- **Dopamine**-containing neurons are found in midbrain regions, notably the substantia nigra and ventral tegmentum. Neurons in the substantia nigra send axons to the basal ganglia via the *nigrostriatal pathway*.

  Degeneration of these dopaminergic fibers occurs in Parkinson's disease (see later).

  The midbrain sends other dopaminergic connections to the forebrain, particularly the nucleus accumbens, where they may play a role in feelings of pleasure and reward. Dopamine is sometimes an inhibitory neurotransmitter, but may not be in every instance.

  Dopamine is removed from the synaptic cleft mainly by uptake mechanisms (involving a dopamine transporter molecule) that return it to the cytoplasm of the presynaptic neuron (for the effect of cocaine on this uptake process, see Section E).

  Neurons that use dopamine as a neurotransmitter are called **dopaminergic**.

2. **Serotonin.**

   Serotonin is present in high concentration in neurons found in certain regions of the brain stem, in nuclei that make up the raphe, which is centered around the reticular formation. These neurons may be involved in regulating sensory perception, onset of sleep and control of mood and emotions.

   **Brain disorders** – serotonin has also been implicated in depression, aggressive and impulsive behavior, and in suicidal tendencies. Serotonin seems to be mainly an excitatory neurotransmitter.

Neurons that use serotonin as a neurotransmitter are called **serotonergic**.

## C. Amino Acids

1. **Glutamic acid.**

   Glutamic acid is one of the most prevalent **excitatory** neurotransmitters in the brain, and is found in many neurons (aspartic acid is also used by the brain as an excitatory neurotransmitter).

   **Cerebrovascular accident (stroke)** – glutamic acid may be involved in cell death following a *stroke*. A stroke occurs when a blood vessel bringing oxygen and nutrients to the brain bursts or is clogged by a blood clot. Lack of blood causes cells to die within minutes. The cells closest to the injury die of oxygen deprivation, but it seems that as they die they release large quantities of neurotransmitters, particularly glutamic acid, from their endings. Cells exposed to an overdose of glutamic acid become **overexcited**, swell and die. This is called *excitotoxicity*. Thus, a widening area of neuronal cell death can develop around the original oxygen-deprived area.

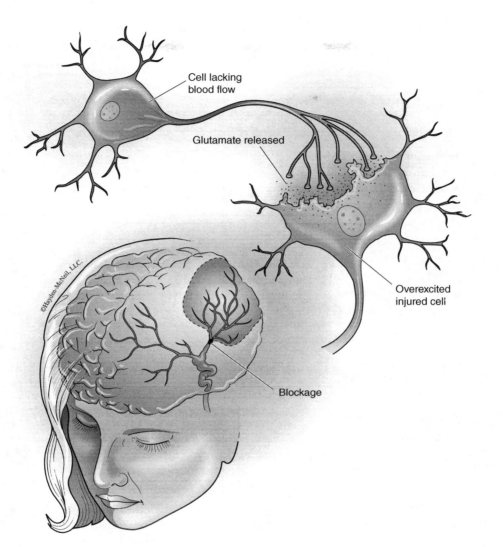

Cell lacking
blood flow

Glutamate released

Overexcited
injured cell

Blockage

**Figure 18-3.** Glutamic acid and stroke.

The destruction of cells following exposure to excess amounts of the excitatory neurotransmitter glutamic acid is called *excitotoxicity*. Drugs that block glutamic acid (e.g. its receptors) or combat the excitotoxicity it causes would be therapeutically important in limiting neuronal cell death after a stroke.

The cause of excitotoxicity may be sustained entry of calcium ions into the neurons via special glutamic acid receptors called *NMDA receptors*. This could trigger apoptosis, or induce the formation of the enzyme that synthesizes nitric oxide, the NO· form of which could diffuse to neighboring neurons and kill them.

An additional problem is that glutamic acid transporter molecules found in the membranes of astrocytes that normally keep the glutamic acid concentration low in the extracellular space, may get knocked out as a result of depolarization and an increase of extracellular $K^+$.

Drugs that block the action of glutamic acid (e.g. by blocking the NMDA receptors) are being tested for their ability to minimize neuronal cell death after a stroke. Unfortunately, all the NMDA blockers tested to date have had serious side effects. Modifying their chemical structures may result in effective drugs. Inhibitors of the enzyme that manufactures nitric oxide, substances that inhibit the formation of $NO\cdot$, and substances that enhance the formation of $NO^+$ may also be important in future therapies.

Neurons that use glutamate as a neurotransmitter are called **glutaminergic**.

2.   **Gamma-amino butyric acid (GABA).**

GABA may be the most prevalent **inhibitory** neurotransmitter in the brain, perhaps being used in as many as one-third of all brain synapses. It is found in some neurons of the basal ganglia, and in certain cell types in the cerebellum as well as in some spinal interneurons. Neurons that use GABA are called **GABA-ergic** neurons.

---

Glycine is another inhibitory amino acid neurotransmitter released by certain spinal interneurons.

---

**Epilepsy and anxiety** – GABA functions to damp down neuronal chatter, and prevents chaos in the brain's system of communication. If levels of GABA are too low, the result may be an epileptic seizure or the development of a state of clinical anxiety resulting from the overactivity of certain neuronal circuits in the brain.

---

Note that similar effects could, in theory, be produced by an overactivity of systems using glutamic acid, the brain's most prevalent excitatory neurotransmitter. In at least one very rare type of epilepsy, it seems that glutamate is the culprit.

---

Loss of GABA-ergic neurons seems to be involved in the early stages of Huntington's disease (see later), a condition where there is excessive involuntary movement.

## D. Neuroactive Peptides (Neuropeptides)

Relatively recently, it has been found that certain cells release peptides that act at very low concentrations to excite or inhibit neurons. These peptides range in length from two amino acids to about 40 amino acids. Neuropeptides are extremely important physiologically.

Close to 50 neuropeptides have been identified in the brain.

Neuropeptides may act as:

- **Hormones** that are released into the blood, and reach their target cells through the circulation. They will be discussed next semester.

- **Neurotransmitters** that change the conductance of the postsynaptic membrane to one or more ions.

- **Neuromodulators** that modulate synaptic transmission, either by affecting the release of another neurotransmitter at the presynaptic ending or by altering the response of the postsynaptic cell.

It is sometimes difficult to decide whether a neuroactive peptide acts as a true synaptic transmitter or as a synaptic modulator, so we will not attempt to distinguish these two forms of action when we discuss specific neuroactive peptides.

1. **Opioid neuroactive peptides.**

   Humans have used **opiates** such as morphine and heroin to deaden pain (produce analgesia) and generate euphoria. Originally, opiates were derived from the juice of the opium poppy, and they are sometimes useful clinically. Unfortunately, these powerful analgesics also produce addiction.

   The brain synthesizes neuroactive peptides that are very similar to morphine. They are called **opioid** neuroactive peptides. Opiate receptors (and other brain neurotransmitter receptor molecules) are specific proteins on the plasma membranes of neurons. At present, there are four subtypes of opiate receptor ($\mu$, $\delta$, $\epsilon$, and $\kappa$). Some have been cloned. Opiate drugs bind to these receptors as well, and therefore exert a similar action on cells that possess such receptors.

   There are three classes of endogenous opioid neuroactive peptides.

   - **Enkephalins** (means "in the head")
   - **Endorphins**
   - **Dynorphin**

   Opioid neuroactive peptides probably play a role in response to injury stress and in pain perception (Chapter 14). Enkephalin-containing synapses overlap the synapses relaying pain in the spinal cord. These synapses contain substance P (see the following page).

   It is possible that opioid neuroactive peptides are released during exercise, and may be responsible for the feeling of well-being that exercise often engenders. They may also be responsible for the "withdrawal" effects when a person who has exercised on a regular basis suddenly stops, but this is pure speculation.

   The release of opioid neuroactive peptides in the body in times of stress may explain why minor injuries received during athletic events are often not noticed until many hours later. For the same reason, wounds received on the field of battle sometimes go unnoticed until later (we discussed this matter in Chapter 14).

2. **Non-opioid neuroactive peptides.**

   These have their own receptors that do not bind opiates. In the brain, their functions are not always well-understood, but many of them also occur in the gastrointestinal tract. One example is cholecystokinin, a hormone secreted by the small intestine (next semester).

381

A non-opioid neuroactive peptide is **substance P**, which is the suspected neurotransmitter in the pain pathway in the spinal cord.

Neurons that use neuroactive peptides as neurotransmitters are called **peptidergic**.

## E. Cocaine and Dopamine

Crack *cocaine* enters the bloodstream through the lungs. Within seconds it is carried to the brain where it acts in the limbic system, specifically on a limbic region called the *nucleus accumbens,* which is involved in feelings of pleasure and reward.

Cocaine exerts its effects at synapses. Normally, a dopaminergic transmitting cell in the limbic system relays a signal by releasing dopamine into the synaptic cleft. To end the signal, dopamine molecules are taken up into the presynaptic terminal to be recycled. Cocaine **blocks removal** of **dopamine** from the synaptic cleft. It does this by specifically blocking the dopamine transporter (it also has the same effect on the norepinephrine transporter, an effect that is important when we consider the lethal effects of cocaine on the heart). In consequence, dopamine accumulates progressively. This continuously stimulates the receiving cell and causes a "high."

Cocaine also inhibits the reuptake of **serotonin** and **norepinephrine**. The action on norepinephrine reuptake affects the **heart**, and may cause death from heart failure (see later).

Other drugs of abuse probably operate by increasing dopamine levels in the nucleus accumbens. These drugs include amphetamines and morphine. It has been shown that nicotine has the same effect, supporting the thesis that this substance is addictive [Pontieri et al. (1996). *Nature 382,* 255].

## II. Brain Conditions Believed to Involve Neurotransmitters

Neurotransmitter problems may be implicated in a number of brain conditions.

| | |
|---|---|
| **Dopamine** | – *schizophrenia* (glutamate may also be involved), *Parkinson's disease* |
| **Serotonin, norepinephrine** | – *clinical depression* |
| **GABA** | – *Huntington's chorea, clinical anxiety,* some cases of *epilepsy* |
| **Glutamate** | – some cases of *epilepsy, schizophrenia* |

## A. Schizophrenia

**Schizophrenia** is characterized by marked disturbances in thinking, emotional responses and social behavior. There is a sense of persecution by others, voices are heard and there are sometimes bizarre delusions of grandeur. Schizophrenia leads to social withdrawal and may be a factor in many cases of homelessness. A person afflicted with schizophrenia was responsible for the shooting of two Capitol Hill policemen in July, 1998. This event alone emphasizes the seriousness of finding effective treatments for the condition.

Monkeys and humans with a damaged *prefrontal cortex* seem to have many of the same problems as schizophrenics, including disorders of *working memory*. Dysfunction of working memory could explain the loose associations, inattention and disordered thought processes in schizophrenics.

The prefrontal cortex has one of the highest concentrations of nerve fibers using the neurotransmitter **dopamine**. In fact, it has been suggested that schizophrenia may be caused either by excessive dopamine release by dopaminergic neurons in the limbic regions of the brain or by abnormal sensitivity to dopamine. *Antischizophrenic drugs* (chlorpromazine, haloperidol, clozapine) either reduce secretion of dopamine, or bind to dopamine receptors, so competing with dopamine and reducing the effects of the excessive quantities of this neurotransmitter.

The antischizophrenic drugs mentioned above are not always effective, however, and some recent evidence suggests that **glutamate** may also be involved. Much work remains to be done in this area.

## B. Clinical Depression

In any given year, severe depression (including manic-depressive illness) affects 17 million people in the United States (121 million worldwide). Women are affected 2–3 times more often than men. Depression is almost always a factor in the more than 30,000 suicides that occur in the United States each year. As many as 1 in 5 individuals suffering from the manic-depressive (bipolar) form of the illness will die by their own hands.

Clinical depression is characterized by loss of interest, sleep disturbance, diminished appetite, loss of energy, diminished sex drive, difficulty in concentrating, and guilty, suicidal or pessimistic thoughts. Depression affects us all to a certain degree at some time or another, but in clinical depression, these feelings may persist unrelentingly day-in, day-out for many months at a time.

> *"Always alone, though in the midst of men, I go back home that I may give myself up to my lonely dreams and to the waves of my melancholy. Whither now, do my thoughts bend? Toward death."* [Attributed to Napoleon Bonaparte]

The *biogenic amine hypothesis* of depression suggests that there is diminished activity of **norepinephrine** and **serotonin** pathways in the brain. It is believed that these pathways normally function to provide drive to the limbic system. Although it is not the whole answer to the problem, this hypothesis has proved extremely useful in the treatment of clinical depression.

In 70–80% of clinically diagnosed cases, certain drugs have proved very effective in combating clinical depression. These drugs either act by inhibiting the enzyme monoamine oxidase, which destroys serotonin and norepinephrine, or they interfere with the transporter molecules that are involved in the reuptake of these neurotransmitters. Some of these drugs act specifically on serotonin reuptake, and are called *serotonin-selective reuptake inhibitors* or *SSRIs* (Prozac and Zoloft are examples of this group of drugs). A consequence of this type of medication is that the brain content of these neurotransmitters either increases or they persist longer at the synapse.

383

## C. Parkinson's Disease

**Dopaminergic** neurons in the substantia nigra send axons to the basal ganglia. Degeneration of these dopaminergic fibers occurs in Parkinson's disease. Attempts at curing the condition include injection of *L-dopa* (a dopamine precursor that can pass from the blood to the brain) and *transplantation* of fetal brain dopaminergic tissue. New strategies to replace dopamine function in Parkinson patients include *stem cell transplantation, gene therapy* and various attempts to *protect* dopaminergic neurons from degeneration and to encourage sprouting of new fibers.

In October, 2001, scientists at a company studying the medical records of the Icelandic population said they had mapped the first gene linked to the main form of Parkinson's disease.

DeCODE Genetics Inc. has bought exclusive access to Iceland's health records and is analyzing the population's unique composition, which has remained stable since the Vikings arrived in the 9th and 10th centuries, to uncover disease–gene links.

Although other researchers have found genetic factors for rarer forms of Parkinson's, this is the first time a gene has been linked to the most common late-onset form. The new gene, which has been mapped to a small region on Chromosome 1, was found after studying data from 51 Icelandic families.

Parkinson's affects from between one and three people per thousand worldwide, and is most common in those over 50.

## D. Huntington's Chorea (Disease)

In its early stages, Huntington's chorea is characterized by hyperactivity of movement. Huntington's patients have *continuous, uncontrollable, quick movements* of the limbs and other parts of the body. It is frequently also associated with personality disorder, possibly because of the connection of the basal ganglia to components of the limbic system. A deficit in inhibitory **GABA-ergic** neurons in parts of the basal ganglia occurs during the early stages of Huntington's disease.

The gene for Huntington's chorea has been identified. It codes for a protein of unknown function called *huntingtin*.

## E. Clinical Anxiety

Anxiety disorders are the most prevalent mental disorders in adults, affecting twice as many women as men. Anxiety disorders include panic disorder, agoraphobia (with and without a history of panic disorder), generalized anxiety disorder (GAD), specific phobia, social phobia, obsessive-compulsive disorder, acute stress disorder, and post-traumatic stress disorder.

GABA is one of the brain's important inhibitory neurotransmitters. It may serve to "damp-down" certain neuronal networks and prevent their overactivity. A deficiency of GABA in certain parts of the amygdala, and hence *overactivity* of neurons in that brain region, has been strongly implicated in at least some clinical anxiety conditions. Anti-anxiety drugs such as the benzodiazapines bind to, and increase the responsiveness of GABA receptors to GABA, so enhancing the effectiveness of GABA and depressing the overactivity of neurons in the amygdala.

### F. Epilepsy

Epilepsy affects about 2.5 million people in America. It results from neuronal hyperexcitability. Generally, anti-epileptic drugs control excess neuronal activity by enhancing inhibitory GABA-ergic pathways, inhibiting excitatory glutaminergic pathways or acting on ion channels such as voltage-gated sodium channels.

## III. The Cerebellum

The cerebellum is easy to identify, and looks like a separate little brain detached from the cerebrum by a transverse fissure.

The cerebellum is a major region of the brain that is concerned with the planning, execution and smooth coordination of **movements** and **posture**. Diseases of this part of the brain cause marked impairment of motor function. Additionally, it is believed that the cerebellum may play an important role in the **learning of motor skills**, such as typing and playing the violin.

The above functions make it imperative that the cerebellum is kept well *informed*. In fact, it is one of the best informed motor structures in the nervous system and is able to process a vast mass of incoming information (most of it sensory) related to movements. In turn, the cerebellum must be able to send its output to the motor systems of the brain, so that it can modify their activity.

### A. Anatomy

The cerebellum constitutes about one-eighth of the total mass of the brain. It is separated from the cerebrum by a *transverse fissure* and by an extension of the dura mater called the *tentorium cerebelli*.

The cerebellum is shaped rather like a butterfly. There is a central constricted area called the *vermis* and the two wings called the **hemispheres**. These hemispheres are partially separated by a layer of dura mater called the *falx cerebelli*.

385

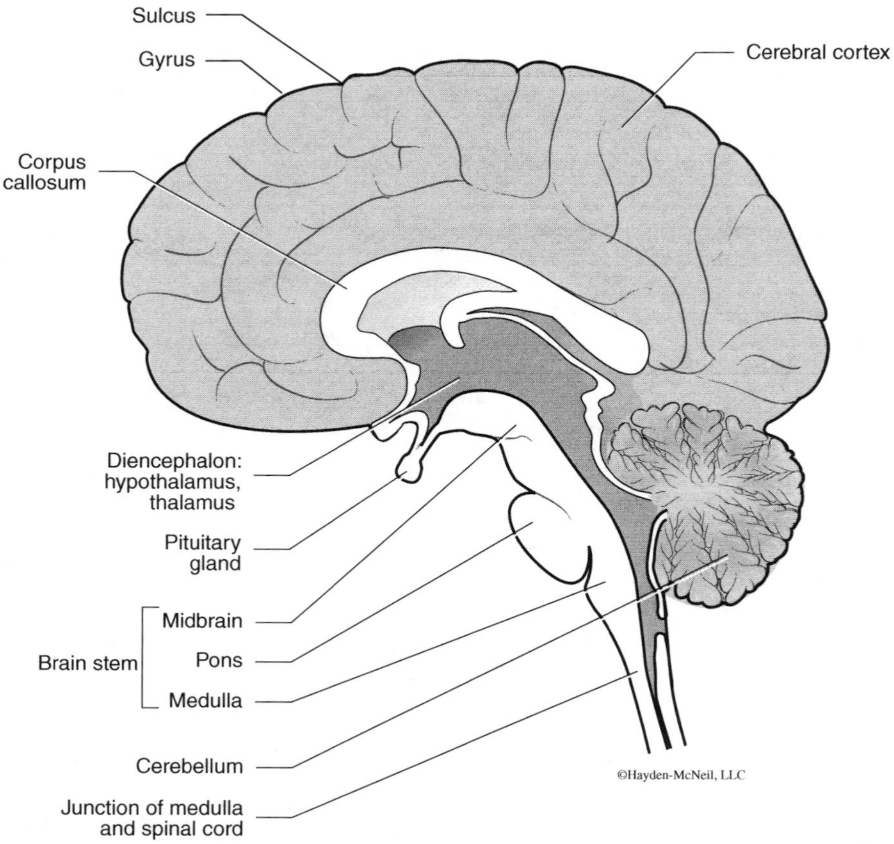

**Figure 18-4.** Location of cerebellum.

Like the cerebrum, the cerebellum is composed mainly of white matter with a thin layer of gray matter, the **cerebellar cortex**, on its surface. Purkinje cells are the major output cells of the cerebellar cortex, and are very prominent in histological sections.

Beneath the gray matter are white matter tracts that resemble the branches of a tree, and are called *arbor vitae*.

Deep within the white matter are three masses of gray matter called the *cerebellar nuclei*. They are the:

- **fastigial nucleus**
- **interposed nucleus**
- **dentate nucleus**

These nuclei are concerned with conveying information from the cerebellum to other parts of the nervous system (other brain centers and the spinal cord).

Another important nucleus that is closely associated with the cerebellum is the:

- **vestibular nucleus**

This nucleus (there is actually a group of them) is involved in conveying information from the vestibular apparatus of the inner ear to the cerebellum and in conveying commands from the cerebellum to the motor neurons controlling muscles affecting balance and posture.

Finally, there is the:

•   **olivary nucleus**

This nucleus plays an important role in motor learning.

## B. Connections—Input and Output Pathways

The cerebellum is connected to the brain stem by three paired fiber tracts called the *cerebellar peduncles*.

•   *inferior cerebellar peduncle* (mainly afferent) connects with the medulla
•   *middle cerebellar peduncle* (mainly afferent) connects with the pons
•   *superior* cerebellar peduncle (the major output pathway) connects with the midbrain

1.   **Input to the cerebellum.**

     Various types of information are provided to the cerebellum.

     a.   **Somatic sensory** information is provided via the *spinocerebellar tracts* (or via the cranial nerves) and includes information from *muscle spindles, Golgi tendon organs, joint* and *cutaneous receptors.*

     b.   Information important in **balance** arrives via the vestibular nucleus of cranial nerve VIII from the *utricle, saccule* and the *semicircular canals* of the inner ear.

     c.   **Visual** information is provided by the eye.

     d.   **Auditory** information is provided by the ear.

     e.   Information about **plans for movement** is relayed to the cerebellum from the *cerebral cortex.*

2.   **Output from the cerebellum.**

     The cerebellum is concerned with the planning, initiation, timing and execution of movements as well as with balance and eye movements. After being relayed through the cerebellar nuclei (dentate, fastigial, interposed) and the lateral vestibular nucleus found in the medulla, the output from the cerebellum goes to many areas of the brain that are involved in movements. These areas of the brain include the following:

     a.   parts of the *cerebral cortex* involved in movement (via another relay in the thalamus).

     b.   *brain stem* – the red nucleus in the midbrain, the reticular formation.

     c.   *vestibular nucleus* – the vestibulospinal tracts provide input to spinal motor neurons involved in posture and balance.

## C. Functions of the Cerebellum—An Overall View

The cerebellum is *not* necessary for **basic** perception or for **basic** muscle movement.

1.   With the cerebral cortex, the cerebellum is involved in **planning** and **programming** of voluntary movements.

2.  The cerebellum is involved in the **execution** of smooth, coordinated voluntary movements. It regulates the rate, range, force, direction, and timing of movements by controlling the activities of agonist, antagonist, and synergist muscles.

    In this respect, the cerebellum appears to be a device that **compares** intended with actual movements. When the actual movement deviates from that which has been planned, the cerebellum issues compensatory commands via the motor systems.

3.  The cerebellum is involved in **posture**, **balance**, and **equilibrium**.

4.  The cerebellum may have a role in **learning motor skills**.

In order to fulfill its role, the cerebellum must be kept **well informed**. In fact, it is one of the best informed motor structures in the nervous system and is able to process a vast mass of incoming information related to movements. In turn, the output of the cerebellum must be able to **modify the activity of the motor systems.**

*   The cerebellum receives information from the cerebral cortex about plans for movement.

*   The cerebellum receives information about motor performance—that is, ongoing movements—from sensory feedback.

*   The cerebellum sends its output to the motor systems of the brain.

388

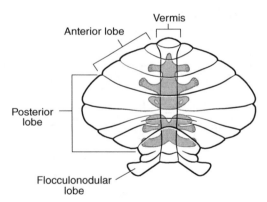

**Figure 18-5.** Parts of the cerebellum showing topographical maps of the body.

## D. Functional Divisions

From the point of view of physiology, the cerebellum has three main functional divisions. They are as follows.

1.  The **vestibulocerebellum** – receives input from the vestibular apparatus of the inner ear and controls balance and eye movements, coordinating movements of the head and eyes.

2.  The **spinocerebellum** – contains topographical maps of the body that receive sensory information from the spinal cord. Parts of it also receive auditory and visual information. The spinocerebellum is mainly concerned with the execution of movements and the regulation of muscle tone. It smoothes out physiological tremors and compensates for variations in muscle loading during movement.

3.  The **cerebrocerebellum** – receives input from wide areas of the cerebral cortex. It does not receive peripheral sensory input. The cerebrocerebellum coordinates the planning of limb movements.

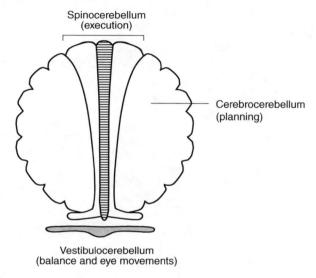

**Figure 18-6.** Functional divisions of the cerebellum.

## E. Motor Disorders Resulting from Lesions of the Cerebellum

Cerebellar disease causes **motor abnormalities**. The coordinated contractions of agonist and antagonist muscles to generate smooth, well-coordinated and well-controlled movement may be destroyed.

The result may be *dysmetria*, or inaccurate range and direction of movements, coupled with overshoot or undershoot when reaching for an object.

There may also be **unsteady walking** and *tremor.* **speech articulation** may be affected, and there may be problems in carrying out **rapid**, **alternating movements** (such as patting the thighs palms up, palms down, palms up, etc.).

A patient with a right cerebellar hemisphere lesion noted:

> *"The movements of my left (unaffected) arm are done subconsciously but I have to think out each movement of my right (affected) arm."*

In a normal person, the cerebellum spares us that mental effort. Like an army command center, our **cerebral cortex** appears to issue **general commands for movements**, but leaves the **specific details for execution** of these movements to subcortical, notably **cerebellar** mechanisms.

390

# 19

# CENTRAL NERVOUS SYSTEM V

Integration of Sensation, Motor Function, Motivation, the "Limbic System,"
Social Behavior and the Brain

391

## CHAPTER OUTLINE

## DESCRIPTION AND INTRODUCTION

This is the last chapter on the central nervous system. We will look at the brain and spinal cord, plus their inputs and outputs, as part of a complete, integrated system that functions as a whole. **As with the other chapters on the central nervous system, the material is often substantially different from the textbooks.**

Some of you have difficulty in understanding the difference between **ascending** and **descending** tracts (pathways) in the spinal cord.

- An *ascending* tract (pathway) is made up of the axons of neurons that have their cell bodies in the **spinal cord**. An ascending tract carries information from the spinal cord to neurons in the brain.

- A *descending* tract (pathway) is made up of the axons of neurons that have their cell bodies in various parts of the **brain**. A descending tract carries commands from the brain to neurons in the spinal cord.

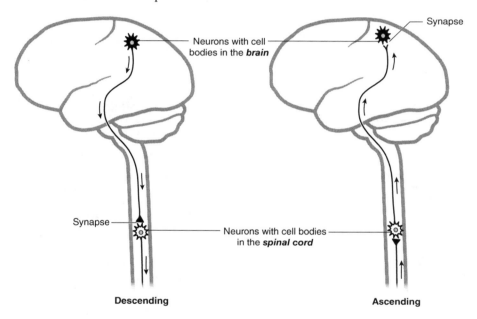

**Figure 19-1.** Ascending and descending tracts.

## OBJECTIVES

After listening to the lecture and reading this chapter, you should be able to:

1. Describe how three functional systems of the central nervous system **integrate** in catching a baseball.
2. List the **two major ascending tracts** (pathways) that carry information from the sensory periphery for use by the cerebral cortex.
3. Describe the three ways in which the **somatic sensory cortex** is organized.
4. Nerve tracts consist of the axons of neurons. State where the cell bodies of these neurons are located in (a) **ascending** tracts in the spinal cord; (b) **descending** tracts in the spinal cord.
5. Describe the **information** that is carried by **ascending** tracts in the spinal cord.
6. Describe the **information** that is carried by **descending** tracts in the spinal cord.

7. List the five brain regions involved in **motor** function and how they are connected.

8. List the **origin** of the two groups of tracts that carry motor commands to the skeletal muscles.

9. Describe two consequences of a **lesion of the corticospinal tract**.

10. List three functions of the **cerebellum**.

11. Draw a simple **diagram** illustrating the relationship of the **basal ganglia** and the **cerebellum** to the motor system of the body.

12. Describe how the basal ganglia and cerebellum differ with respect to receiving **afferent sensory information**.

13. Describe how the basal ganglia and cerebellum differ with respect to **sending commands to brain stem nuclei** that give rise to descending motor tracts (pathways).

14. List six components of the **limbic** system.

15. Name the important **fiber tract** that links the **hypothalamus** with the **hippocampus**.

16. List five **functions** of the limbic system.

17. Describe **Phineas Gage's** accident (read the detailed account of his accident in Chapter 17), its consequences, and our conclusions about the region of the brain that may control our behavior.

18. Describe the possible functions of mirror neurons, canonical neurons and von Economo neurons.

19. Describe and contrast feedback and feed-forward regulation of voluntary movement, and give examples of each.

393

## I. Interaction of Functional Systems in a Simple Behavioral Act

It is important to realize that even what we consider simple behavior may recruit the activity of several functional systems of the brain.

Like catching a baseball.

### A. Sensory Input

To catch the ball successfully, we must get the following **information**.

1. **Visual** information about the motion of the ball.

2. **Proprioceptive** and **kinesthetic** information about positions and movements of arms, legs and body in space. This information tells us about the likely effectiveness of the motor program we have developed to catch the ball. It is important because the motor system must be updated on the results of its actions.

3. **Tactile** information provided on impact of the ball with the hand.

### B. Motor Output

We must be able to control our movements in the light of this information. The parietal lobe appears to play an important role in matching motor output with sensory input. This will involve the following actions.

1. **Selection** of appropriate muscles to be activated or not (back, arms, hands, legs, etc.; *antagonists, agonists, synergists*).

2. **Timing** of muscle activity.

3. **Speed** and **extent** of muscle activity.

4. Appropriate control of the muscles involved in **posture** and **balance**.

## C. Motivation

There must be an **interest** in starting and finishing the behavioral sequence. Motivation involves the limbic system, and might also entail coordinating the activity of the voluntary motor system with the autonomic nervous system. For example, the *autonomic nervous system* may cause the heart rate to increase, blood pressure to increase, glycogen may be converted to glucose, etc.

The *degree* of motivation may influence how fast and accurately the ball is caught. If you couldn't care less or just can't be bothered, then chances are you will not catch the ball. On the other hand, if you were an outfielder in a World Series game you would probably be experiencing an intense motivational drive to catch the ball successfully.

## II. Ascending Tracts (Pathways) that Convey Sensory Information to the Cerebral Cortex

**Ascending** tracts carry information **to** the brain **from** the spinal cord. Usually, they are called **spino**_____ tracts, the exception to this rule being the dorsal column tracts.

Two major ascending systems conveying somatic sensory information for use by the *cerebral cortex.* This is an example of the use of parallel pathways. Parallel pathways add subtlety and richness to the sensory experience, and also act as insurance against damage to one of them.

- The *dorsal column tracts* (pathways)
- The **anterior/lateral** tracts or *spinothalamic tracts* (pathways)

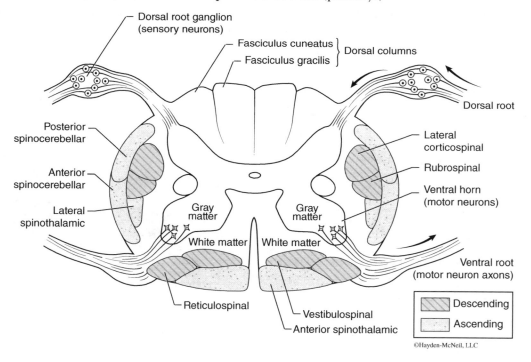

**Figure 19-2.** Ascending and descending tracts in the spinal cord.

A third system carries sensory information mainly for use by the cerebellum—these *spinocerebellar tracts* (pathways) have been discussed previously.

## A. Dorsal Column Tracts (Pathways)

1. The dorsal column tracts carry **fine touch, vibration, pressure, limb movement** and **positional** information.

2. The dorsal column tracts originate mainly from large-diameter afferent fibers from cells in the spinal cord, notably in the ***dorsal root ganglion*** (some fibers represent axons of secondary afferents from neurons in the dorsal horn).

3. The tracts ascend in the ***gracile fascicle*** and ***cuneate fascicle*** of the spinal cord.

4. The fibers form synapses with cells in the *dorsal column nuclei*, i.e. the ***gracile nucleus*** and the ***cuneate nucleus*** of the medulla.

5. The output fibers of the gracile and cuneate nuclei cross over to the opposite side and finally form synapses with neurons in the ***thalamus***.

6. Finally, neurons in the thalamus project to the cerebral cortex, mainly to the primary somatic sensory area in the ***postcentral gyrus***.

## B. Anterior and Lateral Tracts (Spinothalamic Tracts)

1. The spinothalamic tracts carry **crude** touch (including itch, which is related to slow pain, and tickle), **pain** and **temperature**.

2. The spinothalamic tracts originate from neurons in the gray matter of the **spinal cord**.

3. Axons from these neurons cross over to the opposite anterior and lateral columns of the spinal cord (Note—there is a small contingent of uncrossed fibers as well. These fibers sometimes defeat attempts to cure chronic pain by sectioning the spinothalamic tract on the side opposite from the source of the pain).

4. The spinothalamic fibers make synapses with neurons in many parts of the brain, including the:

   - **thalamus**
   - **reticular formation**

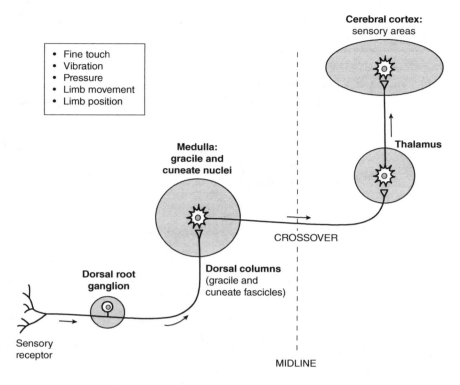

**Figure 19-3.** Ascending pathways—the dorsal column tracts.

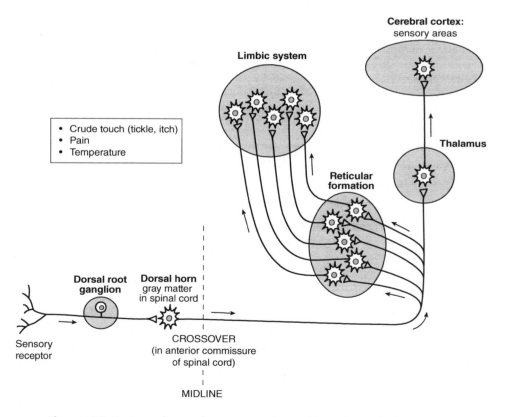

**Figure 19-4.** Ascending pathways—anterior and lateral spinothalamic tracts.

## C. The Spinothalamic Tract and the Perception of Pain

Nerve impulses generated by *nociceptors* are carried by the spinothalamic tract. As noted in Chapter 14, pain is a curious sensation. It has an urgent, anxiety-generating and primitive quality. The sensation can be pricking, burning, aching, stinging or just plain soreness. We also describe it in emotional terms such as unbearable, agonizing, miserable, etc. The sensation of pain, like other sensations, can be modified by our emotions.

Termination of some spinothalamic tract pain fibers in the **reticular formation** may account for the strong effects of pain on arousal of the brain. Severe pain leads to sleeplessness, causes a sense of urgency and causes emotions of fear and anxiety. The conscious sensation of pain and its localization to a particular body region is probably the responsibility of the **cerebral cortex**, utilizing information relayed to it from the **thalamus**.

See Chapter 14 for further discussion of pain.

**Brown-Séquard Syndrome: Hemisection of Spinal Cord**

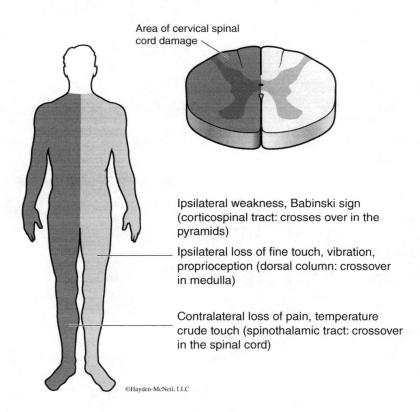

Area of cervical spinal cord damage

Ipsilateral weakness, Babinski sign (corticospinal tract: crosses over in the pyramids)

Ipsilateral loss of fine touch, vibration, proprioception (dorsal column: crossover in medulla)

Contralateral loss of pain, temperature crude touch (spinothalamic tract: crossover in the spinal cord)

©Hayden-McNeil, LLC

**Figure 19-5.**

## D. Organization of the Cerebral Cortex that Receives Sensory Information

The cerebral cortex that receives all this information is highly organized in three ways.

1. It has six discrete **layers** of neurons.
2. The body is mapped on its **surface**.
3. Neurons are segregated into special *cortical columns* that deal with only one type of sensation (called a *sensory modality*).

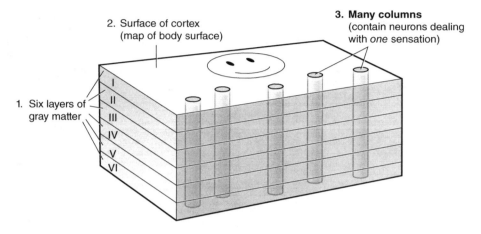

**Figure 19-6.** The somatic sensory cortex is organized in three ways.

## III. The Motor Output System of the Brain

The motor system can be involved in movements as simple and as stereotyped as the stretch reflex and walking, or as complex as the voluntary movements involved in playing the violin, or catching a baseball.

### A. The Five Components of the Motor System

There are five major components of the motor system.

1. **The spinal cord** – final common pathway for all descending tracts from higher brain centers. Contains motor neurons in ventral horns. Additionally, the spinal cord itself organizes the most automatic and stereotyped responses (reflexes such as the knee-jerk, walking).

2. **The brain stem** (medulla, pons, midbrain) – with the exception of the corticospinal (pyramidal) tract, all descending motor tracts (pathways) in the spinal cord originate from nuclei in the brain stem (e.g. the red nucleus, tectum, vestibular nuclei).

3. **Primary motor area of the cerebral cortex**, and other nearby motor areas *(premotor area, supplementary motor area)* – involved in making voluntary movements. The primary motor cortex in the precentral gyrus sends commands via the *corticospinal tract*, and also sends commands to the *red nucleus* in the *brain stem*.

Voluntary movement needs preparation and a plan of action: this plan of action is called the *central motor program*. The premotor and supplementary motor areas of the cortex input into the primary motor cortex and are important in the following:

*   orienting the body, arms and limbs toward a target
*   programming motor sequences
*   planning complex movements

**Motor activity is often context-dependent.**

Motor activity is adaptable, and can be modified according to context. Suppose you go to pick up a glass of water that you think is cold, but is actually boiling hot. As soon as you touch the glass, you pull your hand back in what is essentially a withdrawal reflex. Now suppose your child tries to grab the hot glass. Your child's safety comes first, the reflex is inhibited and you grab the glass first. Now, if you know the glass is made of fine crystal, you might handle it more carefully.

### Ready, Set, Go

"Ready": parietal and frontal lobes, subcortical structures involved in vigilance and attentiveness.

"Set": supplementary and premotor cortical areas, where the strategies for movement are developed and held in check until the "Go!" signal.

"Go!": (outside or internal command) activates primary motor cortex, which executes action.

### Mirror and Canonical Neurons

**Mirror neurons** in the premotor cortex: activated when you perform an action yourself and also when you see someone else performing it.

**Canonical neurons:** activated when you see an object that can be grasped — as if your brain were foreseeing a possible interaction with this object and preparing itself.

Both generate an internal representation of an action, whether you are carrying it out, anticipating carrying it out, or watching someone else carrying it out.

Mirror neurons may help us to understand other people's actions and intentions.

### Grid Cells, Place Cells, and Head Cells

**The brain's inner GPS**

**Grid cells** in the *entorhinal cortex* network with **place cells** in the *hippocampus.*

They tell you **where you are** in space, **where you are going**, and what **landmarks** you are near.

Grid cells appear to be dysfunctional in Alzheimer's Disease.

The function of grid and place cells is complemented by **head cells**, which respond to head direction. They are found in a number of different areas of the brain, including the entorhinal cortex.

The central motor program also involves the basal ganglia and the cerebellum (see below).

The above three "core" components of the motor hierarchy interact with, and are regulated by:

4.  The **cerebellum** – also involved in the central motor program.

5.  The **basal ganglia** – also involved in the central motor program.

1.  Finger flexion

    —simple execution

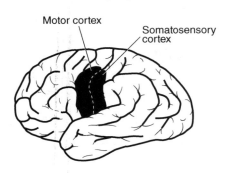

2.  Sequence of finger movements

    —execution

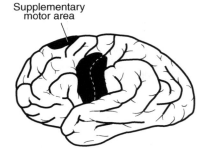

3.  Mental rehearsal of finger movement sequence

    —NO actual performance

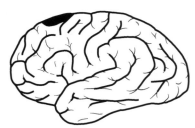

**Figure 19-7.** Planning and carrying out a movement—activity in TWO separate areas of cortex (Black areas = areas of increased blood flow measured by Positron Emission Tomography, PET).

400

*Control of Movement – Feedback and Feed-Forward Systems*

Many voluntary movements involve initiation of a movement and then controlling it by monitoring sensory signals from a variety of sources that include proprioception and vision.

However, a baseball hitter eyeing a fastball does not swing at what he sees. The neural networks that make up his sensory systems are too slow. "Everything we sense is a little bit in the past," (R. A. Andersen, California Institute of Technology). To circumvent sensory feedback delays in fast movements, current motor control theories postulate the existence of anticipatory "forward" models, combining sensory inputs with motor commands to maintain a continuous estimate of movement state. Feed-forward control is therefore essential for rapid actions. Although such feed-forward control can be very fast, accuracy requires learning from previous experience.

According to recent hypotheses, both the PPC and the cerebellum would be part of forward models. Therefore, the brain generates an internal "forward motor model" which allows you to combine sensory inputs and past experience to predict the appropriate output. These visualizations appear to run at actual speed in the posterior parietal cortex.

## B. Descending Tracts (Pathways)

**Descending** tracts carry commands **from** the brain **to** the spinal cord. Usually, they are called _____ **spinal** tracts.

There are two groups of descending tracts distinguished according to whether they originate in the cerebral cortex or in the brain stem.

- Descending tracts (pathways) that originate in the **cerebral cortex** are called *corticospinal tracts*.

- Descending tracts (pathways) that originate in the **brain stem** are called **brain stem/ spinal tracts**. They have different names depending on their origin in the brain stem.

These descending tracts terminate:

- on *interneurons* in the gray matter of the spinal cord.
- or directly on *motor neurons* in the ventral horn of the spinal cord gray matter.

1. The **corticospinal** tracts (sometimes called the *pyramidal tracts*) cross over to the contralateral side of the brain in the *pyramids* of the medulla. They descend in the spinal cord mainly as the *lateral corticospinal tract*. Fine movements of the distal limb and digit muscles are usually directed by impulses passing down this tract.

2. The **brain stem/spinal** tracts originate in various parts of the brain stem, as follows.

   a. In the *red nucleus* (which receives input from the ipsilateral cerebral cortex), which gives rise to the *rubrospinal tract*. The rubrospinal tract crosses over to the other side of the brain, and then descends in the dorsal and lateral region of the spinal cord white matter. This tract has a similar function to the corticospinal tract, but the movements are coarser and not so finely regulated.

b.   In the ***reticular formation*** of the pons and medulla, and other regions of the brain stem including the *vestibular nuclei* that are concerned with information from the semicircular canals of the ear. The tracts include the ***vestibulospinal tract, tectospinal tract*** and ***reticulospinal tract*** that run in the ventral and medial region of the spinal cord white matter. These tracts innervate muscles of the trunk and upper limbs on both sides of the body, and are involved in posture control.

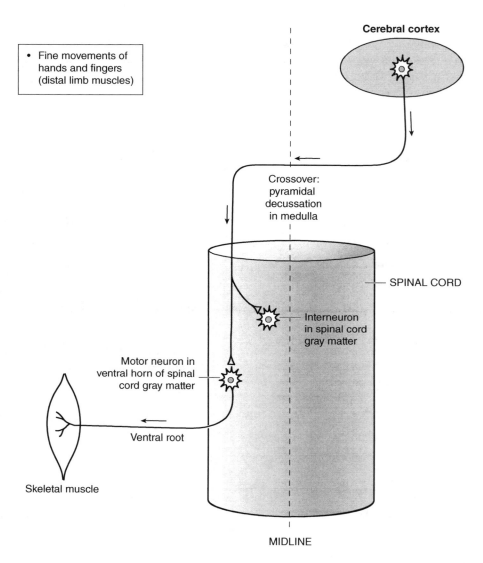

**Figure 19-8.** Descending pathways—lateral corticospinal tract.

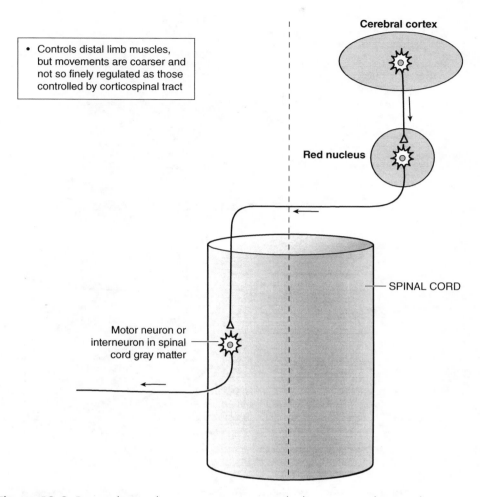

- Controls distal limb muscles, but movements are coarser and not so finely regulated as those controlled by corticospinal tract

**Cerebral cortex**

**Red nucleus**

SPINAL CORD

Motor neuron or interneuron in spinal cord gray matter

403

**Figure 19-9.** Descending pathways—tracts arising in the brain stem: rubrospinal tract.

These pathways are ventral and medial in the spinal cord. They are complex, but most of them control proximal limb and trunk muscles on **both sides of the body.**

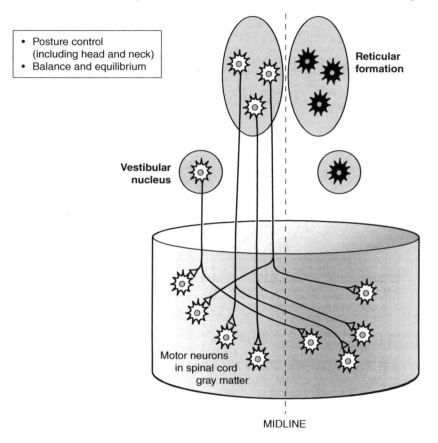

- Posture control (including head and neck)
- Balance and equilibrium

Reticular formation

Vestibular nucleus

Motor neurons in spinal cord gray matter

MIDLINE

**Figure 19-10.** Descending pathways—tracts arising in the brain stem: vestibulospinal, tectospinal, and reticulospinal tracts.

## C. Regulation and Control by the Cerebellum and Basal Ganglia

### 1. The cerebellum

The cerebellum updates and controls movements when they deviate from a planned trajectory.

The cerebellum compares intention with performance and carries out the necessary corrections.

The cerebellum coordinates the various aspects of movement, and is involved in the planning stage and in learning of motor skills. There is evidence that as we learn to walk, to speak, to play the violin or piano, the necessary detailed control information is stored in the cerebellum, and can be recalled by commands from the cerebral cortex.

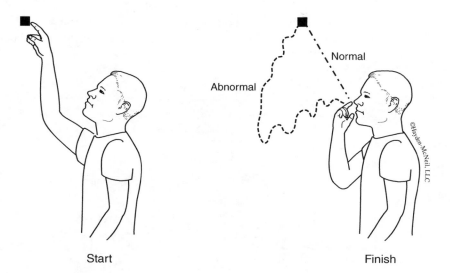

Start                                             Finish

**Figure 19-11.** Attempt by a patient with cerebellar disease to touch the tip of his nose. The diseased cerebellum cannot correct for deviations in trajectory, and there is therefore a marked discrepancy between intention and performance.

2.   **The basal ganglia**

In some ways, the basal ganglia are less well understood than the cerebellum. Some regions are involved in facilitating movemets, others in suppressing or toning down movements. There are also connections between certain parts of the basal ganglia and the limbic system.

Diseases of the basal ganglia produce a unique set of motor disturbances. Huntington's chorea and Parkinson's disease are examples. The basal ganglia also seem to be involved in executing patterns of movement and also in more complex movements (timing, scaling).

The following is a comparison of the basal ganglia and the cerebellum in the motor hierarchy.

| Basal Ganglia | Cerebellum |
| --- | --- |
| Major input from the entire cerebral cortex | Input from cerebral cortex is more restricted – from sensory and motor areas only |
| Major output via thalamus to many areas of cerebral cortex – prefrontal, premotor, supplementary motor, primary motor cortex | Output to cerebral cortex is more restricted – a major component is via the thalamus back to the motor cortex |
| Do NOT receive afferent sensory information from spinal cord | Receives somatic sensory information direct from spinal cord |
| Do NOT project to brain stem nuclei | Projects to those brain stem nuclei that give rise to descending motor tracts |

405

The general relationships of the basal ganglia and cerebellum to the motor system (vastly simplified!) are given in Figure 19-12. There are four loops in the motor control system.

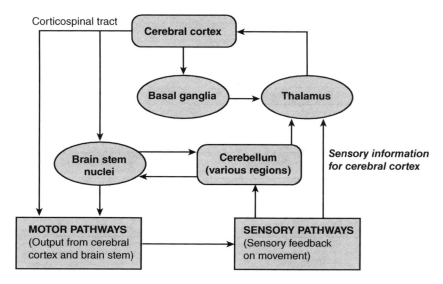

1. Cerebral cortex – corticospinal tract – sensory feedback – cerebral cortex
2. Cerebral cortex – brain stem – cerebellum – thalamus – cerebral cortex
3. Cerebral cortex – basal ganglia – thalamus – cerebral cortex
4. Brain stem nuclei – motor pathways – sensory feedback – cerebellum – brain stem nuclei

NOTE: The various thalamic and brain stem nuclei involved in these circuits are not specified.

**Figure 19-12.** Very simplified relationship of the basal ganglia and the cerebellum to the motor system of the brain.

## IV. Behavioral and Motivational Mechanisms—The Limbic System

### A. Structural Components

The limbic system consists of a number of gyri and associated structures that **roughly encircle the diencephalon and corpus callosum**. In turn, it is encircled by the temporal, occipital, parietal and frontal lobes.

The cortical components of the limbic system are among the oldest, from the evolutionary standpoint.

Components of the limbic system include the following:

- **limbic cortex** (includes the **cingulate gyrus**)

- **olfactory cortex** (= part of the cerebral cortex concerned with the sense of smell, or olfaction)

- **hippocampus** (involved in memory formation and short-term memory)

- **amygdala** (involved in fear, anxiety, recognition of emotions on people's faces, may play a role in violent behavior)

- **nucleus accumbens**

- **prefrontal cortex** (involved in working memory, personality, possibly has a role in modulating and damping down the activity of the amygdala, which has functions summarized above)

- **hypothalamus**

- other areas that will not be discussed

Additionally, there are important and often prominent fiber tracts that link various regions of the limbic system, often in arcs or circles. For example, the tract called the *fornix* links the hippocampus with the hypothalamus. Another tract links the hypothalamus with the thalamus, and yet another tract links the thalamus with one of the gyri of the limbic system.

## B. Functions

Many functions of the limbic system are similar to those of the hypothalamus, the major output path. They include the following:

- **self-preservation** (feeding, fighting, fleeing, drinking).

- **reproduction** (mating, procreation, care of offspring).

- **emotions and goal-directed behavior** (feelings of reward, pleasure, punishment, depression, elation, fear) – there are many regions of the limbic system involved. Different parts of the *amygdala* appear to be involved in the emotions of fear, and anxiety. In humans, we now know that the amygdala is very important in the recognition and interpretation of emotional signals in people's faces (e.g. fear, disgust, etc.).

- **memory** – this involves the *hippocampus*. It is also interesting that the olfactory cortex is part of the limbic system: odors and perfumes are very powerful agents for triggering memories. The establishment of memories connected with acquiring certain **motor skills**, however, is believed to be associated with the *cerebellum*.

407

**Personal Memories:**

*Posterior medial cortex*: most active when people recall details of their own pasts. Strongly suppressed during math calculations. *Proc. Nat. Acad. Sci.,* 2012, Parvizi et al.

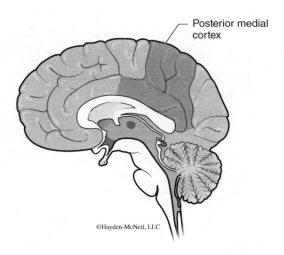

©Hayden-McNeil, LLC

**Figure 19-13.**

- via the hypothalamus, the limbic system provides a **link between the conscious, intellectual functions of the cerebral cortex and the autonomic nervous system and endocrine system.**

- **social and ethical behavior** (see next section).

- **drug addiction** – many drugs act on the nucleus accumbens in the septal region. Cocaine's primary action is on the dopaminergic neurons in the ventral tegmentum, which project to the nucleus accumbens. Intense romantic love seems to function much like an addiction. Other limbic regions that may be important in drug addiction include the amygdala, hippocampus, and part of the prefrontal cortex.

> Drug addiction: many drugs act on the *nucleus accumbens* in the septal region.
>
> Cocaine's primary action is on the dopaminergic neurons of the ventral tegmentum, which project to the nucleus accumbens (part of the brain's pleasure/reward circuit).

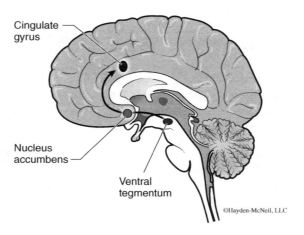

Figure 19-14.

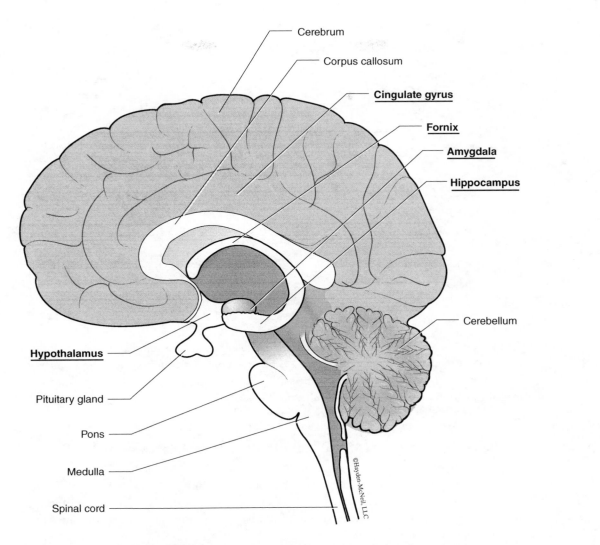

**Figure 19-15.** Limbic system (components underlined).

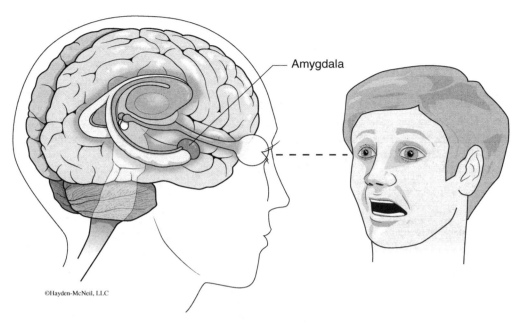

©Hayden-McNeil, LLC

**Figure 19-16.** A quick look at this man's face will tell you that he is afraid. The amygdala is a part of the brain's limbic system that seems to be important in recognizing emotion in people's faces. Our ability to do this is very important in social interactions. A person with damage to the amygdala is unable to identify facial expressions (such as fear, disgust, happiness) in photographs, even though they can recognize the person in the photograph.

410

## C. The Frontal Lobes—Are They Important in Rational Behavior and in Controlling Violent Urges?

Review again the horrible accident that happened to Phineas Gage (Chapter 17), and how his *personality* changed dramatically afterward. Although his memory and high intelligence remained intact, he had lost his ability to function socially and became rude, impulsive, and erratic.

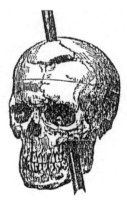

**Figure 19-17.** The horrible accident of Phineas Gage.

Many patients with frontal lobe damage similar to Phineas Gage's have problems in making rational decisions in their personal life and social affairs. They also have problems in dealing with their emotions. These people are found to be no longer trustworthy and are impossible to employ.

Therefore, we believe that there is a region in the frontal lobes that is involved in decision-making on social questions. An individual in whom this region is damaged may still be smart and may perform well on intelligence tests. However, such an individual will behave totally irrationally when it comes to personal and social behavior.

It is also possible that the prefrontal cortex can act as a brake on areas of the brain that are involved in fearful and aggressive behavior. One such area is the *amygdala*. Some experiments carried out in the '70s showed that when the *prefrontal cortex* of cats was stimulated electrically, they stopped attacking rats. Consequently, it has been suggested that malfunction of the prefrontal cortex leads to violent behavior. This idea has been supported by brain imaging and psychological studies (some admittedly preliminary) on murderers, on individuals with extensive criminal records, and on people who were just functioning in society but who had violent and antisocial tendencies.

There has also been a recent study on children with damage to the prefrontal cortex that occurred before the age of 7. Such children have difficulty in controlling their frustration, anger and aggressive urges.

411

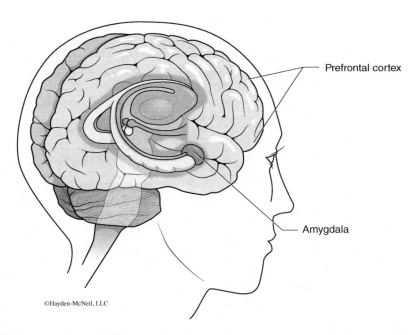

©Hayden-McNeil, LLC

**Figure 19-18.** Violence. Malfunctioning of some brain areas may contribute to violence. These areas include the prefrontal cortex, which may suppress areas such as the amygdala, which is involved in fear and aggression.

## D. Von Economo Neurons

**Von Economo neurons** are found in humans, the great apes, elephants, and whales. These are all social animals with large brains. They are very large, cigar-shaped, tapered at each end, and have only a few dendritic processes. They are localized in the frontoinsular and the anterior cingulate cortices. Von Economo neurons may relay a fast intuitive assessment of complex social situations to facilitate the rapid adjustment of behavior (Allman et al., 2005). Some people have called von Economo neurons the "brain cells for socializing."

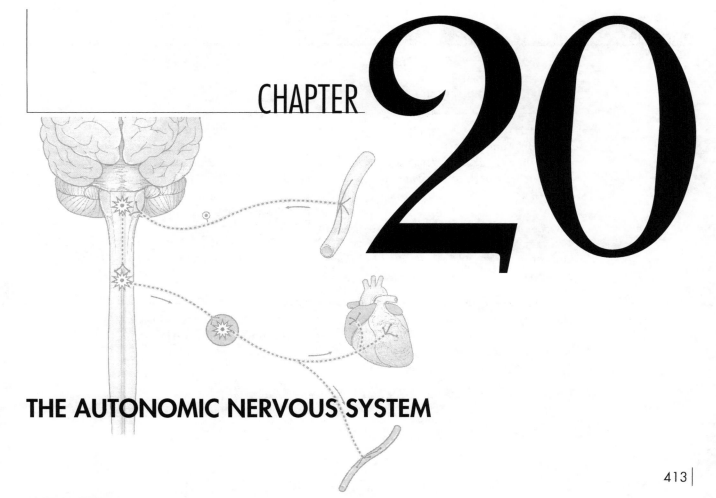

CHAPTER

20

# THE AUTONOMIC NERVOUS SYSTEM

413

## CHAPTER OUTLINE

## DESCRIPTION AND INTRODUCTION

You are expected to know the structure of *peripheral nerves* and the anatomical arrangement of the *spinal nerves* (recognize the *dorsal roots* and *ventral roots; dorsal root ganglion; dorsal branches* and *ventral branches; white rami* and *gray rami; paravertebral ganglia; collateral ganglia*). Know all the *cranial nerves* and their functions, especially the *vagus nerve (X)*, which contains predominantly efferent fibers (axons) that represent as much as 75% of all the fibers of the parasympathetic division of the autonomic nervous system.

Smooth muscle, cardiac muscle and many glands are controlled by the **autonomic nervous system**.

The autonomic nervous system consists of visceral efferent neurons organized into **nerves**, **ganglia**, and **plexuses**. Although the autonomic nervous system is generally an involuntary, automatic system, it nevertheless comes under control from certain brain centers located in the cerebral cortex, hypothalamus and medulla oblongata.

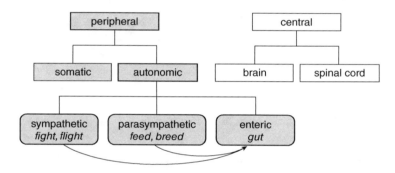

**Figure 20-1.**

The autonomic nervous system is divided into three branches, the **sympathetic, parasympathetic**, and the **enteric**. The enteric branch of the autonomic nervous system is represented by a complex network of neurons found in the gut. In this course, we shall concentrate mainly on the first two branches—the **sympathetic** and **parasympathetic**.

The autonomic nervous system controls smooth muscle in the gut (in conjunction with the enteric nervous system) and in various blood vessels, cardiac muscle and various glands (e.g. digestive and sweat glands). It regulates heart rate, blood pressure, breathing rate, body temperature and other activities involved in maintaining homeostasis.

The sympathetic branch of the autonomic nervous system becomes highly activated during times of emotional or physical stress, or when intense stress is anticipated. One important function of this branch of the autonomic nervous system is to prepare the body to meet the demands of strenuous physical activity—*fighting* or *fleeing*.

## OBJECTIVES

After listening to the lecture and reading this chapter, you should be able to:

1. Provide some **general characteristics** of the autonomic nervous system.
2. Name the **three branches** of the autonomic nervous system.

3.  Compare the **sympathetic** and **parasympathetic** branches of the autonomic nervous system with the **somatic efferent system** in terms of their **effectors, control, pathways, actions**, and **neurotransmitters**.

4.  Describe how sympathetic and parasympathetic efferent pathways differ from **somatic** efferent pathways.

5.  List the three general groups of **autonomic ganglia**, and state which division of the autonomic nervous system they are associated with.

6.  Describe the pathways of **pre-** and **postganglionic** fibers in the sympathetic branch of the autonomic nervous system.

7.  Describe the **origins** and **pathways** of nerve fibers in the parasympathetic division of the autonomic nervous system.

8.  Describe the **neurotransmitters** used by neurons in the sympathetic and parasympathetic divisions of the autonomic nervous system.

9.  List the **neurotransmitters** found in neurons of the sympathetic branch of the autonomic nervous system.

10. List the **neurotransmitters** found in neurons of the parasympathetic branch of the autonomic nervous system.

11. List the sympathetic and parasympathetic **neurotransmitter receptors**.

12. Compare the actions of the sympathetic and parasympathetic nervous systems on the **pupil** of the eye, **salivary** and **gastric glands, stomach** motility, **heart, bronchi** of the lungs, **arterioles** of the skin and viscera, **basal metabolic rate, penis, glycogen** metabolism, **intestinal** motility.

13. Describe the **components** of an autonomic (visceral) reflex, and describe the example given in these notes.

14. List the four components of the loose **hierarchy** that controls the sympathetic and parasympathetic branches of the autonomic nervous system.

15. Describe the relationship of the cells of the **adrenal medulla** to the sympathetic branch of the autonomic nervous system.

16. Define the difference between a **cholinergic** neuron and an **adrenergic** neuron.

415

## I. Some General Characteristics of the Autonomic Nervous System

Skeletal muscles are controlled by the motor side of the *somatic* nervous system. Movement of skeletal muscles occurs in response to commands that are usually under conscious control (exceptions are certain postural and spinal reflexes).

The three branches of the *autonomic* nervous system are called the **sympathetic, parasympathetic** and the **enteric**. The enteric branch is represented by a highly complex network of neurons found in the walls of the gut. We will concentrate on the sympathetic and parasympathetic branches.

Note that we regard the autonomic nervous system as mainly *motor*. However, reflexes of the autonomic nervous system respond to sensory information flowing into the central nervous system through afferent nerves having their sensory receptors in the skin or in the viscera (blood vessels, gastrointestinal tract, etc.). Much of the input from our viscera is not perceived by our conscious being (that is, it does not reach the cerebral cortex), but is evaluated and acted upon at the subconscious level (subcortical structures such as nuclei in the hypothalamus, pons and medulla) via *autonomic reflexes*.

The autonomic nervous system controls the following *effectors*:

- cardiac muscle
- smooth muscle
- glandular epithelium

The important distinctions between the parasympathetic and sympathetic branches of the autonomic nervous system on the one hand and the somatic nervous system on the other are as follows.

- In the **somatic** nervous system, a motor neuron in the spinal cord sends an axon through a peripheral nerve and makes a direct synapse (called a neuromuscular junction) with skeletal muscle fibers.

- In the parasympathetic and sympathetic branches of the **autonomic** nervous system, motor neurons in the spinal cord send out axons that make synapses with groups of second-order neurons located entirely *outside of the central nervous system* in structures referred to collectively as **ganglia** (singular = **ganglion**).

- In the sympathetic and parasympathetic branches of the autonomic nervous system, the axons of these second-order neurons make synaptic connections with the **cardiac muscle**, **smooth muscle** or **glandular epithelium**. The axons of the first neurons are called *preganglionic axons*, and the neurons themselves are called *preganglionic neurons*. The axons of the second-order neurons are called *postganglionic axons*. The neurons themselves are called *postganglionic neurons*, even though their cell bodies are within the ganglia.

Comparison of Somatic Efferent and Parasympathetic and Sympathetic Branches
of the Autonomic Nervous System

|  | **Somatic Efferent** | **Parasympathetic and Sympathetic** |
|---|---|---|
| effectors | skeletal muscles | cardiac muscle, smooth muscle, glandular epithelium |
| control | voluntary | involuntary |
| pathway | axon of motor neuron in CNS synapses with skeletal muscle fibers | axon of motor neuron in CNS synapses with a *second* neuron in a *ganglion*: this second neuron sends axon that synapses with visceral effector |
| action | always excites (i.e. muscle always contracts) | may be excitatory or inhibitory, depending on whether innervation is sympathetic or parasympathetic |
| neurotransmitters | acetylcholine | acetylcholine or norepinephrine |

- Neurons that release **acetylcholine** at their axon terminals are called *cholinergic*.
- Neurons that release **norepinephrine** at their axon terminals are called *adrenergic*.

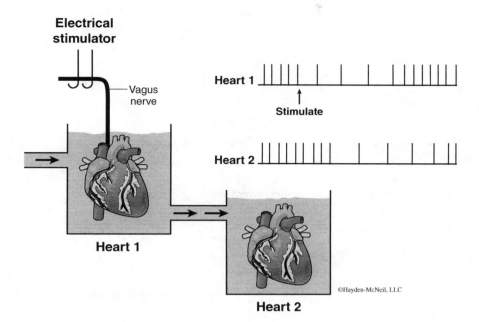

**Figure 20-2.**

Acetylcholine was discovered by Otto Loewi in Vienna and chemically identified by Sir Henry Dale in England. In Loewi's experiment carried out in 1921, he placed two beating hearts in separate chambers. Ringer's solution flowed through the first chamber into the second. When the vagus nerve to the first heart was electrically stimulated, the first heart slowed down. After a delay, Loewi observed that the second heart also slowed down. This demonstrated that a substance released by vagus nerve stimulation was carried to the second heart. Loewi called it Vagusstoff (literally vagus stuff). Dale subsequently characterized it chemically as acetylcholine. For this work, Loewi and Dale shared the 1936 Nobel Prize in physiology or medicine.

417

Usually, organs are innervated by fibers from both the parasympathetic and sympathetic branches of the autonomic nervous system. This is called dual innervation. Generally (but not always), commands through one branch are excitatory whereas commands through the other division are inhibitory.

## II. Anatomy of the Autonomic Nervous System

### A. Parasympathetic and Sympathetic Efferent Pathways Differ from Somatic Efferent Pathways

The **first** motor neurons of the sympathetic and parasympathetic branches of the autonomic nervous system are in the **spinal cord**, as in the case of the somatic nervous system. However, the efferent pathways of the sympathetic and parasympathetic autonomic nervous system involve groups of second-order neurons that are located in autonomic **ganglia** outside of the central nervous system. The axons of the first motor neurons synapse with these second-order neurons, which in turn send their axons to the visceral effectors, i.e. cardiac muscle, smooth muscle or glandular epithelium.

---

Don't confuse the ganglia of the sympathetic and parasympathetic branches of the autonomic nervous system with dorsal root ganglia. Dorsal root ganglia consist of masses of *sensory* neuron cell bodies, and have no synapses in them.

---

There are three general groups of ganglia in the parasympathetic and sympathetic branches of the autonomic nervous system.

1. The first group is associated with the **sympathetic division.** The ganglia in this group have many alternative names—we will call them **paravertebral** ganglia. The paravertebral ganglia are arranged like a string of beads along either side of the vertebral column. The beads are the ganglia, and the whole string is the *sympathetic trunk.*

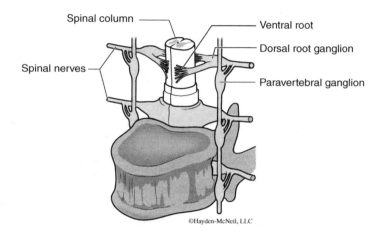

Spinal column

Ventral root

Dorsal root ganglion

Spinal nerves

Paravertebral ganglion

©Hayden-McNeil, LLC

**Figure 20-3.** Paravertebral ganglia—strung like pearls
down both sides of the vertebral column.

2. The second group is also associated with the **sympathetic division.** Ganglia in this group are called **collateral** ganglia.

3. The third group is associated with the **parasympathetic division.** Ganglia in this group are called *terminal ganglia* or *intramural ganglia.* They belong to the parasympathetic division, and are located either very close to the organ being innervated or are actually *within the walls* of the organ itself. In the gut, neurons in these ganglia input into the enteric branch of the autonomic nervous system.

## B. Sympathetic Division

Myelinated preganglionic axons of the sympathetic division exit with somatic efferents through the ventral roots of spinal cord segments T1–T12 and L1–L2.

Once outside of the vertebral column, **white rami** branch away from the spinal nerve and connect with a **paravertebral** ganglion. The white rami are white because their fibers are myelinated.

Once they have entered the paravertebral ganglion, the preganglionic fibers may:

1.  Form synapses with second-order neurons in the paravertebral ganglion. The fibers of these second-order neurons are *unmyelinated*. These postganglionic fibers (= axons) emerge from the paravertebral ganglia in the **gray rami** and join the spinal nerve again. They innervate many organs, including the iris of the eye, the salivary glands, lungs, heart.

2.  Alternatively, the preganglionic fibers may pass straight through the paravertebral ganglion without synapsing (they are still called preganglionic because they haven't synapsed yet). Thereafter, these preganglionic fibers may do one of two things.

    a.  The preganglionic fibers may emerge from the paravertebral ganglion and pass up or down the sympathetic trunk before forming synapses with second-order neurons in other paravertebral ganglia. The unmyelinated axons of the post-ganglionic, second-order neurons rejoin the spinal nerves via the gray rami.

    b.  Instead of passing up and down the sympathetic trunk, the preganglionic fibers may emerge from the paravertebral ganglion in nerves called the *splanchnic nerves*, and form their first synapses with second-order neurons in the **collateral** ganglia. Collateral ganglia include the *celiac ganglion*, the *superior mesenteric ganglion* and the *inferior mesenteric ganglion*.

        From the second-order neurons in the collateral ganglia, unmyelinated post-ganglionic axons distribute themselves to many organs. In the case of the celiac ganglion, these organs include the stomach, spleen, liver, kidney and small intestine.

3.  The **adrenal glands** – in one apparent exception to the general rule of two neurons in the efferent pathways of the sympathetic and parasympathetic branches of the autonomic nervous system, some preganglionic axons from first neurons in the sympathetic splanchnic nerves synapse directly on cells in the *adrenal medulla*. However, these cells of the adrenal medulla may be regarded as second-order neurons that have become *neurosecretory cells*. That is, they *secrete* their neurotransmitters into the bloodstream. These neurotransmitters, more correctly called *hormones*, are norepi-nephrine and its close relative *epinephrine* (= *adrenalin*).

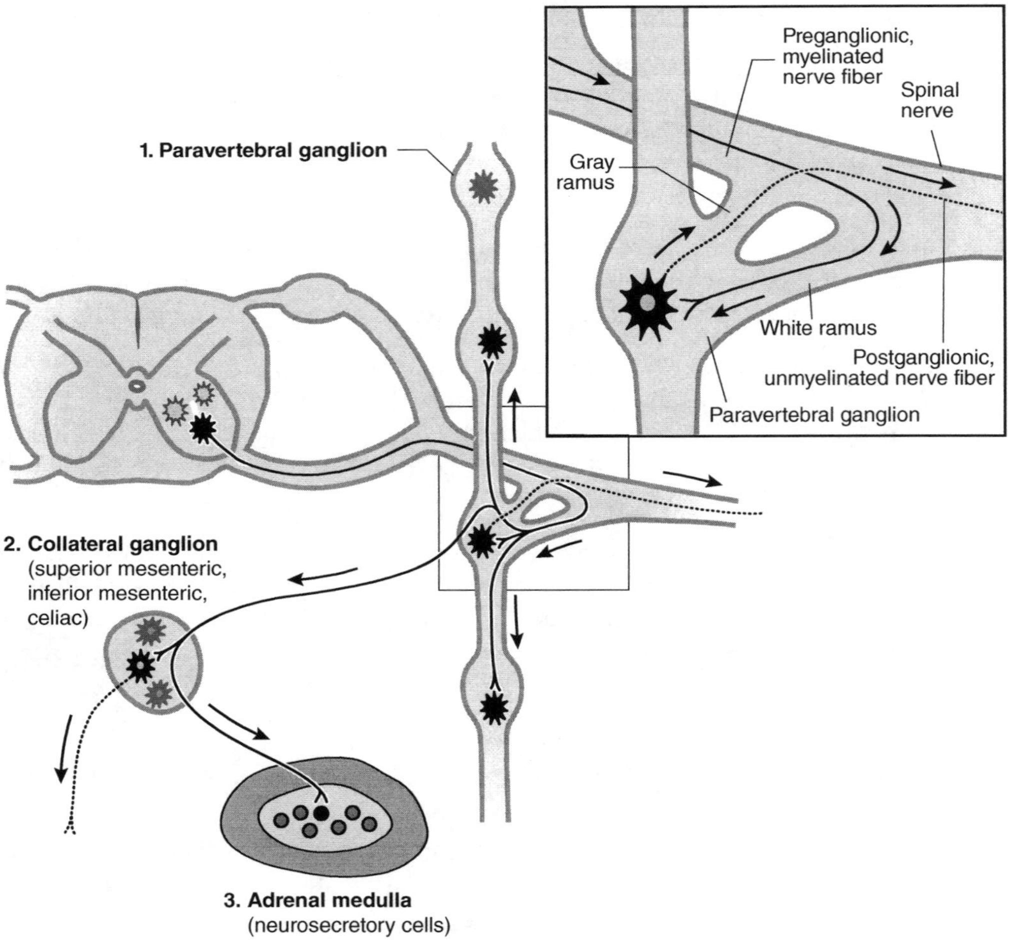

**Figure 20-4.** Sympathetic nervous system.

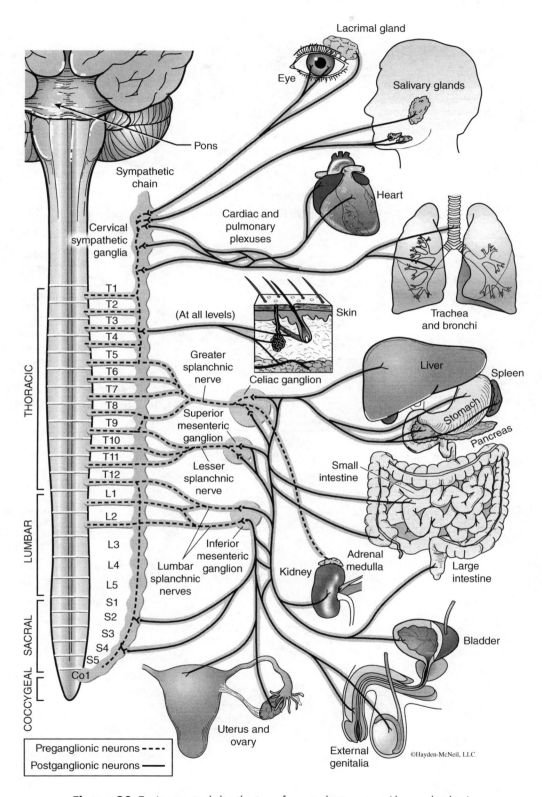

**Figure 20-5.** Anatomical distribution of sympathetic output (thoracolumbar).

## C. Parasympathetic Division

The parasympathetic division of the autonomic nervous system has its first neurons in two widely-separated locations of the central nervous system—the head (**cranial**) end, and the tail (**sacral**) end.

The cranial group of parasympathetic neurons is found in certain cranial nerve nuclei of the midbrain, pons and medulla.

The sacral group of parasympathetic neurons is found in the gray matter of spinal cord segments S2–S4.

1.  **Head (cranial) end of the parasympathetic division.**

    Parasympathetic preganglionic fibers exit in cranial nerves III (oculomotor), VII (facial), IX (glossopharyngeal) and X (the vagus). The locations of the second, postganglionic neurons are listed below.

| Cranial Nerve | Ganglion | Organ(s) |
|---|---|---|
| III (oculomotor) | *ciliary* | iris |
| VII (facial) | *pterygopalatine* | lacrimal (tear) glands and nasopharyngeal mucosa |
| | *submandibular* | salivary glands |
| IX (glossopharyngeal) | *otic* | parotid salivary glands |
| X (the vagus) | has its second neurons in the walls of organs (intramural ganglia) | lungs, heart, liver, stomach, small intestine, ascending colon |

2.  **Tail (sacral) end of the parasympathetic division.**

    Collectively, the sacral parasympathetic outflow emerges as preganglionic fibers from the ventral roots of S2–S4. These fibers constitute the ***pelvic splanchnic nerves***. They synapse with second, postganglionic neurons in the walls of the urinary bladder, rectum, genital organs. These synapses are called intramural synapses.

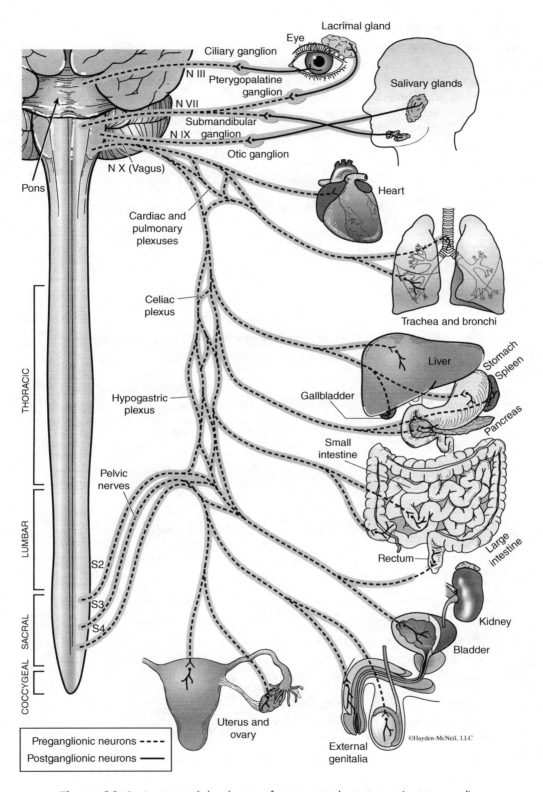

**Figure 20-6.** Anatomical distribution of parasympathetic output (craniosacral).

423

## D. Enteric Division

There are extraordinarily complex neuronal networks in the walls of the stomach, small intestine and large intestine. The small intestine alone has over 100,000,000 neurons! Although it is effectively an extension of the parasympathetic branch of the autonomic nervous system, most researchers regard these networks (or **plexuses**) as a *third* branch of the autonomic nervous system, called the enteric nervous system. Practically every neurotransmitter in the brain has also turned up in the enteric nervous system. The enteric nervous system appears to have a role in coordinating the activities of the gut, including movement and the secretion of digestive juices. It receives important input from the parasympathetic branch of the autonomic nervous system.

Some functions of the enteric division include:

- Control of motility
- Regulation of fluid exchange and local blood flow
- Regulation of gastric and pancreatic secretion
- Regulation of gastrointestinal endocrine cells
- Entero-enteric reflexes

## III. Sympathetic and Parasympathetic Neurotransmitters

There are two major neurotransmitters of the sympathetic and parasympathetic branches of the autonomic nervous system:

- **Acetylcholine** binds to two types of cell surface *receptor*:
  - **nicotinic receptors**
  - **muscarinic receptors**

- **Norepinephrine** binds to two types of cell surface receptor:
  - **α-adrenergic receptors**
  - **β-adrenergic receptors**

These receptors will be discussed in more detail in the next section.

Additionally, it is now realized that many neuroactive peptides are released by autonomic nervous system neurons.

**Neurotransmitters in each branch of the autonomic nervous system.**
- Sympathetic and parasympathetic preganglionic neurons are **cholinergic**.
- Parasympathetic postganglionic neurons are **cholinergic**.
- Most sympathetic postganglionic neurons are **adrenergic**, *except* for sympathetic postganglionic neurons innervating eccrine sweat glands, which are **cholinergic**.

**Distribution of neurotransmitter receptors.**
- The membranes of sympathetic and parasympathetic postganglionic neurons have **nicotinic** acetylcholine receptors.
- **α**- and **β-adrenergic** receptors are found on the membranes of cells that respond to norepinephrine.
- **Muscarinic** acetylcholine receptors are found on the cells that respond to acetylcholine released from autonomic nerve endings.

EXCEPTION – the sympathetic postganglionic neurons that innervate eccrine sweat glands of the skin are cholinergic, not adrenergic and act on muscarinic receptors.

### Adrenal medulla.

The cells of the **adrenal medulla** are modified postganglionic sympathetic neurons. When stimulated by preganglionic neurons they release the catecholamines *epinephrine* (80%) and norepinephrine (20%) into the blood (epinephrine is another name for *adrenalin*). From the adrenal medulla, these *catecholamines* are swept by the bloodstream to many tissues and organs, so that sympathetic stimulation of the adrenal can have widespread actions throughout the body.

Acetylcholine is rapidly destroyed by the enzyme **cholinesterase**, and its actions are short-lived.

Norepinephrine is removed by **reuptake** mechanisms and also destroyed by the enzyme *monoamine oxidase* found in the synaptic terminals.

## IV. Receptors for Sympathetic and Parasympathetic Neurotransmitters

Acetylcholine and norepinephrine (like other neurotransmitters) act on the postsynaptic membrane by binding to special proteins in the membranes called **receptors** (see diagram).

425

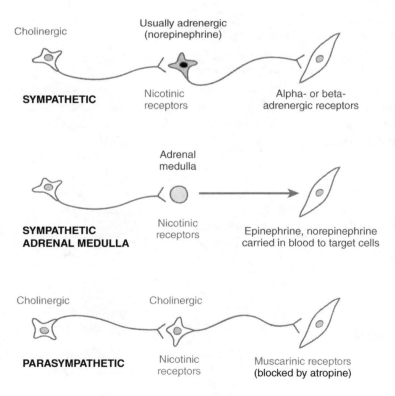

**Figure 20-7.**

There are two types of receptors for acetylcholine.

- **Nicotinic receptors.**

    One receptor for **acetylcholine** is found in the postsynaptic membrane of both sympathetic and parasympathetic postganglionic neurons, and is called a **nicotinic receptor** (so-called because nicotine binds to them and has the same effect as acetylcholine itself: that is, nicotine is an *agonist*). The motor endplate of the neuromuscular junction also has nicotinic receptors. Nicotinic acetylcholine receptors are also found in the brain, where they are responsible for the effects of nicotine and nicotine addiction from cigarette smoking. The nicotinic receptor is an example of a *ligand-gated ion channel*.

- **Muscarinic receptors.**

    The second receptor for **acetylcholine** is found in the postsynaptic membranes of synapses formed by the second neurons of the parasympathetic division with visceral effectors. This receptor is called the **muscarinic receptor** (so called because the toadstool toxin called muscarine acts as an agonist).

**Norepinephrine** (= *noradrenalin*) and **epinephrine** (= *adrenalin*) combine with two major types of **adrenergic** receptor.

- **α-adrenergic receptors** – bind both epinephrine and norepinephrine. α-adrenergic receptors are found in the walls of blood vessels, for example.

- **β-adrenergic receptors** – bind norepinephrine and epinephrine. Certain blood vessels have β-adrenergic receptors as well as α-adrenergic receptors in their walls. β-adrenergic receptors mediate the increase in force and rate of contraction of the heart when the sympathetic system is stimulated.

The effects of epinephrine and norepinephrine on a tissue are determined by the relative numbers of these two types of receptor (actually, both receptor types are further subdivided, but don't worry about that now).

## V. Actions of the Sympathetic and Parasympathetic Branches of the Autonomic Nervous System on Effector Organs—Autonomic (Visceral) Reflexes

### A. Actions

Most visceral effectors are innervated by both the sympathetic and parasympathetic divisions. In these cases, one division is usually excitatory and the other division is inhibitory. The excitatory action may be either sympathetic or parasympathetic.

In the case of the heart, sympathetic stimulation *increases* heart rate and force of contraction, whereas parasympathetic stimulation *decreases* heart rate but has no effect on the force of contraction.

On the other hand, in the case of the digestive system, sympathetic stimulation *decreases* digestive activities whereas parasympathetic stimulation *increases* digestive activities.

In general, the parasympathetic division is concerned with activities that conserve and restore body energy during times of rest and recuperation.

In general, the sympathetic division is involved in the ***fight-or-flight response***. That is, activation of the sympathetic division of the autonomic nervous system has the following effects.

1. Pupils of the eyes dilate.
2. Heart rate and force of contraction increase.
3. Blood vessels in skin and viscera contract.
4. Dilation of bronchioles to allow faster movements of air into and out of the lungs.
5. Blood vessels in skeletal muscles dilate.
6. Liver glycogen is converted to glucose.
7. Epinephrine and norepinephrine are secreted by the adrenal medulla.
8. "Non-essential" activities are inhibited (e.g. activity of the gastrointestinal tract, such as digestive secretion and movement).

### Some Actions of the Sympathetic and Parasympathetic Branches of the Autonomic Nervous System

| Effector | Sympathetic Stimulation (generally adrenergic except for the eccrine sweat glands, which are cholinergic) | Parasympathetic Stimulation (generally cholinergic) |
|---|---|---|
| pupil of eye | dilated | constricted |
| glands | | |
| lacrimal | no action | strong stimulation |
| salivary | slight stimulation ($K^+$ and $H_2O$) | strong stimulation ($K^+$ and $H_2O$) |
| sweat | strong stimulation (**cholinergic**) | no action |
| gastric | inhibition | stimulation |
| stomach | decreased motility | increased motility |
| heart | increased rate and force of contraction | decreased rate (strong stimulation causes "vagal arrest") |
| lungs (smooth muscle in the bronchi and bronchioles) | dilated | constricted |
| arterioles (skin, viscera) | constricted | not innervated |
| veins and muscular venules | constricted | not innervated |
| basal metabolism | increased | no effect |
| penis | ejaculation | erection (also of clitoris in female) |
| liver | glycogen → glucose | moderate glycogen synthesis |
| intestine | decreased mobility, tone | strongly increased mobility, tone |

427

## B. Autonomic (Visceral) Reflexes

In most respects, an autonomic reflex arc is similar to a somatic reflex arc. The autonomic reflex arc involves:

1. a **receptor**
2. a **sensory afferent** neuron
3. one or more **interneurons**
4. a **preganglionic motor** neuron
5. a **postganglionic motor** neuron in an autonomic ganglion
6. an **effector** (smooth muscle, cardiac muscle, glandular epithelium)

The only real difference from a somatic reflex arc is the presence of **two** motor neurons in the efferent motor pathway, the second one being housed in a sympathetic or parasympathetic autonomic ganglion.

### Important Example of an Autonomic Reflex

Blood pressure is controlled by the *baroreceptor reflex. Study it. **I will expect you to know it for the upcoming examination, and we will come back to it later in more detail when we discuss the cardiovascular system.***

1. A fall of blood pressure causes special *stretch receptors* (**baroreceptors**) in the aortic arch and carotid artery to become less stretched and to **reduce** their firing rate. This reduces the frequency of action potentials passing up the sensory axons to neurons in the medulla.

2. This **increases** the firing rate of a group of neurons in the medulla.

3. The neurons in the medulla signal to sympathetic motor neurons, which (via postganglionic neurons) cause the heart to increase its **rate** and force of contraction.

4. The sympathetic motor neurons also cause smooth muscle contraction in the blood vessels, **narrowing** them ( = vasoconstriction).

5. **Speeding up the heart rate and narrowing the blood vessels** raise the blood pressure back to normal.

Sensory nerve impulses generated in the viscera and elsewhere do not always reach the cerebral cortex. Under normal conditions, you are not aware of muscular contractions in the digestive organs, changes in the diameter of blood vessels, changes in blood pressure, etc. Many autonomic (visceral) reflexes involve neurons in many regions of the spinal cord, medulla or hypothalamus. Examples are as follows.

*Medulla*
- cardiac
- respiratory
- vasomotor
- swallowing
- vomiting

*Hypothalamus*
- temperature regulation

428

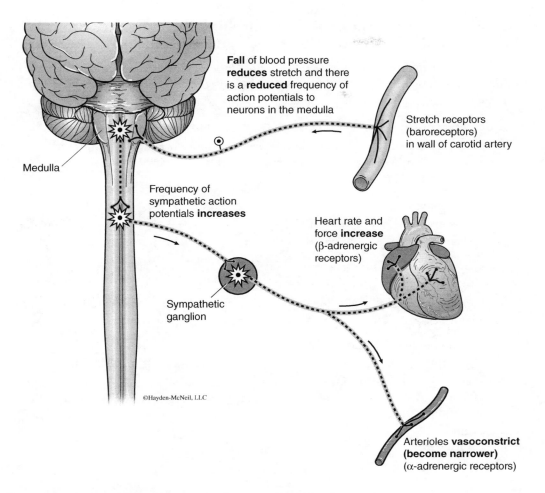

Fall of blood pressure **reduces** stretch and there is a **reduced** frequency of action potentials to neurons in the medulla

Stretch receptors (baroreceptors) in wall of carotid artery

Medulla

Frequency of sympathetic action potentials **increases**

Heart rate and force **increase** (β-adrenergic receptors)

Sympathetic ganglion

Arterioles **vasoconstrict (become narrower)** (α-adrenergic receptors)

©Hayden-McNeil, LLC

429

**Figure 20-8.** The *baroreceptor reflex* for controlling blood pressure—an important autonomic reflex that you must learn. This diagram is simplified. We will add more to it when we discuss how blood pressure is controlled.

Sometimes these sensory impulses **do** reach the cerebral cortex, when we become conscious of feelings of hunger, thirst, nausea, fullness of the urinary bladder and rectum and pain from damaged viscera. In these cases, we are not really dealing with autonomic reflexes because the action taken in response to these sensations is often under voluntary control. Examples are eating when we are hungry, drinking when we are thirsty and urinating when the bladder feels full.

## VI. Hierarchy of Brain Regions Controlling the Sympathetic and Parasympathetic Branches of the Autonomic Nervous System

The autonomic nervous system is regulated and controlled by a variety of regions in the brain. They can be regarded as a loose hierarchy, with the cerebral cortex at the top and the medulla and pons at the bottom.

- **Cerebral cortex.**

  Control of the the sympathetic and parasympathetic branches of the autonomic nervous system by the cerebral cortex seems to occur primarily during emotional stress (fear, anxiety, etc.).

- **Limbic system.**

  The cerebral cortex operates through the limbic system. Note, however, that some components of the limbic system are actually cerebral cortex (e.g. the *cingulate gyrus*), as we have seen.

- **Hypothalamus.**

  The hypothalamus is the major output pathway of the limbic system, and the hypothalamus controls and integrates the autonomic nervous system.

- **Pons and medulla.**

  The hypothalamus in turn can stimulate centers in the pons and medulla. For example, the cardiac and vasomotor centers in the medulla can increase heart rate, force of heart contraction, and may raise the blood pressure. The micturition center in the pons regulates *micturition*. *Respiratory* centers are found in the pons and medulla.

## CHAPTER 21

# SPECIAL SENSES I
The Eye, Smell, and Taste

## CHAPTER OUTLINE

## DESCRIPTION AND INTRODUCTION

The sensory receptor cells for the special senses are located in the head, often associated with complex sensory organs such as the eye. The sensory receptors for vision are photoreceptors. Mechanoreceptors are involved in hearing and balance, and chemoreceptors for the chemical senses of taste and smell.

1. **The eye is the organ of vision**, and provides us with information about objects that may be quite distant from the body. Early humans would have used their sight to detect a herd of mammoth (food), a sabertooth tiger (danger), or other humans. Sight could be used in navigation, in recognizing familiar rock formations, trees, streams, caves and so forth. Sight would also be the sense that was used to observe gestures and actions by other humans, and therefore may have subserved one form of communication. Nowadays, sight is also important in reading, writing and pictorial communication such as art, TV and the movies.

2. **The ear is the organ of hearing and balance.** It therefore has to provide us with two types of information.

   - **Hearing** – the sense that permits us to detect and analyze minute pressure changes that come to us as **sound waves** in the air (or water, if we are underwater). Sound is important in detecting danger, listening to music and in verbal communication.

   - **Balance** – not a sense that particularly impinges on our consciousness, but vitally important in controlling a variety of reflexes involved in **preventing us from falling over** when we are standing still or when we are running and walking. This sense is also important in stabilizing the direction of gaze of the eyes.

3. The twin senses of *taste* (in the **mouth**; buccal cavity) and *smell* (in the **nose**; nasal cavity) have receptor cells for detecting chemicals. These cells have either *olfactory receptor proteins* or *taste receptor proteins* in their membranes. These proteins bind to, and respond to, smelly or tasty molecules dissolved in the mucus of the nose or the saliva of the mouth. These smelly and tasty molecules may be released into our environment by a variety of agents. Through taste and smell, these molecules may tell us of danger (smell of smoke), they may evoke pleasure (fragrance of a rose), arouse sexual sensations (certain perfumes and odors released by our bodies), or give us feelings of unease (an unidentified odor may do this). Such molecules also give us important information about the food we are eating or the fluid we are drinking. They may warn us of something that should be avoided (a putrid, rotten odor, or an unpleasant taste) or identify something that should be sought after (sweet tastes, smell of turkey roasting).

   **Taste** may be a *screening mechanism* for what we eat, helping us to select food that is safe, palatable and nutritious (Andrew Spielman, NYU College of Dentistry), and to avoid eating other substances that are toxic.

   **Smell** is very primitive. Smell is unique in that its pathways first connect with more ancient parts of the cerebral cortex before going on to the thalamus and the evolutionarily newer parts of the cerebral cortex (the *neocortex*).

Some people say that human beings have lost their sense of smell. True, we have fewer olfactory receptor cells than, say, a bloodhound. However, we still have the ability to enjoy our food and surroundings, appreciate perfumes, avoid smoke from a fire, avoid putrid and dangerous foods, and perhaps seek out our mates. So humans still use their sense of smell.

The receptor cells for both taste and smell adapt rapidly, and plug into neuronal circuitry that controls "feeling states" of the mind as well as memories, both good and bad. We all know that certain smells and tastes, sometimes in unique combinations, can be strongly evocative of memories of events and emotions in the distant past, or of places visited.

In the present chapter, we will discuss the anatomy and physiology of the senses of **smell** (= olfaction), **taste** and **sight**.

## OBJECTIVES

After listening to the lecture and reading this chapter, you should be able to:

1. Distinguish between **somatic** and **special** senses.
2. Explain the importance of **vision** in our lives.
3. Explain the importance of **smell** and **taste** in our lives.
4. Describe the **olfactory receptor cells**, an olfactory **glomerulus**, the olfactory **pathway** and the regions of the b**rain** that receive information on odors transmitted through this pathway.
5. Describe the **physiology** of olfaction.
6. Describe how the **menstrual cycles** of women living together might become **synchronized**.
7. Describe the **anatomy** of **taste receptors** and the taste **pathway**.
8. Describe the **physiology** of taste.
9. Explain the relationship between **smell**, **taste** and **flavor**.
10. Name the parts of the **eye** and explain the function of each part.
11. **Draw a diagram** of the **neural retina**, showing the arrangement of the five neural cells found in it.
12. Name the cell layer that makes up the **non-neural** retina.
13. Give the name of the glial cell found in the retina.
14. **Draw a rod**, showing outer segment, mitochondria, nucleus and synapse.
15. Explain how the **cornea** and **lens** function to form an **image** of the external scene on the retina.
16. List five examples of **refractive problems** with the eye, and how they may be corrected.
17. Explain what is meant by a **visual pigment**, and explain the importance of vitamin A in vision and in the structure of rhodopsin.
18. Explain the basis of **color** vision and of color **blindness**.
19. Name four types of **defective color vision**.
20. Explain how light affects the **membrane potential** of a photoreceptor.

21. Define what is meant by **dark adaptation** and explain its molecular basis (see how far you can take this without referring to these notes a second time!).

22. **Draw a diagram** to show the nervous connections between the retina and the **visual cortex**.

23. Predict the consequences to vision of cutting **one optic nerve** (refer to the diagram of the visual pathway at the end of these notes).

24. Predict the consequences to vision of **cutting one optic tract** (refer to the diagram of the visual pathway at the end of these notes).

25. Predict the consequences to vision of making a **longitudinal** cut at the **optic chiasma** (refer to the diagram of the visual pathway at the end of these notes).

## I. Sense of Smell (Olfactory Sense)

### A. Olfactory Receptors

The sense of smell is associated with olfactory receptor cells in the upper region of the nasal cavity. The olfactory receptor cells are confined to a yellowish brown patch of specialized epithelium, the *olfactory epithelium*.

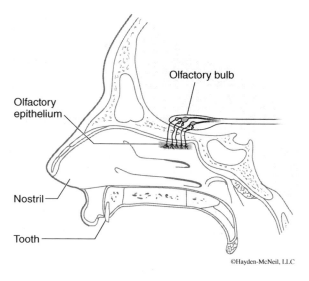

©Hayden-McNeil, LLC

**Figure 21-1.**

The olfactory receptor cells are bipolar neurons embedded in a layer of columnar epithelial cells, which have microvilli and are covered with a film of mucus.

One end of the olfactory receptor cell protrudes slightly beyond the surface of the epithelium, and gives rise to hair-like *olfactory cilia*, which form a dense mat on the surface. These cilia contain integral membrane **olfactory receptor proteins** that bind to, and interact with odor-producing molecules. In mammals, odor-producing substances are thought to be recognized by up to a thousand different olfactory receptor proteins, coded by the same number of *olfactory receptor genes* (in humans, the number of olfactory receptor proteins and olfactory receptor genes is probably about 500).

The other, more central, process of the olfactory receptor neuron consists of an unmyelinated axon that runs from the nasal cavity to the part of the brain called the *olfactory bulb*. Between 10 and 100 of these axons form a bundle surrounded by Schwann cell processes.

To reach the olfactory bulb, the axons pass through fine perforations in the *cribriform plate* of the *ethmoid bone*.

In humans, there are believed to be more than 100 million olfactory receptor cells (bloodhounds have 4 *billion*). Like taste receptor cells, the olfactory receptor cells die, and are replaced by new ones. In this case, the cycle takes 60 days. Special *basal cells* that lie near the basement membrane of the olfactory epithelium are responsible for the generation of new olfactory receptor cells, which they do by a process of differentiation.

This replacement is remarkable, because olfactory receptor cells are neurons, and when they differentiate, their axons must grow and make the appropriate synapses with neurons in the olfactory bulb. It would be of immense clinical value if it could be determined how the basal cells differentiate into olfactory receptor cells and how these cells form the correct connections with the mitral cells in the olfactory bulbs. It is also important to understand how all the special *olfactory receptor genes* in olfactory receptor cells get turned on during this differentiation process.

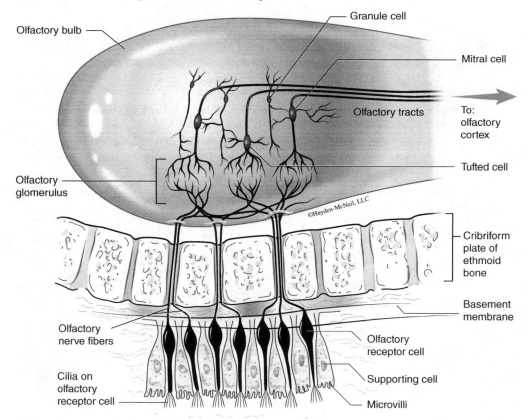

**Figure 21-2.** Olfactory system. Basal cells that regenerate are NOT shown.

## B. Physiology of Olfaction

There are thousands of distinct odors, and up to 1000 different olfactory receptor proteins encoded by a corresponding number of genes. At least one kind of olfactory receptor cell has seven subtypes that are involved in perception of the seven so-called "primary" odors. This kind of olfactory receptor responds to a range of molecules that have certain properties in common. For example, the molecules of substances that generate the primary odor *floral* all have a similar shape and bind to and stimulate the floral receptor. The same can be said of receptors for *putrid, camphoraceous, musky, pepperminty, ethereal* and *pungent* odor producers. However, as we shall see in a moment, the broad features of smells are also determined when olfactory information is processed in the olfactory bulb.

Each odor-producing chemical binds to an olfactory receptor protein in the cilia of groups of olfactory receptor cells in different regions of the olfactory epithelium. Recently, researchers have discovered an enormously large family of genes in rats that code for between 500 and 1000 different types of olfactory receptor proteins. This enables animals to detect a correspondingly enormous variety of odors.

When a molecule binds to its olfactory receptor protein, it produces a **generator potential** that increases the rate of impulse firing of the receptor cell in proportion to the intensity of the stimulus. In this case, the intensity of the stimulus is determined by the number of molecules of odoriferous substance dissolved in the mucus covering the olfactory epithelium.

436

For reasons not understood, older people are much less sensitive to certain odors.

> The **vomeronasal organ** – in many animals, the nasal cavity contains a vomeronasal organ, which has a second kind of olfactory receptor cell believed to be sensitive to **pheromones**. Pheromones were originally identified as sex attractants in insects, but there are now plenty of examples of pheromones being used by mammals for signalling, particularly in sexual and territorial marking situations. There is now some evidence that humans emit pheromones (see below), although whether humans have a **functional** vomeronasal organ has been seriously questioned. [See Meridith M. (2001). Human vomeronasal function: a critical review of best and worst cases. *Chem Senses 26*, 433–445. Lledo, P.-M., Gheusi G., and Vincent, J.-D. Information processing in the mammalian olfactory system. *Physiol Rev 85*(1), 281–317, January 1, 2005.]

> **Pheromones in humans?** The menstrual cycles of women who live together or who are close friends and see a lot of each other tend to synchronize. There is some scientific evidence that this is due to pheromones. In a 1998 study by Stern and McClintock (*Nature 392*, 177–179, 1998) axillary body odor was collected on cotton pads from a number of female donors. The pads were then wiped under the noses of a number of female recipients. Depending on the time in the menstrual cycle of the female donors, the menstrual cycle of the female recipients was advanced or delayed in phase. For further information, consult the original article cited above, or see the review in the same issue of *Nature 392*, 126–127 (1998). The scientific journals *Nature* and *Science* are available in the Life Sciences Library in Lilly Hall of Life Sciences (second floor, above my office).

### C. Olfactory Pathway

The **olfactory bulb** is the first site for olfactory information processing in the brain. The unmyelinated axons of olfactory receptor cells that respond to similar odor-producing compounds may converge in large numbers onto special structures called *olfactory glomeruli*, which are really complex synapses with the dendrites of the *mitral cells*.

At this point, there is a certain amount of information processing.

Mitral cell axons exit the olfactory bulbs in the *olfactory tracts*, which terminate in the *olfactory cortex*. Information on odor is then directed to two different locations in the brain.

1.  The **limbic system** – some regions of the olfactory cortex make connections with the **hippocampus** and **amygdala**, both structures being components of the *limbic system* (see Chapter 19). These regions may be involved with the emotional and memory-retrieving aspects of smells, perhaps influencing our behavior and thought processes. The growing multi-billion dollar fragrance industry capitalizes on this.

2.  The **frontal lobes** – other regions of the olfactory cortex make connections with the frontal lobes via the **thalamus**. These regions are believed to be involved with the conscious perception of smell.

HHMI researcher and Nobel Prizewinner Linda Buck showed that each odorant is recognized by a combination of receptors, and that each receptor can recognize multiple odorants. "So, the odorant receptor family is being used combinatorially," she said. "Just like letters of the alphabet are used in different combinations to form different words, the odorant receptors are used in different combinations to detect different odorants and encode their unique identities."

437

**Olfactory Pathways to the Brain**

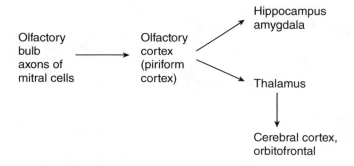

**Figure 21-3.**

## II. Sense of Taste (Gustatory Sense)

Taste is important in helping us evaluate the food we eat. Foods that taste delicious are hopefully good for you (I wonder if they really are!) and things that taste nasty are very likely to be bad for you.

### A. Taste Receptor Cells

**Taste receptor cells** are modified *epithelial* cells, NOT neurons. Taste cells are bundled together in groups of about 40–60 contained in a *taste bud*. Taste receptor cells die every 10 days, and are replaced by new taste receptor cells formed from cells called basal cells.

The taste bud is embedded in the epithelium of the tongue and connected to the tongue's surface by a *taste pore*. Microvilli or *taste hairs* extend from the apical surfaces of the taste receptor cells, and project through the taste pore to make contact with the saliva bathing the tongue. The plasma membranes of the taste hairs contain *taste receptor proteins* that bind to specific tasty molecules dissolved in the saliva.

At the base of each taste receptor cell there is a *synaptic* contact with a branch of an *afferent nerve fiber*. One afferent fiber may carry the signals from many receptors. The various taste chemicals either depolarize or hyperpolarize taste cells, so regulating neurotransmitter release from the taste cells.

On the tongue, collections of taste buds occur in three different types of structures called *papillae*. There are *circumvallate*, *foliate*, and *fungiform* papillae.

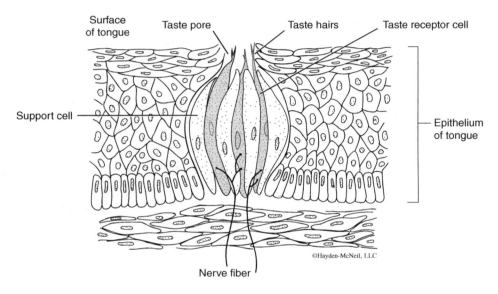

**Figure 21-4.** Taste bud.

## B. Physiology of Taste

Humans classify tastes in five groups. It appears that combinations of five basic tastes can account for most tastes:

- bitter
- salty
- sweet
- sour
- *umami*, a unique taste associated with protein-rich foods and produced by monosodium glutamate (MSG). The umami receptor is an amino acid receptor. Since amino acids are essential for building proteins, the receptor is important in helping to identify and seek out these substances in the diet. The mouse umami receptor responds to nearly all of the 20 amino acids found in protein, whereas the human umami receptor is most sensitive to monosodium glutamate, which is one of the commonest amino acids in our diet and gives high-protein food a meaty, attractive flavor.

It has been suggested that there are other receptors, such as alkaline and metallic, but this is controversial.

A single taste **bud** contains 50–100 **taste cells** representing **all five** taste sensations (*the classic textbook pictures showing separate taste areas on the tongue are completely wrong*).

In addition to the tongue, there are also taste buds on the epiglottis, the upper third of the esophagus and on the soft palate.

Salts and acids seem to depolarize taste receptor cells *directly*. However, it seems that the tastes of bitter, sweet and umami involve guanine nucleotide binding proteins (also known as G proteins: more in BIOL 204).

## C. Genetics of Taste

The ability to taste different substances often varies between people. In some cases, the variation is genetic. For example, about a quarter of the population can taste the chemical *propylthiouracil* (PROP), finding it intensely bitter. About half the population find it somewhat bitter, and the remaining quarter of the population cannot taste PROP at all. "Supertasters," those who can taste PROP, have more *fungiform* papillae on the tips of their tongues. You can see them by dabbing some blue food dye on the tongue—the tongue stains blue, but the fungiform papillae remain pink. Supertasters are more sensitive to bitter substances in coffee and grapefruit juice, find saccharin and sucrose sweeter than most people do, and are more sensitive to the burning sensation of chili peppers.

439

One of the twenty receptor molecules for bitter taste has now been cloned.

## D. Flavors, Tastes, and Odors

Taste and odor usually go hand in hand to generate a particular *flavor*. Stimulating both taste and olfactory receptor cells produces the "flavor" of chocolate and coffee, for example. This is the reason that when you have a cold, and your nose is all bunged up, foods appear to be tasteless. Some foods may even go so far as to stimulate *pain/heat* receptors on the tongue. An example might be your favorite Tex-Mex chili recipe, or some homegrown jalapeño peppers (definitely not to be eaten by the faint-hearted). Apparently the hot ingredient in these dishes is a substance called *capsaicin*, which binds to a special ion channel called the *vanilloid receptor*. When the channel opens, it allows the influx of calcium ions and sodium ions into the receptor cell. Painful heat acts on the same receptors (see *Nature 389*, 783 and 816, 1997).

## E. Taste Pathway

Signals from the taste buds in the tongue, epiglottis and esophagus travel *via* cranial nerves **VII**, **IX** and **X** to the medulla, where they synapse with neurons in the *gustatory nucleus,* which is part of the *nucleus of the tractus solitarius.*

From the medulla, signals pass to the **thalamus**, which relays them to the post-central gyrus and insula of the **cerebral cortex,** close to the somatosensory area for the tongue.

**Sensory Innervation of the Tongue**

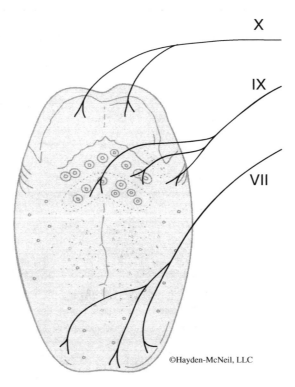

©Hayden-McNeil, LLC

**Figure 21-5.**

## III. Sense of Sight (Visual Sense, Vision)

Both the eye and the ear provide us with information about events that are compara-tively distant from the body. The eye is a complex organ designed to throw an **image of the external scene** on a carpet of photoreceptor cells that are found in a special photo-sensitive layer of neurons within the eye. This layer is called the **retina**.

The **photoreceptor cells** respond to different **colors** of light, and are also able to signal the **intensity** of the light. Some preliminary processing of these signals takes place in the neural networks of the retina, which develops as an outgrowth of the neural tube. In some ways, the retina can be considered as a small brain.

In addition to the eye itself, there are a number of accessory structures associated with it.

## A. Accessory Structures Associated with the Eye

1. **Eyelids** – moved by the *orbicularis oculi* and *levator palpebrae superioris* muscles. The *conjunctiva* is a mucous membrane that lines the eyelids and extends over the ante-rior surface of the eye with the exception of the *cornea*.

2. **Lacrimal apparatus** (generates tears) – consists of the *lacrimal gland* located in the orbit and a series of tubes that convey the tear fluid into the nasal cavity.

3. **Extraocular muscles** – move the eye. There are six of them, as follows.
   - *inferior rectus* rotates the eye downward and toward the midline
   - *lateral rectus* rotates the eye away from the midline
   - *medial rectus* rotates the eye toward the midline
   - *superior rectus* rotates the eye upward and toward the midline
   - *inferior oblique* rotates the eye upward and away from the midline
   - *superior oblique* rotates the eye downward and away from the midline

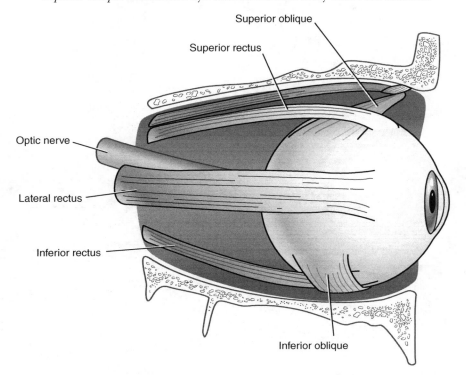

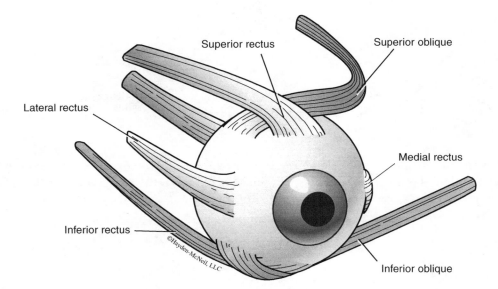

441

**Figure 21-6.** Extraocular muscles.

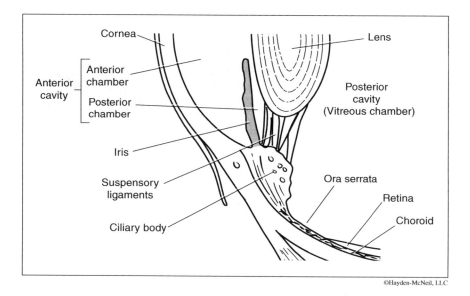

©Hayden-McNeil, LLC

**Figure 21-7.** The eye.

The main thrust of this discussion on the sense of sight will be on the structure of the eye, and on the *retina* in particular. It is the retina that is involved in detecting light, in processing signals, and in transmitting this information via the thalamus to the posterior occipital cortex.

## B. Structure of the Eye

The eye consists of three basic layers.

1.  Outer layer.

    a.  **Sclera** – in the posterior part of the eye, the outer layer makes up the white of the eye, and is composed of dense fibrous connective tissue. The collagenous fibers in the sclera are not organized, and they scatter light so much that the sclera looks white.

    b.  **Cornea** – in the anterior part of the eye, the outer layer becomes the transparent window of the eye. The cornea is transparent because it has few cells and no blood vessels, and (unlike the sclera) the layers of collagenous fibers are so regularly arranged that very little scattering occurs as light passes through it. The cornea has many naked nerve endings that transmit **pain**. That is why anything that touches your cornea causes a painful sensation.

2.  **Uveal layer** (**middle layer**) – typically highly vascular (that is, it contains many blood vessels).

    a.  **Choroid** – in the posterior part of the eye, the uveal layer is called the **choroid**. The choroid contains numerous blood vessels and *melanocytes*. The melanocytes contain *melanin granules*, which assist in preventing light from being reflected around in the interior of the eye and confusing the image (the interior of a camera is painted matte black for the same reason). The blood vessels of the choroid are very important in conveying nutrients to the retinal pigmented epithelium and the neural retina.

    b.  **Ciliary body** and **iris** – in the anterior part of the eye, the choroid gives way to the **ciliary body** and the **iris**. The ciliary body has ciliary muscles and a series of foldings called *ciliary processes*, which are connected to the *suspensory ligaments* that hold the *lens* in position. The *ciliary muscles* are involved in altering the shape of the lens during accommodation, which will be discussed below. Cells in the ciliary body are responsible for secreting the *aqueous humor*.

    The iris is attached to the ciliary body. It confers color to the eyes – a darkly pigmented iris gives a person brown eyes, and an iris that has little pigmentation gives a person blue eyes. The blue color is not caused by a blue pigment, but by light scattering. The sky looks blue for the same reason. In albinos, there is no pigmentation at all, and the eye looks pink because we see the blood in the blood vessels of the iris.

    In the center of the iris is the black hole of the *pupil*. It looks black because practically no light is reflected back out of the eye. In bright light the pupil is very small, because the iris has contracted (it contains smooth muscle). This reduces the amount of light entering the eye. In dim light the pupil can be very large, increasing the amount of light entering the eye. The iris is therefore equivalent to the *iris diaphragm in a camera*.

    Certain drugs and brain damage can also affect the size of the pupil.

443

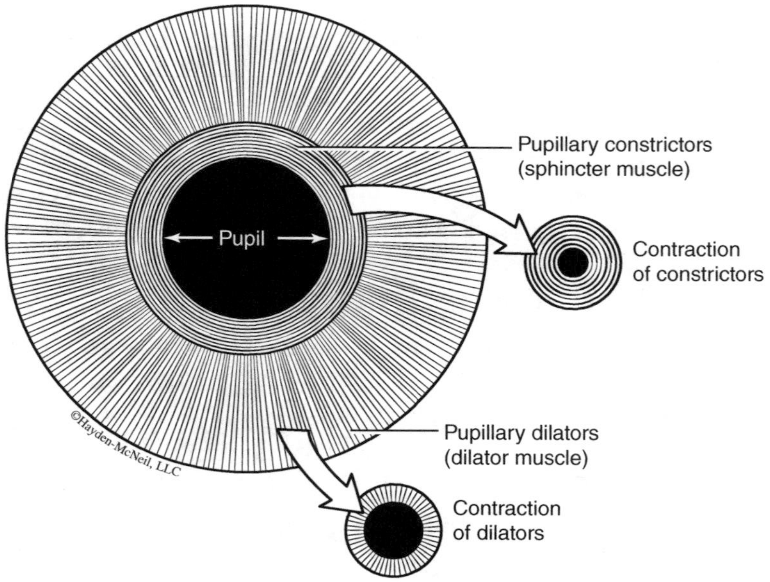

**Figure 21-8.**

3.  **Retina (innermost layer)** – the retina actually consists of the *neural retina* and the non-neural retina or *pigmented epithelium* (= retinal pigmented epithelium). It will be discussed in detail later.

444

## C. Cavities and Chambers of the Eye—Aqueous Humor and Vitreous Humor

The eye is divided into an *anterior cavity* and *posterior cavity* by the **lens**. Additionally, the anterior cavity is divided into the *anterior chamber*, which lies anteriorly to the iris, and the *posterior chamber*, which lies behind the iris.

A watery fluid called **aqueous humor** is secreted into the posterior chamber by the **ciliary body**. The aqueous humor flows through the aperture of the iris into the anterior chamber and then out of the eye into the blood by a channel called the *canal of Schlemm*. Factors that increase the secretion of aqueous humor or block its outflow cause an increase in the *intraocular pressure*. This occurs in the condition called *glaucoma*, which can lead to blindness due to retinal degeneration.

The posterior cavity of the eye is filled with a transparent, jelly-like body called the **vitreous humor**.

## D. Refraction of Light through the Eye

In the eye, an image of the external scene must be formed on the light-sensitive layer of the retina. In a camera (where the film replaces the retina), this is done by the lens. In the eye, however, about **75%** of the refracting power is due to the *cornea*, only about **25%** being due to the *lens*.

This is why vision is blurred when you open your eyes under water. The water has the same refractive index as the cornea and aqueous humor, so no refraction occurs at the corneal interface. However, if you put on an air-filled face mask, then sharp vision is restored.

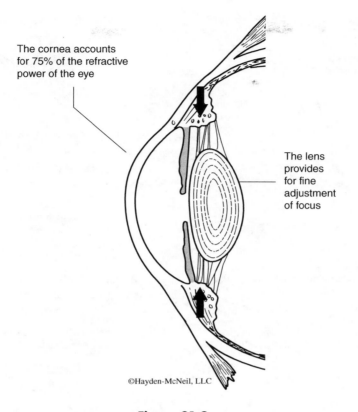

The cornea accounts for 75% of the refractive power of the eye

The lens provides for fine adjustment of focus

©Hayden-McNeil, LLC

**Figure 21-9.**

The lens of the eye functions to adjust the refracting power of the eye so that images are always sharply focused on the retina irrespective of the distance of the object being viewed. This process of adjusting the power of the lens depending on whether we are viewing a near or a distant object is called *accommodation*.

1.  **Viewing a near object.**

    The lens assumes a more powerful, spherical shape because the muscles in the ciliary body *contract*. This reduces the pull on the suspensory ligaments and allows the lens to round up because of its natural elasticity. This increases the refractive power of the lens.

2.  **Viewing a distant object.**

    The lens becomes more flattened and therefore weaker because the muscles in the ciliary body *relax*. This increases the pull on the suspensory ligaments, which in turn pull on the lens and flatten it. This reduces the refractive power of the lens.

**Focusing (viewing) a NEAR object**    **Focusing (viewing) a FAR object**

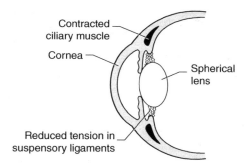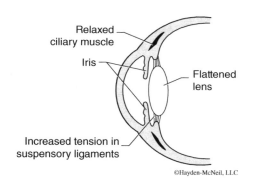

**Figure 21-10.** Accommodation.

**Accommodation for near vision**

- Ciliary muscles contract
- Pull on suspensory ligaments is reduced
- Lens becomes more spherical and optically more powerful

**Accommodation for distant vision**

- Ciliary muscles relax
- Pull on suspensory ligaments increases
- Lens flattens and becomes optically weaker

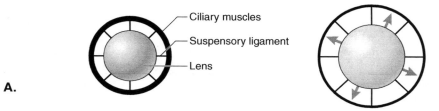

**A.**

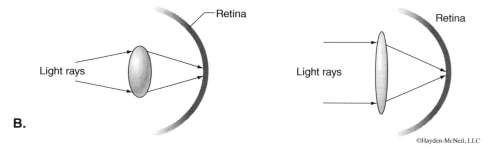

**B.**

**Figure 21-11.** A. Front view of ciliary muscles, suspensory ligaments and lens.
B. Side view of lens and retina.

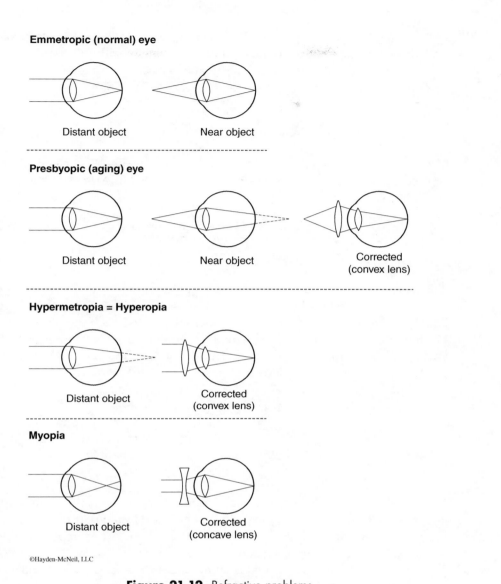

Emmetropic (normal) eye

Distant object          Near object

Presbyopic (aging) eye

Distant object          Near object          Corrected
(convex lens)

Hypermetropia = Hyperopia

Distant object          Corrected
(convex lens)

Myopia

Distant object          Corrected
(concave lens)

©Hayden-McNeil, LLC

**Figure 21-12.** Refractive problems.

## E. Refractive Problems

1. **Presbyopia and aging** – as a person ages, the natural elasticity of the lens is lost and it is unable to assume the more spherical shape necessary for viewing near objects. Objects such as the printed page tend to be held further away from eyes, because the lens cannot be made powerful enough to bring them into focus if they are held closer. The eye is then said to be **presbyopic**, and requires the assistance of a **convex** lens to *increase the power of the eye* and focus near objects on the retina.

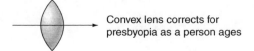

Convex lens corrects for
presbyopia as a person ages

2. **Hyperopia** – farsightedness, caused by the eyeball being a little too short, and the light rays converge toward a point behind the retina. As with presbyopia, a **convex** lens is needed to *increase the power of the eye* and correct the problem.

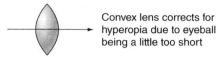

Convex lens corrects for hyperopia due to eyeball being a little too short

3. **Myopia** – nearsightedness, because the eyeball is a little too long, and light rays are focused in front of the retina. A **concave** lens is needed to *decrease the power of the eye* and correct the problem.

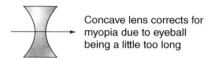

Concave lens corrects for myopia due to eyeball being a little too long

4. **Astigmatism** – most often caused by irregular curvature of the cornea. A person with astigmatism might be able to bring vertical lines into focus, but horizontal lines become blurred. If the horizontal lines are focused, then the vertical lines are blurred. A **cylindrical** lens can sometimes correct the problem. The cylinder below is exaggerated — normally, a cylindrical lens in prescription glasses is not noticeable unless you look through the lens and carefully rotate it).

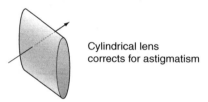

Cylindrical lens corrects for astigmatism

5. **Cataract** – a condition where the lens loses its transparency and becomes opaque, either partially or completely. Cataract can be caused by a variety of factors, including chemical agents, ultraviolet and infrared radiation. For example, glassblowers can be exposed to infrared radiation for much of their working lives, and before protective glasses became mandatory they used to get "glassblower's cataract." If clear vision is lost, then the lens may need to be removed by cataract surgery.

## F. The Retina

The retina consists of the *neural retina* and the non-neural retina or *pigmented epithelium* (= retinal pigmented epithelium).

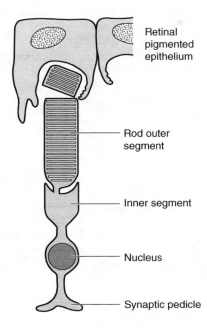

**Figure 21-13.** Retinal pigmented epithelial cell phagocytizing
the detached tip of a rod outer segment.

449

1. **Non-neural retina** – the **retinal pigmented epithelium** is a single layer of melanin-containing cells that is sandwiched between the neural retina and the choroid. The retinal pigmented epithelium has the following functions:

   a. Regulates the passage of nutrients from the choroid to the photoreceptors.

   b. Stores retinol (vitamin A) and supplies it to the photoreceptors.

   c. Plays a critical role in the regeneration of rhodopsin.

   d. Phagocytizes the shed tips of the growing rod outer segments.

2. **Neural retina** forms in the embryo as an outgrowth of the brain. Its primary function is to detect light, and therefore the neural retina acts like the film in a camera. It does more than a film, however, because its neuronal networks also carry out a preliminary analysis of the spatial patterns and movement of the image. It relays this information to the brain via the optic nerve.

   The neural retina contains *five* different types of **neuron** and one type of **glial** cell. They are as follows.

   - **Photoreceptors** (the *rods* and *cones*) are modified, elongated neurons that detect light.

   - **Bipolar cells** are neurons that relay signals from the photoreceptors to the ganglion cells (see Figure 21-14).

- **Ganglion cells** are neurons with axons that exit from the posterior part of the eye, and form the **optic nerve**. The optic nerve carries signals (action potentials) from the retina to the brain.

- **Amacrine cells** are neurons that are involved in lateral interactions between the above cell types.

- **Horizontal cells** are neurons that are also involved in lateral interactions between the aforementioned cell types. Lateral interactions can be responsible for certain illusions, such as that seen in the Hermann grid (see Figure 21-14).

- **Mueller cells** are *glial* cells (not shown in the diagram).

The cone photoreceptors are concentrated in a central part of the retina called the yellow spot or **macula lutea**. It looks yellow because it contains a mixture of zeaxanthin and lutein. Both are derived from the diet and are related to $\beta$-*carotene*. They may have a protective function. In the center of the macula lutea is a depression called the **fovea**. This is the area of sharpest **visual acuity** in the retina.

The point at which the optic nerve fibers exit the retina is called the **optic disk**. Blood vessels also enter the eye at this point, and nourish the inner surface of the retina. Because there are no photoreceptors at the optic disk, this area is called the **blind spot**.

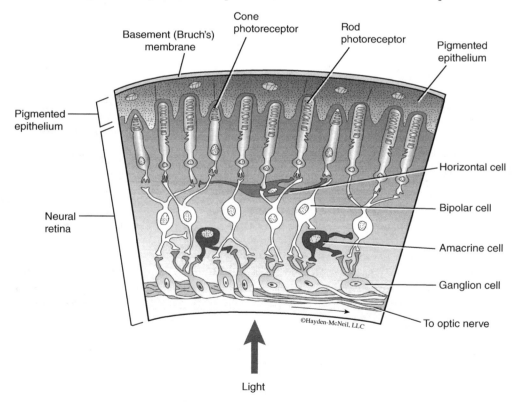

**Figure 21-14.** Retinal cells (Mueller cells not shown).

***Lateral inhibition*** **in the retina** – in the *Hermann grid* of black squares below there appear to be darker spots at the corners of the squares.

**Can you see these spots?**

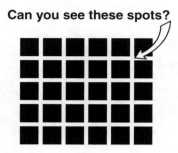

**Figure 21-15.** Hermann grid.

The illusion of the darker spots is because cones within the black areas inhibit cones receiving light at the corners. *Which cells in the neural retina might be involved in this effect?*

## G. Photoreceptor Cells, Visual Pigments and Vision

There are two types of photoreceptor cell in the retina – the **rods** and **cones**. Rods provide *poor-acuity black-and-white vision in dim light.* Cones provide *high-acuity color vision in bright light.*

Rods have a low visual acuity because many of them tend to be wired to one ganglion cell (via the bipolar cells, an example of *convergence*). Cones have a high visual acuity because few cones (sometimes even one cone) are wired to one ganglion cell.

1. **Photoreceptors are light-sensitive because they contain** *visual pigments.*

   A photoreceptor cell is an elongated neuron with an outer segment at one end and a synaptic pedicle (or ending) at the other. The photoreceptor outer segments, which consist of stacks of membranes (disks), contain integral membrane proteins called **visual pigments**. In rods, the visual pigment is reddish in color and is called ***rhodopsin***.

2. **Visual pigments are chemically changed when they absorb light.**

   The visual pigment **rhodopsin** consists of an integral, transmembrane protein called ***opsin*** that has bound to it the aldehyde of ***vitamin A*** which is called ***retinal***. Retinal can exist in a number of molecular shapes, or *isomers*. The isomer in rhodopsin is a bent molecule called ***11-cis*** ***retinal***.

   When rhodopsin absorbs light, it is changed chemically. The chemical change involves straightening out the bent molecule of 11-*cis* retinal to form **all-trans** ***retinal***. The protein part of the rhodopsin molecule (opsin) then changes its shape and is activated.

   Ultimately, the all-*trans* retinal is hydrolyzed from the opsin and is then converted by an enzyme (retinol dehydrogenase) into ***all*-trans** ***retinol*** (vitamin A). In the process, rhodopsin loses its color and is said to bleach. This process is reversed during dark-adaptation (see later).

451

- Outer segments contain visual pigments that absorb light.

- Visual pigment in rods is called rhodopsin.

- Visual pigments are integral membrane proteins to which are attached molecules of 11-*cis* retinal = aldehyde of vitamin A (retinol).

- Light chemically changes (bleaches) visual pigments, transforming 11-*cis* retinal to all-*trans* retinal.

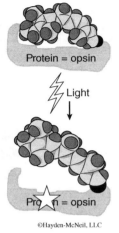

Protein = opsin

Light

Protein = opsin

©Hayden-McNeil, LLC

**Figure 21-16.**

3. **When activated by the absorption of light, rhodopsin initiates a series of events that lead to membrane *hyperpolarization*** (not *depolarization*, as occurs in most sensory receptors).

This is because the membrane is leaky to sodium ions in darkness, so the membrane is always partly depolarized (i.e. the membrane potential has moved toward the Nernst potential for sodium). In the light, the sodium channels are ***closed***, *and so the membrane potential moves toward the Nernst potential for potassium. That is, it hyperpolarizes.*

In a complex way (see below), the ultimate result of photoreceptor membrane hyperpolarization is an increase in the firing rate of the ganglion cells, which transmit action potentials up their axons to the ***lateral geniculate nucleus*** of the thalamus (remember that the optic nerve is made up from the axons of the ganglion cells).

Light-activated rhodopsin has the following actions.

a.  It interacts with a G protein called transducin.

b.  This causes activation of an enzyme called cyclic GMP phosphodiesterase (cGMP = cyclic guanosine monophosphate).

c.  This breaks down cGMP, reducing its amount in the photoreceptor.

d.  Reduction in the amount of cGMP causes closure of sodium (and calcium) channels in the plasma membrane and hyperpolarization of the cell membrane.

The signal from bleached rhodopsin is then turned off by phosphorylation (by the enzyme rhodopsin kinase). The phosphorylated rhodopsin is then inactivated by a protein called arrestin.

A parallel system appears to occur in the cones.

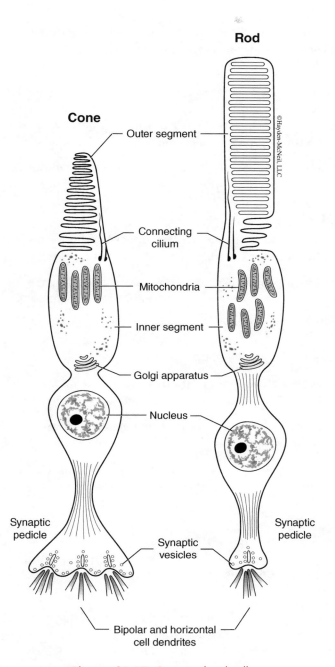

**Figure 21-17.** Cone and rod cells.

453

## H. Color Vision

The cones are responsible for our ability to see colored light. All colors are made up of three primary colors—**red**, **green**, and **blue** light. This is the basis of the **Young–Helmholtz** *trichromatic theory* of color vision. Humans and Old World monkeys all have trichromatic vision, which allows them to distinguish between blue, green and red colors. Some researchers have suggested that the evolution of trichromacy helped early primates to find ripe fruits and tender young red leaves in the greenery of their forest homes. Many primate species evolved red skin and hair after they had acquired color vision.

Trichromatic vision involves three types of cone that respond to red light, green light and blue light. Each of these cone types has a different visual pigment that absorbs red, green or blue light.

In agreement with the **labeled line code** principle, the *type* of cone stimulated determines the perceived color. When all three cone types are stimulated equivalently, we perceive **white** light. When only one type of cone is stimulated, we perceive **red**, **green**, or **blue** light (depending on the cone). **Other colors** result from stimulation of several cone types.

The **brightness** of the perceived light is determined by the intensity of stimulation, and is encoded by the **frequency** of impulses passing up the optic nerve.

## I. Defective Color Vision

**Trichromats** (91.8% of the population) have normal color vision, and can match all colored lights with a mixture of red, green and blue light.

**Dichromats** (nearly always males), need only two colors to match any color or white light. There are three types: protanopes, deuteranopes and tritanopes.

- **Protanopes** (1.2% of the population) are dichromats who can match all colors with green and blue. They are insensitive to red light, and confuse reds, yellows and greens, which look the same to them.

- **Deuteranopes** (1.4% of the population) are dichromats who can match all colors with red and blue. They also confuse reds, yellows and greens.

- **Tritanopes** are rare dichromats who can match all colors with red and green. They are insensitive to blue light.

**Monochromats** are people who cannot distinguish colors at all. They are truly color blind, and can match any two colored lights simply by adjusting their intensities.

## J. Dark Adaptation

When you enter a darkened movie theater it is at first difficult to see objects and find a seat. After a while, however, the sensitivity of the eyes increases and you are able to see quite well. This increase in sensitivity is called **dark adaptation** (the converse is called light adaptation).

Much of the increase in sensitivity of the eye in dim light is due to the *regeneration* of rhodopsin molecules that have been bleached in the daylight outside. The process involves the pigment epithelium, which converts the all-*trans* isomer back to 11-*cis* and returns it to the retina.

In the rod outer segment, bleached rhodopsin releases all-*trans* retinal, which is promptly reduced to all-*trans* retinol (vitamin A).

The all-*trans* retinol leaves the rod outer segment and passes into the pigment epithelium. It is then isomerized back to 11-*cis* retinol, converted to 11-*cis* retinal, and transported back to the rod outer segment.

In the rod outer segment the 11-*cis* retinal combines with opsin to regenerate rhodopsin.

The above process is sometimes called the "visual cycle."

Cones are able to regenerate their visual pigments much more rapidly by a process that may not involve the pigmented epithelium (but we don't know for sure), and even in bright light they always have enough visual pigment to be able to function.

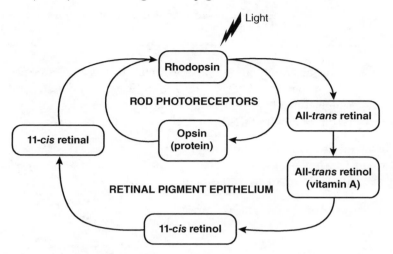

**Figure 21-18.** The visual cycle for rods. (Cones can regenerate their visual pigments much more rapidly, and the process is believed to occur entirely in the retina without involvement of the retinal pigment epithelium.)

### K. Visual Pathway

455

Information from both retinas is processed and transmitted to the cerebral cortex via the visual pathway.

One important aspect of this integration of visual information is that information from both eyes is used in the perception of depth and distance. This is called **binocular vision** or stereoscopic vision.

The two **optic nerves** are composed of the axons of the ganglion cells of the retinas.

Just anterior to the pituitary gland, the optic nerves form the X-shaped **optic chiasma**. Within the optic chiasma some fibers cross over. That is, there is a partial *decussation* of the fibers. Fibers from the left visual field (nasal half of left eye retina, temporal half of the right eye retina) are segregated to form the **right optic** tract. Fibers from the right visual field (temporal half of the left eye, nasal half of the right eye) are segregated to form the **left optic** tract. The fibers in these tracts synapse with neurons in the corresponding **lateral geniculate** nuclei of the **thalamus.**

- Nerve impulses originating in the retina from objects in the **left** visual field therefore arrive in the **right** lateral geniculate nucleus.

- Nerve impulses from objects in the **right** visual field arrive in the **left** lateral geniculate nucleus.

Neurons in the lateral geniculate nucleus send their axons to the *visual cortex* (in the posterior **occipital** lobe) along prominent nerve tracts called the *optic radiations*.

An object in the *left* visual field therefore activates neurons in the right occipital cortex.

An object in the *right* visual field therefore activates neurons in the left occipital cortex.

The usefulness of this arrangement is that if we need to bat away a bee approaching from the left, the information about the bee in our left visual field arrives in the right cerebral cortex, which controls the left hand. So we do not have to wait for information to be transferred from one half of the brain to the other via the corpus callosum.

**Pathways involved in controlling eye movements** – some fibers diverge from the optic tracts and synapse with neurons in other parts of the brain, such as the ***superior colliculus***. These pathways are involved in eye movements.

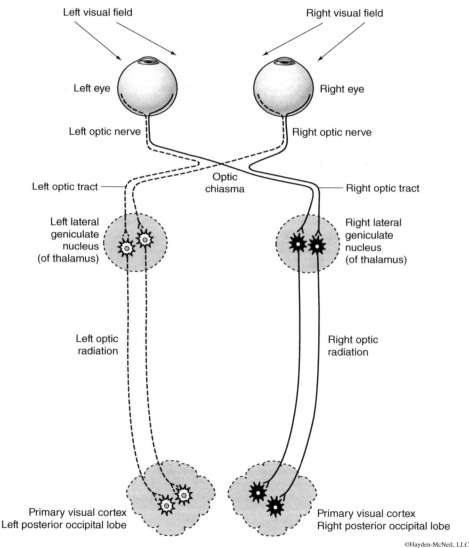

©Hayden-McNeil, LLC

**Figure 21-19.**

# CHAPTER 22

## SPECIAL SENSES II
The Ear: Hearing and Balance

457

## CHAPTER OUTLINE

## DESCRIPTION AND INTRODUCTION

### Lateral Lines—precursor of the auditory system

Fish and some amphibians have a sensory organ—the lateral line system—that other species have lost. Sometimes referred to as the "sense of distant touch," lateral lines convert changes in water pressure into electrical pulses similar to the way our inner ear responds to sound waves. Running lengthwise down each side of the body and over the head, these pressure-sensing organs help the fish avoid collisions, participate in schooling behavior, orient to water currents, elude predators and detect prey.

Lateral lines are composed of neuromasts (hair cells surrounded by a protruding jelly-like cupula) that usually lie at the bottom of a pit or groove. These hair cells—the same sensory cells found in all vertebrate ears—convert mechanical energy into electrical energy when moved.

The lateral line and similar types of structures don't work well in air because the transfer of sound from air to solid or water isn't very efficient. The ear of terrestrial vertebrates evolved by two modifications: First, a fluid-filled channel in the inner ear improved efficiency of sound transmission to the hair cells. Second, the bones in the mammalian middle ear evolved from the jaw hinge, specifically the temporomandibular joint. These structures improve the efficiency of transmission of sound from air to the hair cells of the inner ear.

Two different regions of the ear are involved in two senses – **hearing** and **balance**.

- **Hearing** is the sense that permits us to detect and analyze the minute pressure changes generated by **sound** waves in the air (or water, if we are underwater). These pressure changes are converted into neural signals by receptor cells in the *cochlea* of the *inner ear*.

- **Balance** is a sense that does not particularly impinge on our consciousness. However, it is vitally important in controlling a variety of reflexes that prevent us from falling over when we are standing still, running, walking or turning around. These reflexes maintain our balance or equilibrium. This sense is also important in stabilizing the direction of gaze of the eyes. Balance is detected by receptor cells in the *vestibular system* of the inner ear. The vestibular system consists of the following structures.

  - **utricle** and **saccule** – detect head tilt and linear acceleration or deceleration
  - **semicircular canals** – detect head rotation in all three planes of space

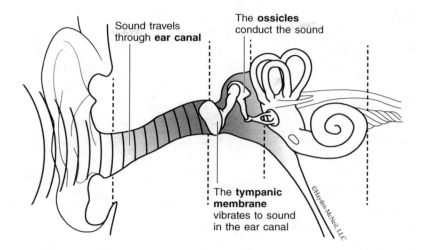

Sound travels through **ear canal**

The **ossicles** conduct the sound

The **tympanic membrane** vibrates to sound in the ear canal

©Hayden-McNeil, LLC

**Figure 22-1.**

## OBJECTIVES

After listening to the lecture and reading this chapter, you should be able to:

1. **Draw a diagram** showing the general plan of **receptor cells** and **pathways** subserving **hearing** and b**alance**.
2. Describe the importance of the sense of **hearing**.
3. Name the **structures** found in the **three parts** of the **ear**.
4. Describe how sound is transmitted from the **external auditory meatus** into the **cochlea**.
5. Describe the anatomy of the **organ of Corti**, and how it **functions** in hearing.
6. State which **cranial nerve** carries **auditory information** to the brain.
7. State which **cranial nerve** carries information from the **vestibular apparatus** to the brain.
8. Name the **sensory ganglion** and **nucleus** in the **medulla** concerned with the **vestibular** pathway.
9. Name the **sensory ganglion** and **nucleus** in the **medulla** concerned with the **cochlear** pathway – describe the remainder of the pathway to the **auditory cortex**.
10. Describe the **importance** of our ability to sense b**alance** and **motion**.
11. Define the part of the vestibular system involved in sensing **head tilt**.
12. Define the part of the vestibular system involved in sensing **up** and **down movements** (such as in an elevator).
13. Define the part of the vestibular system involved in sensing **linear horizontal acceleration** or **deceleration** (e.g. when you are in an automobile that speeds up or slows down).
14. Define the part of the vestibular system involved in sensing **head rotation**.
15. Name the anatomical components of the **utricle** and **saccule**.
16. Name the anatomical components of the **semicircular canals**.
17. List four sensory mechanisms **in addition** to the vestibular apparatus that are concerned with sensing **balance** and **equilibrium**.

459

## I. Introduction

### A. Sense of Hearing

Detects **sound**, and can discriminate between a wide range of sound **frequencies**.

### B. Sense of Balance

Detects the body's **orientation** and **movement** in space. In a nutshell, the sense of balance detects whether the body is vertical, horizontal, upside down, tilted, accelerating, decelerating, or rotating.

This involves detecting:

- the **tilt** of the head with respect to the direction of gravity – the ear structures involved are the **utricle** and the **saccule**.

- **linear acceleration and deceleration** (horizontal, as when you are in an automobile, or vertical, as when you are in an elevator) – again, the ear structures involved are the **utricle** and the **saccule**.

- head **rotation** – the ear structures involved are the **semicircular canals**.

The utricle, saccule and semicircular canals are grouped together under the name of the **vestibular apparatus**.

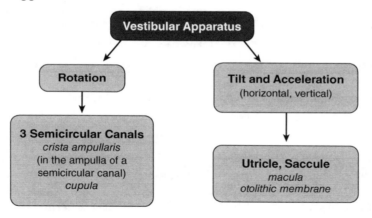

**Figure 22-2.** Vestibular apparatus.

### C. All the Receptor Cells Have a Common Motif

All this can be very confusing, but it gets simpler if you realize that the receptor cells in all these structures have a common motif, as described in 1, 2, and 3 that follow. Read these paragraphs very carefully, and study the diagram.

1. First of all, the receptor cells in the ear are all *hair cells*, irrespective of whether they are found in the cochlea or in the vestibular apparatus. Hair cells are *mechanoreceptors* with stiff, hair-like processes projecting from one end. They are stimulated when these processes are *bent to one side*.

2.  Secondly, the tips of these hair-like processes are always embedded in a gelatinous material.

    *   In the **cochlea**, this material makes up the *tectorial membrane*.
    *   In the **semicircular canals** this material constitutes the *cupula*.
    *   In the **utricle** and **saccule** it is called the *otolithic membrane* because it contains calcium carbonate crystals called *otoliths* that make it heavier.

3.  In every part of the ear (i.e. in the cochlea, utricle and saccule), the cells are stimulated when there is relative movement between the hair cell and the gelatinous material in which the tips of its hairs are embedded. This relative movement bends the hair-like processes. This movement can be caused by:

    *   **Sound vibrations** – detected in the cochlea.
    *   **Head tilt** and **linear acceleration** or **deceleration** – detected in the utricle and saccule.
    *   **Head rotation** – detected in the semicircular canals.

The brain receives information from the utricle, saccule, semicircular canals and cochlea via a sensory ganglion (see table below) and the **VIII cranial nerve**—called the *vestibulocochlear nerve*. The nerve fibers form synaptic-like contacts with the hair cells at their peripheral ends, and at their central ends form synapses with neurons in the *vestibular nucleus* or the *cochlear nucleus* in the medulla. The nerve cell bodies that give rise to these fibers are located in sensory ganglia that are analogous to dorsal root ganglia in the spinal cord. The following is a brief summary.

461

| Structure | Vestibular Apparatus | Cochlea |
|---|---|---|
| Sense | balance (tilt, movement) | hearing |
| Receptor | hair cell (utricle, saccule) or semicircular canals | hair cell |
| Gelatinous "membrane" | otolithic (utricle, saccule) cupula (semicircular canals) | tectorial |
| Nerve | vestibular branch of VIII | cochlear branch of VIII |
| Ganglion | vestibular ganglion | spiral ganglion |
| Nucleus in medulla | vestibular nucleus | cochlear nucleus |

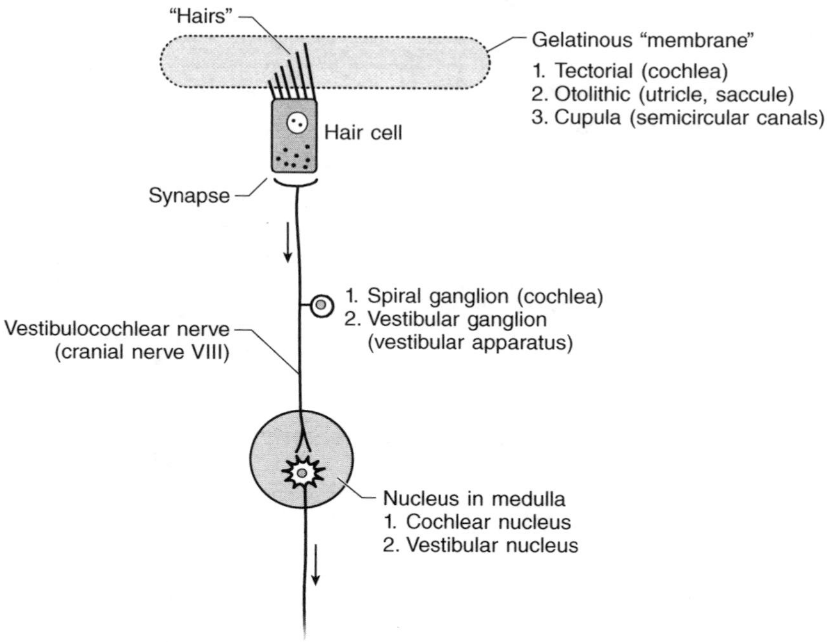

**Figure 22-3.** General plan of receptor cells and pathways subserving hearing *and* balance.

## II. Hearing

In addition to primitive ears, fish and some amphibians have a pressure-sensing structure that works well in water. This structure is called the lateral line. It runs down each side of the body and is important in detecting predators and prey.

The lateral line consists of hair cells surrounded by a jelly-like material lying at the bottom of a pit or a groove. The hair cells are the same sensory cells found in all vertebrate ears. Therefore, it seems that the ear and the lateral line evolved in close association with each other. Once vertebrates started to emerge onto land, the lateral line proved virtually useless because sound vibrations in the air were transferred poorly to the hair cells. The lateral line gradually disappeared, and the ear became the dominant structure for reception of sound. A fluid-filled tube in the inner ear improved the efficiency of sound transmission to the hair cells, and one of the jaw bones evolved into the stapes, a small ossicle found in the middle ear.

The sense of hearing serves a number of important purposes, including survival and communication.

Hearing in terrestrial vertebrates, including humans, involves the *external ear*, *middle ear* and the **cochlea** of the *inner ear*.

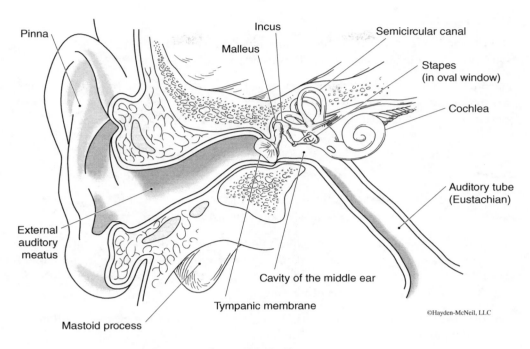

**Figure 22-4.** The ear.

463

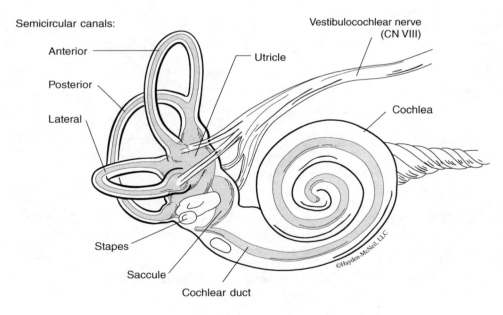

**Figure 22-5.** The inner ear.

## A. External Ear

The external ear consists of an outer, funnel-like flap called the *auricle* or *pinna*, and an S-shaped tube called the *external auditory meatus*.

The auricle helps to localize sounds as we turn our heads. As noted previously, the epithelium of the external auditory meatus contains *ceruminous glands* that secrete a waxy substance.

## B. Middle Ear

The entrance to the middle ear is sealed by the *eardrum*, or *tympanic membrane*.

The cavity of the middle ear is filled with air, and contains three little bones (*auditory ossicles*) known as the **hammer** (*malleus*), **anvil** (*incus*) and **stirrup** (*stapes*).

The auditory ossicles are firmly attached to one another and move as a unit. The base of the malleus is attached to the tympanic membrane, and the footplate of the stapes is attached to a membrane covering an opening leading to part of the cochlea in the inner ear. This opening is called the *oval window*.

The oval window has a membranous covering that separates the **air**-filled middle ear from the **liquid**-filled cochlea in the inner ear.

The eardrum vibrates in response to sound waves that travel down the external auditory meatus. The auditory ossicles assembly vibrates in turn, and the footplate of the stapes vibrates against the oval window, so transmitting the sound waves to the liquids of the inner ear.

Two small skeletal muscles are attached to the ossicles. One is the *tensor tympani*, which is inserted into the malleus, and the other is the *stapedius*, which is inserted into the stapes.

These muscles operate in the *tympanic reflex*, or *attenuation reflex*, which is a response to loud sounds and makes the bridge of ossicles more rigid.

The function of these muscles is as follows.

- Muscles contract in response to loud sounds, making the bridge of ossicles more rigid and reducing the effectiveness of the ossicles in transmitting loud sounds to the inner ear (**attenuation reflex, tympanic reflex**). This protects the auditory apparatus from damage.

- The attenuation reflex also masks out low-frequency sounds in loud environments, so that we can concentrate on the sounds of voice communication, which are at higher frequencies.

- Both muscles are activated at the same time that the brain activates the voice mechanism, which decreases our hearing sensitivity to our own speech.

- An additional function of the tensor tympani muscle is to maintain a steady pull on the eardrum, keeping it taut.

Connecting the air-filled cavity of the middle ear with the *pharynx* is a tube called the *Eustachian tube* (= auditory tube). This helps to equalize the air pressure in the middle ear with that of the atmosphere. The function of this system is particularly noticeable when ascending or descending in an aircraft.

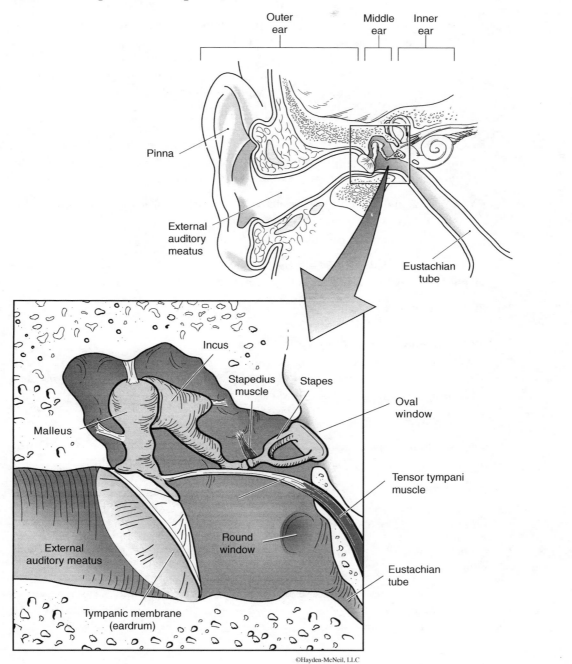

©Hayden-McNeil, LLC

**Figure 22-6.** Middle ear.

### C. Inner Ear—Contains the Vestibular Apparatus (Semicircular Canals, Utricle, Saccule) and the Cochlea

The equipment of the inner ear is housed in a *bony labyrinth* (= osseous labyrinth) carved out of the **temporal** bone.

The equipment of the inner ear consists of a system of interconnected membranous tubes and chambers (called the *membranous labyrinth*) that fits snugly into the mold of the bony labyrinth. The space between the membranous labyrinth and the walls of the bony labyrinth is filled with *perilymph*, which is almost identical with cerebrospinal fluid. The interior of the membranous labyrinth is filled with *endolymph*.

The membranous labyrinth is composed of:

*   The **vestibular apparatus,** which represents the balance-sensing part of the inner ear and will be discussed in a later section. At this point, we should note that the vestibular apparatus consists of the following components.

    *   Tubes making up the three **semicircular canals** or ducts: near one end of each canal is an enlargement called the *ampulla.*
    *   Two large chambers called the **utricle** and **saccule.**

*   A coiled tube called the *cochlear duct* or *scala media*, which makes up part of the **cochlea.** The cochlea is the part of the inner ear involved in hearing.

We will focus first on hearing.

466

### D. Functional Anatomy of the Cochlea

The cochlea is a system of coiled tubes within the bony labyrinth. The coiling is irrelevant to function, but arises because 34 mm of the sound-sensitive *basilar membrane* must be tucked into each temporal bone, and coiling it is the best way to do it.

The cochlea is partitioned into three tubes.

*   **Scala vestibuli**, filled with *perilymph.* Perilymph is almost identical with cerebrospinal fluid. One end of the scala vestibuli is sealed off by the **oval window.**

*   **Scala media** (cochlear duct), filled with *endolymph.* The composition of endolymph is similar to intracellular fluid in that it has a very high concentration of potassium ions and a very low concentration of sodium ions.

*   **Scala tympani**, filled with *perilymph.* The *round window* seals off one end of the scala tympani.

The scala vestibuli and scala tympani are connected at their opposite ends by an opening at the apex of the cochlea called the *helicotrema.* They also communicate with the subarachnoid space around the brain.

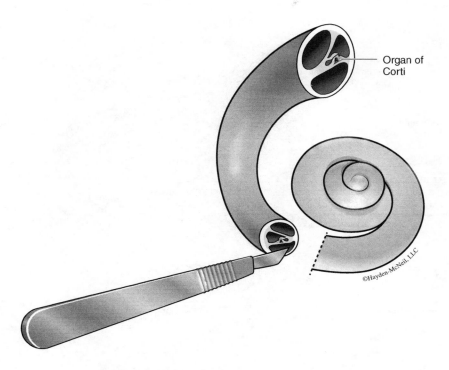

Organ of
Corti

©Hayden-McNeil, LLC

**Figure 22-7.** The cochlea consists of three tubes:
the scala vestibuli, scala media, and the scala typani.

467

The partitions between these three tubes are formed from two longitudinally-running membranes.

- The thin and flexible *Reissner's membrane* (= the *vestibular membrane*), separates the scala vestibuli from the scala media.

- The **basilar membrane** separates the scala media from the scala tympani. On the surface of the basilar membrane lies the *organ of Corti*, which contains the auditory receptor cells, or **hair cells**. There are actually two types of hair cell, called inner and outer hair cells, but we will not discuss this further.

- The scala media is therefore bounded by the basilar membrane and Reissner's membrane.

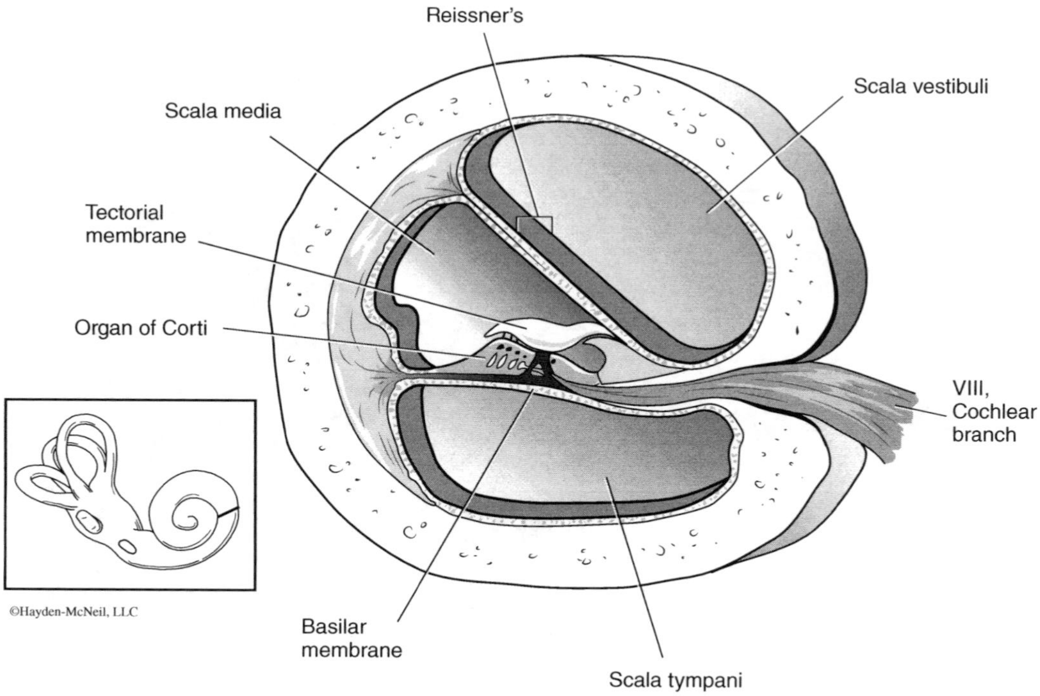

**Figure 22-8.** Cochlea.

468

## E. Transmission of Sound Waves in the Ear

Sound waves are transmitted in the ear as follows.

1.  Sound waves transmitted through the outside air and the air in the external auditory meatus make the tympanic membrane (eardrum) vibrate.

2.  The vibrations of the tympanic membrane are transmitted via the malleus, incus and stapes to the oval window.

3.  Vibration of the oval window causes vibration of the perilymph in the scala vestibuli.

4.  Sound vibrations are transmitted through Reissner's membrane and then through the endolymph of the scala media.

5.  The sound waves transmitted through the endolymph of the scala media set up a resonating wave of vibration in the basilar membrane (this results in stimulation of the hair cells in the organ of Corti).

6.  The perilymph in the scala tympani picks up these vibrations, transmitting them back to the round window, which is in contact with the air-filled cavity of the middle ear. So, when the oval window moves in, the round window moves out, and *vice versa*. The helicotrema facilitates the equalization of pressure between the scala vestibuli and the scala tympani.

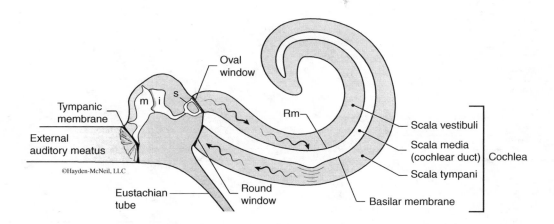

©Hayden-McNeil, LLC

1. Sound waves make tympanic membrane vibrate

2. Vibrations are transmitted via malleus (m), incus (i) and stapes (s) to oval window

3. Vibration of oval window causes perilymph vibration in scala vestibuli

4. Vibration is transmitted through Reissner's membrane (Rm) through endolymph in scala media

5. Basilar membrane vibrates in response to vibration of endolymph in scala media, stimulating hair cells in Organ of Corti (see notes for further details)

6. Vibrations are then transferred via the perilymph in the scala tympani to the round window

7. Vibration of the round window is dissipated in the air of the middle ear

**Figure 22-9.**

469

## F. The Basilar Membrane and Resonance in the Cochlea

Different parts of the basilar membrane resonate to different sound frequencies, enabling us to distinguish between them.

While Reissner's membrane is a very loose, thin membrane that serves only to separate the scala vestibuli from the scala media, the basilar membrane has another, very important function.

Different parts of the basilar membrane resonate to different sound frequencies. The basilar membrane is able to do this because it contains a meshwork of stiff, collagen fibers. These fibers have different lengths and thicknesses. They are fixed at one end to the bony central structure of the cochlea, and are free at their other ends.

Consequently, the fibers in the basilar membrane can *vibrate like the reeds of a harmonica*. The short, stiff ones are near the oval window and vibrate in response to high frequencies, while the long, more flexible fibers near the apex vibrate in response to low frequencies.

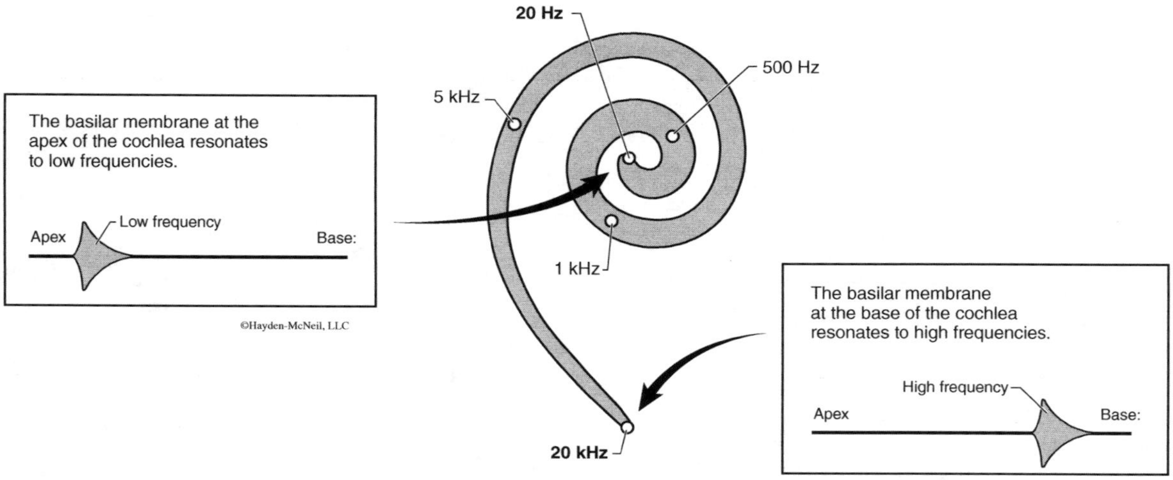

The basilar membrane at the apex of the cochlea resonates to low frequencies.

Apex    Low frequency    Base:

©Hayden-McNeil, LLC

20 Hz

500 Hz

5 kHz

1 kHz

20 kHz

The basilar membrane at the base of the cochlea resonates to high frequencies.

Apex    High frequency    Base:

**Figure 22-10.**

How are these vibrations converted into nerve impulses passing up the eighth nerve? This is done by the **organ of Corti**, which lies on the basilar membrane.

## G. The Organ of Corti and the Detection of Sound Waves

*The organ of Corti sits on the basilar membrane, and is the receptor organ that generates nerve impulses in response to vibration of the basilar membrane.*

470

The receptor cells of the organ of Corti are **hair cells**. Each hair cell has about 100 hair-like processes called *stereocilia* projecting from its apical surface. At birth, 30,000 of these hair cells detect the motion of the basilar membrane.

They can be damaged by infection, aging, genetic diseases and certain drugs. The result is nerve deafness, which affects 14 million Americans. Noises louder than 90 decibels (motor cycle engine, rock bands) can also cause nerve deafness. In general, damaged hair cells do not regrow in adult humans. However, sharks, frogs and chicks can easily grow new hair cells. In the last few years, it seems that small numbers of supporting cells can multiply in the inner ear of guinea pigs, rats, mice and humans after damage. Supporting cells are not hair cells, but there is some hope that growth factors may be used to cause hair cell regeneration in humans. The clinical use of regeneration as a cure for nerve deafness, however, is at least 10 years away, perhaps longer.

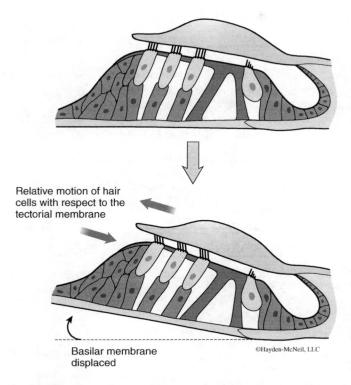

Relative motion of hair
cells with respect to the
tectorial membrane

Basilar membrane
displaced

©Hayden-McNeil, LLC

**Figure 22-11.** The hair cells in the organ of Corti convert basilar membrane
vibrations into electrical signals.

471

How do hair cells detect the vibrations of the basilar membrane? The tips of their stereocilia are embedded in a gelatinous, immovable "membrane" called the ***tectorial membrane***, which projects out from a bony shelf of the cochlea.

When the basilar membrane moves upward in response to sound vibrations, the stereocilia are bent in one direction because of their attachment to the immovable tectorial
membrane. This bending of the stereocilia causes the hair cells to depolarize, producing a *generator potential.*

The hair cell is not a true neuron, and has no dendrites or axon. However, the dendrites
of sensory neurons that have their cell bodies in the ***spiral ganglion*** make a synaptic connection with the hair cells.

When they are depolarized, it is believed that the hair cells release a neurotransmitter
that depolarizes the afferent nerve endings that form synapses with them. As noted
above, the cell bodies of these sensory nerves lie in a ganglion called the spiral ganglion
(this ganglion is similar to a dorsal root ganglion). The axons of the neurons in the
spiral ganglion make up the *cochlear branch* of the vestibulocochlear (VIII) cranial nerve.

There are also *efferent* nerve fibers that innervate the hair cells. In some way, they are
believed to be able to modulate the response of the hair cells, but not much is known
about this.

## H. Auditory Nerve Pathways

The processing of signals in the auditory pathways enables us to detect sounds of different pitch, loudness and points of origin in the space around us. We also have the ability to attend selectively to sounds of particular interest (the so-called "cocktail party effect," where we can concentrate attention on one person speaking, and somehow tune out the background of other people's loud conversation).

Auditory signals are conveyed to the brain via the eighth cranial nerve.

The vestibulocochlear or eighth cranial nerve (VIII) has two branches.

* The **cochlear** branch innervates the receptor cells of the cochlea.
* The **vestibular** branch innervates the receptor cells in the semicircular canal, the utricle and the saccule.

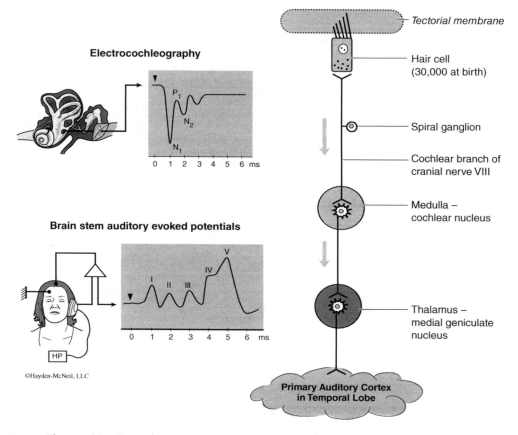

**Figure 22-12.** Auditory pathway from the cochlea to the primary auditory cortex.

The axons of the neurons comprising the cochlear branch of the vestibulocochlear nerve make synapses in the **cochlear nucleus** of the medulla. The nerve fibers carrying responses from different regions of the cochlea, and therefore representing *different sound frequencies*, arrive in *different areas* of the cochlear nucleus.

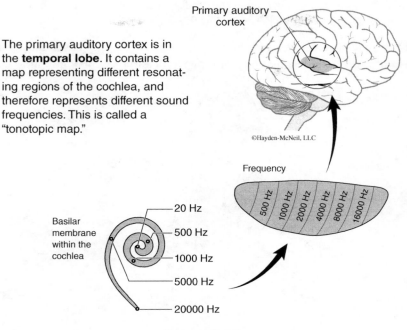

The primary auditory cortex is in the **temporal lobe**. It contains a map representing different resonating regions of the cochlea, and therefore represents different sound frequencies. This is called a "tonotopic map."

©Hayden-McNeil, LLC

Frequency

500 Hz, 1000 Hz, 2000 Hz, 4000 Hz, 8000 Hz, 16000 Hz

Basilar membrane within the cochlea

20 Hz
500 Hz
1000 Hz
5000 Hz
20000 Hz

**Figure 22-13.**

After that, the auditory pathway is complex, and will not be described here. Some auditory signals are transmitted to the cerebral cortex, where they produce the sensation of sound. Like other sensory information destined for the cerebral cortex, these signals arrive at synapses with neurons in the *thalamus* (the ***medial geniculate nucleus***). From the thalamus, these signals are relayed to the ***primary auditory cortex*** in the **temporal lobe**.

## III. Balance—The Vestibular System of the Inner Ear

Our ability to sense the balance and motion of our bodies is essential in all of the following activities.

- Standing
- Walking
- Running
- Turning
- Complex movements
- Stabilizing eyes during body movements

The vestibular system of the ear has two major functions, which are:

1. Maintenance of body **balance**.

2. During head movements, the vestibular system maintains **stable eye position** with respect to visual objects. This is rather like the telescopes on certain orbiting satellites. These telescopes are stabilized with computers so that they remain trained on an object in outer space irrespective of rolling or oscillatory movements of the satellite.

Vestibular illusions are common and potentially dangerous when piloting an aircraft. Several of these illusions will be described in this chapter.

All the motor pathways involved in maintenance of balance project via the **vestibulospinal**, **tectospinal** and **reticulospinal** tracts to the **trunk** and **proximal limb muscles**.

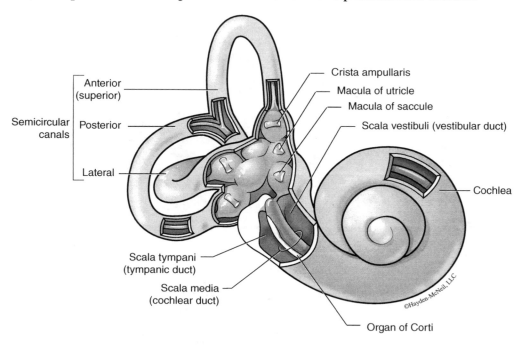

**Figure 22-14.** The vestibular system of the inner ear.

## A. The Utricle and Saccule Detect Head Tilt and Linear Acceleration or Deceleration

The utricle and saccule—the otolith organs—each contain a small patch of hair cells and supporting cells in a sensory area called a *macula*.

The hairs of the hair cells are in contact with the **otolithic membrane**. The otolithic membrane is a sheet of gelatinous material, made twice as dense as endolymph because it contains many small calcium carbonate crystals—*statoconia* or *otoliths* (= ear stones).

The hair cells are stimulated when their hairs are bent, as occurs when the heavy gelatinous otolithic membrane moves relatively to the hair cell. This happens when the head is *tilted* (gravity) or when the body moves *horizontally*, or *vertically up and down* (Newton's first law of motion). Since the membrane does not project into the lumen of the vestibular apparatus, movements of endolymph caused by angular rotation of the head do NOT affect it.

The utricular macula is oriented at right angles to the saccular macula. Therefore, its hair cells respond to head tilt and *horizontal* linear acceleration and deceleration. The saccular macula is oriented so that *vertical* linear acceleration or deceleration (jumping and falling, moving up or down in an elevator) causes the hair cells to respond.

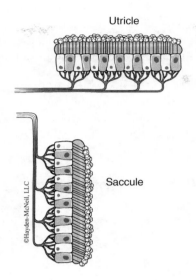

Utricle

Saccule

©Hayden-McNeil, LLC

**Figure 22-15.**

But if the utricular macula responds to both head tilt AND horizontal linear acceleration, how do we tell the difference? We have to supplement the information from the utricular macula with visual cues. These can be lacking in certain situations. For example, a pilot accelerating in an aircraft in a featureless sky may experience a "heads up" illusion, and think the nose of the plane is tilting upward. This may cause the pilot to make a correction. However, since the plane is actually flying on the level, the result is that the nose is pushed downward and the plane may crash. Pilots are always taught to rely on their instruments in order to avoid these types of illusion.

475

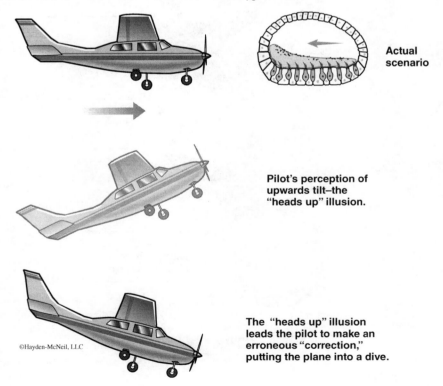

Actual scenario

Pilot's perception of upwards tilt—the "heads up" illusion.

©Hayden-McNeil, LLC

The "heads up" illusion leads the pilot to make an erroneous "correction," putting the plane into a dive.

**Figure 22-16.**

In summary, the utricle and saccule are important in detecting movements such as falling or accelerating in an automobile, and are the sensory structures involved in maintaining balance when standing still or walking.

*Example* – suppose you are standing on a platform that is suddenly moved forward. There is the sensation of falling backward and the body also tends to tilt backward. The appropriate muscles are activated so that the body leans forward to counteract this effect. Therefore, we do not fall backward.

## B. The Semicircular Canals Detect Head Rotation

There are three semicircular canals. Two of the semicircular canals stand vertically at right angles to each other, and the other is horizontal. In other words, they represent all three planes in space.

Each ampulla of each semicircular canal houses a sense organ called a *crista ampullaris*, or just *crista*.

Each crista is composed of groups of hair cells and supporting cells.

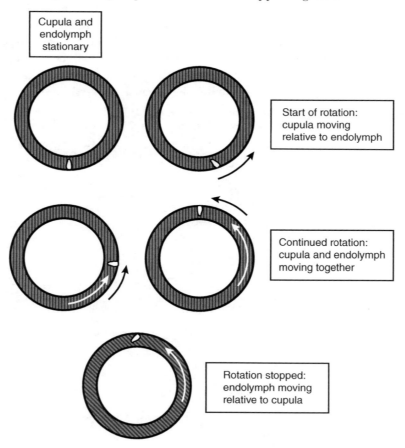

Cupula and endolymph stationary

Start of rotation: cupula moving relative to endolymph

Continued rotation: cupula and endolymph moving together

Rotation stopped: endolymph moving relative to cupula

**Figure 22-17.**

As in the maculae, the hairs of the hair cells extend upward into a gelatinous mass. In this case, the mass is called a *cupula*.

The cupula does NOT contain otoliths. In fact, it has the same specific gravity as endolymph and, unlike the otolithic membranes of the utricle and saccule, it is NOT affected by gravity.

When the head suddenly begins to rotate in any direction, the inertia of the endolymph in the semicircular canals tends to keep this fluid stationary while the cristae move. The cupula tends to remain stationary with the endolymph, so bending the hairs of the hair cells. Obviously, the direction of bending is opposite to the direction of movement of the head.

If we keep spinning round and round, the endolymph finally "catches up" and moves at the same speed as the cupula. The hair cells resume an upright position, and the only cues we have that we are spinning come from visual and proprioceptive information. Little kids do this when they are playing "airplanes." The problem is when they stop spinning. Now the endolymph keeps going, and the hairs of the hair cells bend and signal that they are spinning in the opposite direction. A powerful set of postural reflexes come into play, and they try to compensate for the apparent spin. Since the person is stationary and not spinning, these reflexes result in loss of equilibrium and falling down.

This is the cause of the "graveyard spiral" and the "graveyard spin" in an aircraft.

### Comparison of the cupula with the otolithic membrane.
The cupula projects into the endolymph of the semicircular canal, and is deflected by movements of the endolymph caused by head rotation. Unlike the otolithic membrane in the utricle and saccule, gravity has no effect on the cupula, because the cupula lacks otoliths that would make it heavier than the endolymph in which it floats and sways.

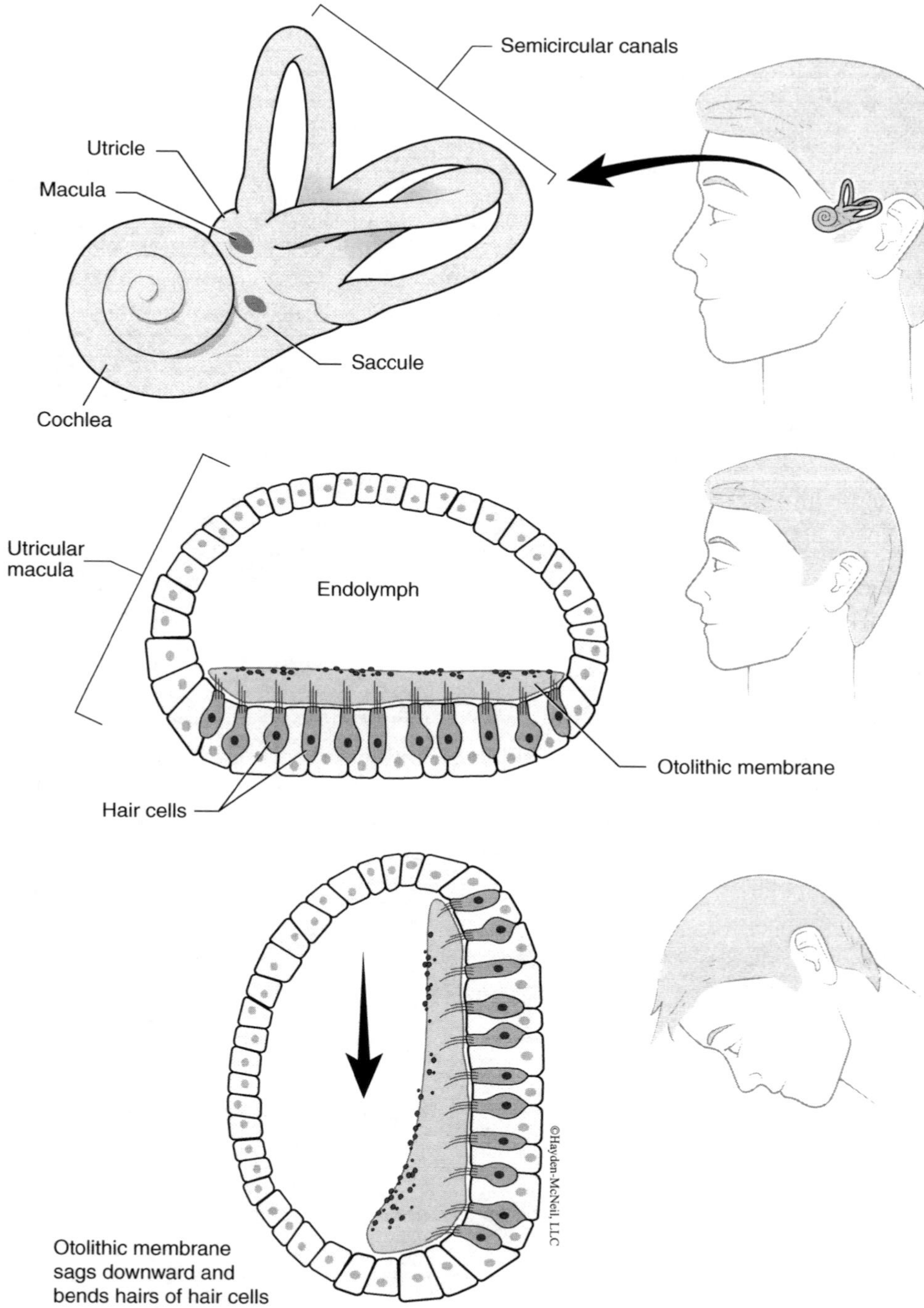

Semicircular canals

Utricle

Macula

Saccule

Cochlea

Utricular macula

Endolymph

Otolithic membrane

Hair cells

©Hayden-McNeil, LLC

Otolithic membrane sags downward and bends hairs of hair cells

**Figure 22-18.** Forward tilt. Utricular macula is detector (also detects horizontal linear acceleration).

# Head Rotation
Semi-circular canals and crista ampullaris are detectors

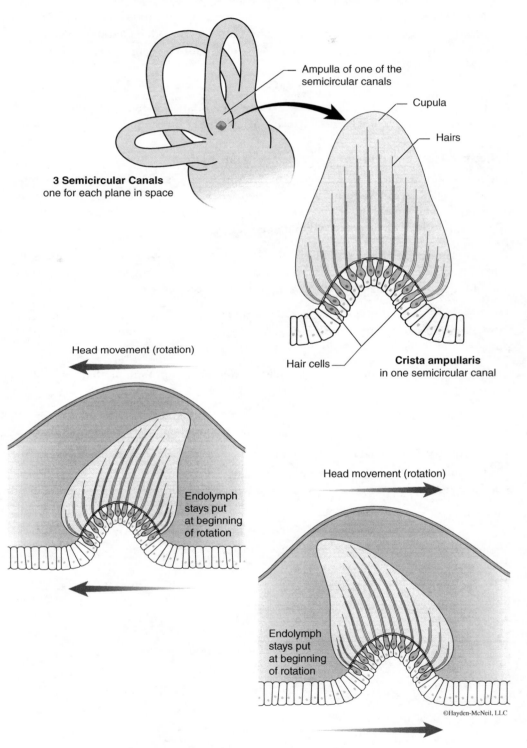

479

**Figure 22-19.** Head rotation. Semicircular canals and crista ampullaris are detectors.

One role of the semicircular canals is in maintaining body balance during the performance of rapid and intricate body movements.

> ***Example*** – if a person is running forward in a straight line and by error starts to turn to one side or the other, this rotation movement is detected by the crista ampullaris structures in the semicircular canals and corrections can be made before the person falls off balance.

Another function of the semicircular canals is to maintain a stable image on the retina by stabilizing the direction of gaze, irrespective of head movements.

## C. Central Nervous Pathways of the Vestibular System

The hair cells of the vestibular system have synaptic contacts with the dendrites of bipolar neurons with cell bodies in the ***vestibular ganglion***. The axons of these neurons and the axons of neurons in the ***spiral ganglion*** (associated with the cochlea) together make up the vestibulocochlear nerve (cranial nerve VIII).

The fibers in the **vestibular** branch of the eighth nerve make synapses with neurons in a collection of nuclei in the medulla beneath the floor of the fourth ventricle. This collection of nuclei is known as the ***vestibular nucleus*** or the ***vestibular nuclear complex***.

The output of the vestibular nucleus goes to many areas of the brain. However, signals from the vestibular system are NOT relayed to the cerebral cortex, and consequently are not consciously perceived.

The signals relayed through the vestibular nuclei go to destinations that include the following:

- brain areas that control *eye movements*
- brain areas that help to control movements of the *head* and *neck*
- via the vestibulospinal tracts to skeletal muscles that control *body posture* in response to head movements
- the *cerebellum* (particularly the vestibulocerebellum)

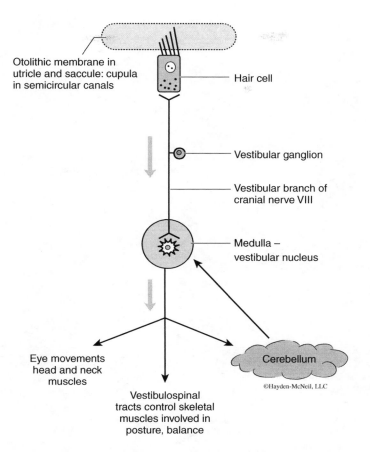

Figure 22-20. Pathways from the vestibular apparatus to central nervous system destinations.

## D. Other Sensory Mechanisms Concerned with Sensing Balance

There are many sensory mechanisms in addition to the vestibular apparatus that are concerned with sensing the body's balance or equilibrium. They include the four following:

1. **Neck proprioceptors** – proprioceptors in the joints of the neck inform the neurons in the vestibular nuclear complex of the position of the head as it relates to the rest of the body. This information can be transmitted to the cerebellum.

2. **Proprioceptive** information that tells us about the relative positions of other body parts (such as bending and extension of the limbs, bending of trunk) is also important for the maintenance of balance.

3. **Exteroceptive** information, such as pressure sensations from the soles of the feet, can tell you whether the weight is distributed equally between the two feet, and whether the weight is forward or backward on the feet.

4. **Visual** information can also be important, because movement of the body shifts the position of an image on the retina. It is interesting that persons with lesions in their vestibular apparatus can still maintain their balance provided their eyes are open and provided they move slowly. If they close their eyes, they lose their balance and fall over.

482

# CHAPTER 23

# CARDIOVASCULAR SYSTEM I
Function, Basic Arrangement, Blood Vessels, Development of the Heart

483

## CHAPTER OUTLINE

I. Function of the cardiovascular system
   A. Reason for having a cardiovascular system
   B. Prevention of blood loss (hemostasis)

II. Basic arrangement of the cardiovascular system

III. The tubing: structure and function of blood vessels
   A. Types of blood vessels
   B. Layers in the walls of blood vessels
   C. Vascular endothelial cells are very important
   D. Arteries
   E. Arterioles
   F. Capillaries
   G. Venules and veins
   H. Vasoconstriction and vasodilation

IV. The pump—structure of the heart
   A. The pericardium
   B. The heart wall
   C. The chambers of the heart
   D. Great vessels entering and leaving the heart
   E. Arteries branching from the aorta
   F. Valves of the heart
   G. The skeleton of the heart
   H. The blood supply to the heart walls

V. Development of the heart

VI. Fetal circulation

*Important Message Concerning Your Health*

SMOKING CAUSES CARDIOVASCULAR DISEASE, LUNG CANCER, RESPI-
RATORY DISEASE AND CANCER OF THE LARYNX. SMOKING KILLS 1 IN
10 ADULTS AND IS THE LEADING PREVENTABLE CAUSE OF DEATH.

 Did you know that in women, lung cancer from smoking
has surpassed breast cancer as the leading cause of cancer
deaths?

As well as having the same smoking-related health problems
as men, smoking women have increased risk of cervical cancer, early menopause, and increased risk of coronary artery
disease if oral contraceptives are used. Pregnant women who
smoke run an increased risk of having still-born or premature babies.

DON'T LET YOUR HEALTH GO UP IN SMOKE.

IF YOU SMOKE, QUIT. IF YOU DON'T SMOKE, DON'T START.

## DESCRIPTION AND INTRODUCTION

484

*The heart of creatures is the foundation of life, the Prince of all, the sun of their microcosm,
from where all vigor and strength does flow.* [William Harvey, *De Motu Cordis*, 1628.]

One of the most influential works ever published in physiology and medicine, William
Harvey's *De Motu Cordis* (*On the Motion of the Heart*) is the foundation of modern cardiovascular physiology. In it, Harvey outlined the basic principles of cardiac function and
development. His work established the basic concepts of the heart as a muscular pump
in which the right and left ventricular chambers performed distinct functions, the circulatory system as a closed circuit, and the conservation in structure and function of the
heart throughout the animal world.

The remaining six chapters deal with the **cardiovascular system** – that is, the **heart** and
**blood vessels**. Diseases of the cardiovascular system are a major cause of death in this
country. We will study the normal physiology of the heart and blood vessels. Then we'll
discuss what happens when things go wrong.

In the present chapter, I shall describe the basic arrangement of the cardiovascular system, and I will introduce you to the structure of the blood vessels and the heart. We will
also touch on the development of the heart and the fetal circulation.

## OBJECTIVES

After listening to the lecture and reading this chapter, you should be able to:

1.  List the seven **functions** of the blood circulation.
2.  **Draw a labeled diagram** showing the basic arrangement of the cardiovascular system.
3.  Describe the **layers** found in the **walls** of blood vessels.
4.  Explain **vasoconstriction** and **vasodilation**, and why these processes are important.
5.  Explain the importance of **vascular endothelial cells** in the cardiovascular system, and list the vasoconstrictor and vasodilators they secrete.
6.  List the six main **types** of blood vessels and their structures.
7.  Explain two benefits arising from the fact that the large arteries near the heart are very **elastic**.
8.  Name the blood vessels that control **peripheral resistance**.
9.  Name the blood vessels that control the **capacity** of the circulatory system.
10. Describe the structure of the **heart** and the **layers** of its wall.
11. Name the **valves** of the heart and their locations.
12. Name the **great vessels** entering and leaving the heart.
13. Name the major arteries branching off from the **aorta**, and the regions they supply.
14. Name the major **veins** of the body, and the regions they drain.
15. Describe the **skeleton of the heart**.
16. Summarize the **development** of the heart in the fetus at the third, fourth, fifth and eighth weeks.
17. Name the systems that are **not** functional in the **fetus**, and the structure that substitutes for them, describe how this has led to a change in the design of the fetal circulation compared with that of the adult, and describe the degree of oxygenation of the blood and its direction of flow in the umbilical artery and vein.
18. Define **hemostasis**.

485

## I. Function of the Cardiovascular System

Simple, unicellular organisms such as an amoeba do not require a cardiovascular system. The cardiovascular system appeared when animals evolved to larger, multicellular organisms.

### A. Reason for Having a Cardiovascular System

The cardiovascular system consists of the heart that pumps blood into branching networks of variously-sized tubes (blood vessels) that distribute it to all parts of the body and return it back to the heart.

The blood circulation fulfills the following purposes.

1.  **Gaseous exchange** – delivery of oxygen from the lungs to the tissues and organs, and removal of carbon dioxide from the tissues and organs and delivery to the lungs.

2. **Delivery of major nutrients** to tissues and organs, and removal of waste metabolites from tissues and organs. Examples of major nutrients are glucose, amino acids and fatty acids. These substances may originate directly from the digestion of foodstuffs, or they may be produced by mobilization of storage depots (e.g. glucose from glycogen, fats from adipose tissue). An example of a waste metabolite is urea, much of which is delivered to the kidney for elimination from the body by way of the urine.

3. **Delivery of "micronutrients"** to tissues and organs. Examples of micronutrients are the vitamins (vitamin A, for example) and certain metals (iron, copper, zinc, magnesium, calcium, etc.).

4. **Delivery of hormones** from the endocrine glands to distant target tissues (oxytocin, thyroxin, aldosterone, etc.).

5. **Defense** – the bloodstream carries leukocytes and antibodies.

6. **Thermal exchange** – heat conservation and heat loss. The blood plays an important role in removing heat from the "core" of the body (in particular, the muscles) and delivering it to the skin, where it is lost by radiation and convection. Conversely, vasoconstriction of the skin blood vessels helps to conserve this heat by preventing its loss.

7. **Transportation of water** around the body.

## B. Prevention of Blood Loss (Hemostasis)

486

Not only must the blood be pumped around the body (circulated), but the body needs to prevent blood loss in the case of injury. This process is called *hemostasis*.

When a blood vessel is cut, there is formation of a blood *platelet plug*, blood *coagulation* to form a blood clot, and finally **growth of fibrous tissue** into the blood clot to close the hole permanently.

## II. Basic Arrangement of the Cardiovascular System

In a person at rest (not exercising) the heart beats about 75 times per minute, and ejects about 75 mL of blood with each beat. That means that it pumps about 338 liters per hour.

But the body contains only about five liters of blood. **We must therefore conclude that the blood circulates.** This important deduction was first made from similar calculations by William Harvey in the year 1628.

The cardiovascular system contains several basic components, and is arranged as follows:

- One basic component is the *heart*, which is really two pumps set up side by side. The **right** heart pumps the blood through the lungs (the *pulmonary circuit*) into the left heart. The **left** heart then pumps the blood through the rest of the body, the *systemic circuit*.

- Both the pulmonary and systemic circuits contain a continuous pipeline of *arteries*, *arterioles*, *terminal arterioles*, *capillaries*, *venules* and *veins* (terminal arterioles, which connect arterioles with capillaries, are sometimes called *metarterioles*). Blood leaves the heart via the arteries, and returns to it via the veins.

- The systemic circuit distributes blood from the left heart via the *aorta* to the organs and tissues, and returns the blood to the right heart *via* the venae cavae.

- The pulmonary circuit is a simple loop. **Deoxygenated** blood is pumped from the **right** heart into the lungs, and **oxygenated** blood is returned from the lungs to the **left** heart.

- The systemic circuit is actually numerous circuits arranged in parallel. This means that there is wide latitude for altering blood flow through a particular organ without necessarily altering the total flow through the system. If they were in series (one after the other), then cutting down the flow in one part would also cut down the flow in all successive parts.

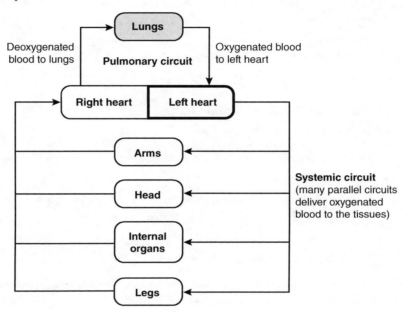

**Figure 23-1.** The cardiovascular system.

Four very important properties of the cardiovascular system are as follows. All can be altered by the autonomic nervous system, specifically the sympathetic branch.

1. **Vascular capacity** – this represents the volume of the cardiovascular system, where most of the blood in the circulatory system is contained in the **veins** and **venules.**

2. **Vascular resistance** – the heart pumps blood through a system of tubes called blood vessels. The diameter of these blood vessels affects the *resistance* of the system. This resistance component is made up mainly by the **arterioles**. The arterioles therefore constitute the resistance component of the cardiovascular system. The resistance depends on their *diameter*. When their diameter is small, the resistance is high. When their diameter is large, their resistance is low. Activation of the sympathetic branch of the autonomic nervous system narrows (constricts) the arterioles, and raises the resistance.

3. **Heart** – rate and force of contraction.

4. **Volume** of blood in the circulation – regulated by the kidneys and fluid intake.

These variables have a central role to play in adjustments that the circulatory system makes in response to (for example) blood loss or a heart attack. More later.

487

## III. The Tubing: Structure and Function of Blood Vessels

### A. Types of Blood Vessels

The tubes through which the blood circulates are called *blood vessels*. There are six types of blood vessels:

1. **arteries**
2. **arterioles**
3. **terminal arterioles**, connect arterioles with capillaries – the terminal arterioles are neither true arterioles nor true capillaries
4. **capillaries**
5. *muscular venules* and *non-muscular venules*
6. **veins**

### B. Layers in the Walls of Blood Vessels

The walls of most blood vessels have three layers.

1. An inner layer of a specialized squamous epithelium called ***vascular endothelium***. This layer is called the ***tunica intima***.

2. A middle layer composed of smooth muscle fibers, usually with some elastic connective tissue. This layer is called the ***tunica media***.

3. An outer layer composed of connective tissue with elastic and collagenous fibers. This layer is called the ***tunica adventitia***.

An exception is the *capillaries*, which are tubes consisting only of vascular endothelial cells sitting on a basement membrane.

*Arteries*, on the other hand, have very thick walls with an abundance of elastic fibers and smooth muscle fibers.

*Arterioles* are particularly noted for the large amount of smooth muscle in the tunica media.

***Smooth muscle fibers are found in all blood vessels except for the capillaries and non-muscular venules.***

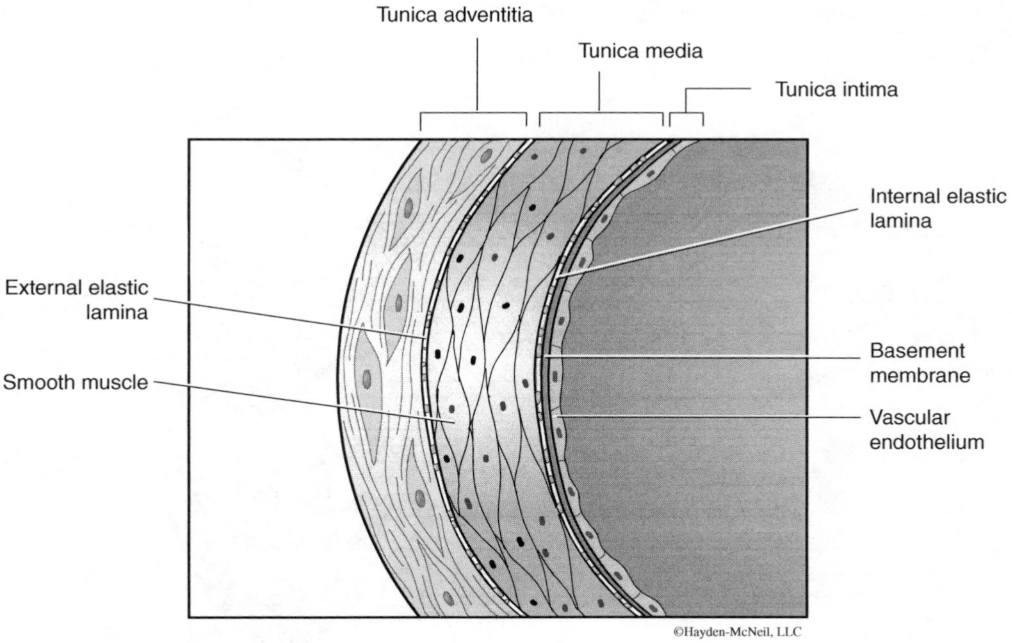

Tunica adventitia

Tunica media

Tunica intima

External elastic lamina

Smooth muscle

Internal elastic lamina

Basement membrane

Vascular endothelium

©Hayden-McNeil, LLC

**Figure 23-2.** Layers in the walls of blood vessels.

## C. Vascular Endothelial Cells Are Very Important

*Vascular endothelial cells* line the walls of all the blood vessels and the heart. Three important features of these cells are as follows:

1. **Smooth surface** – allows blood cells and platelets to flow past without adhering to the blood vessel wall or becoming damaged by the force of the blood flow.

2. **Secrete vasoactive substances** – these important substances cause blood vessels to contract and relax. They include *endothelin*, *nitric oxide*, and *prostacyclin*.

3. **Damage and dysfunction** – linked with vascular disease such as *atherosclerosis*.

## D. Arteries

The arterial side of the systemic circuit contains blood flowing away from the heart at **high pressure**. Arteries have all three layers in their walls. The tunica media, however, makes up the bulk of the arterial wall, which is very thick and contains an abundance of elastic and smooth muscle fibers.

The ratio of smooth muscle fibers to elastic fibers in the tunica media of arteries increases as the distance from the heart increases. In the large arteries near the heart, therefore, the elastic component of the tunica media is very prominent. These large, **elastic arteries** include the *aorta, carotids, common iliacs*.

The elasticity of the arteries near the heart allows them to *distend* at each heart beat. Arteries with weakened walls (e.g. in Marfan syndrome) can progressively distend, forming dangerous aneurysms.

489

Normal arterial elasticity has the following effects:

1.  **Smooths** out the pressure wave from the pulse.

2.  The **elastic recoil** of these arteries continues to propel blood through the systemic circuit in the interval between heart beats.

Arteries lose this elasticity and harden in the disease condition known as *arteriosclerosis*; this will be discussed later, when we also talk about *hypertension*.

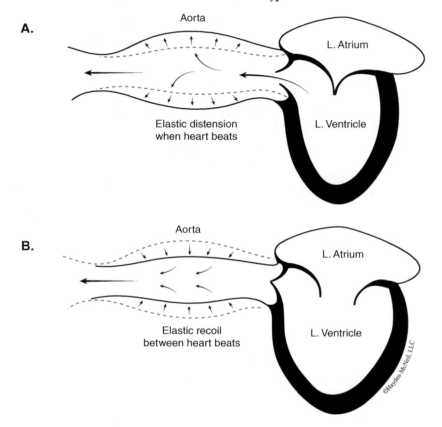

**Figure 23-3.** Elasticity of large arteries allows distension at each heart beat
  • This cushions pressure shock waves
  • Stores elastic energy that propels blood onward *between* heart beats
  This elasticity is lost in **arteriosclerosis**.

In the pulmonary circuit, the blood in the pulmonary arteries is at much lower pressure than in the systemic arteries.

### E. Arterioles

The large arteries make many branches, the diameter of the walls in each branch becoming progressively smaller and smaller. The smallest vessels are called arterioles.

Arterioles are smaller versions of arteries, but the smooth muscle component of the tunica media is very prominent. This allows for strong vasoconstriction when the sympathetic nervous system is activated.

The arterioles are the most important blood vessels involved in controlling blood flow through organs and tissues, and in determining the total peripheral resistance.

The **terminal arterioles**, which develop from arterioles proper, have structures that are intermediate between arterioles and capillaries.

## F. Capillaries

Terminal arterioles deliver blood into the capillaries. Capillaries have only the tunica intima. Essentially, they are tubes of endothelial cells sitting on a basement membrane. Interchange between the blood and interstitial fluid takes place across their walls.

**Pericytes – cells that are** often found wrapped around the endothelial cells of capillaries. These cells are called *Rouget cells* or "pericytes." The cells play an important role in growth of new blood vessels (*angiogenesis*).

Capillaries are responsible for *delivering* nutrients, hormones, oxygen, etc. to the tissues, and they are also responsible for *removing* carbon dioxide and other metabolic products such as lactic acid and urea.

## G. Venules and Veins

The pressure of blood in the venous part of the systemic circuit is much *lower* than on the arterial side.

491

Blood passes from the capillaries into venules, which merge together to form veins. The veins are responsible for returning the blood to the heart to complete the circuit.

An additional important point is that the veins have a large capacity for blood, and can act as blood reservoirs. This will be discussed in the context of hemorrhage and shock.

The smallest venules lack smooth muscle in their walls. They are **non-muscular venules**. The larger venules have all three layers. They are the **muscular venules**. The veins also have all three layers. However, their walls are much thinner and are less elastic than the walls of arteries and arterioles. Veins have a thick tunica adventitia composed of fibrous connective tissue.

In sum, therefore, venules and veins have a large diameter with little elasticity in their walls, giving them *large capacities at low pressures*.

Many veins, particularly those in the arms and legs, contain flap-like *valves*, which project inward from their inner linings. These valves assist in returning the blood to the heart by preventing backflow due to gravity.

### H. Vasoconstriction and Vasodilation

The smooth muscle fibers of the tunica media contract or relax in response to sympathetic stimulation, certain hormones (e.g. epinephrine, endothelin), and certain chemicals (e.g. $H^+$, $CO_2$). If the blood vessels become narrower, the effect is called ***vasoconstriction***. When the smooth muscle fibers relax, the blood vessels open up again. This is called ***vasodilation***. One important vasodilator is nitric oxide, sythesized and released by the vascular endothelium. Another is prostacyclin, also produced by the vascular endothelium.

**Vasoconstriction and vasodilation affect:**

1. blood flow through tissues and organs

2. venous capacity

3. systemic vascular resistance (SVR) = total peripheral resistance (TPR), governed by arterioles

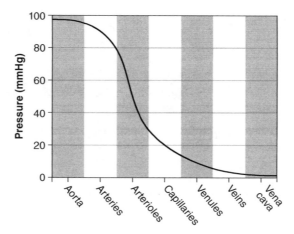

Low TPR          High TPR

**Figure 23-4.** Vasoconstriction and vasodilation.

Vasoconstriction and vasodilation control:

1.  **flow** of blood through organs and tissues
2.  **resistance** of the systemic circuit (also known as the ***total peripheral resistance*** or ***TPR***)
3.  **capacity** of the blood vessels in the cardiovascular system.

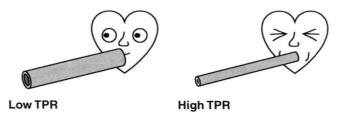

**Figure 23-5.** Vascular pressures.

## IV. The Pump — Structure of the Heart

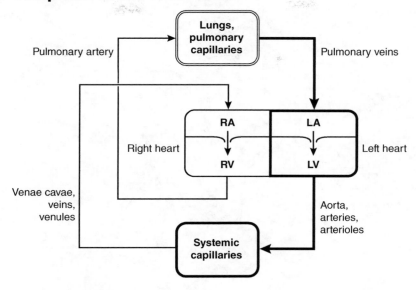

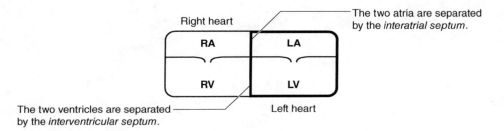

**Figure 23-6.** Schematic of blood circulation through the heart.

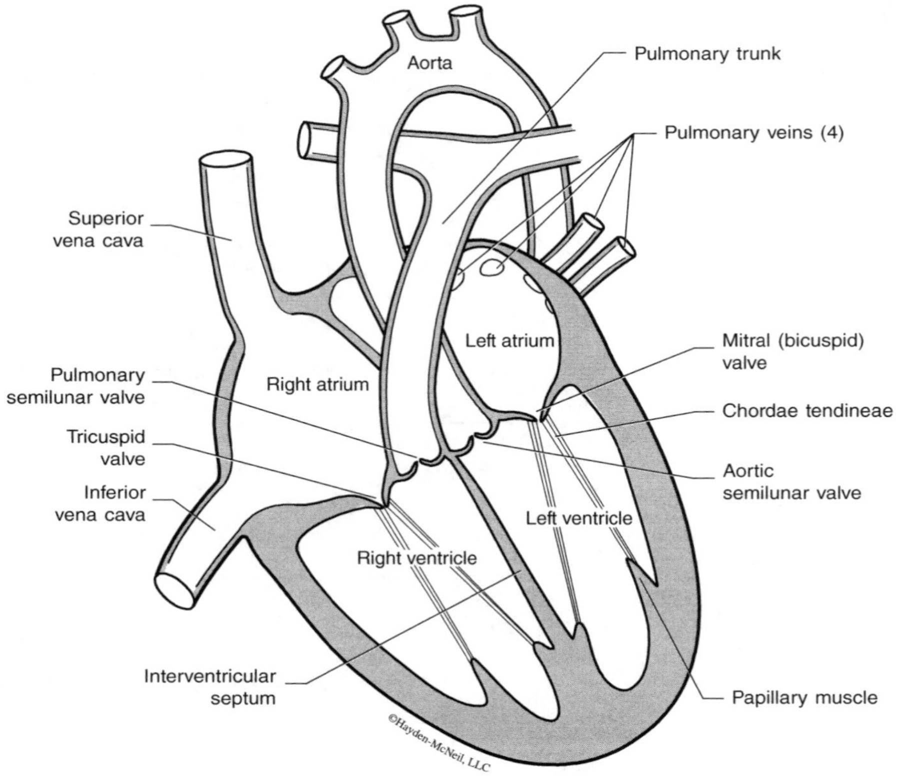

**Figure 23-7.** The heart.

The relatively thin-walled **atria** act mainly as the receiving chambers for blood returning from the systemic or pulmonary circulation, and the thicker-walled **ventricles** are the major pumping chambers.

## A. The Pericardium

The heart and the roots of the great blood vessels that emerge from it are enclosed in a double-layered serous membrane called the **pericardium**.

The pericardium confines the heart to its position in the **mediastinum**, while allowing the heart freedom of movement so that it can contract vigorously and rapidly whenever the need arises.

The **parietal pericardium** consists of an inner layer of serous membrane and an outer layer of fibrous connective tissue.

The **visceral pericardium** is firmly attached to the muscular wall of the heart (see below). The visceral pericardium is also referred to as the **epicardium**.

Between the visceral and parietal pericardium is a thin film of serous fluid (**pericardial fluid**) that acts as a lubricant and reduces friction as the heart contracts and relaxes.

Inflammation of the pericardium is called **pericarditis**, and can lead to excessive buildup of pericardial fluid in the *pericardial cavity* between the parietal and visceral layers of the pericardium. This can cause compression of the heart, and may lead to a life-threatening situation.

## B. The Heart Wall

Like most blood vessels, the wall of the heart has three layers.

1.  **Epicardium** (= visceral pericardium).

    This is the outer layer.

2.  **Myocardium.**

    This is the middle, muscular layer that makes up the bulk of the heart and does all the pumping; i.e. it accounts for the contractility of the heart. The myocardium is made up of interlacing bundles of cardiac muscle fibers. These bundles are specially arranged so that the heart acts as a very efficient pump. As we have already described, cardiac muscle cells are involuntary, striated and branched.

    The inner surface of the myocardium is sculpted into a complex series of ridges and valleys called the ***trabeculae carneae***. These prevent the wall of the heart from wrinkling when it contracts.

    The myocardium is more prominent in the ventricles than in the atria. The myocardium is thinnest in the right ventricle, and is thickest in the left ventricle. This is because the right ventricle does less work than the left ventricle. The right ventricle only has to pump blood through the lungs at comparatively low pressure, while the left ventricle has to pump blood to all parts of the body at comparatively high pressure.

3.  **Endocardium.**

    This is the inner layer that lines the cavities of the heart. It consists of a thin layer of vascular endothelial cells overlying a thin layer of connective tissue. The layer of vascular endothelium is continuous with the layer of vascular endothelium in the blood vessels that emerge from the heart.

495

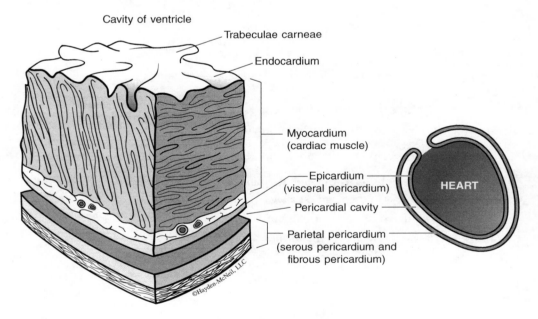

**Figure 23-8.** The heart wall.

## C. The Chambers of the Heart

The heart consists of two pumps mounted side by side, each consisting of two intercon-nected chambers. The upper chamber that receives blood is called the **atrium**, and the lower chamber that does nearly all the work of pumping this blood is called the **ventricle**.

The wall that separates the two atria from each other is called the *interatrial septum*.

The wall between the two ventricles is called the *interventricular septum*.

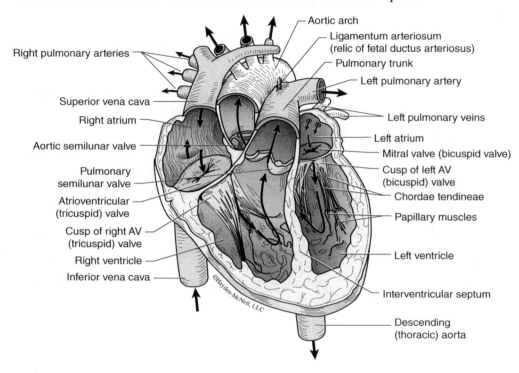

**Figure 23-9.** Sectional anatomy of the heart.

## D. Great Vessels Entering and Leaving the Heart

Blood enters and leaves the heart through the following great vessels:

* Blood enters the right heart through the *superior vena cava* and *inferior vena cava*.

* Blood leaves the right heart through the *pulmonary trunk*, that branches into the **left** *pulmonary arteries* and the **right** *pulmonary arteries*.

* Blood enters the left heart via the **left** and **right** *pulmonary veins*.

* Blood leaves the left heart via the **aorta**.

Although they are not considered to be great vessels, we include the *coronary arteries* that provide blood to the heart wall, the *cardiac veins* and the *coronary sinus* that drains into the right atrium.

Blood flows through these great vessels and the heart as follows.

1.  **Right side** – receives blood from all parts of the body and pumps it through the lungs, where it loses its carbon dioxide and takes on oxygen.

    The right atrium receives deoxygenated blood laden with carbon dioxide from all parts of the body (except the lungs, of course). The major vessels are the **superior** and **inferior vena cavae**, which collect blood from the superior and inferior regions of the body and deliver it to the right atrium. The **coronary sinus** drains blood from the walls of the heart.

    The right ventricle receives blood from the right atrium and pumps it to the lungs through the **pulmonary trunk**, which divides into the **left** and **right pulmonary arteries**.

2.  **Left side** – receives oxygenated blood from the lungs and pumps it to the rest of the body.

    The left atrium receives oxygenated blood from the lungs via four **pulmonary veins**.

    The left ventricle receives oxygenated blood from the left atrium and pumps it into the **aorta**. The aorta distributes this oxygenated blood into the **coronary arteries** and the other major arteries.

## E. Arteries Branching from the Aorta

You should know all the arteries branching from the aorta, and the regions supplied. Study and learn all the Arteries I list.

497

| | |
|---|---|
| **Ascending Aorta** | Right and left coronary arteries |
| **Aortic Arch** | Brachiocephalic (right common carotid, right subclavian)<br>Left common carotid<br>Left subclavian |
| **Thoracic Aorta**<br>(above diaphragm) | Pericardial<br>Bronchials<br>Esophageals<br>Mediastinal<br>Posterior intercostal |
| **Abdominal Aorta**<br>(below diaphragm) | Phrenics<br>Celiac<br>Superior mesenteric<br>Suprarenals<br>Renals<br>Gonadals<br>Inferior mesenteric<br>Lumbar<br>Middle sacral<br>Common iliacs |

You should also be familiar with the corresponding veins.

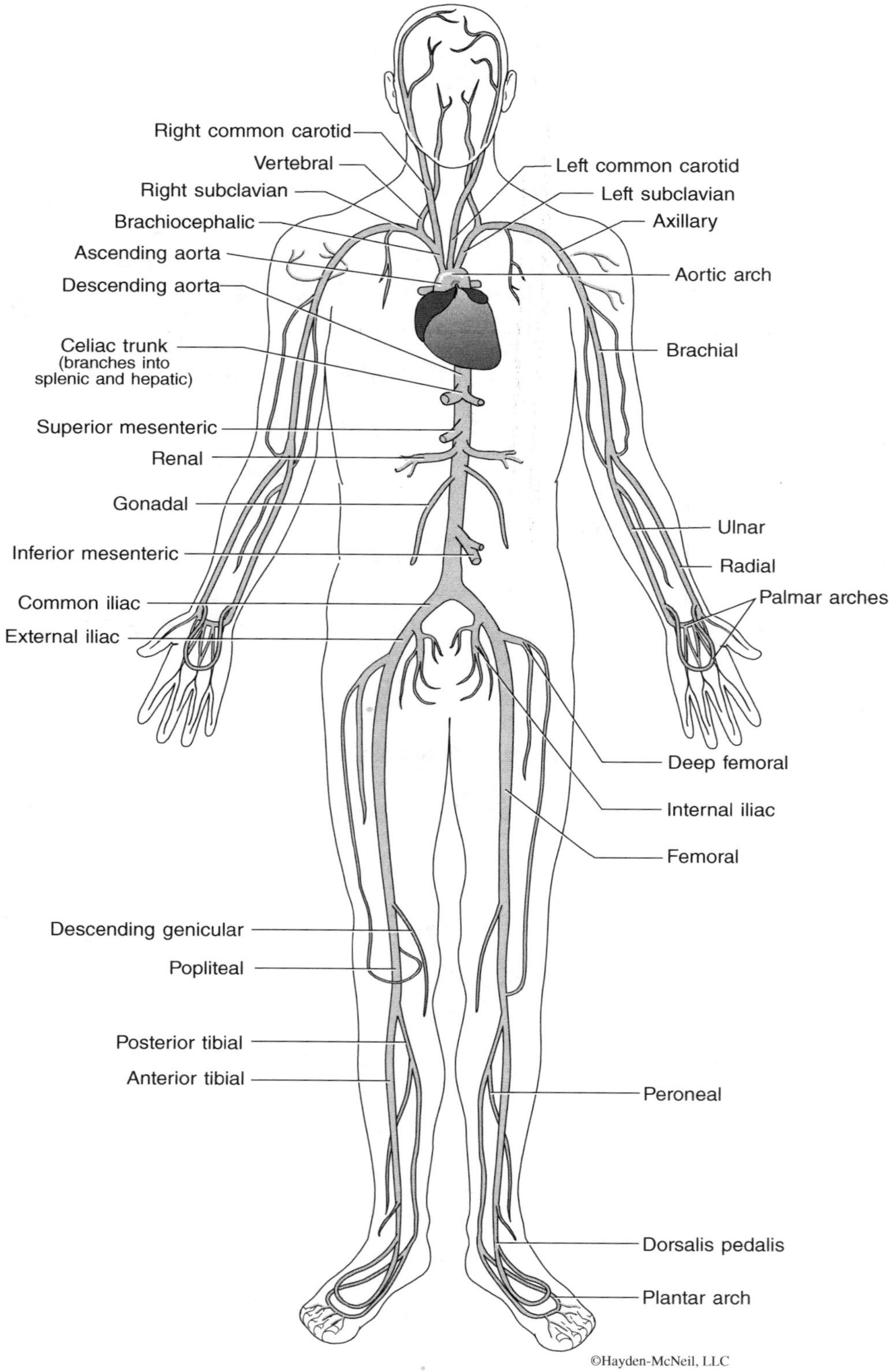

Right common carotid
Vertebral
Right subclavian
Brachiocephalic
Ascending aorta
Descending aorta
Celiac trunk
(branches into
splenic and hepatic)
Superior mesenteric
Renal
Gonadal
Inferior mesenteric
Common iliac
External iliac

Left common carotid
Left subclavian
Axillary
Aortic arch
Brachial
Ulnar
Radial
Palmar arches
Deep femoral
Internal iliac
Femoral

Descending genicular
Popliteal
Posterior tibial
Anterior tibial
Peroneal
Dorsalis pedalis
Plantar arch

©Hayden-McNeil, LLC

**Figure 23-10.** Arterial system.

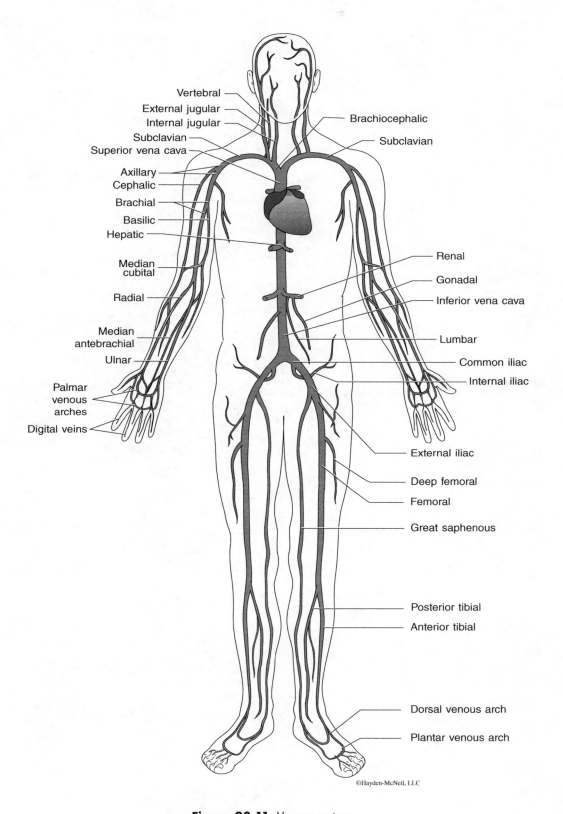

**Figure 23-11.** Venous system.

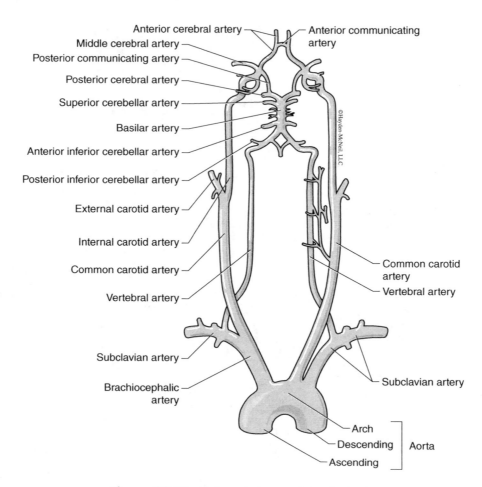

Anterior cerebral artery
Middle cerebral artery
Posterior communicating artery
Posterior cerebral artery
Superior cerebellar artery
Basilar artery
Anterior inferior cerebellar artery
Posterior inferior cerebellar artery
External carotid artery
Internal carotid artery
Common carotid artery
Vertebral artery
Subclavian artery
Brachiocephalic artery

Anterior communicating artery
©Hayden-McNeil, LLC

Common carotid artery
Vertebral artery
Subclavian artery

Arch
Descending        Aorta
Ascending

**Figure 23-12.** Major arteries supplying the brain.

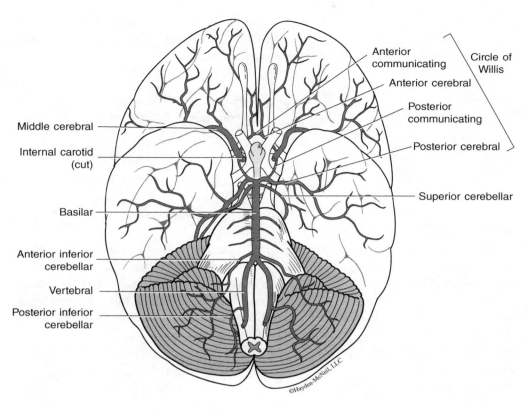

**Figure 23-13.** Arteries of the brain.

## F. Valves of the Heart

In a normal, healthy individual, blood passes through the heart in one direction only. It can only do this because one-way valves guard the openings leading from the atria to the ventricles and from the ventricles to the arterial trunks.

> It is important to understand that the opening and closing of these valves is purely passive, and occurs in response to changing pressure differentials across them.

Valves called *atrioventricular valves* (**A-V** valves) guard the entrances to the two ventricles from the two atria.

Valves called *semilunar valves* guard the exits from the two ventricles.

1.  **Right side valves.**

    The right A-V valve is called the *tricuspid valve* [an aid to remembering which side this is on is to think of it as the tRI(GHT)cuspid]. It consists of three leaflets. Tendon-like fibrous cords called *chordae tendineae* connect the pointed ends of the leaflets to finger-like muscular projections (*papillary muscles*) on the inner surface of the right ventricle. The chordae tendineae and the papillary muscles prevent the valve from turning inside out into the atrium when the ventricle contracts.

The **right** semilunar valve guards the opening from the right ventricle into the pulmonary trunk. The valve consists of three semilunar (half-moon shaped) cusps, and is called the **pulmonary** or **pulmonic semilunar** valve.

2.  **Left side valves.**

    The left A-V valve is called the *bicuspid valve* or *mitral valve*. It has only two cusps, but has chordae tendineae attached to papillary muscles just like the tricuspid valve on the right side of the heart.

    The **left** semilunar valve guards the opening from the left ventricle into the aorta. Like the pulmonary semilunar valve, this valve has three cusps. It is called the **aortic semilunar valve**.

## G. The Skeleton of the Heart

Rings of dense fibrous connective tissue surround the pulmonary trunk and the aorta at their proximal ends. Rings of fibrous connective tissue also surround the tricuspid and mitral valves. The four rings are connected rather like the six plastic rings that secure the cans in a six-pack of soda. The muscle bands, arterial trunks and valves are all attached to this framework, called the *skeleton of the heart*.

## H. The Blood Supply to the Heart Walls

Blood is supplied to the tissues of the heart, notably the cardiac muscle, by the **right** and **left coronary arteries**. These arteries exit from the aorta just beyond (distal to) the aortic semilunar valve.

After blood has passed through the capillary beds of the heart wall, most of the venous blood is collected by the **cardiac veins**, which drain into the wide **coronary sinus**. The coronary sinus drains into the right atrium. This topic will be dealt with in more detail when we discuss heart failure.

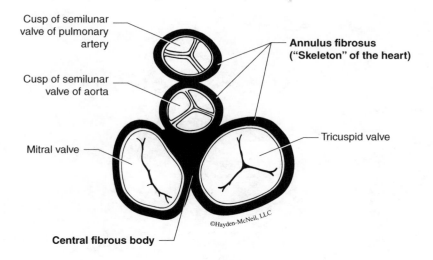

Cusp of semilunar valve of pulmonary artery

Cusp of semilunar valve of aorta

**Annulus fibrosus ("Skeleton" of the heart)**

Mitral valve

Tricuspid valve

**Central fibrous body**

©Hayden-McNeil, LLC

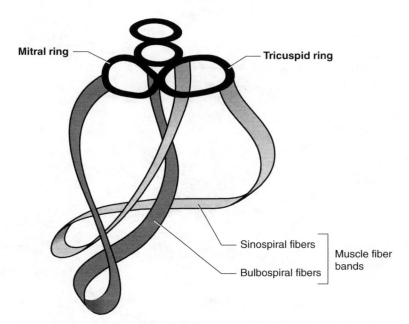

**Mitral ring**

**Tricuspid ring**

Sinospiral fibers

Bulbospiral fibers

Muscle fiber bands

Muscle bands, arterial trunks, valves are all attached to this framework

**Figure 23-14.** "Skeleton" of the heart.

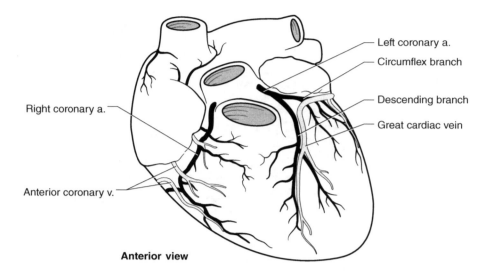

Right coronary a.

Anterior coronary v.

Left coronary a.

Circumflex branch

Descending branch

Great cardiac vein

**Anterior view**

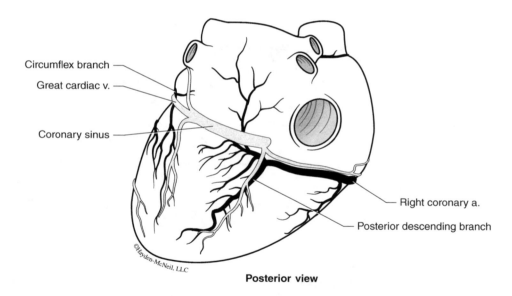

Circumflex branch

Great cardiac v.

Coronary sinus

Right coronary a.

Posterior descending branch

©Hayden-McNeil, LLC

**Posterior view**

**Figure 23-15.** The coronary circulation.

## V. Development of the Heart

The cardiovascular system develops rapidly and early. Long before development of any other major organ, the heart and its vessels have taken shape and the heart is beating. This is necessary, because the body is making rapid growth, and tissues and organs are developing.

By the end of the third week after conception, cells have already arranged themselves into tubes forming primitive vessels. The most prominent of these tubes will become the heart itself.

- *Third week* – a single-chamber "heart" is present.

- *Fourth week* – the heart begins to beat, and the tube begins to grow.

- *Fifth week* – four chambers are visible, but not fully divided from each other.

- *Eighth week* – all four chambers are distinct and contracting; all four valves are operational.

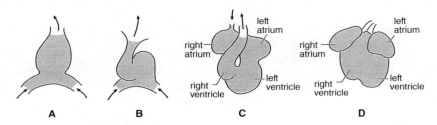

505

**Figure 23-16.** A tubular heart (A) is formed from two cardiac crescents (not shown). The tubular heart then undergoes changes (B, C) that lead to the development of a four-chambered heart (D).

## VI. Fetal Circulation

The fetus does not feed or breathe in the same way as an infant. The fetus lacks functioning lungs to provide it with oxygen and remove carbon dioxide, and a functional digestive system to provide it with nutrients. Instead of lungs and digestive system, the fetus has the *placenta*.

The fetal circulation therefore differs from the adult in that the system is designed to bring oxygen and nutrients from the placenta via a special blood vessel called the **umbilical vein**. Carbon dioxide and waste products are returned to the placenta via the **umbilical artery**.

A full description of the fetal circulatory system will be deferred until next semester.

## CHAPTER 24

# CARDIOVASCULAR SYSTEM II
The Cardiac Cycle, Sources of Energy, Important Parameters,
Equations and Calculations, Heart Sounds and Murmurs, Control of
Cardiac Output, Starling's Law of the Heart, Autonomic Nervous System

507

## CHAPTER OUTLINE

## DESCRIPTION AND INTRODUCTION

A healthy heart in a resting 154 lb adult pumps about six liters of blood per minute. Because the total blood volume in a healthy adult is about 5.2 liters, this means that the heart pumps the equivalent of the body's total blood volume in less than a minute. It can keep this up for 90 years or more, during which time it will have pumped *283 million liters* of blood. And that is only if the owner of the heart has been at rest all that time. It will be much more than that if he or she has exercised. Think about this remarkable performance—any man-made pump would have needed frequent servicing and would probably have worn out by then.

The present chapter describes the cardiac cycle, the sources of energy that the heart uses to power itself, and some of the factors that determine how much blood the heart pumps out per minute. This is the *output of the heart*, which is called the **cardiac output**.

Finally, we discuss the way the autonomic nervous system controls the heart.

## OBJECTIVES

After listening to the lecture and reading this chapter, you should be able to:

1. Explain how the heart beat is regulated and synchronized.
2. Explain with **diagrams** the action of the **heart valves** during contraction and relaxation of the heart.
3. **Draw a graph** illustrating the changes in **pressure** in the **aorta**, **left ventricle** and **left atrium** during the cardiac cycle.
4. Relate the events in 3. above with the **electrocardiogram** and the **heart sounds**.
5. Describe how **blood pressure** is measured in humans; name the **instrument** most commonly used in the doctor's office.
6. Describe the **heart sounds**, and how they are produced.
7. Define what is meant by a **murmur**, and give examples of the causes of **systolic** and **diastolic** murmurs.
8. List the two main types of food molecule providing **energy** for cardiac contraction, and their relative importance.
9. List and define **11 important parameters** that relate to the functioning of the heart, and **give equations** for calculating them.
10. List the four important factors that affect **cardiac output**.
11. Define **preload**.
12. Define **afterload**, and list three factors that affect it.
13. Define **myocardial contractility**, and three factors that increase it.
14. Explain **Starling's Law of the Heart**.
15. Describe how the **sympathetic** and **parasympathetic** branches of the autonomic nervous system affect the **heart** and influence **cardiac output**.

## I. Heart Contraction and Relaxation—the Cardiac Cycle

Nearly all the pumping action of the heart is due to *ventricular* contraction. The heart functions so that blood rushes from the veins through the open atria and on into the ventricles. The atria then contract, and force a little more blood into the ventricles. The atria relax, then the ventricles contract vigorously, forcing the blood into the pulmonary and systemic circuits. Finally, the ventricles relax, and the cycle is repeated.

a.   At rest, the heart pumps 5–6 liters of blood per minute = the *cardiac output*

b.   Cardiac output: multiply *heart rate* by the *volume pumped per beat* (= stroke volume):

$$CO = HR \times SV$$

c.   The ventricles do nearly all of the pumping

d.   Contraction = *systole* (ventricular, atrial)

e.   Relaxation = *diastole* (ventricular, atrial)

f.   The valves ensure one-way flow

g.   The opening and closing of the valves is purely passive, determined by the pressure differential across them

h.   Heart beat is regulated and synchronized by *pacemaker cells* in the sinoatrial node

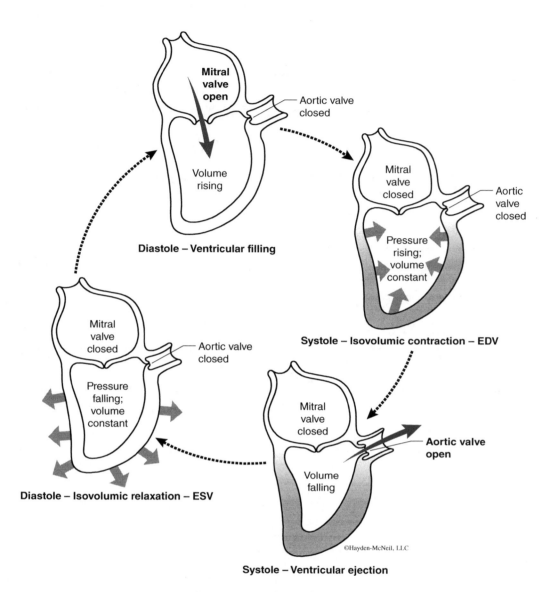

©Hayden-McNeil, LLC

**Figure 24-1.** The cardiac cycle.

## A. Stages in Contraction and Relaxation—Action of the Valves

The pumping action of the heart is divided into a number of distinct stages. They are as follows:

**Stage 1. Filling** – the atria and ventricles are relaxed. This state is called *diastole*.

> The mitral and tricuspid valves (the A-V valves) are wide open, the aortic and pulmonary semilunar valves are closed.

> The pressure in the venae cavae and atria is slightly higher than in the ventricles. Therefore, blood rushes from the venae cavae into the atria and on into the ventricles. About 70% of the ventricular filling occurs during this phase.

**Stage 2. Atrial systole** – the atria contract, forcing the remaining 30% of blood into the ventricles. The atria then relax, a stage known as *atrial diastole*.

**Stage 3.** *Isovolumic ventricular contraction* **–** this is the first phase of ventricular systole.

When the ventricles contract, pressure rises in their interiors and exceeds the pressure in the atria. This causes the A-V valves to close, which occurs passively in response to the pressure differential.

As the ventricles contract, the papillary muscles also contract, pulling on and tensing the chordae tendineae. This prevents the A-V valves from turning inside out into the atria.

The ventricles continue to contract with all four valves closed, raising the pressure still more.

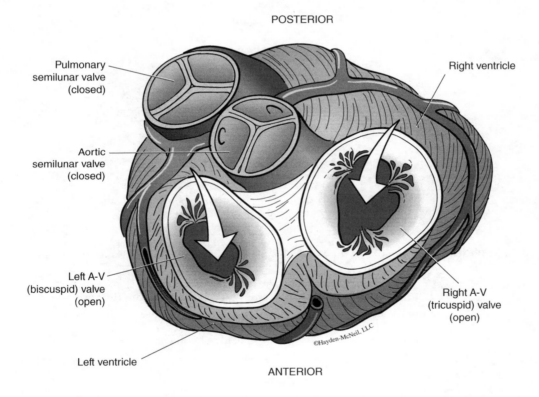

**Transverse section, Superior view**
**Ventricular diastole - filling phase**

**Figure 24-2.** Transverse section, superior view. Ventricular diastole—filling stage.

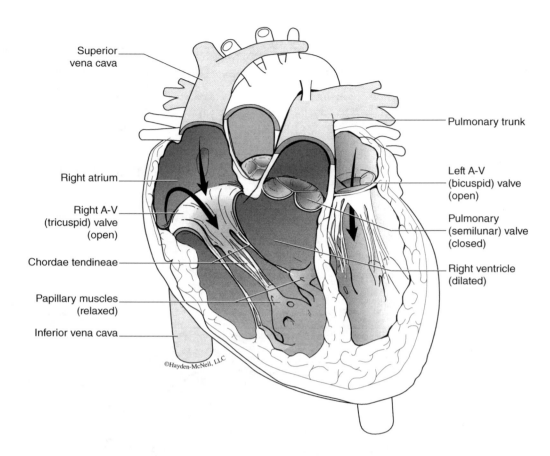

Superior
vena cava

Pulmonary trunk

Right atrium

Left A-V
(bicuspid) valve
(open)

Right A-V
(tricuspid) valve
(open)

Pulmonary
(semilunar) valve
(closed)

Chordae tendineae

Right ventricle
(dilated)

Papillary muscles
(relaxed)

Inferior vena cava

©Hayden-McNeil, LLC

512

**Figure 24-3.** Frontal section. Ventricular diastole—filling stage.

**Stage 4. Ejection** – pressure in the ventricles reaches the point where it exceeds the pressure in the pulmonary arteries and aorta.

The semilunar valves open passively, and blood is ejected from the ventricles into the pulmonary and systemic circuits, at first rapidly, then at a reduced rate.

As blood is ejected, the pressure in the ventricles starts to fall, an effect that is accentuated when the ventricles cease to contract and enter the phase known as *ventricular diastole*.

**Stage 5. *Isovolumic relaxation*** – pressure in the ventricles drops below the pressures in the pulmonary arteries and the aorta. The result is that the semilunar valves close passively. The pressure in the ventricles continues to fall. At this stage, all four valves are closed.

**Stage 6. Onset of filling** – once the pressure in the ventricles falls below the pressure in the atria, the A-V valves open, allowing blood to rush into them and on into the relaxed ventricles. Filling with blood is at first rapid, then its rate is reduced. This phase of reduced filling is sometimes called *diastasis*.

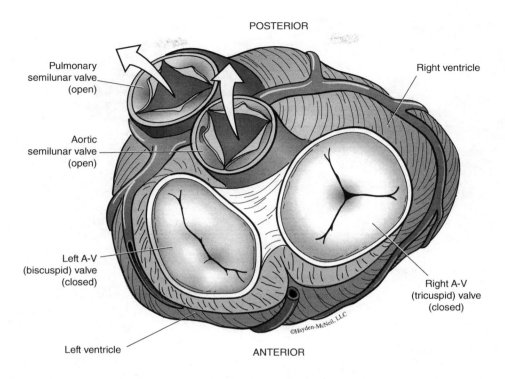

POSTERIOR

Pulmonary
semilunar valve
(open)

Aortic
semilunar valve
(open)

Left A-V
(biscuspid) valve
(closed)

Left ventricle

Right ventricle

Right A-V
(tricuspid) valve
(closed)

©Hayden-McNeil, LLC

ANTERIOR

**Figure 24-4.** Transverse section, superior view. Ventricular systole—ejection stage.

513

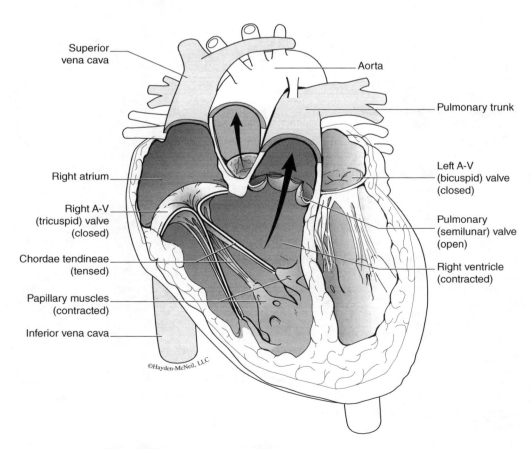

Superior
vena cava

Right atrium

Right A-V
(tricuspid) valve
(closed)

Chordae tendineae
(tensed)

Papillary muscles
(contracted)

Inferior vena cava

Aorta

Pulmonary trunk

Left A-V
(bicuspid) valve
(closed)

Pulmonary
(semilunar) valve
(open)

Right ventricle
(contracted)

©Hayden-McNeil, LLC

**Figure 24-5.** Frontal section. Ventricular systole—ejection stage.

**1. Ventricular filling**

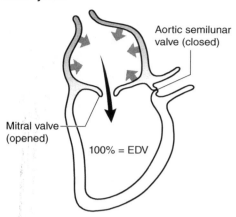

Left atrium

Aorta

Left ventricle

70%

**2. Atrial systole**

Aortic semilunar valve (closed)

Mitral valve (opened)

100% = EDV

**3. Isovolumic ventricular contraction**
(no volume change)

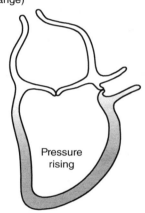

Pressure rising

**4. Ejection into aorta**
(rapid, then reduced)

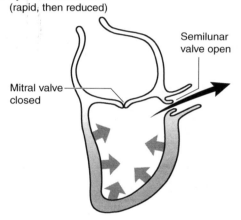

Semilunar valve open

Mitral valve closed

**5. Isovolumic ventricular relaxation**
(no volume change)

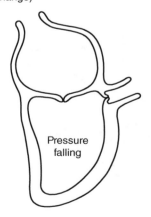

Pressure falling

**6. Ventricular filling**
(rapid, then reduced, diastasis)

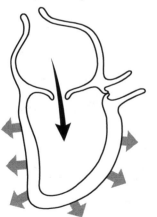

**Figure 24-6.** This figure shows the cardiac cycle only for the *left* atrium and *left* ventricle, where blood is ejected into the *aorta*. The same events are going on simultaneously in the right atrium and right ventricle, where blood is ejected into the pulmonary trunk.

## B. Intracardiac Pressure during One Cardiac Cycle

The changes in pressure in the aorta, left ventricle and left atrium during one cardiac cycle are shown in Figure 24-7. Just after the aortic semilunar valve closes there is a rapid oscillation of aortic pressure that is sometimes called the *incisura* or *dicrotic notch.*

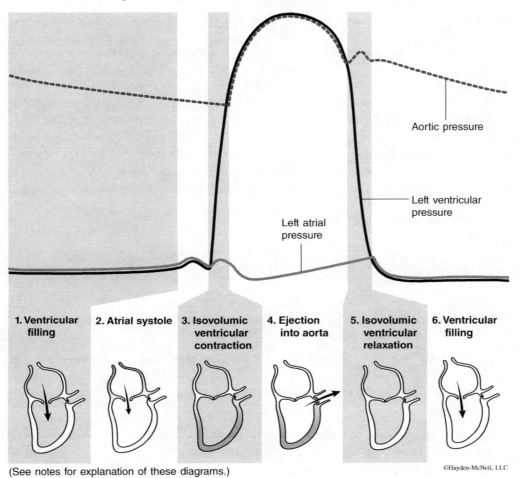

Aortic pressure

Left ventricular pressure

Left atrial pressure

| 1. Ventricular filling | 2. Atrial systole | 3. Isovolumic ventricular contraction | 4. Ejection into aorta | 5. Isovolumic ventricular relaxation | 6. Ventricular filling |

(See notes for explanation of these diagrams.)                    ©Hayden-McNeil, LLC

**Figure 24-7.** Intracardiac pressure curves and stages in filling and ejection.

515

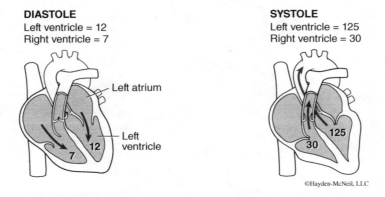

**DIASTOLE**
Left ventricle = 12
Right ventricle = 7

**SYSTOLE**
Left ventricle = 125
Right ventricle = 30

Left atrium

Left ventricle

7    12

30    125

©Hayden-McNeil, LLC

**Figure 24-8.** Left versus right ventricular pressures in mmHg.

## C. Blood Pressure Measurement in Humans

In hospital intensive care units, needles or catheters may be introduced into peripheral arteries, or into the heart chambers, and the pressure measured directly with strain gauges or similar devices.

Ordinarily, however, the blood pressure (by which we usually mean the *arterial* pressure) is measured indirectly by means of a **sphygmomanometer**. This consists of an inflatable bag contained in an inextensible cuff. The cuff is wrapped around the arm (occasionally the thigh), and inflated to a pressure somewhat in excess of arterial **systolic pressure**. This pressure is determined by a measuring device called a manometer. The pressure is then released slowly. When the pressure falls just below the systolic level, small spurts of blood escape through the brachial artery. They may either be detected by *palpating* (feeling with your fingertips) the radial artery at the wrist, or by listening with a **stethoscope** applied to the skin of the antecubital space over the brachial artery. This latter method is called *auscultation*. The sounds that are first heard are called *Korotkoff sounds*. The Korotkoff sounds disappear once the cuff pressure drops below **diastolic pressure**.

## D. Heart Sounds

The cardiac cycle is not a silent process. The sounds of the cardiac cycle are heard with the aid of a stethoscope, and the technique is called *auscultation*. Instead of a stethoscope, a microphone can be used, and the sounds recorded to produce a *phonocardiogram*.

A normally functioning heart produces two basic heart sounds: $S_1$ and $S_2$. There are two other sounds ($S_3$ and $S_4$) that are difficult or impossible to hear (although they can be detected with a microphone), and need not concern us here.

1. **First heart sound, $S_1$** – occurs at the onset of ventricular systole. It is due to the *closure of the A-V valves* (the mitral and tricuspid valves) and the tensing of the chordae tendineae. The mitral valve closes slightly ahead of the tricuspid valve, generating two components to $S_1$ that are called $M_1$ and $T_1$.

2. **Second heart sound, $S_2$** – occurs when *the semilunar valves close*, and marks the end of ventricular systole. The aortic valve closes slightly ahead of the pulmonic valve, generating two components to $S_2$ that are called $A_2$ and $P_2$.

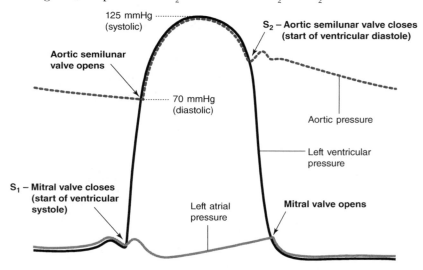

**Figure 24-9.** Opening and closing of the valves—the heart sounds.

### E. Murmurs

**Murmurs** are abnormal sounds that may be heard during ventricular systole or diastole. There are many types, but we shall describe just two. See Figures 24-10 and 24-11.

1.  **Systolic murmurs.**

    A systolic murmur can occur when the tricuspid or mitral valves do not close properly during systole. This causes blood to regurgitate into the corresponding atrium during ventricular systole and during isovolumic ventricular relaxation, a time when the A-V valves should be tightly closed.

2.  **Diastolic murmurs.**

    A diastolic murmur can occur when the aortic or pulmonic (pulmonary) valves do not close properly. This allows blood to regurgitate into the ventricles during ventricular diastole, a time when the aortic and pulmonic valves should be tightly closed.

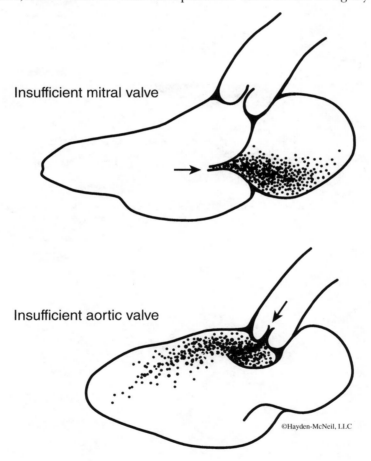

**Figure 24-10.** Insufficient valves.

517

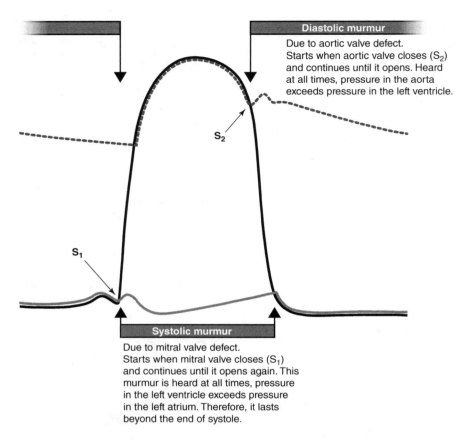

**Diastolic murmur**

Due to aortic valve defect.
Starts when aortic valve closes ($S_2$)
and continues until it opens. Heard
at all times, pressure in the aorta
exceeds pressure in the left ventricle.

$S_2$

$S_1$

**Systolic murmur**

Due to mitral valve defect.
Starts when mitral valve closes ($S_1$)
and continues until it opens again. This
murmur is heard at all times, pressure
in the left ventricle exceeds pressure
in the left atrium. Therefore, it lasts
beyond the end of systole.

**Figure 24-11.** Heart murmurs.

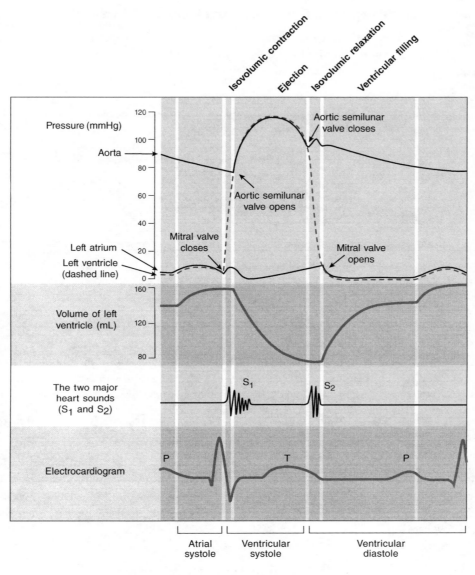

**Figure 24-12.** Cardiac cycle.

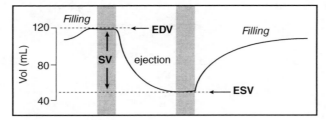

- Stroke volume – the volume of blood ejected per beat = EDV – ESV

- Ejection fraction = $\dfrac{SV}{EDV}$

- Cardiac output = stroke volume x heart rate

**Figure 24-13.** Volume of left ventricle.

## II. Source of Energy for Cardiac Muscle Contraction

The heart converts the energy generated by the metabolism of its cells into ATP, and this ATP is used to generate the force necessary to maintain blood pressure and ensure adequate blood flow through the tissues of the body.

You will recall that skeletal muscle gets much of its energy from glucose and its storage form, glycogen. Skeletal muscle can also use fatty acids as an energy source. In cardiac muscle, **fatty acids** are the preferred source of energy.

Utilization of Various FUELS by the Heart
for Energy Production

| Fuel substrate | % |
|---|---|
| Glucose | 17.9 |
| Lactate | 16.5 |
| Pyruvate | 0.5 |
| Fatty acids | 67.0 |
| Amino acids | 5.3 |
| Ketoacids | 4.3 |

In the table above, you will notice that cardiac muscle also uses *lactic acid* as an energy source (it first converts it to *pyruvic acid*). This is very useful, because during heavy exercise, skeletal muscle produces large amounts of lactic acid, and some of this is utilized by the heart.

The glycogen stored in cardiac muscle is primarily used as a reserve. It can be mobilized by sympathetic stimulation of the heart.

As in skeletal muscle, there is a phosphagen system, where creatine phosphate serves as a reservoir for high-energy phosphate. The creatine phosphate is manufactured from ATP by the enzyme *creatine phosphokinase* (*CPK*). The enzyme found in cardiac muscle is different from that in skeletal muscle, and if there is damage to the heart (e.g. in a *heart attack*), we can sometimes detect the cardiac CPK (*CPK-MB*) in the blood.

## III. Important Parameters, Equations, and Calculations

The following is a list of parameters relating to the heart. They are important. Make yourself familiar with them, and how they are calculated.

| Parameter | Measured In: | Example |
|---|---|---|
| 1.   Heart rate (HR) | beats per minute | 70 |
| 2.   Cardiac output (CO) | liters per minute | 5.6 |
| 3.   Stroke volume (SV) | mL per beat | 80 |
| 4.   End diastolic volume (EDV) | mL | 145 |
| 5.   End systolic volume (ESV) | mL | 65 |
| 6.   Diastolic aortic pressure | mm mercury | 65 |
| 7.   Systolic aortic pressure | mm mercury | 125 |
| 8.   Mean arterial pressure (MAP) | mm mercury | 85 |
| 9.   Pulse pressure | mm mercury | 60 |
| 10.  Total peripheral resistance (TPR) | mm mercury per liter per min | 15.2 |
| 11.  Ejection fraction |  | 0.55 |

Calculations and equations:

- **Stroke volume** = end diastolic volume – end systolic volume
- **Pulse pressure** = systolic aortic pressure – diastolic aortic pressure
- **Mean arterial pressure** = diastolic aortic pressure + 1/3 pulse pressure
- **Cardiac output** = heart rate × stroke volume
- **Total peripheral resistance** = mean blood pressure / cardiac output
- **Mean arterial** (blood) **pressure** = total peripheral resistance × cardiac output. This is an important equation that helps you to understand *hypertension*. Generally, in hypertensives there is an increase in total peripheral resistance without much change in cardiac output.
- **Ejection fraction** = stroke volume/end diastolic volume. A low ejection fraction (e.g. 0.4) indicates that the heart is pumping inefficiently and may be failing.

## IV. Four Factors that Affect Cardiac Output

Cardiac output is the amount of blood pumped by the blood per minute. Therefore it is a very important index of the functioning of the heart. During a heart attack, for example, there is usually a drop in the cardiac output.

Four factors are important determinants of cardiac output.

- **Preload** – the amount of blood returning to the heart (end diastolic volume)
- **Afterload** – the resistance to ejection of blood from the ventricles
- **Heart rate**
- **Myocardial contractility** – strength of cardiac muscle contraction

521

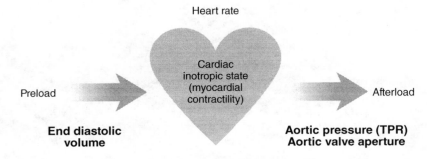

**Figure 24-14.** Four factors affect cardiac output: preload, heart rate, cardiac inotropic state (myocardial contractility), and afterload.

We will now consider each of these in turn.

### A. Preload—The Amount of Blood Returning to the Heart, End Diastolic Volume

Suppose a person's blood volume is 5.00 liters. Further, let us suppose that the output of the right ventricle is 5.00 liters/minute and the output of the left ventricle is 4.95 liters/minute. If this situation persisted and the blood volume remained constant, then an extra 1 liter of blood would accumulate in the lungs every 20 minutes. This emphasizes the importance of a control mechanism to keep a long-term balance between the outputs of each side of the heart.

This control mechanism lies within the heart itself. The heart behaves as a *self-regulating* pump, ensuring not only that what is pumped out by the right heart is also pumped out by the left heart, but also that the whole heart pumps out into the aorta what it gets from the venae cavae. *If it pumped out less than it received from the veins, it would become distended and would finally fail.*

The more blood that returns to the heart while the heart is in diastole, the greater will be the filling of the ventricles, the greater will be their end diastolic volume. This means that their walls will be stretched. This volume or stretching factor is called the **PRE-LOAD**, because it is a load applied to the heart *before* the ventricles contract. An increase in preload increases the force of contraction and increases the stroke volume. This is a property of the cardiac muscle. Muscle fibers that are stretched (provided the stretching is not excessive) contract more forcefully. This is known as ***Starling's Law of the Heart***, after the English physiologist Ernest Starling.

---

**Starling's Law of the Heart** – within limits, the greater the *preload* or stretch (and hence, the greater the length of the muscle fibers in the myocardium), the greater will be the *force of contraction*, the smaller will be the *end systolic volume*, and therefore the larger will be the *stroke volume*. Starling's law therefore ensures that the heart pumps into the aorta the same amount of blood it receives from the veins.

---

Starling's Law of the Heart is an **intrinsic property of cardiac muscle** and there is no change in myocardial contractility (see Section D). It does not depend on any nervous reflex, and can be observed in a heart that has been totally isolated from the autonomic nervous system (see Section B).

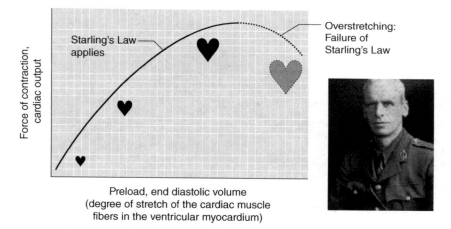

**Figure 24-15.** Starling's Law of the Heart. (Sizes of heart icons indicate end diastolic volume.) Force of contraction and cardiac output increase with increasing preload until the cardiac muscle fibers in the myocardium are overstretched and Starling's Law fails (this can occur in congestive heart failure). Starling's Law ensures that the heart pumps out the same volume of blood that it receives from the veins. Above is a photo of Ernest Starling in World War I uniform. He is buried in Jamaica.

## B. Afterload—Resistance to Ejection of Blood from the Ventricles

The resistance to ejection of blood from the ventricles is called the **AFTERLOAD**, because it is a load that occurs *after* the ventricles have started to contract.

For the left ventricle, the resistance to ejection (afterload) is affected by the:

1. **Pressure in the aorta** – the higher the pressure, the higher the resistance, and the tougher it is for the heart to pump against it (like pumping up a bicycle tire).

2. **Total peripheral resistance** – determined by the arteriole diameters, and therefore by vasoconstriction (like blowing through a narrow tube compared with a wide tube).

3. **Pathological changes** that lead to a narrowing (*stenosis*) of the aortic valve or a narrowing (stenosis) of the aorta itself – the effect is similar to an increase in total peripheral resistance.

## C. Heart Rate

Since the cardiac output is the heart rate multiplied by the stroke volume, any factor that changes the heart rate is likely to change the cardiac output. This is illustrated in the following table.

| Condition | Heart Rate (beats/min) | Stroke Volume (mL) | Cardiac Output (liters/min) |
|-----------|------------------------|--------------------|-----------------------------|
| Rest | 60 | 92 | 5.52 |
| | 90 | 97 | 8.72 |
| Exercise | 100 | 109 | 10.90 |
| | 120 | 112 | 13.74 |

In this table, the heart rate **doubles** during exercise (from 60 to 120 beats per minute). However, the cardiac output **more than doubles** because of an increased **stroke volume**, and goes up from 5.52 liters per minute to 13.74 liters per minute.

The heart rate is affected by a number of factors in addition to exercise, including the autonomic nervous system (see below).

## D. Myocardial Contractility—Strength of Contraction

Myocardial contractility is the force of contraction of the cardiac muscle at a **given fiber length.**

Myocardial contractility does *not* change during the operation of Starling's Law of the Heart, which is the result of increased force of contraction when the fibers **increase in length** during stretching.

523

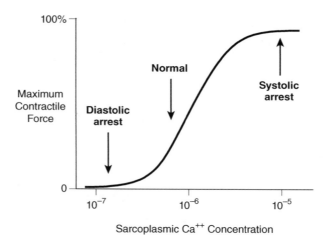

**Figure 24-16.** Diastolic arrest, systolic arrest.

Myocardial contractility depends on the levels of intracellular calcium, and is increased by a number of factors. They include:

1.  **Norepinephrine** and **epinephrine** (increase the heart rate as well).
2.  **Increased extracellular calcium**.
3.  *Digitalis,* which increases intracellular calcium.

524

## V. Autonomic Nervous System, Heart Rate and Myocardial Contractility

The autonomic nervous system can modify heart rate and myocardial contractility (strength of contraction). Starling's Law of the Heart is an intrinsic property of the cardiac muscle fibers, and has nothing to do with the autonomic innervation of the heart.

In normal adults at rest, the average heart rate is 70 beats per minute (in well-trained athletes the rate at rest may be only 50 or fewer beats per minute). During sleep, the rate is usually 50–60 beats per minute. During emotional excitement or muscular activity it may accelerate to rates up to 190 beats per minute. This acceleration of the heart is due to input from the autonomic nervous system.

The heart receives input (is *innervated*) by both the sympathetic and parasympathetic branches of the autonomic nervous systems.

### A. Sympathetic Branch

The heart is innervated by postganglionic sympathetic nerve fibers that release the neurotransmitter **norepinephrine**, which binds to β-**adrenergic receptors** in the myocardial cell membranes.

Sympathetic stimulation acts on two regions of the heart:

1.  **Sinus node,** causing the heart rate to **increase**.
2.  **Cardiac muscle** of the ventricles (less importantly of the atria), causing it to increase its contractile force. An increase in contractile force is spoken of as an increase in **myocardial contractility**. An increase of myocardial contractility will usually increase the stroke volume, because the end systolic volume is diminished by the more forceful systole of the ventricles.

Since cardiac output is dependent on heart rate multiplied by the stroke volume, sympathetic stimulation will increase cardiac output.

## B. Parasympathetic Branch

**Parasympathetic** nerve fibers from the left and right **vagus (X)** nerves innervate mainly the sinus and A-V nodes (*not* the ventricular myocardium), and cause the heart to beat more slowly.

The preganglionic parasympathetic nerve endings release **acetylcholine**, which binds to **nicotinic receptors** on postganglionic (intramural) neurons found in the heart. These postganglionic neurons also release **acetylcholine**, which binds to **muscarinic receptors** on the membranes of the pacemaker cells. These receptors are blocked by *atropine*.

Normally at rest, the parasympathetic inflow to the heart dominates over the sympathetic. This holds the heart rate in check. If the parasympathetic system is blocked (or the vagus nerves cut), there is a marked increase in heart rate.

**Autonomic Nervous System and Cardiac Output**

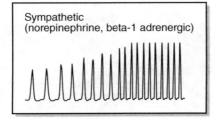

Sympathetic
(norepinephrine, beta-1 adrenergic)

Increased cardiac output caused by:

• Increased heart rate
• Increased myocardial contractility

525

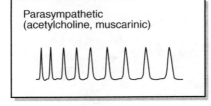

Parasympathetic
(acetylcholine, muscarinic)

Decreased cardiac output caused by:

• Reduced heart rate

**Figure 24-17.** Autonomic nervous system and cardiac output.

## C. Central Control of the Heart

Central control of the heart is primarily from a region of the medulla called the *vasomotor center* or *cardiac center*. Output from this center controls both sympathetic outflow to the heart and the flow of nerve impulses down the vagus nerve. In turn, the vasomotor center is under higher control from many areas of the brain, including the *hypothalamus*, *reticular formation* of the brain stem, and the *limbic system*.

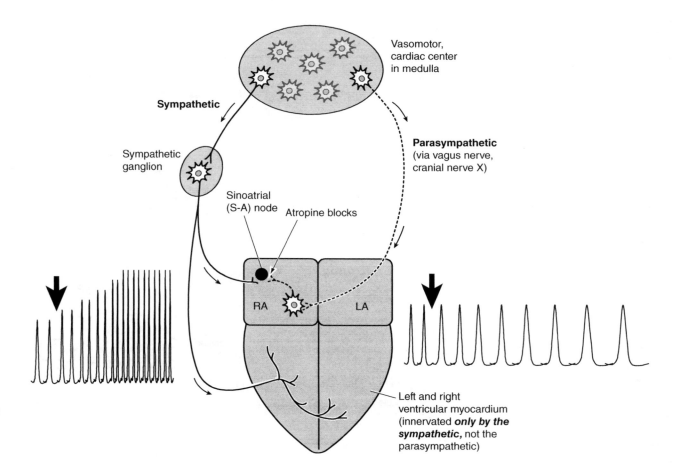

### Sympathetic

1. Accelerates heart rate (S-A node).
2. Increases force of contraction of the ventricular myocardium.
3. *Norepinephrine* is released at sympathetic nerve terminals and acts on β-*adrenergic* receptors in the pacemaker cells of the sinoatrial node and on cardiac muscle cells of the ventricles.
4. Action of norepinephrine (and epinephrine) on the heart is blocked by β-*blockers*.

### Parasympathetic

1. Slows heart rate (S-A node).
2. Does *not* alter force of contraction of ventricles because it doesn't innervate them.
3. *Acetylcholine* is released at parasympathetic nerve terminals and acts on *nicotinic* receptors on intramural neurons which also release acetylcholine, which binds to *muscarinic* receptors in the pacemaker cells of S-A node.
4. Muscarinic receptors are blocked by *atropine*.

**Figure 24-18.** Actions of the autonomic nervous system on the heart.

# CARDIOVASCULAR SYSTEM III
The Electrical Activity of the Heart—Action Potentials,
Electrocardiogram, Arrhythmias

## CHAPTER OUTLINE

## DESCRIPTION AND INTRODUCTION

As the heart beats, the mass of cardiac muscle that makes up the myocardium goes through repetitive, cyclic waves of depolarization and repolarization. This pulsating electrical activity can be recorded by attaching wires to the skin of the chest and other parts of the body. The electrical potentials can then be recorded on a strip chart or oscilloscope, and the record is called an *electrocardiogram (ECG or EKG)*.

The electrocardiogram can be recorded from a patient at rest, or while the patient is working out on a treadmill. In that case, the procedure is called a *stress test*. The electrocardiogram is a very important, non-invasive diagnostic tool. It is usually the first test carried out on a patient who has had a heart attack, and will often dictate the initial treatment. When examined by skilled medical personnel, the electrocardiogram can often reveal the nature of a heart problem, and what should be done about it.

This chapter analyzes the electrical activity of the heart, including the action potential of a cardiac muscle cell, the pacemaker and conduction system, and the electrocardiogram. We shall also deal with some simple **cardiac arrhythmias** (also known as *dysrhythmias*), some of which may be life-threatening, and finally the effect of cocaine on the heart.

## OBJECTIVES

After listening to the lecture and reading this chapter, you should be able to:

1.  Describe how the **action potential** of a cardiac muscle cell differs from that of a neuron.
2.  **Provide a diagram** of the action potential of a cardiac muscle, and identify its four phases (0, 1, 2, 3).
3.  Describe opening and closing of the **ion channels** that give rise to each phase of the cardiac action potential.
4.  Describe what is meant by a **pacemaker cell**.
5.  Describe the sequence of events that follows depolarization of cells in the **sinoatrial node** of the heart.
6.  Describe how an electrocardiogram is **recorded** and list the **twelve leads**.
7.  **Draw an electrocardiogram**, label its components, and describe what they represent.
8.  Define a cardiac **arrhythmia** (dysrhythmia).
9.  List the five **areas** of the heart that can give rise to cardiac arrhythmia (dysrhythmia).
10. Describe and distinguish first, second and third degree **A-V block**.
11. Describe what is meant by **bundle branch block**, and describe some possible consequences.
12. Describe at least three cardiac arrhythmias (dysrhythmias), including one that is life-threatening.
13. Explain why **cocaine abuse** can have lethal effects on the heart.
14. Explain the significance of a **lengthened P-R interval**.
15. Following what event might you see an elevated or depressed **S-T segment**, possibly with an **inverted T wave** and an **increased Q wave**?
16. Discuss the effects and mechanism of action of the drugs called **beta-blockers**.
17. Describe and explain commotio cordis.

## I. Action Potential of a Cardiac Muscle Cell

The potentials illustrated here are recorded intracellularly. A glass micropipette electrode with a tip diameter of 10–20 micrometers is filled with NaCl or KCl solution and a chlorided silver wire is inserted down the center. The wire is connected to a recording and display device.

To carry out the recording, the tip of the micropipette is advanced until it contacts the plasma membrane of the cell, then with a sharp movement it penetrates into the cell interior. At this point, the recorded potential abruptly changes from zero to the resting potential of the cell (in Figure 25-1, this is shown as −70 mV).

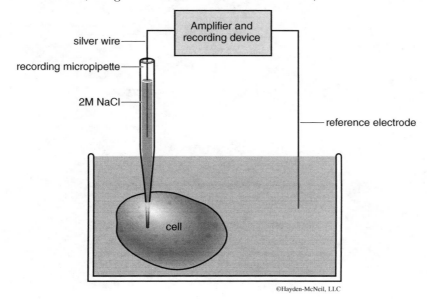

©Hayden-McNeil, LLC

529

**Figure 25-1.**

The action potentials of single cardiac muscle cells vary in shape, depending on the cell. Figure 25-2 gives three examples—ventricle, S-A node and atrium. For starters, we shall concentrate on the action potential measured in a cell from one of the ventricles.

There are two important differences between the action potential of a cardiac muscle cell and that of a skeletal muscle cell or of a nerve.

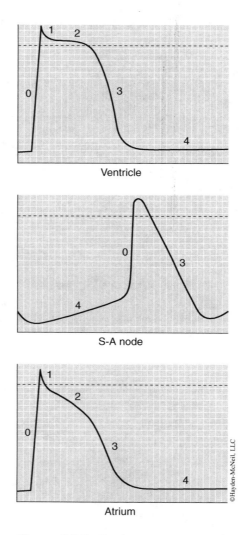

**Figure 25-2.** Cardiac action potentials.

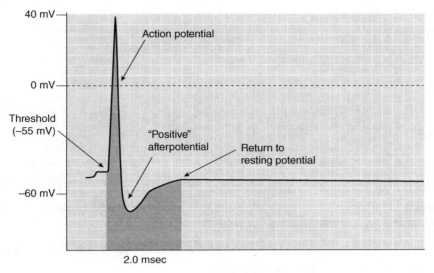

**Nerve action potential**

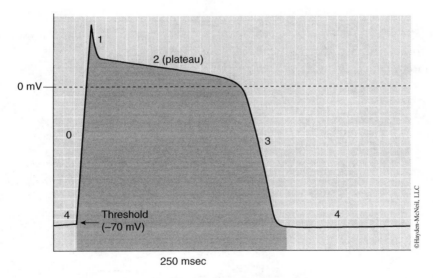

**Cardiac muscle action potential**
(Note difference in shape and duration)

**Figure 25-3.** Nerve vs. cardiac muscle action potentials.

- **Duration.**

  A cardiac action potential lasts as long as 250 milliseconds, whereas a skeletal muscle or nerve action potential lasts only a few milliseconds (a millisecond is 1/1000 of a second).

- **Shape.**

  A cardiac muscle action potential has a very pronounced *plateau*, which is not present in a skeletal muscle or nerve action potential.

## A. Phases of the Cardiac Action Potential

The phases of the action potential of a single cardiac muscle cell are shown in Figure 25-3.

- **Phase 0** is the same as nerve or skeletal muscle. It is caused by the rapid **opening** of the usual **voltage-gated sodium channels**.

- **Phase 1** is also similar to nerve and skeletal muscle, and is due to the **closing** of the **voltage-gated sodium channels**.

- **Phase 2** (the plateau) – *this is the phase that makes cardiac muscle different.* The sarcolemma of cardiac muscle, unlike nerve and skeletal muscle plasma membranes, has a very large population of slow, **voltage-gated calcium channels**. These calcium channels open at the beginning of Phase 2 and remain open throughout the plateau part of the action potential. During this period, calcium ions flow into the cell.

Unlike skeletal muscle, there is also a **reduction of potassium permeability** of the membrane, which lasts throughout the plateau phase of the cardiac action potential.

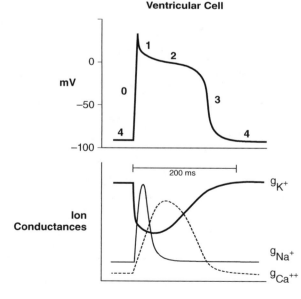

**Figure 25-4.**

**Excitation-contraction coupling** – the calcium that enters the myocardial cells during the plateau phase triggers the release of calcium from the sarcoplasmic reticulum, causing an increase in the calcium concentration of the sarcoplasm. As in skeletal muscle, this calcium binds to troponin, which then causes a conformational change in tropomyosin that permits myosin to bind to actin, causing the muscle to contract. Note that these events take time, and therefore the electrical changes always precede the mechanical response.

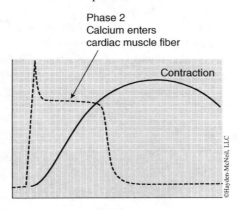

**Figure 25-5.** Excitation–contraction coupling.

**Catecholamines (epinephrine and norepinephrine)**, which are released at sympathetic nerve terminals or from the adrenal medulla during sympathetic activation, increase the inward calcium current. This is how sympathetic stimulation enhances cardiac contractility.

**Beta-blockers** – the action of catecholamines on the heart is blocked by a group of drugs called beta-blockers. They derive their name from the fact that they bind to, and block, β-adrenergic receptors. These drugs are used clinically to moderate the effect of sympathetic stimulation on the heart, which includes acceleration of heart rate and increased contractility of the cardiac muscle cells. This decreases the strain on the heart during stress, and diminishes the frequency and severity of **anginal** attacks (see later).

- **Phase 3** is due to the **closing** of the slow calcium channels, and is accompanied by an increase of potassium permeability back to normal.

- **Phase 4** represents the resting potential.

During most of the plateau phase (2), the arrival of a second depolarizing impulse has no effect—this period is called the ***effective refractory period***. Because it lasts for quite a long time, cardiac muscle cannot display tetanus when stimulated at high frequency, as is observed in skeletal muscle.

## B. Pacemaker Cells

The heart beats in response to a continuous train of electrical signals (action potentials) generated by rhythmic depolarization of a special region in the posterior wall of the right atrium below the opening of the superior vena cava. This region is often called the **pacemaker**, and its anatomical name is the **sinoatrial node** (or S-A node).

The cells in the S-A node are specialized cardiac muscle fibers containing very few contractile elements. They are capable of entirely *spontaneous*, *rhythmic* depolarization and repolarization. They are continuous with the true muscle fibers of the atrium, and therefore any action potentials that begin in the S-A node spread immediately into the myocardium of the atria, causing the two atria to contract almost simultaneously. As we shall see in the next section, this wave of depolarization ultimately spreads via special pathways into the ventricles and into the ventricular myocardium.

Pacemaker cells are rather different from other cells. They are always leaky to sodium ions, and this tends to depolarize them. Further, unlike nerve and skeletal muscle fibers, their action potentials are **NOT** generated by voltage-gated sodium channels, but by voltage-gated **calcium** channels.

The rhythmic and spontaneous depolarization that is seen in pacemaker cells depends on a very complex interplay between channels for **sodium**, **calcium** and **potassium**. These channels can be affected both by drugs and by neurotransmitters of the autonomic nervous system. Parasympathetic and sympathetic stimulation alter the rate of firing of the pacemaker cells by acting on the *potassium* channels.

- **Parasympathetic** stimulation releases **acetylcholine**, which binds to **muscarinic** receptors on the pacemaker cells and causes an increase in potassium permeability, lengthening the time it takes for an action potential to be generated. Therefore, the rhythmic activity of the sinoatrial node is slowed, and this *reduces* the heart rate. This action is blocked by **atropine.**

- **Sympathetic** stimulation releases **norepinephrine**, which binds to β-**adrenergic** receptors on the pacemaker cells and increases the rate of closure of voltage-gated potassium channels. This *increases* the heart rate.

If the cells in the S-A node fail, their pacemaker function is taken over by cells at the A-V node or even the Purkinje fibers. The rhythm of these cells is slower than that observed with the S-A node, and therefore the heart beats at a slower rate in these cases.

| | |
|---|---|
| Cells of the S-A node | = 60–90 beats per minute |
| Cells of the A-V node | = 40–60 beats per minute |
| Purkinje fibers | = 20–30 beats per minute |

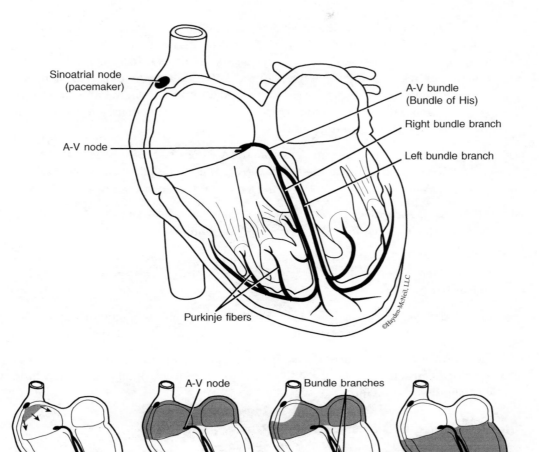

**Figure 25-6.** Heart conduction pathway.

## II. The Cardiac Pacemaker and Conduction System

Contraction of the myocardium is normally triggered by rhythmic depolarization of the pacemaker cells in the sinoatrial node. The wave of depolarization initiated by these cells spreads to the ventricles via specialized myocardial cells that make up the conduction system of the heart. The sequence of events is as follows:

1.  The cells in the **sinoatrial node** depolarize.

2.  A wave of depolarization spreads over the surface of the **atria**, causing them to contract.

3.  The wave of depolarization arrives at the *atrioventricular node (A-V node)*.

    Because the atria and ventricles are electrically insulated from each other by the fibrous four-ringed "skeleton of the heart," the wave of electrical depolarization can only reach the ventricles by passing through the A-V node.

When it hits the A-V node, the wave of depolarization suddenly slows down, causing a delay in conduction of the electrical pulse through the node. This delay (about 0.13 seconds) gives the atria time to contract before the ventricles start to contract. It is caused by the fact that the fibers of the A-V node are very **thin**, and therefore conduct electrical changes very slowly (just like in nerve, where conduction rate decreases as the diameter of the nerve fiber decreases). Also, there are very **few gap junctions** between the conducting cells.

4.  When the electrical impulse emerges from the A-V node it speeds up again as it enters the *A-V bundle* (also known as the *bundle of His*). The A-V bundle then divides into **left** and **right** *bundle branches*, which serve the left and right ventricles, respectively.

5.  The *Purkinje fibers* then carry the cardiac impulse at a speed of 2–4 meters per second into the inner, endocardial layer of myocardium.

6.  From the endocardial surface, excitation spreads outward at the slower rate of 0.3–0.5 meters per second through the thickness of the **myocardium** toward the epicardial surface.

Depolarizing impulses arrive via the Purkinje fibers almost simultaneously in all parts of the ventricles, so permitting these parts to contract synchronously.

After the myocardium has become depolarized, and has contracted, the process of repolarization begins. In humans, the apical surface of the myocardium repolarizes a little earlier than the basal region.

## III. Recording the Electrocardiogram

The pulsating electrical activity that occurs as the heart muscle contracts and relaxes sets up a flow of current in the chest resistance that may be detected as voltage by attaching electrical leads to the skin at a number of standard locations on the surface of the body.

An **electrocardiogram** can be recorded through any one of *twelve* leads.

*   Three *standard limb leads* are designated I, II, and III. They are attached to the two wrists and the left leg (a "ground" lead is usually attached to the right leg).

*   Six *chest leads* (= *precordial leads*) are attached to specific points on the chest wall, and are designated V1 through V6.

*   Three other leads are referred to as *augmented leads* (aVL, aVR, and aVF). They are obtained by connecting the three leads from the limbs in a different way.

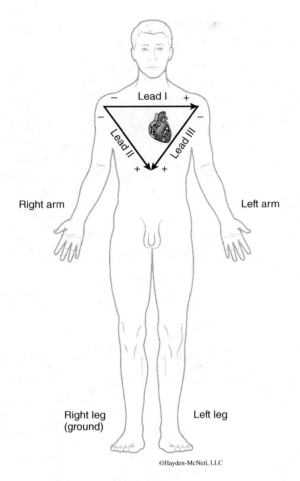

©Hayden-McNeil, LLC

**Figure 25-7.**

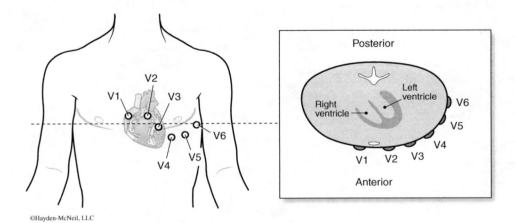

©Hayden-McNeil, LLC

**Figure 25-8.**

The leads are connected through a specially-designed electrical circuit to a sensitive and stable **amplifier** (you will see this in laboratory).

The output of the amplifier goes to a **recording** device—an oscilloscope, computer, or a pen that moves over a paper strip chart recorder. In our laboratory, the output goes into the computer, and the data can be printed out.

The electrical wave that is recorded on the strip chart (or is observed on the oscilloscope or computer screen) is called an **electrocardiogram** (**ECG** or **EKG**). Abnormalities in the ECG reflect abnormalities in the heart. By carefully examining the ECG, it is possible to determine whether the patient has a cardiac problem, where it is, what it is, and what to do about it.

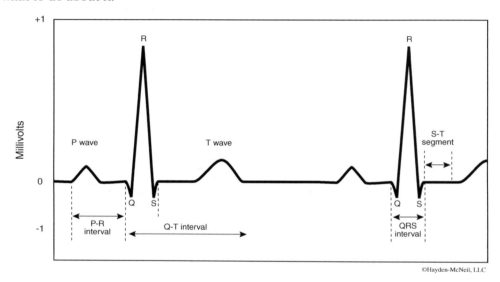

©Hayden-McNeil, LLC

**Figure 25-9.** Electrocardiogram.

## IV. The Electrocardiogram

A typical electrocardiogram consists of the following five major components. Because we are recording the massed depolarizations of many cardiac muscle cells at the surface of the body, the electrocardiogram does not look like the action potential of a single cardiac muscle cell.

- **P wave**
- **P-R interval**
- **QRS complex**
- **T wave**
- **S-T segment**

You are expected to know what these components represent in the cardiac cycle. There will be questions on them in the lecture examination and in the laboratory tests.

| Component of ECG | Origin |
|---|---|
| P wave | Depolarization of the atria, indicates S-A node function. *The onset of the P wave precedes the onset of atrial contraction.* |
| P-R interval | Indicative of the time it takes for the impulse to pass through the A-V node into the ventricles (atrioventricular conduction time). |
| QRS complex | Depolarization of the ventricles – the QRS duration indicates the time in which ventricular depolarization occurs. *The onset of the QRS wave precedes the onset of ventricular contraction.* |
| T wave | Repolarization of the ventricles, at which time they are ready to be stimulated again. |
| S-T segment | The part of the electrocardiogram between the S wave of the QRS complex and the T wave. Its elevation or depression with respect to the baseline can be important in diagnosing a ***myocardial infarction***. |
| PQRSTP | One complete cardiac cycle |

There is also a wave representing atrial repolarization, but it is buried in the much larger QRS complex wave that is caused by ventricular depolarization.

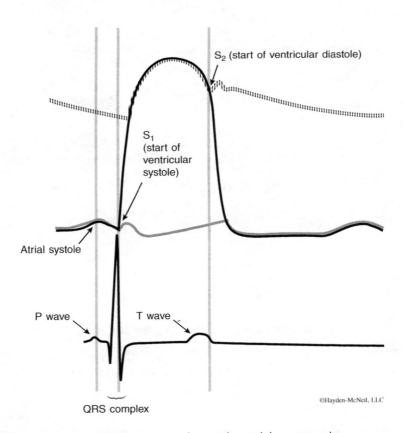

**Figure 25-10.** The electrocardiogram, cardiac cycle, and the intracardiac pressure curves.

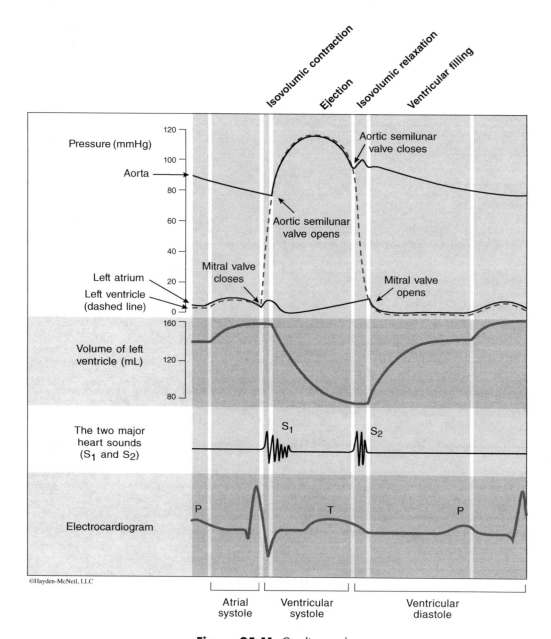

**Figure 25-11.** Cardiac cycle.

## V. Cardiac Arrhythmias (Dysrhythmias) and Conduction Problems— Some Examples

A **cardiac arrhythmia** (also known as a dysrhythmia) is an abnormal cardiac rate or rhythm.

Arrhythmias and conduction problems may be caused by a variety of conditions. Conditions that cause arrhythmias include lack of oxygen, drug effects, electrolyte imbalance and myocardial or conduction system damage due to myocardial ischemia.

Arrhythmias and conduction problems may arise from factors operating in the following areas.

- Sinus node = sinoatrial (S-A) node
- Atria
- A-V nodal (junctional)
- A-V block and bundle branch block
- Ventricles

## A. Sinus Node

1. **Sinus tachycardia** is an elevation in heart rate observed at rest. It is caused by an increased rate of depolarization and repolarization of the sinus node. The rhythm is often normal, but the rate is usually greater than 100 beats per minute. Sinus tachycardia may sometimes be a normal, physiological condition due to elevated body temperature or sympathetic stimulation. At other times, sinus tachycardia may be brought on by drugs or certain toxic conditions.

2. **Sinus bradycardia** is a slow heart rate at rest caused by a decreased rate of depolarization and repolarization of the sinus node. The heart rate is below 60 beats per minute, and may be quite normal in a trained athlete. In that event, the slow heart rate is probably caused in part by an increase in the frequency of nerve impulses in the parasympathetic vagus nerve.

## B. Atria

541

**Atrial flutter** is one example of an atrial arrhythmia. Atrial flutter can be caused by waves of depolarization circling around the bands of atrial muscle fibers. In atrial flutter, the atria may beat as fast as 250–300 beats per minute. Not all these impulses may succeed in passing through the A-V node, so the ventricular rate may be fairly regular and moderate (e.g. 75 beats per minute). Atrial flutter can progress to *atrial fibrillation*.

## C. A-V Nodal (Junctional)

**A-V nodal arrhythmias (junctional arrhythmias)** occur when various parts of the A-V node take over the pacemaker duties of the S-A node, possibly because of damage to the S-A node. Generally, the rate of the A-V node is lower than the rate of the S-A node, so the ventricles may beat at the rate of 40–60 beats per minute.

The P wave may be lost in the QRS complex and appear to be absent, or it may be inverted because the depolarization moves in a direction opposite to normal.

## D. A-V Block and Bundle Branch Block

In **A-V block** and *bundle branch block* the atrial rate is normal but there is a problem with conduction of the wave of depolarization from the atria to the ventricles or through one of the bundle branches.

Blocks occur when damage caused by a myocardial infarction, rheumatic fever or diphtheria (for example), or by drug toxicity leads to impaired conduction through the A-V node, the A-V bundle, or through the right or left bundle branches.

1. **First degree A-V block.**

   Each P wave is followed by a QRS but the P-R interval is prolonged (normally it is 0.2 seconds or less).

2. **Second degree A-V block.**

   This is an intermittent block. Some QRS are dropped, so that not every P wave is followed by a QRS. For example, every second atrial beat may fail to get through to the ventricles—therefore, the atrial rate will be twice the ventricular rate, and this particular example of a second degree block is called a 2:1 block.

3. **Third degree A-V block.**

   This is a complete heart block. The atria and ventricles beat independently of each other, so there is no relationship between the P waves and the QRS. The QRS rate always has a lower frequency than the P wave rate. For example, the Purkinje cells of the ventricles may take over as pacemakers and cause the ventricles to beat at between 20 and 30 times per minute (the atria, of course, will beat at their normal rate). This abnormally slow ventricular rate causes an inadequate cardiac output, and calls for immediate action by the cardiologist.

**Bundle branch block** – there can be a conduction delay or block in the bundle branches. Usually, bundle branch block is not total, but leads to a conduction delay. This means that one ventricle may depolarize somewhat later than the other, giving rise to a broadened QRS complex, or even one with two R waves. Since the two ventricles do not contract nearly synchronously, there will be abnormal "splitting" of the $S_1$ heart sound and also abnormal "splitting" of the $S_2$ heart sound (**WHY?**—think about that for a moment).

## E. Ventricles

Arrhythmias of the ventricles are always serious. The ventricles are the chambers that pump blood into the aorta, and if the heart is to function efficiently as a blood pump, the contraction of the ventricles must be properly coordinated.

1. **Premature ventricular contraction (PVC).**

   One example of a ventricular arrhythmia is called a premature ventricular contraction (PVC). This occurs before it is expected in a normal series of ECGs. Premature ventricular contractions often generate wide and bizarre QRS complexes that do not have a preceding P wave.

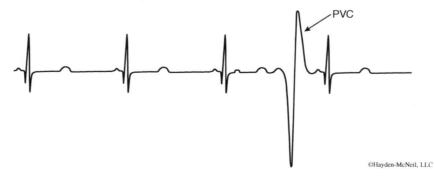

©Hayden-McNeil, LLC

**Figure 25-12.** ECG illustrating ventricular arrhythmia.

A premature ventricular contraction is caused by what is called an ***ectopic focus*** in one of the ventricles. An ectopic focus is a small region of the ventricular myocardium that decides to depolarize all on its own, possibly because of inflammatory disease, lack of blood or drugs. The depolarization from such an ectopic focus may then travel throughout the myocardium of the ventricles, causing the ventricles to contract.

In itself, a premature ventricular contraction is not life-threatening. However, it has the *potential to be dangerous* if it occurs during the ventricular repolarizing phase. This *vulnerable* phase corresponds to the point in the ECG when the T wave is being generated.

The danger arises because at this time some of the cells are repolarized and therefore excitable, while others are still refractory.

2.  **Ventricular tachycardia.**

    If an ectopic focus generates a depolarizing stimulus during the T wave, it can set up circular waves of depolarization that pass repeatedly around the ventricular walls. This can cause ventricular tachycardia, where the ventricles can beat at 250–350 contractions per minute. Under these conditions, the pumping efficiency of the heart is very poor because the ventricles do not have time to fill and empty properly.

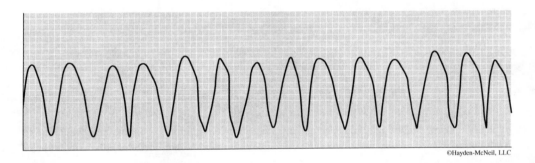

©Hayden-McNeil, LLC

**Figure 25-13.** ECG illustrating ventricular tachycardia.

3.  **Ventricular fibrillation.**

    Ventricular tachycardia can lead to the lethal condition known as ventricular fibrillation. The electrical record in ventricular fibrillation is rapid and chaotic. Parts of the myocardium contract at random, and without any coordination. Consequently, the heart no longer pumps blood, and death will follow unless action is taken.

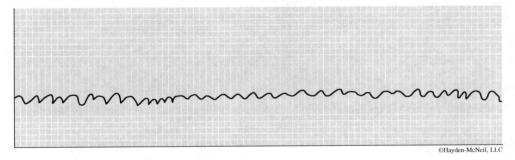

©Hayden-McNeil, LLC

**Figure 25-14.** ECG illustrating ventricular fibrillation.

543

The only effective treatment for a fibrillation episode is to use a **defibrillator** to administer a **direct-current shock** to the thoracic region over the heart. This defibrillating shock stimulates and depolarizes all parts of the ventricle simultaneously, and causes the whole myocardium to become refractory at the same time. All activity stops, then after 3–5 seconds the heart may begin to beat normally again, either with the S-A node or another pacemaker.

Revival after a fibrillation episode may be facilitated by first administering *cardiopulmonary resuscitation* or *CPR*. The purpose is to force oxygenated blood into the aorta and more importantly into the coronary circulation. A defibrillating shock may then be successful, because some oxygenated blood is available for use by the reactivated myocardium. As usually applied, CPR is a combination of rescue breathing and chest compression. There has been recent discussion concerning the effectiveness of rescue breathing versus compression only.

### Commotio cordis
Sudden death from Vfib triggered by a precordial blow to the chest wall (ball, puck, kick). Young athletes lacking adequate chest protection are most at risk. The "window of vulnerability" is during the period when only a part of the ventricular myocardium is repolarized, just before the peak of the T wave.

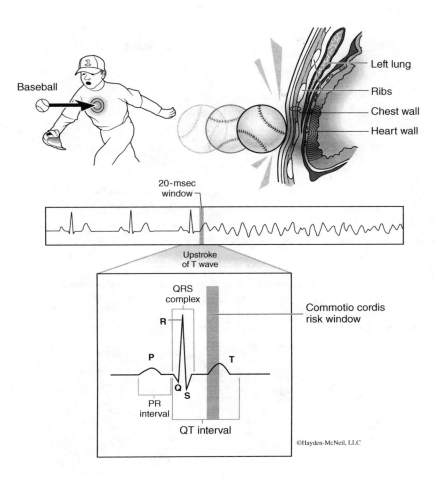

**Commotio cordis –** a sharp blow to the chest during the "vulnerable period" of the ECG (on the rising phase of the T wave) can trigger ventricular fibrillation.

The vulnerable period is a time when some parts of the ventricles have repolarized, but others are still depolarized. Less than one person in five survives.

**Figure 25-15.** Commotio cordis.

## VI. Changes in the Electrocardiogram Following a Myocardial Infarction

A *myocardial infarction* is a *heart attack*. It is caused by part of the myocardium receiving insufficient blood, possibly because of blockage or thrombosis of a coronary artery. The result is injury or death of cardiac muscle cells.

Following a myocardial infarction, it is possible that changes will be observed in one or more of three regions of the electrocardiogram.

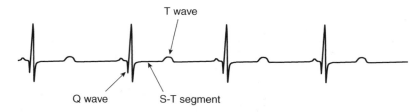

**Figure 25-16.** The three regions of the electrocardiogram that can be affected following a myocardial infarction.

1.  **S-T segment** – the S-T segment can be important diagnostically. Normally, this part of the ECG is close to the baseline (that is, it is "isoelectric"). However, it may be elevated or depressed following a myocardial infarction. If the S-T segment becomes elevated or depressed during a stress test, this indicates that the person may be at risk for a myocardial infarction.

2.  **T wave** – the T wave may be inverted after a myocardial infarction.

3.  **Q wave** – the Q wave may increase in size following a myocardial infarction (cardiologists sometimes speak of this as a "Q wave infarction").

546

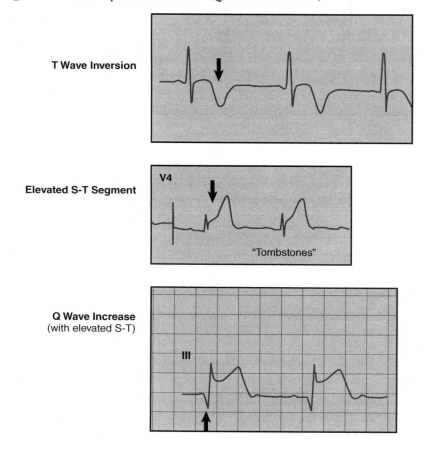

**Figure 25-17.** Reading an ECG.

## VII. Cocaine and the Heart

Death from cocaine abuse is usually caused by lethal cardiac events, including myocardial infarction, ventricular fibrillation and other rhythm disorders. Partly this is caused by direct action on the heart (cocaine is a local anesthetic that blocks sodium channels) and also to the fact that cocaine can potentiate the effects of sympathetic stimulation by **inhibiting the reuptake of norepinephrine** at axon terminals in the heart (similar to its action on dopamine in the limbic system). An increase in the levels of norepinephrine in the heart can cause premature depolarization events, such as a premature ventricular contraction, leading to fibrillation and death.

**Central Importance of the ECG in Patient Evaluation in the Emergency Department**

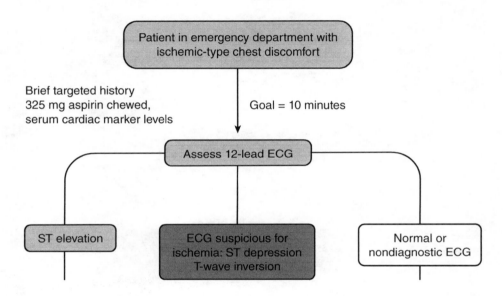

**Figure 25-18.**

548

# CARDIOVASCULAR SYSTEM IV
Blood Vessels, Capillaries and the Control of Blood Pressure

## CHAPTER OUTLINE

## DESCRIPTION AND INTRODUCTION

First of all, we shall review the structure of blood vessels. Then we discuss how the capillaries function in the transfer of substances between the circulating blood and the interstitial fluid that bathes the cells of the body. We then consider the factors that affect blood flow through tissues and that influence blood pressure.

Finally, we discuss the control of blood pressure. A knowledge of the factors that control blood pressure is very important to an understanding of the causes and treatment of *hypertension*, dealt with in the next chapter.

## OBJECTIVES

First of all, from the earlier chapters on the cardiovascular system you should be able to:

- List the six basic types of blood vessels.
- Describe the organization of the circulatory system.
- Describe the structure of each type of blood vessel.

Make sure you can do the above three objectives before proceeding with the following objectives, which are based primarily on the present material.

1. Explain the **resistance** of the circulatory system.
2. Explain the **capacity** of the circulatory system.
3. **Draw a diagram** of the circulatory system, and indicate the peripheral resistance and capacity components.
4. Describe what is meant by the **venous pump**, and describe **varicose veins**.
5. Describe (**with a diagram**) the structure of a **capillary bed.**
6. Describe how materials **move in** and **out** of capillaries.
7. Describe the factors that influence the fluid content of the **interstitial space**.
8. Describe the four causes of **edema**.
9. Describe one cause of **pulmonary** edema and its consequences.
10. Explain how **blood flow** through tissues is affected by different factors.
11. Describe **angiogenesis** and its importance in health and disease.
12. Describe what is meant by an **angiogenic factor**.
13. List four factors that determine **blood pressure**.
14. Describe the two basic **systems** that govern blood pressure.
15. Explain the **baroreceptor reflex**, and describe its functional importance.
16. Describe the reflex that represents the "last-ditch stand" by the brain in a case of **severe hemorrhage**.
17. **Draw a diagram** illustrating how the baroreceptor reflex operates if blood pressure suddenly increases above normal.
18. **Draw a diagram** illustrating how the baroreceptor reflex operates if blood pressure suddenly decreases below normal.
19. Describe what you think would happen to the blood pressure if the **sensory nerves from the baroreceptors were cut**.
20. Define **active hyperemia.**

21. Name four **vasoconstrictors** and two **vasodilators**.

22. Explain **orthostatic hypotension** and **Shy-Drager syndrome**.

23. Name the different **types** of capillary, and in what **tissues** they are found.

24. Describe the **renin-angiotensin-aldosterone** system, and draw a diagram illustrating how it operates (in other words, be able to draw *from memory* the diagram in these notes).

25. List the two actions of **angiotensin II**.

## I. The Four Variables of the Cardiovascular System

1. The heart (cardiac output)

2. Total peripheral resistance = systemic vascular resistance

3. Capacity

4. Blood volume

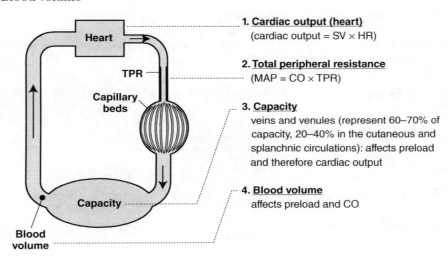

**1. Cardiac output (heart)**
(cardiac output = SV × HR)

**2. Total peripheral resistance**
(MAP = CO × TPR)

**3. Capacity**
veins and venules (represent 60–70% of capacity, 20–40% in the cutaneous and splanchnic circulations): affects preload and therefore cardiac output

**4. Blood volume**
affects preload and CO

551

**Figure 26-1.** The four variables that control mean arterial pressure.

## II. Blood Vessels—Capacity and Resistance

The various blood vessels of the cardiovascular system exercise an important influence on its **capacity** to hold fluid and its **resistance** to blood flow. The **arterioles** are mainly involved in determining the resistance segment of the circulation, while the **veins** determine the capacity.

Resistance and capacity are *variable*. Sympathetic stimulation can:

* increase the resistance by causing vasoconstriction of the arterioles.
* decrease the capacity of the system by causing vasoconstriction of the veins.

## A. Resistance of the Circulatory System—Importance of the Arterioles

The arterioles control the blood **flow** into the capillary beds and into the collecting muscular and non-muscular venules and veins. They also control the **total peripheral resistance**. In consequence, the arterioles are sometimes referred to as the *resistance vessels* of the cardiovascular system, and the total peripheral resistance depends on whether they are undergoing vasoconstriction or vasodilation.

A chronic elevation of the total peripheral resistance by narrowing of the lumens of the arterioles appears to be the important factor that elevates the blood pressure in **hypertension** (see later). Many drugs for treating hypertension act by reducing the total peripheral resistance. That is, they dilate the arterioles.

The mean arterial pressure (what we usually refer to simply as "blood pressure") varies in proportion to cardiac output and total peripheral resistance. This statement can be expressed in the following equation.

**mean arterial pressure = cardiac output × total peripheral resistance**

For example, an increase in total peripheral resistance with unchanged cardiac output will elevate the mean arterial pressure (= blood pressure).

## B. Capacity of the Circulatory System—Importance of the Veins

The average human being has a total of about 5.2 liters of blood in the body. This is distributed as follows.

| Lungs | 10–12% |
|---|---|
| Heart | 8–11% |
| Systemic arteries | 10–12% |
| Capillaries | 4–5% |
| Systemic veins and venules | 60–70% |

The systemic veins and venules contain about two thirds of the blood in the body. Therefore, the veins and venules control the **capacity** of the circulation. The venous capacity is relatively small in muscles and the kidney, but relatively large in the *skin* and in the *gastrointestinal tract*.

The veins and venules are important in *hemorrhage*. Loss of blood usually leads to activation of the sympathetic nervous system and arteriolar vasoconstriction, which can cause a decrease in pressure downstream in the veins. Loss of distending pressure will allow the natural *elastic recoil* of the veins to cause venous capacity to decrease *passively*. Additionally, there may be *active* constriction of the veins *via* the sympathetic nervous system, which can further reduce the capacity of the circulation and assist in maintaining the blood pressure.

After a *hemorrhage (loss of blood)*, the **capacity** of the veins and venules in the systemic circulation (particularly in the skin and gastrointestinal tract) is **reduced**. This compensates for the reduction of blood volume, and assists in the maintenance of cardiac output and arterial blood pressure. We will discuss this in more detail later.

### C. "Venous Pump"

The venous pump operates in three regions of the body. The first is the plantar pump, which is driven by changing pressure on the soles of the feet during walking. The second is the muscular pump of the legs. This is made possible because the long veins of the arms and legs contain flap-like **valves** that project inward from their linings. These valves have two semilunar leaflets that are arranged so that the direction of blood flow can only be toward the heart. When the muscles of the legs or arms contract, they massage the veins and help to propel the blood toward the heart.

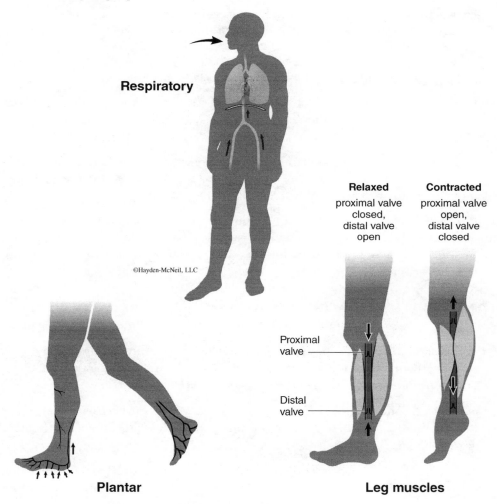

**Figure 26-2.** The venous pump.

If you stand absolutely still, the pumping doesn't occur. Pressure in the veins and capillaries then increases. The feet and legs swell because fluid leaks out from the capillaries into the tissue spaces (the effect is called *edema*). This effect can also be observed during periods of sitting without leg movement on long airline trips.

The third pumping system is the respiratory pump, which is driven by changing pressures in the thoracic cavity during respiration.

*Varicose veins*—the valves in the long veins of the legs do not function properly and pressure in the veins increases. Increased venous pressure leads to leakage of fluid from the capillaries, which causes edema in the legs when one has been standing for a few minutes. There is progressive distortion of the veins. The condition prevents adequate diffusion of nutritional materials from the capillaries to the muscle and skin cells, leading to painful and weak muscles and skin ulceration.

## III. The Capillary Bed

The capillary bed is the place in the circulatory system where exchange of substances can occur between the blood and the interstitial fluid that fills the space around the cells of the body.

### A. Structure of a Capillary Bed

Capillaries branch off from **terminal arterioles**. The terminal arterioles are intermediate in structure between arterioles and capillaries, and have some smooth muscle in their walls.

At the point where the true capillaries originate from the terminal arterioles, one or two smooth muscle fibers encircle the capillary. This is called the *precapillary sphincter*, which can open up or close down the entrance to the capillary.

Blood from the capillaries is collected by venules. At first, the venules have little or no muscle in their walls, and are called **non-muscular venules**. As they approach the veins, however, the amount of muscle increases, they become larger in diameter and they are called **muscular venules**.

### B. How Materials Move in and out of Capillaries

Capillaries in various parts of the body differ in the structure of their endothelial walls.

*   In the **brain** and **retina**, the vascular endothelial cells are relatively tall, and connected by **tight junctions** that prevent many substances from passing through them. They constitute a barrier called the *blood-brain barrier* (see below).

*   In the **liver, bone marrow** and **spleen**, the vascular endothelial cells have enormous gaps between them. These gaps allow proteins and other large molecules to move through them.

*   In the **skin, muscle, lungs, gastrointestinal tract, many glands** and in the **kidneys** the walls of the capillaries lie between these two extremes and will be discussed in more detail later.

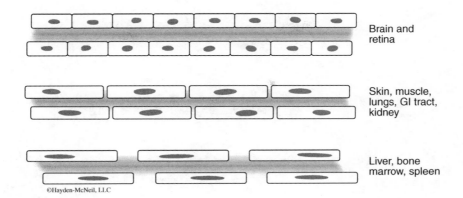

Brain and retina

Skin, muscle, lungs, GI tract, kidney

Liver, bone marrow, spleen

©Hayden-McNeil, LLC

**Figure 26-3.** Three types of capillaries and their locations.

Substances move across the walls of the last group of capillaries by three processes.

1. **Diffusion.**

   Diffusion is a passive process that causes substances to move down their concentration gradients. Substances such as carbon dioxide and oxygen are lipid-soluble and diffuse through the endothelial cell wall of the capillary, carbon dioxide inward and oxygen outward. There is no net transfer of water by this process.

   Other, water-soluble substances diffuse out from the capillary through *pores* that are actually clefts between two endothelial cells. In general, no protein escapes from the capillaries, except when the pores are very large (in liver, spleen and bone marrow).

   ***Blood-brain barrier*** – there are no pores in the capillaries of the cerebral and retinal circulations, where there is a blood-brain barrier that prevents many small molecules (e.g. certain hormones) from getting into the brain. Special carrier molecules in the membrane ensure that essential nutrients such as glucose and amino acids can be delivered to the brain's cells.

2. **Pinocytosis.**

   Small quantities of substances with large, lipid-insoluble molecules are transferred across the capillary wall by pinocytosis. Pinocytotic vesicles are formed by pinching off of the plasma membrane.

3. **Filtration (movement of fluid).**

   Filtration is the principal mechanism for controlling the balance between interstitial fluid volume and plasma volume. The filtrate passing out of a capillary wall consists mainly of water, ions and small solutes. It contains negligible quantities of plasma proteins.

   Net protein osmotic and hydrostatic forces determine the extent and direction of capillary filtration (see next page).

555

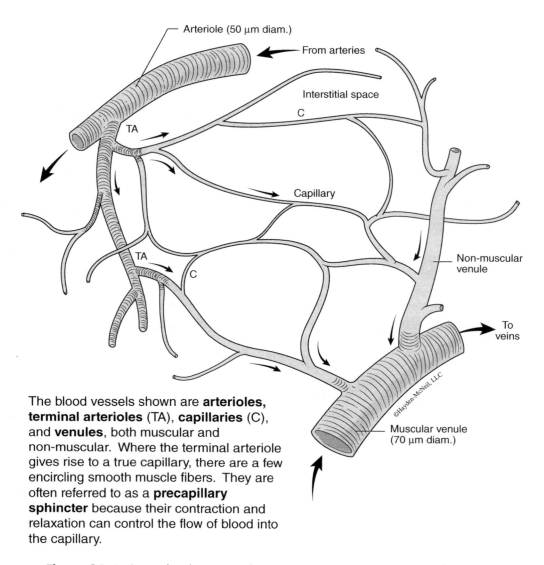

The blood vessels shown are **arterioles, terminal arterioles** (TA), **capillaries** (C), and **venules**, both muscular and non-muscular. Where the terminal arteriole gives rise to a true capillary, there are a few encircling smooth muscle fibers. They are often referred to as a **precapillary sphincter** because their contraction and relaxation can control the flow of blood into the capillary.

**Figure 26-4.** Generalized structure of a capillary bed with associated blood vessels.

### C. How Capillaries Function in the Exchange of Fluid between the Blood and the Interstitial Space

- The main force that drives fluid OUT of a capillary is the **blood pressure** (hydrostatic pressure) inside the capillary. The pressure inside the capillary is opposed by the pressure of the interstitial fluid, which is normally negligible but can be increased in inflammation (see BIOL 204 notes, next semester).

- The main force that draws fluid INTO a capillary is the blood osmotic pressure, which is higher in the blood than in the interstitial fluid because the blood contains *proteins* which are lacking in the interstitial fluid (*salt* concentration is the same in blood and interstitial fluid, so the osmotic pressures due to salt cancel out). The blood protein osmotic pressure (= blood *oncotic* pressure) is opposed by the interstitial fluid protein osmotic pressure, which is normally less than that of the blood unless there has been extensive leakage of proteins from the blood into the interstitial space, as could happen in inflammation.

The balance between these forces determines whether fluid enters the capillary from the interstitial space or leaves the capillary and enters the interstitial space.

Generally speaking, the blood pressure at the **arterial** end of a capillary is greater than the blood osmotic pressure. Therefore, fluid leaves the capillary at its arterial end.

On the other hand, the blood pressure at the **venous** end is less than the blood osmotic pressure. Therefore, fluid is withdrawn from the interstitial space into the blood at the venous end of a capillary.

At some point in between, there is no net flow either inward or outward.

Normally, a little more fluid leaves the capillaries than returns to them. About 10% remains in the interstitial space. The excess is collected as *lymph* by a network of *lymphatics*, blind-ended vessels with valves, and returned to the venous circulation near the junction of the subclavian and internal jugular veins (the lymphatic system will be discussed next semester).

Flow across the capillary wall is governed mainly by the hydrostatic pressure inside the **capillary, which tends to drive fluid out, and the protein osmotic pressure of the blood (the oncotic pressure),** which tends to draw fluid back in.

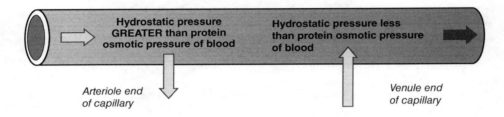

Hydrostatic pressure GREATER than protein osmotic pressure of blood

Hydrostatic pressure less than protein osmotic pressure of blood

Arteriole end of capillary

Venule end of capillary

Net Flow is out of the capillary at the arteriole end, and into the capillary at the venule end.

10% does not return to the venule and is removed by the lymphatics

**Figure 26-5.** Fluid exchange across the capillary wall.

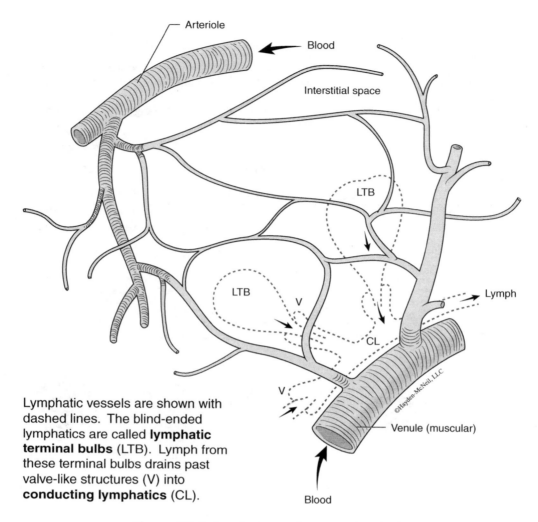

558

Lymphatic vessels are shown with dashed lines. The blind-ended lymphatics are called **lymphatic terminal bulbs** (LTB). Lymph from these terminal bulbs drains past valve-like structures (V) into **conducting lymphatics** (CL).

**Figure 26-6.** Lymphatic vessels in a capillary bed.

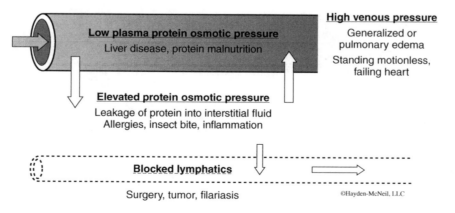

**Figure 26-7.** Four causes of edema.

## D. Edema

**Edema** is tissue swelling caused when an abnormal excess of fluid builds up in the interstitial space. You need to know the four principal causes of edema.

1.  **Increased venous hydrostatic pressure**
    *   standing for a long time
    *   failing heart

    Simply standing for a long time without moving the leg muscles can impair the venous pump and raise the pressure at the venous end of the capillaries in the legs and feet, causing edema in this part of the body (see previous page). Edema can also be caused by increased pressure in the veins produced by a failing heart.

2.  **Reduced plasma osmotic pressure**
    *   malnutrition
    *   liver disease

    Loss of plasma proteins in malnutrition and liver disease cause edema because of the decrease in the plasma protein osmotic pressure.

3.  **Increased interstitial fluid osmotic pressure**
    *   buildup of proteins in the interstitial space

    Substances that increase the permeability of the capillary walls to plasma proteins also cause edema. The plasma proteins accumulate in the interstitial fluid, and therefore increase the interstitial fluid protein osmotic pressure. Histamine, which is released during inflammation (see next semester), is an example of a substance that has this effect on capillary walls.

4.  **Blocked lymphatics**
    *   surgery
    *   tumor
    *   parasitic infection (*filariasis*)

## E. Pulmonary Edema

Efficient gas exchange in the lungs requires that the surfaces of the air sacs in the lungs (the *alveoli*) be kept dry and free of accumulated fluid.

As with other tissues, there is a small, continuous leak of fluid out of the lung capillaries into the interstitial space surrounding the cells in the lung. This fluid is normally removed by a gentle suction effect by the lymphatic vessels, which also sucks the air sacs dry.

*Pulmonary edema* can be caused by a rise in pressure in the capillaries. One cause is **failure of the left ventricle**—the right ventricle continues to pump blood into the lungs, but the left ventricle cannot pump it away at the same rate. Therefore, there is a rise of pressure in the pulmonary veins, and therefore in the pulmonary capillaries.

Because efficient gas exchange cannot occur across the swollen respiratory membrane, death due to pulmonary edema can occur very quickly.

## IV. Factors that Affect Blood Flow through Tissues

### A. Local Regulation of Blood Flow

The smooth muscle fibers of the terminal arterioles and precapillary sphincters are only sparsely innervated by the autonomic nervous system. They are controlled by **local** factors within the tissue. Local factors that have a vasodilator effect and increase blood flow through a capillary bed include the following.

1. High carbon dioxide
2. Low oxygen
3. Low pH (e.g. from accumulation of lactic acid in the tissue)
4. Other agents that need not concern us here

An increase in metabolic rate would generate more carbon dioxide, reduce the amount of oxygen, and reduce the pH because of formation of lactic acid. Therefore, as the metabolic rate of a tissue increases, we see an increase in the blood flow through that tissue. For example, the blood flow through a muscle increases during exercise, when the metabolic rate of the muscle increases. Also, the blood flow through regions of the brain increases when those regions become very active during mental activity.

The increase in blood flow through a tissue that has become more metabolically active is called **active hyperemia** (*metabolic hyperemia*).

### B. Hormones and Other Related Chemicals

There are many compounds that have important vasodilator and vasoconstrictor effects on blood vessels. An understanding of how these substances function is essential if we are to achieve effective methods of treatment for peripheral vascular disease, particularly hypertension.

1. **Vasoconstrictors**

   Important *vasoconstrictors* include:

   a. **Norepinephrine** and **epinephrine** (*catecholamines*) – norepinephrine is released at sympathetic nerve terminals, and both norepinephrine and epinephrine are released into the blood by the adrenal gland.

   b. **Angiotensin II** (an eight amino acid peptide involved in the renin-angiotensin-aldosterone system – see later).

   c. **Vasopressin** (released from the pituitary gland – next semester).

   d. **Endothelin** (secreted by the vascular endothelial cells).

2. **Vasodilators**

   Important *vasodilators* include:

   a. **Nitric oxide** is a vasodilator that has attracted a lot of attention recently. Like the vasoconstrictor endothelin mentioned above, nitric oxide is produced by the vascular endothelium and may be important in the maintenance of normal blood pressure. It is also important in penile erection.

   b.  **Histamine** is released from mast cells in allergic reactions (histamine also increases the porosity of the capillary wall, an effect that is unrelated to its vasodilator action).

There are also a variety of vasodilator drugs that are used therapeutically. They include *nitroglycerin, nitrites, hydralazine,* and agents used in hypertensive therapies such as *calcium channel blockers* and *angiotensin receptor blockers*.

## C. Nervous Control

Generally, the effects of the parasympathetic nervous system on blood vessels are not important (but see next semester, when we discuss the reproductive system). However, stimulation of the sympathetic nervous system has a very potent vasoconstrictor effect on those blood vessels that receive sympathetic innervation (not all blood vessels are innervated, however).

Sympathetic arteriolar vasoconstriction is especially potent in the **kidneys, gut, spleen** and **skin**. It is less important in the blood vessels supplying the skeletal muscles, brain and myocardium (coronary circulation), all of which are under overriding local control related to their metabolic activity.

The sympathetic sends a constant stream of nerve impulses to the blood vessels, causing a continual ***sympathetic vasoconstrictor tone***. Sympathetic tone maintains the total peripheral resistance. This tone is lost if the spinal cord is severed or if transmission in the spinal cord is blocked with a local anesthetic. This causes a large drop in the total peripheral resistance, and the blood pressure can drop dangerously.

Sympathetic stimulation causes release of epinephrine and norepinephrine by the adrenal glands. These substances pass into the circulation and cause vasoconstriction in blood vessels that lack a sympathetic innervation (e.g. terminal arterioles).

Don't forget the actions of the autonomic nervous system on the **heart**. Sympathetic stimulation increases the force of contraction and accelerates the rate. Parasympathetic stimulation slows the heart but has a negligible effect on the force of contraction of the ventricles.

561

## V. Growth of New Blood Vessels

## A. Angiogenesis

Over many days and weeks, there may be a change in the number of blood vessels in a tissue (i.e. a change in the tissue **vascularity**). There can be an increase in tissue vascularity if there has been a prolonged increase in metabolic rate of a tissue. An example is a rapidly growing tumor, which becomes invaded by blood vessels (see the following page). The development or growth of new blood vessels is called ***angiogenesis***, and the process seems to be regulated by a class of peptides called ***angiogenic factors***.

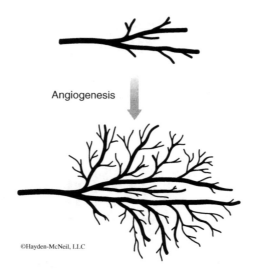

Angiogenesis

©Hayden-McNeil, LLC

**Figure 26-8.** Angiogenesis.

## B. Angiogenic Factors

Angiogenic factors work on the vascular endothelial cells that make up the inner walls of blood vessels, notably the capillaries. An example of one of these factors is *vascular endothelial growth factor* (VEGF). Endothelial cells always have the capacity to multiply under suitable conditions, and will even migrate and multiply to line plastic tubing used surgically to replace damaged blood vessels. The cells that surround capillaries—*pericytes*—seem to have an important role to play here, because they normally prevent the endothelial cells from multiplying.

## C. Importance of Angiogenesis

The process of angiogenesis is important in the following cases.

1.  Development of blood vessels in *ischemic tissue* (blood-deficient tissue).

2.  In *deep wounds* where there is little oxygen ("hypoxic wounds": one of the angiogenic factors is now being used clinically to promote angiogenesis in such wounds, and accelerate healing).

3.  During *embryonic* development.

4.  During the *menstrual cycle*.

Under *physiological* conditions, the process of angiogenesis is highly regulated—the production of angiogenic factors may be turned on in response to a number of stimuli, of which low *oxygen* seems to be one of the most important. However, many *disease* states seem to be driven by unregulated angiogenesis.

*For example –*

- In *tumors*, where the new vessels not only provide nourishment for the growing tumor but also provide new gateways for *metastasis*. Quantitation of angiogenesis in biopsy specimens of breast cancer has been used as an indication of future metastatic risk.

- In *arthritis*, new blood vessels invade the joint and destroy the cartilage.

- In *diabetes* (diabetic retinopathy).

- *Ocular neovascularization*, such as retrolental fibroplasia, a condition of vascular proliferation in the retinas of infants (usually premature infants) that have been exposed to high oxygen conditions and then placed in an atmosphere that contains a normal level of oxygen.

## VI. Factors that Determine Blood Pressure

The term **blood pressure** in the context of the present discussion refers to the **mean systemic arterial blood pressure** (**MAP**).

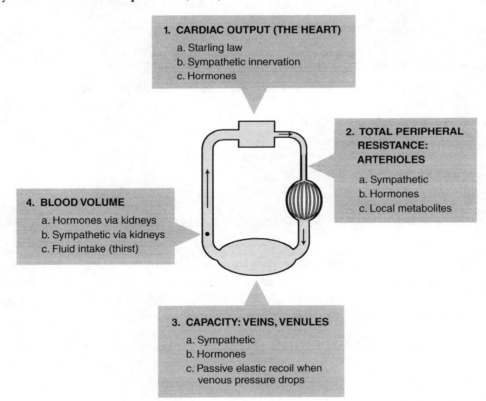

**Figure 26-9.** The four variables come under a variety of controls, the main one being the sympathetic nervous system.

The blood pressure is determined by a number of factors. They include the following four factors (see Figure 26-9 and diagram in Chapter 27). All are under a variety of controls, the main one being the sympathetic nervous system.

- **Cardiac output** – a function of the heart:

  cardiac output = stroke volume × heart rate

- **Total peripheral resistance** – determined mainly by vasoconstriction or vasodilation of the arterioles.

  mean arterial pressure = cardiac output × total peripheral resistance

- **Capacity of the venous system** – affected by venous constriction and dilation. If the capacity suddenly increases, as might happen with venous dilation, then the blood pressure will drop.

- **Volume of fluid in the circulatory system** – reduced by hemorrhage, increased by *antidiuretics*, which reduce the volume of urine. Certain hormones have an important effect on the volume of fluid in the body, as we shall see. If the volume of fluid in the circulation increases there would be an increase in blood pressure.

**Viscosity** of the blood can also be important in some conditions.

## VII. Control of Blood Pressure

A list of factors that determine blood pressure was given in the previous section. In the next two chapters, we shall show how these come into operation during exercise, shock and cardiovascular disease including myocardial infarction.

### A. The Two Basic Systems that Determine Blood Pressure

There are two basic systems that determine blood pressure. They are as follows.

1. **The sympathetic nervous system**

   The sympathetic nervous system deals with changes in blood pressure over a short time period (seconds, minutes).

   The sympathatic nervous system exercises strong control over the first, second and third factors listed above, i.e. the cardiac output (increased rate and force of contraction), the peripheral resistance and the capacity of the venous system. As we shall see, it also acts on the kidneys to affect the volume of blood in the circulation.

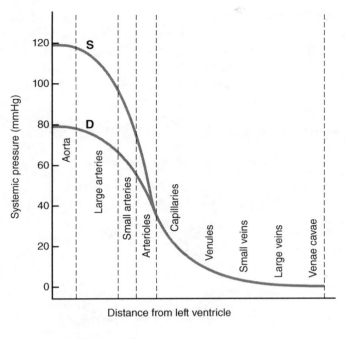

S = systolic pressure
D = diastolic pressure

- A difference between systolic and diastolic pressures in the aorta, arteries, and proximal regions of the arterioles means that a **pulse** would be felt in these vessels

**Figure 26-10.** Blood pressure in the systemic circulation.

Excitation of the sympathetic nervous system raises the blood pressure, as follows.

- The sympathetic nervous system **increases cardiac output** by increasing heart rate and the force of contraction (increases stroke volume by reducing end systolic volume).

- The sympathetic nervous system raises the **total peripheral resistance** by causing vasoconstriction of the arterioles.

- The sympathetic nervous system **reduces the capacity** of the venous side of the circulation by constricting the veins. This raises the venous pressure and increases the volume of blood returned to the heart. This causes an increase in the cardiac output, because the heart always pumps what it receives (Starling's Law of the Heart).

- The sympathetic nervous system also acts on the *kidney*, causing it to release *renin* into the circulation (next section).

2.    **The renin-angiotensin-aldosterone system**

The volume of fluid in the circulatory system (the fourth factor in the previous section) comes under a very complex system of hormonal control that acts primarily in handling fluid and salt retention. The substances involved are the enzyme *renin* (released by the kidneys), and the hormones *angiotensin II* (formed by renin and angiotensin-converting enzyme) and *aldosterone* (released by the adrenal cortex).

The **renin-angiotensin-aldosterone** system has a particularly important role in long-term effects on the cardiovascular system, compared with the other actions of the sympathetic nervous system, which deal primarily with short-term events.

The system operates through the kidney. It works like this. When there is a fall of blood pressure, the sympathetic nervous system is activated via the *baroreceptor reflex* (to be discussed later in this chapter). Sympathetic stimulation of the kidney leads to:

- release of the enzyme *renin* from the kidneys

- **angiotensin I** is formed when renin acts on a protein called *angiotensinogen*, which is found in the blood

- conversion of angiotensin I to **angiotensin II** by *angiotensin-converting enzyme (ACE)*

- angiotensin II-induced release of *aldosterone* from the adrenal glands

[We shall add more details in BIOL 204.]

The effects are to cause **vasoconstriction** coupled with **retention of water and salt** (= reduction of urine volume).

## Renin-Angiotensin-Aldosterone System

This system is fundamentally important. The renin-angiotensin-aldosterone system is the target of many drugs that control blood pressure. Study it and understand it. You will not only be expected to know it in detail this semester, but we will be dealing with it again next semester in BIOL 204.

The following diagram shows how it is activated by a fall of blood pressure, perhaps because of a hemorrhage (loss of blood) or a heart attack (myocardial infarction).

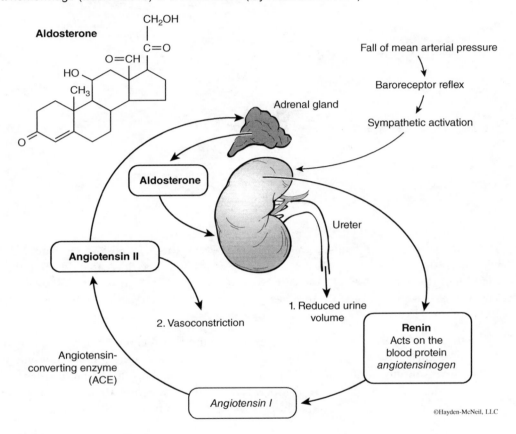

Angiotensin II has *two* actions:

1.  It stimulates the adrenal cortex to release aldosterone, which reduces urine volume and therefore conserves body fluid.
2.  It is a vasoconstrictor, and therefore raises the total peripheral resistance. ACE inhibitors and angiotensin receptor blockers are used in hypertensive therapies.

**Figure 26-11.** Renin-angiotensin-aldosterone system.

## B. The Baroreceptor Reflex and the Control of Arterial Pressure

An important part of the sympathetic control of blood pressure is the **baroreceptor reflex**, which we discussed earlier when we were looking at autonomic reflexes. The *baroreceptors* are specialized mechanoreceptors (they are also interoceptors) located in the walls of the **aortic arch** and in the **carotid sinuses**.

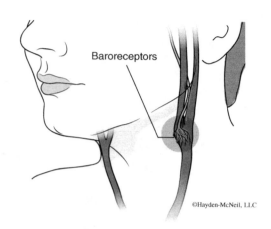

**Figure 26-12.**

The baroreceptors are really *stretch* receptors. Consequently, most of the time, the baroreceptors are continually firing. A drop in aortic pressure decreases the stretch in the wall of the aortic arch and the carotids, and therefore the baroreceptors fire more slowly. A rise of aortic pressure stretches the walls of the arteries, and the baroreceptors increase their firing rate.

1.  If the mean arterial pressure *drops below normal*, the baroreceptors *reduce* their rate of firing. This causes decreased inhibition of the vasomotor center, increasing sympathetic vasomotor tone and causing constriction of the veins, muscular venules and arterioles. Additionally, there is inhibition of the vagal center that normally holds down the heart rate and an increase in sympathetic outflow to the heart.

    **Results?**

    *   **Increase of total peripheral resistance** due to vasoconstriction of the arterioles.

    *   **Increased cardiac output** due to increased venous return caused by vasoconstriction of veins and muscular venules, increased heart rate and force of contraction.

    *   Therefore, **mean arterial pressure increases**.

2.  When the mean arterial pressure *rises above normal*, the baroreceptors *increase* their rate of firing. This inhibits the vasoconstrictor center in the medulla and diminishes the sympathetic vasomotor tone. Excitation of the vagal center sends inhibitory impulses to the heart. There is also inhibition of the sympathetic outflow to the heart.

    **Results?**

    *   **Lowering of total peripheral resistance** due to reduction of sympathetic tone in the arterioles, causing them to dilate.

    *   **Decreased cardiac output** due to decreased venous return caused by vasodilation of veins and muscular venules, decreased heart rate and force of contraction.

    *   Therefore, **mean arterial pressure decreases**.

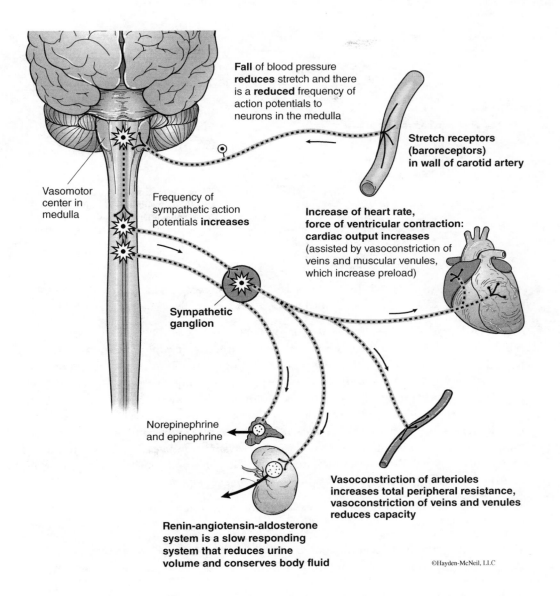

**Fall** of blood pressure **reduces** stretch and there is a **reduced** frequency of action potentials to neurons in the medulla

**Stretch receptors (baroreceptors) in wall of carotid artery**

Vasomotor center in medulla

Frequency of sympathetic action potentials **increases**

**Increase of heart rate, force of ventricular contraction: cardiac output increases** (assisted by vasoconstriction of veins and muscular venules, which increase preload)

**Sympathetic ganglion**

Norepinephrine and epinephrine

**Vasoconstriction of arterioles increases total peripheral resistance, vasoconstriction of veins and venules reduces capacity**

**Renin-angiotensin-aldosterone system is a slow responding system that reduces urine volume and conserves body fluid**

©Hayden-McNeil, LLC

569

**Figure 26-13.** The baroreceptor reflex for controlling blood pressure — some details have been added to Figure 20-5 in Chapter 20.

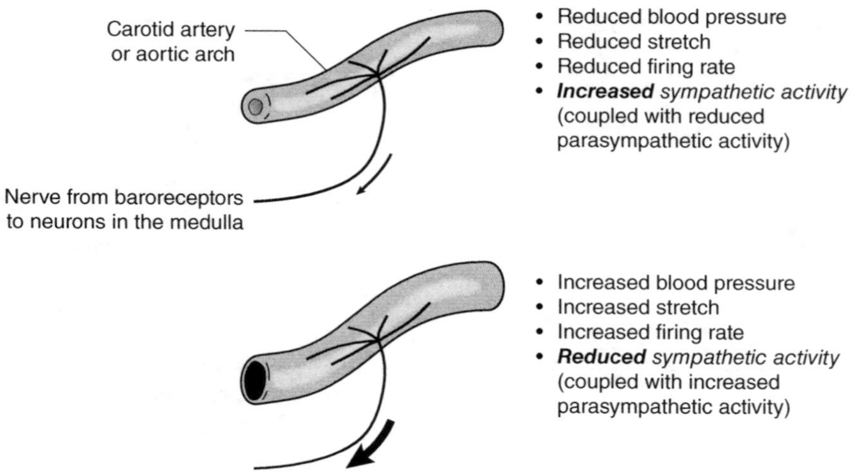

- Reduced blood pressure
- Reduced stretch
- Reduced firing rate
- **Increased** *sympathetic activity* (coupled with reduced parasympathetic activity)

Carotid artery or aortic arch

Nerve from baroreceptors to neurons in the medulla

- Increased blood pressure
- Increased stretch
- Increased firing rate
- **Reduced** *sympathetic activity* (coupled with increased parasympathetic activity)

**Figure 26-14.** The baroreceptors are stretch receptors in the walls of the carotid artery or the aortic arch.

The physiological importance of the baroreceptor reflex is that it protects the arterial pressure against wild fluctuations due to posture, for example. If you move from a lying-down to a standing position, about one-fifth of the blood in the heart and lungs is displaced to the legs. The preload is decreased, which means that the end diastolic volume is decreased, and therefore the stroke volume is decreased. Cardiac output drops, and therefore the blood pressure drops. The baroreceptor reflex kicks in, and restores the blood pressure back to normal. Patients in which this reflex is impaired are liable to faint on standing suddenly, and are said to have **orthostatic hypotension**. This condition is seen in patients with degeneration of neurons in the autonomic nervous system, causing central autonomic failure which produces **Shy-Drager syndrome**.

As we shall see, the baroreceptor reflex is also important in maintaining blood pressure when there is blood loss, and when there has been a heart attack.

Unfortunately, the baroreceptor system adapts to changes in blood pressure over a 1–3 day period, and therefore it is not important in controlling chronic hypertension.

## C. Central Nervous System Ischemic Response

Reflexes in addition to the baroreceptor reflex play a role in regulating arterial pressure, but only one need concern us here. It is called the central nervous system ischemic response. It is the most powerful of all the activators of the sympathetic vasoconstrictor system.

This reflex seems to be a last-ditch stand by the brain when the blood pressure has dropped to the point where blood flow to the brain is diminished to close to lethal levels. This could happen in the event of a severe hemorrhage. The stimulus seems to be a sharp rise in carbon dioxide and a drop in pH within the vasomotor center. The sympathetic vasoconstriction is sometimes so intense that peripheral blood vessels are closed off and all urine production by the kidney is shut down.

Figure 26-15 summarizes the effects of a fall in mean arterial pressure (renin-angiotensin-aldosterone system omitted).

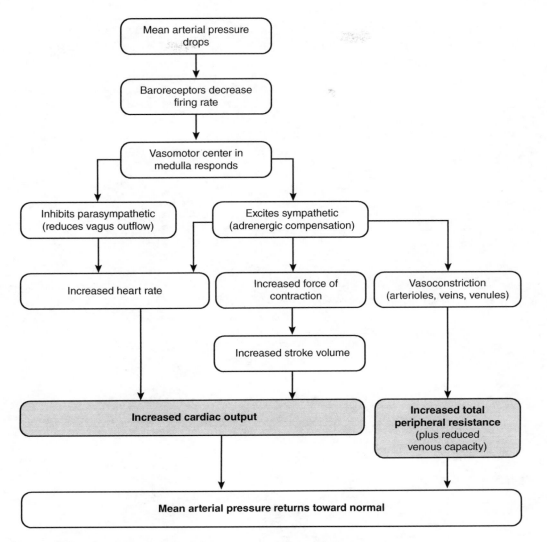

Mean arterial pressure = Cardiac output × Total peripheral resistance

**Figure 26-15.** Effects of a fall in mean arterial pressure.

572

# CARDIOVASCULAR SYSTEM V
Exercise, Hemorrhage, Hypertension, Atherosclerosis, the Coronary Circulation

## CHAPTER OUTLINE

---

Smoking, in addition to causing *lung cancer*, is a major risk factor in cardiovascular and other diseases. If you don't smoke, *don't start*. If you do smoke, *quit now*.

---

## DESCRIPTION AND INTRODUCTION

We will now start applying the knowledge you have gained from the previous four chapters to the whole cardiovascular system. We shall see how the cardiovascular system functions in its entirety, both in health and disease.

We will first talk about *exercise*, a normal activity that causes a number of changes to take place in the circulation in response to the activity of the skeletal muscles.

We then move on to discuss the adjustments that the cardiovascular system makes in response to a loss of blood—*hemorrhage*.

We then discuss some important aspects of cardiovascular disease, notably the twin killers *hypertension* and *atherosclerosis*.

Finally, as a prelude to our last chapter on heart disease, we describe the anatomy, physiology and pathology of the *coronary circulation*, which provides the heart muscle with the oxygen and nutrients it needs to carry out its vital function of pumping blood to all parts of the body.

## OBJECTIVES

After listening to the lecture and reading this chapter, you should be able to:

1. Describe the two important factors operating on the cardiovascular system during a bout of **exercise**.
2. Itemize seven **physiological changes** that occur during exercise.
3. Describe the effect of **athletic conditioning** on stroke volume, heart rate and cardiac output.
4. Define **circulatory shock**.
5. List four conditions that can cause **hypovolemic** shock.
6. Define hemorrhage and explain the two phases of the physiological response to **hemorrhage**.
7. Describe and explain two symptoms that appear in a person who has had a hemorrhage.
8. Define **hypertension** and the changes in the cardiovascular system that accompany it.
9. Describe how essential hypertension is **treated**.
10. Define **atherosclerosis**.
11. Explain the stages in **development** of atherosclerosis.
12. Describe the anatomy of the **coronary circulation**.
13. Describe the changes in **blood flow** through the coronary circulation during systole and diastole.
14. Give the single, **most important** determinant of coronary blood flow.
15. Explain the meaning and causes of **cardiac ischemia**, **angina pectoris** and **myocardial infarction**.
16. List four **treatments** for coronary artery blockage.

## I. Exercise

### A. Introduction

In endurance events it is usually believed that performance is limited by the cardiovascular system. The goal of cardiovascular function during exercise is to deliver oxygen and nutrients (glucose, fatty acids) to the active muscles and remove carbon dioxide and lactic acid from them. It is also vital that the myocardium receives enough oxygen and nutrients so that the heart can deliver an adequate cardiac output. Mean arterial pressure must also be maintained in events requiring the activity of many muscles, because the total peripheral resistance can drop dramatically as a result of active hyperemia.

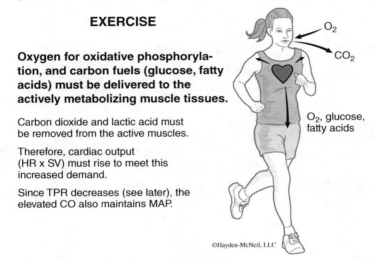

**EXERCISE**

**Oxygen for oxidative phosphorylation, and carbon fuels (glucose, fatty acids) must be delivered to the actively metabolizing muscle tissues.**

Carbon dioxide and lactic acid must be removed from the active muscles.

Therefore, cardiac output (HR x SV) must rise to meet this increased demand.

Since TPR decreases (see later), the elevated CO also maintains MAP.

$O_2$

$CO_2$

$O_2$, glucose, fatty acids

©Hayden-McNeil, LLC

**Figure 27-1.**

575

Circulatory changes during exercise affect primarily the heart (heart rate, myocardial contractility, stroke volume, and therefore cardiac output) and the blood flow through the skin, muscles and viscera.

---

In exercise, there is an increase in cardiac output and a redistribution of blood flow so that a larger proportion of the cardiac output is diverted to the active muscles.

---

In intense exercise the demand of the muscles for oxygen may increase 20 times. To meet this increase in oxygen demand, the cardiac output would also have to increase by 20 times, to about 100 liters per minute. The heart can't deliver this amount of blood, so there must be adjustments to ensure that a larger *proportion* of the cardiac output goes to the *active* muscles.

The following are circulatory changes occurring during exercise.

- **heart** – increase cardiac output
- **blood flow**

  - increase in **active muscles**
  - decrease in the **viscera**
  - initial decrease in the **skin**, followed by an increase as body warms up

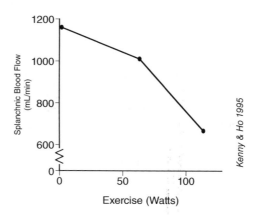

**Figure 27-2.**

The two important controls acting on the cardiovascular system during a bout of exercise are as follows.

1. **Neural.**

   Effects are mainly sympathetic and therefore *adrenergic*. Cerebrocortical input activates the sympathetic nervous system ("sympathetic drive") and inhibits the parasympathetic nervous system. These effects may be coupled with sympathetic activation arising from stimulation of stretch and tension mechanoreceptors in active muscles.

   Even the *anticipation* of physical activity causes cerebrocortical activation of the sympathetic nervous system, and inhibits parasympathetic vagus nerve discharge to the heart. The result is that the heart rate and force of contraction increase ($\beta_1$-adrenergic receptors) and there is increased vasoconstriction ($\alpha$-adrenergic receptors). This increased vasoconstriction affects mainly the **skin** and abdominal **viscera**: the effect is quite mild in the muscles, and there may even be vasodilation via $\beta_2$-adrenergic receptors activated by low levels of *epinephrine* released by the adrenal medulla. The result is that a higher proportion of the cardiac output is available to flow through the muscles.

   There are sympathetic vasodilators that utilize *acetylcholine* in the muscles of cats and dogs. They have not been demonstrated in humans.

2. **Local–active hyperemia.**

   Local–active hypermia caused by the release of vasodilator substances such as carbon dioxide and lactic acid serves to increase the blood flow through active muscles. Local factors are also responsible for the increase in flow through the coronary circulation.

   Local factors are responsible for the striking increase in blood flow through the active muscles during exercise, as shown in the table below.

| Condition | mL Blood/100 gm muscle/min |
|---|---|
| Resting blood flow | 3.6 |
| Blood flow during maximal exercise | 90 |

## B. Changes during Exercise

It takes several minutes before the muscles receive sufficient blood flow to balance the demand for oxygen, glucose and fatty acids. Metabolism is covered at first by building up an oxygen deficit (oxygen from myoglobin, depletion of creatine phosphate, anaerobic glycolysis forming lactate).

Once exercise has begun, the increased *sympathetic drive* and reduced parasympathetic inhibition of the S-A node continue, and may even be augmented.

1.  Stimulation of the sympathetic system leads to the following.

    a.  **Heart** *rate, force of contraction, stroke volume* and *cardiac output* increase. The heart rate can increase to as much as 180 beats per minute (the maximum heart rate achievable can be calculated from the formula 220—age in years, with a standard deviation of 10–12 beats per minute). In the average individual, there is a modest increase in cardiac output resulting from an increase in stroke volume—between 10 and 35%—caused by increased central venous pressure and end diastolic volume because the veins have constricted and reduced their volume.

        However, at elevated heart rates, the stroke volume may actually decrease, because the heart is beating so fast that efficient filling of the ventricles does not have a chance to occur. Overall, however, there is a steady increase in cardiac output as work performed during exercise is increased, and this increase in cardiac output is achieved mainly by an increase in heart rate. The situation may be different in well-trained long distance runners, where the stroke volume during exercise can double (see the section below on cardiac output and athletic conditioning).

    b.  **Arterioles** are *constricted* mainly in the **skin** and abdominal **viscera**, reducing blood flow through these organs. As soon as the body starts to heat up, the blood vessels in the skin dilate. **The reduction in blood flow through the circulation supplying the gastrointestinal tract can be as much as 70%.**

        Vasoconstriction results from the binding of norepinephrine to α-adrenergic receptors in the arterioles of these organs.

    c.  **Veins** are constricted, reducing the venous capacity and boosting venous return to the heart. Stroke volume is therefore increased, and cardiac output is therefore boosted by the operation of the Starling law.

2.  The **venous pump** (constriction and relaxation of skeletal muscles around the long veins of the legs and arms, which have valves in them) also boosts the amount of blood returning to the heart.

3.  Blood flow through the **brain** does not change significantly.

4.  Blood flow through the **coronary circulation** increases markedly, in response to local vasodilation from factors associated with the increased demand for oxygen by the myocardium.

5.  There is release of vasodilator substances (e.g. carbon dioxide, lactic acid) in the **active** muscles. This leads to the following.

    a.  **Muscle arterioles and precapillary sphincters open up**, allowing blood to flow into all the capillary beds. The effect is known as *capillary recruitment*.

b.  **As a result of a., blood flow through active muscles is increased** – sometimes by as much as 15–20 times, effectively having been diverted from the skin and, more importantly, from the circulation supplying the abdominal viscera.

c.  **Total peripheral resistance is reduced** – the vasodilation in the active muscles is so strong that it actually *reduces* the peripheral resistance, even though the vessels in the skin and abdominal viscera remain constricted. In exercise that involves a large percentage of the body's musculature (running and swimming), the reduction of peripheral resistance may be quite large. The reduction of total peripheral resistance enables the heart to pump more blood more efficiently. This is because the reduction in total peripheral resistance minimizes the rise in mean arterial pressure that could be a consequence of increased cardiac output (see below). In fact, if it were not offset by the increase in cardiac output, the mean blood pressure would drop to 20 mmHg.

6.  When the body temperature rises during strenuous exercise, the heat-regulation center in the hypothalamus is activated, and the **skin** vessels dilate to increase heat loss from the skin. If this occurs, there is a further drop in the peripheral resistance.

---

During exercise, blood flow to the active muscles must be maintained at high level to supply oxygen, glucose and fatty acids. But there must also be a high blood flow to the skin to convey heat to the body surface. When surrounding temperatures are high and there has been fluid loss due to sweating during prolonged exercise, blood volume will decrease and there may be difficulty in meeting high blood flow to BOTH skin and muscle. In this situation, there may be peripheral vasoconstriction to reduce skin blood flow. This will maintain both blood pressure and muscle blood flow. However, body temperature will rise. So maintenance of blood pressure is the top priority for the body, and it will accept a temperature rise rather than have a drop of blood pressure. Obviously, in this situation there is the danger of *hyperthermia* if exercise continues and body temperature rises above a tolerable level.

---

7.  More **oxygen** is extracted from the blood perfusing active muscles. This is caused by an increase in muscle temperature and a reduction of pH, both of which force hemoglobin to give up its oxygen more easily.

## C. Summary of Cardiovascular Changes during Exercise

1.  Cardiac output increases, due mainly to an increase in heart rate, but also because of a modest increase in stroke volume (stroke volume may decrease at elevated heart rates) resulting from an increase in myocardial contractility from sympathetic action (which reduces the end systolic volume) and from an elevated end diastolic volume.

2.  Total peripheral resistance generally decreases in exercise that involves a **large** number of active muscles, mainly due to vasodilation in the active muscles: if the body temperature rises there may also be added vasodilation of the skin vessels.

3.  End diastolic volume increases consequent to increased amounts of blood returning to the heart and therefore produces an increase in cardiac output by the Starling law (i.e. stroke volume increases).

4. The mean arterial pressure increases, but often less than might be predicted from the increased cardiac output because the total peripheral resistance decreases (depends on the amount of muscle tissue involved in the exercise—the greater the mass of muscle, the greater will be the drop in peripheral resistance).

5. Arteriovenous oxygen difference in the muscle blood supply increases, as does oxygen consumption.

6. Strong vasoconstriction is seen in the circulation through the abdominal viscera. There is initial vasoconstriction followed by vasodilation in the cutaneous circulation, vasodilation in the coronary circulation and active skeletal muscles, little change in the cerebral circulation.

During *moderate* exercise, the following changes are likely to be observed.

| | |
|---|---|
| Skeletal muscle flow | increased by 175% |
| Mean arterial pressure | increased by 15% |
| Cardiac output | increased by 120% |
| Heart rate | doubled |
| Stroke volume | increased by 20% |
| Total peripheral resistance | decreased by 50% |

## D. Cardiac Output during Exercise and Athletic Conditioning

579

Aside from promoting muscle development (see the chapters on the muscular system), training has an important effect on the cardiovascular system. The bottom line is that the maximum cardiac output during exercise is much higher in the trained athlete than in an untrained individual. This is obvious from the table below.

| | Cardiac Output |
|---|---|
| Average young man at rest (trained or untrained) | 5.5 liters per minute |
| Maximum output by young untrained man during exercise | 20–22 liters per minute |
| Maximum output during exercise by trained marathoner | 30–40 liters per minute |

Therefore, while an untrained person can increase cardiac output by about four times, a trained marathoner can increase cardiac output by more than seven times.

These results are accounted for by the fact that the heart chambers of the marathoner are about 40% larger and the myocardial mass is also greater than in the untrained individual.

This means that the stroke volume of the marathoner is much greater than in the untrained person. However, because the marathoner's heart rate is much slower, the cardiac output at rest is about the same as for an untrained individual. You can understand this by studying the table below. It is important to understand that heart enlargement and increased pumping capacity occurs in *endurance* types of training, not in *sprint* types.

Cardiac output is calculated by multiplying the stroke volume (mL/beat) by the heart rate (beats/min). The answer is in **mL/min**. You divide by 1000 to get the cardiac output in **liters per minute.**

| | Stroke Vol. (mL/beat) | Heart Rate (beats/min.) | Cardiac Output (liters/min) |
|---|---|---|---|
| Resting | | | |
| Non-athlete | 75 | 73 | 5.5 |
| **Marathoner** | **105** | **52** | **5.5** |
| Maximum | | | |
| Non-athlete | 110 | 195 | 21.5 |
| **Marathoner** | **162** | **185** | **30.0** |

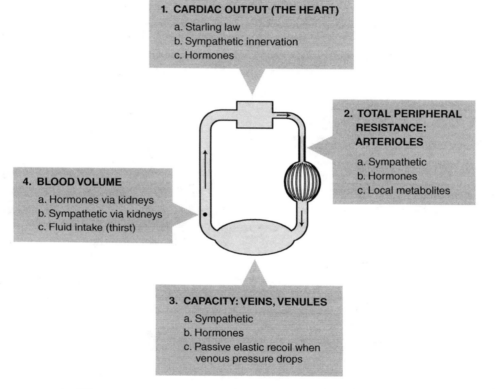

**Figure 27-3.** The four variables of the cardiovascular system.

## II. Hemorrhage—A Particular Case of Shock

**Circulatory shock** is a complex syndrome characterized by inadequate blood flow to such critical organs as the heart, brain, liver, kidneys and the abdominal viscera (mainly the gastrointestinal tract).

**Hypovolemic shock** can be caused by any factor that reduces blood volume. Hypovolemic shock includes the following cases where loss of body fluid has occurred.

- **Hemorrhage** (loss of blood)
- **Severe burns** (loss of plasma)
- **Vomiting** (loss of fluid and electrolytes)
- **Diarrhoea** (loss of fluid and electrolytes: alternative spelling, diarrhea)

Fifty percent of battlefield mortality is attributable to hemorrhage and resulting hypovolemic shock. The combat medic must have the means to replace lost fluid (fluid resuscitation), limit cellular damage, and maintain supply of oxygen and vital nutrients to the tissues of the body.

Hemorrhage causes an immediate lowering of the blood pressure. The body responds in two phases.

1. Reduced firing rate of the baroreceptors in the carotid sinus and aorta rapidly *activates the sympathetic nervous system* – effects on the heart and blood vessels are aimed at maintaining cardiac output and arterial blood pressure.

2. Slower responses
   - conservation of body fluid by reducing urine volume (kidneys)
   - moving fluid from the interstitial space into the circulation
   - restoring lost body fluid by stimulating thirst (hypothalamus)

### A. The Baroreceptor Response

The word **baroreceptor** is derived from *baro-* (for pressure) plus *receptor*. It therefore means **pressure** receptor. Compare the word *barometer*, which means something that measures pressure.

The baroreceptor response is vital to survival. With the baroreceptor reflex fully operational, the body can lose as much as 30–40% of the blood volume in half an hour before death occurs. Without the baroreceptor response, only 15–20% of the blood can be lost.

The baroreceptor response caused by moderate blood loss causes rapid stimulation of the sympathetic nervous system. The result is as follows.

1. **Arteriolar vasoconstriction** increases **total peripheral resistance**. Arteriolar vasoconstriction occurs mainly in the arterioles of the **skin** and **gastrointestinal** tract. In severe hemorrhage there may be intense **renal** vasoconstriction, resulting in cessation of urine formation.

   There is NO vasoconstriction in the **coronary** vessels (which actually dilate) or in the **cerebral** vessels. They supply blood to the heart and the brain, organs that are vital to survival. Blood flow through these organs is primarily determined by local metabolism and oxygen demand.

581

2. **Constriction of the veins and muscular venules** (mainly in the skin and gastrointestinal tract) reduces the **capacity** of the circulatory system.

3. **Heart rate and force of contraction** increase, promoting an increase in **cardiac output**.

All these effects operate to restore the arterial pressure.

Typical symptoms that appear after activation of the sympathetic nervous system are as follows.

• **Blanching** of the skin in pale skinned people due to vasoconstriction of the blood vessels in the skin.

• **Cold sweat**, **cold** and **clammy** skin – the sympathetic nervous system causes sweating, and the skin is cold because of the vasoconstriction of its blood vessels. Sweating causes it to cool even more.

We shall see later that the sympathetic nervous system is also activated during a **heart attack**, producing the same symptoms.

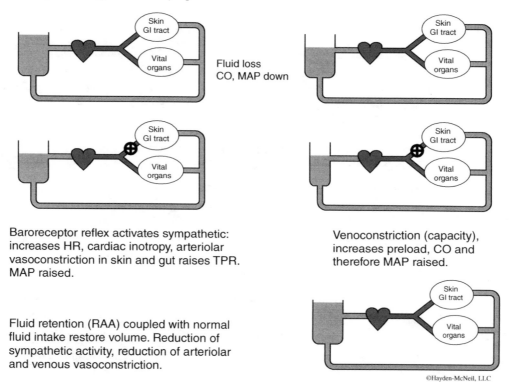

**Figure 27-4.**

## B. The Slow Response that Tends to Return Blood Volume to Normal

At more substantial levels of hemorrhage (greater than about 20%), the aforementioned reflexes are not adequate to maintain arterial pressure, which then starts to drop, accompanied with a further drop in cardiac output.

1. **Retention of salt and water by the kidneys**. The volume of urine is reduced. This is a conservation measure, and minimizes the volume of fluid that would normally be lost via the urine. This is a hormonal mechanism, of which the **renin-angiotensin-aldosterone** system is one of the most important. Others will be discussed next semester.

2. **Movement of fluid from the interstitial space into the capillaries**. This is really the opposite of edema, and is caused by reduction of pressure within the capillaries.

3. **Increased thirst** (appetite for salt may also be increased). This restores lost fluid and electrolytes. These effects are believed to be caused by *angiotensin* and *aldosterone*.

## III. Hypertension and Atherosclerosis

### A. Introduction

Hypertension is a serious problem. In 1985, for example, it affected more than 6 million people in the United States alone. Hypertension is the major risk factor for coronary, cerebral and renal vascular disease. The risk of coronary disease is 2× higher in hypertensives and of stroke is 8× higher than in normotensives (= people with normal arterial pressure).

Symptoms of hypertension generally are absent until the disease is far advanced and has caused cardiac, renal, neural and ocular damage. Hypertension usually means a mean resting arterial pressure of about 110 mmHg, with a diastolic pressure of > 85–90 mmHg and a systolic pressure > 140 mmHg. This applies to a 30-year-old male. However, there are changes in blood pressure with aging and there are also differences according to gender.

**Mean arterial pressure (MAP) = diastolic arterial pressure + ⅓ arterial pulse pressure**

**= diastolic arterial pressure + ⅓ (systolic – diastolic arterial pressure)**

583

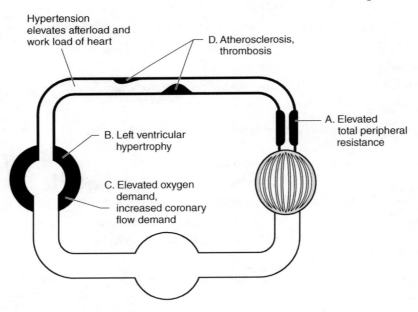

**Figure 27-5.** Hypertension and its effects on the circulation.

If untreated, 50% of hypertensives die from coronary heart disease, 33% from stroke (cerebral infarct), and 10–15% from renal failure.

Hypertension increases the work load of the heart (i.e. afterload is increased), particularly the myocardium of the left ventricle, which initially *hypertrophies* (increases in size), and increases its *oxygen demand*. Therefore, any pathological decrease in coronary flow will have more severe consequences in hypertensive people than in normals. If the left ventricle starts to fail, there may be pulmonary congestion and edema.

Hypertension also leads to vascular pressure damage and associated ***atherosclerosis*** (see later). Effects on the renal circulation include atherosclerotic lesions which can eventually lead to renal failure.

Hypertension can be divided into two categories.

- **Secondary hypertension** is consequent on another condition, which includes a variety of diseases affecting the kidneys and endocrine glands, as well as *pregnancy-induced hypertension*.

- **Primary hypertension,** also known as **essential** or **idiopathic** hypertension, arises from unknown causes and accounts for more than 90% of all known cases of hypertension.

Treatment of hypertension is important in order to minimize damage to cerebral, ocular, renal and cardiac tissues.

Treatment of *essential hypertension*:

- **Lifestyle modification** – reduce sodium intake in the diet and carry out a program of weight reduction. Other factors that may need to be addressed on an individual basis might include ***alcohol*** intake and ***smoking***.

- **Pharmacological** – drugs can be divided into those that affect total peripheral resistance and those that have an effect on cardiac output.

    - **cardiac output** – *diuretics, beta-blockers*
    - **total peripheral resistance** – *calcium channel blockers, angiotensin-converting enzyme inhibitors, angiotensin receptor blockers* and *alpha-blockers*.

Treatment of *secondary hypertension* is based on treating the underlying disease.

## B. Role of the Total Peripheral Resistance

Why is blood pressure high in the hypertensive individual? Recall the equation relating blood pressure, cardiac output and peripheral resistance.

---

mean arterial pressure = cardiac output × total peripheral resistance

---

In older hypertensives, the cardiac output is normal but the peripheral resistance is up by 40–60%. That is, the increased blood pressure is due to a rise in the peripheral resistance, there being no change in the cardiac output part of the equation.

One of the underlying factors in this effect may be vasoconstriction due to augmented intracellular calcium (hence the use of calcium channel blockers such as verapamil in many hypertensive therapies). Intracellular calcium, however, is under the control of many factors, some of them neural, some humoral. Ultimately, however, chronic constriction can lead to thickening of the blood vessel walls. To make matters worse, these thickened walls seem to be more sensitive to vasoconstrictor influences such as norepinephrine. Therefore, under stressful circumstances that increase sympathetic activity, the blood pressure may rocket even higher.

## C. Causes of Essential Hypertension

The causes are unknown. Many *environmental* factors may be implicated in the genesis of essential hypertension, including the following.

1.  Excess dietary $Na^+$ intake (in *some* groups of hypertensives), increased blood volume
2.  Emotional stress (which causes chronic sympathetic activation)
3.  Smoking
4.  Excessive alcohol intake
5.  Obesity
6.  Diabetes

However, there is undoubtedly a *genetic* component in many cases. Children of hypertensives tend to develop hypertension. A number of genes that could be defective in hypertensives are presently being investigated, and include the enzyme in the lungs that converts angiotensin into its active form (angiotensin-converting enzyme, or ACE). ACE inhibitors such as *captopril* and *enalapril* are widely used for hypertension and congestive heart failure.

585

## D. Atherosclerosis

### More quackery – chelation therapy

*"The American Heart Association's Clinical Science Committee has reviewed the available literature on the use of chelation (EDTA) in the treatment of atherosclerotic heart or blood vessel disease and finds no scientific evidence to demonstrate any benefit of this form of therapy. Furthermore, employment of this form of unproven treatment may deprive patients of the well established benefits attendant to the many other valuable methods of treating these diseases."* [http://www.americanheart.org]

Hypertension is one of the classic risk factors for *atherosclerosis*, a chronic inflammatory condition associated with the deposition of plaques containing lipids and cholesterol in the coronary, carotid and aorto-femoral vascular beds. Other risk factors include smoking, diabetes mellitis, obesity, high blood cholesterol, being male rather than female, and advancing age.

Coronary artery disease (CAD) caused by atherosclerosis is the main cause of congestive heart failure and of death in western societies. WHO expects it to be leading cause of death globally within the next 15 years.

[Arteriosclerosis is a term used for hardening of arteries, or loss of elasticity. It is caused by buildup of calcium.]

Inflammation is now believed to play an important role in the pathogenesis of atherosclerosis, together with the established risk factors listed above. The popular current hypothesis involves vascular endothelial damage or dysfunction leading to uptake of LDL (which normally delivers cholesterol to the cells of the body). The LDL is then oxidized in the intima. It accumulates in macrophages and other cells, giving them a foamy appearance. This is the fatty streak lesion. The presence of foam cells initiates activation of cells of the immune system and the development of an inflammatory response.

The atherosclerotic lesion may grow silently for years without producing any clinical symptoms.

Alternatively, it may develop into a vulnerable atheromatous plaque, characterized by numerous inflammatory cells and a thin cap. If such a plaque is activated, the cells start producing proteolytic enzymes that degrade the fibrous cap. It can crack under the influence of hydrostatic pressure, and the inflamed core becomes exposed to the circulating blood. The core contains molecules (e.g. tissue factor) that activate platelets and promote clot formation. Platelets bind, aggregate and a thrombus is formed. There may be a transient vasospasm due to a prostaglandin vasoconstrictor (thromboxane A2) released from activated platelets. The thrombus can grow rapidly. So rapidly, in fact, that it can sometimes block the lumen within minutes. The result is acute myocardial ischemia followed by infarction. Such a vessel must be reopened within a very short time frame by thrombolysis or angioplasty.

## IV. The Coronary Circulation

The survival and proper functioning of the heart depends on the coronary circulation. The blood flow through the coronary circulation is an important 5% of the cardiac output. In exercise, this flow can increase by as much as 4 to 5 times.

### A. Coronary Arteries

The two coronary arteries branch off from the aorta just beyond the aortic semilunar valves.

The *left coronary artery* branches into the *circumflex artery* and the *left anterior descending artery* (sometimes called the anterior interventricular artery).

The *right coronary artery* passes along the atrioventricular sulcus between the right atrium and the right ventricle. It branches into the *posterior interventricular artery* and the *marginal artery*.

### B. Cardiac Veins

Blood is collected from the capillary beds in the heart and drains into the *cardiac veins*. The veins run parallel to the arteries. Finally, the veins drain into the *coronary sinus*, a very large vein that empties into the **right atrium**.

### C. Collateral Circulation in the Heart

Some connections (collaterals) exist between the smaller arteries in the heart. When a sudden blockage occurs in one of the larger coronary arteries, blood flow through these collaterals may be enough to minimize the damage.

## D. Variation of Blood Flow through the Coronary Circulation during the Cardiac Cycle

Changes in the coronary blood flow during systole and diastole are as follows.

- Flow *decreases* during ventricular systole. The reason for this is that there is strong squeezing of the intra-myocardial vessels when the heart muscle contracts during systole.

- Flow *increases* during ventricular diastole. During diastole, the cardiac muscle relaxes completely and no longer prevents blood from flowing through the capillary beds, so that blood flows rapidly during diastole.

Although we haven't mentioned it before, we see just the same effects in skeletal muscles. The blood flow through skeletal muscles falls when they contract, and rises when they relax.

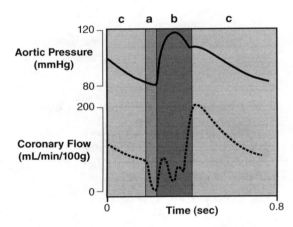

**Figure 27-6.** Pulsatile nature of left coronary artery blood flow. Flow is lower during phases of isovolumetric contraction (a) and ejection (b) than during diastole (c).

587

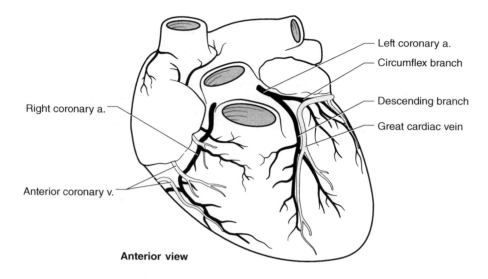

**Anterior view**

588

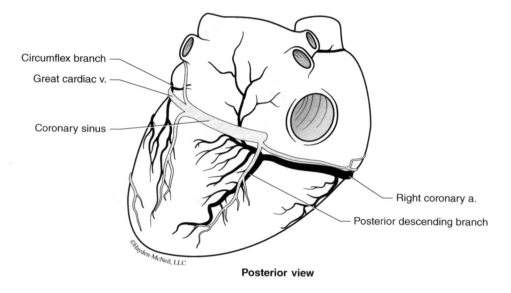

**Posterior view**

**Figure 27-7.** Coronary circulation.

## E. Control of Coronary Flow

**Oxygen demand is the major factor governing coronary flow.** If the heart is beating faster and more forcefully during exercise or during emotional stress, it will require more oxygen, and the flow of blood through the coronary vessels will increase. This is purely a local response to vasodilator substances released during metabolism of the cardiac muscle, and is another example of active hyperemia.

## F. Cardiac Ischemia

Most heart problems (excluding those that result from valve defects) have their roots in a faulty coronary circulation. About 35% of all human beings who die in the U.S.A. die from *myocardial ischemia (= cardiac ischemia)*. *Ischemia* means lack of blood.

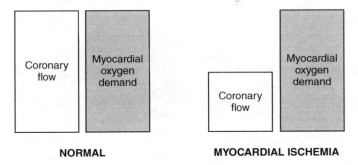

**Figure 27-8.** Myocardial ischemia.

**Myocardial ischemia** occurs when the heart demands more oxygen than the coronary circulation is able to supply.

- **Supply**

  The ability of the coronary circulation to deliver oxygen (and nutrients) can be reduced by formation of a blood clot, thromboembolism, atherosclerosis, a spasm of the artery, or sudden reduction in blood pressure (from hemorrhage or during a heart attack).

589

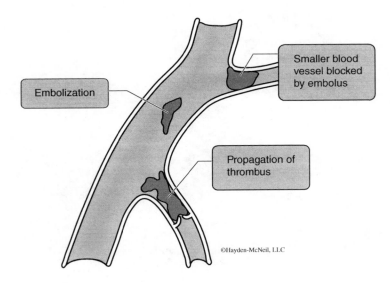

**Figure 27-9.**

- **Demand**

  The demand for oxygen (and nutrients) by the cardiac muscle cells can be increased by exercise or emotional stress.

Often these factors operate together to cause myocardial ischemia. A partly blocked coronary circulation may be adequate to supply the heart's oxygen needs when the person is resting quietly, but may not be able to provide enough oxygen if the myocardial oxygen demand is increased as a result of sudden emotional stress or strenuous exercise.

Therefore, myocardial ischemia will be produced by anything that reduces the ratio:

$$\frac{\textbf{coronary flow}}{\textbf{myocardial oxygen demand}}$$

The consequences of myocardial ischemia will be described and discussed in Chapter 28. They include myocardial infarction (death of cardiac muscle), ventricular arrhythmias and the pain of angina pectoris.

# CARDIOVASCULAR SYSTEM VI
## Heart Disease

591

## CHAPTER OUTLINE

Smoking causes cardiovascular disease and lung cancer. If you don't smoke, *don't start.* If you do smoke, *quit now.*

## DESCRIPTION AND INTRODUCTION

**Major cardiovascular risk factors:**

1. **Hypertension:** component of metabolic syndrome

2. **Tobacco use**, particularly cigarettes, chewing tobacco

3. **Elevated LDL cholesterol** (or total cholesterol ≥ 240 mg/dL) or low HDL cholesterol: metabolic syndrome

4. **Diabetes mellitus:** component of metabolic syndrome

5. **Obesity** (BMI ≥ 30 kg/m2): metabolic syndrome

6. **Age** > 55 years for men or > 65 years for women: increased risk

7. **Glomerular filtration rate** <60 mL/min per 1.73 m2

8. **Microalbuminuria** (moderately increased albuminuria)

9. **Family history** of premature cardiovascular disease (men < 55 years; women < 65 years)

10. **Lack of exercise**

With the exception of valve disorders, most heart problems are caused by a faulty coronary circulation. Therefore, you should first review the coronary circulation in your notes for Chapter 27. A faulty coronary circulation can be caused by an atherosclerotic plaque or an embolus. More rarely, there may be a sudden vasoconstriction (spasm) of the coronary artery. Lack of an adequate circulation to part of the myocardium is called **myocardial ischemia**. It is usually associated with the pain of **angina pectoris**.

In this chapter, we discuss the ways in which the body succeeds in compensating for the effects of a heart attack, and how medication can be used to assist the body in recovering from a severe heart attack.

## OBJECTIVES

After reviewing Chapter 27, Section IV, listening to Lecture 28 and reading these notes, you should be able to:

1. Describe the causes of faulty **coronary circulation**, and how this condition may be treated surgically.
2. Define **myocardial ischemia** and its causes.
3. Explain the **two factors** that can combine to cause myocardial ischemia.
4. Explain how the metabolism of **ATP** may be involved in cell death following myocardial ischemia.
5. Explain what is meant by a **myocardial infarction,** its consequences and how it is diagnosed.

6. Define **Starling's Law of the Heart**, and explain how it helps the cardiovascular system to recover from a moderate heart attack.

7. Explain the function of the **sympathetic nervous system** in the first stage of recovery after a moderate heart attack.

8. Explain why **fluid retention** by the body may be beneficial in the case of a moderate heart attack, but a killer if the heart attack is more severe.

9. List and describe the interventions designed to restore the mismatch between coronary flow and myocardial oxygen demand.

10. Describe **cardiogenic shock**.

11. Explain why there is usually **peripheral edema** after unilateral failure of the **right** ventricle and **pulmonary edema** after unilateral failure of the **left** ventricle.

## I. Myocardial Ischemia

### A. Introduction

In a healthy heart, increased myocardial oxygen demand is met by increased coronary flow. Increased coronary flow results from vasodilation of the coronary arterioles. Vasodilation is caused by locally produced substances such as carbon dioxide, hydrogen ions and adenosine. This is an example of *active hyperemia*.

Myocardial ischemia occurs when the heart demands more oxygen than the coronary circulation is able to supply. Myocardial ischemia can lead to myocardial infarction (death of cardiac muscle), a cause of one third of all the deaths in the U.S. Two factors may operate simultaneously.

593

1. **Impairment of coronary flow.**

    a. atherosclerotic plaques causing narrowing of the artery.

    b. thrombus formation from an unstable plaque causing occlusion.

    c. *coronary artery vasospasm* – contraction of the smooth muscle in the media.

    d. *reduced perfusion pressure* (hemorrhage, heart attack).

2. **Elevated myocardial oxygen demand.**

    a. *exercise* (affects heart rate and inotropic state).

    b. other causes of *sympathetic activation* (e.g. caused by stress).

    c. *cardiac hypertrophy*, which can arise from pressure overloading (e.g. hypertension) or volume overloading (e.g. mitral regurgitation). Cardiac hypertrophy involves an increase in the size of the cardiac muscle cells, not in their numbers.

A partly obstructed coronary circulation may be adequate to supply the heart's oxygen needs for a person at rest, but may be inadequate if the person exercises. Under these conditions, the coronary flow cannot increase enough to satisfy the increased metabolic demand of the myocardium, leading to a decrease in the supply/demand ratio.

## B. Consequences of Myocardial Ischemia

The consequences of myocardial ischemia can be:

- **Myocardial infarction.**

  When the interruption or reduction of coronary blood supply to the myocardium is so severe and long-lasting that function can no longer be sustained, the ischemic cardiac muscle cells that make up the affected myocardium become injured and then die. The condition is then called a myocardial infarction or heart attack.

- **Ventricular arrhythmias (dysrhythmias).**

  Acute myocardial ischemia, aside from leading to cell injury and death, can be an important cause of ventricular arrhythmias. $K^+$ is lost from the injured cells, causing a reduction in the resting membrane potential of normal cells. Changes in refractoriness and conduction also occur. The problem may be worsened if the ventricle has become enlarged as a result of the heart working against a chronically elevated blood pressure, as occurs in hypertensive patients.

- **Angina pectoris.**

  When ischemia occurs, there is the formation of pain-producing substances such as lactic acid coupled with damage to the myocardium and loss of contractility. Lactic acid stimulates the pain endings in the cardiac muscle. The pain is called **angina pectoris**. Angina pectoris is a type of referred pain (see earlier chapter on pain) that is perceived as coming from the chest, arms and other regions of the body. It typically lasts from 1–10 minutes, and may occur only during exertion (when the oxygen demand of the myocardium increases), or it may develop suddenly at rest. When that happens, the cause is usually a sudden blockage caused by development of a clot associated with ruptured, unstable atherosclerotic lesion.

## C. Cardiac Muscle Metabolism and Cell Death Following Myocardial Ischemia

Nearly all the energy liberated by the controlled burning of foods (mainly fatty acids) in cardiac muscle cells is used to synthesize ATP.

A large fraction of this ATP is used to supply the power needed for repeated contraction of the myocardium.

During a bout of ischemia, the myocardium is deprived of oxygen for oxidative phosphorylation, and much less ATP is synthesized. This leads to a loss of contractility of the myocardium.

Another problem can arise when the coronary circulation is restored after a bout of ischemia. Dangerous substances called *free radicals* can be released, and can damage myocardial tissue.

## II. Myocardial Infarction

*Myocardial infarction* is myocardial cell death (necrosis) due to prolonged myocardial ischemia. The pathophysiology of an acute MI involves vessel narrowing by atheromatous plaques, plaque rupture with varying degrees of vasospasm and thrombus forma-

594

tion. Total occlusion for more than 4–6 hours results in irreversible myocardial necrosis. Severe myocardial infarction can be accompanied by intense anginal pain that may persist as long as 15–20 minutes. Infarction of > 40% of the myocardium often leads to cardiogenic shock and death. However, when the areas involved are smaller, there is a good chance for recovery.

The subendocardial region is particularly prone to ischemia, injury and infarction because it gets most of its blood supply during diastole. It also has a higher $O_2$ demand than the more surface portions of the muscle, possibly because it develops a greater intramural tension during systole.

## Diagnosis of Myocardial Infarction

1.  *Clinical signs and family history:* angina, difficulty breathing (dyspnea) and crackling noises on inspiration (caused by pulmonary edema), jugular vein distension, edema of legs and ankles, pale cold sweaty skin (sympathetic activation).

2.  *The initial 12-lead ECG – changes in the S-T segment, T wave, Q wave.*

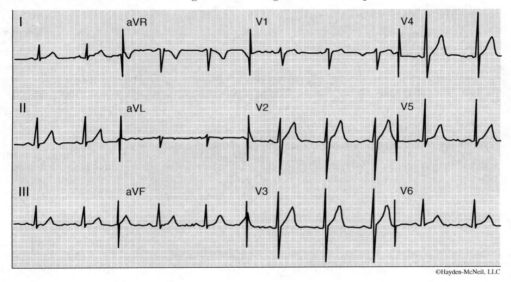

©Hayden-McNeil, LLC

**Figure 28-1.** Normal 12-lead ECG.

3.  *Protein markers.* The definitive diagnosis of a myocardial infarction is the appearance of cardiac-specific proteins in the blood. The current consensus is that if the blood test is positive for cardiac troponins and/or creatine phosphokinase-MB, then the condition can be accurately labeled as an MI. In addition, some clinicians routinely require levels of other proteins/peptides.

4.  *Imaging* (echo, for example)to measure blood flow through the myocardium and abnormalities in wall movement.

595

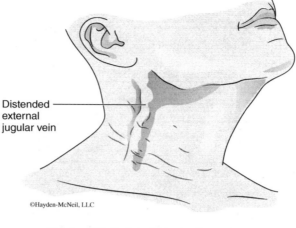

**Figure 28-2.** Jugular vein distension.

## III. Hemodynamic Consequences of a Heart Attack

1. Cardiac output decreases, partly caused by reduced myocardial contractility and partly by loss of contracting myocardium.

2. Venous pressure and right atrial pressure increase because the reduced cardiac output does not match the rate at which blood is returning to the heart from the veins. In other words, we can say loosely that blood is dammed up in the veins. The jugular vein is seen to be distended under these conditions.

3. Because cardiac output has dropped, arterial pressure drops, sometimes causing syncope (fainting) or dizziness.

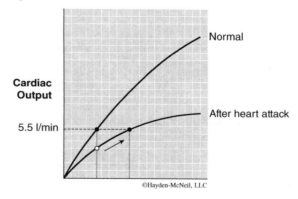

**Figure 28-3.** Starling's law graphs.

## Sympathetic Activation (Neurohumoral Compensation)

1. The drop in arterial pressure activates the sympathetic nervous system via the baroreceptor reflex.

2.  The activation of the sympathetic nervous system results in the following:

    a.  heart rate increases.

    b.  healthy muscle in the heart beats more forcefully.

    c.  vascular effects: vasoconstriction raises the total peripheral resistance and re- duces the capacity of the veins. Vasoconstriction in the skin makes it appear pale and feel cold. It also feels clammy as a result of sympathetic activation of the eccrine sweat glands.

    d.  via the kidneys, activates the renin-angiotensin-aldosterone system. This oper- ates to maintain the volume of the circulating blood, then increase it with nor- mal fluid intake by the patient. One result is a reduction in urine volume.

    e.  release of epinephrine from the adrenal medulla.

    The cardiac output and arterial pressure therefore start recovering.

## IV. Volume Overload, Chronic (Congestive) Heart Failure

If sympathetic (adrenergic) activation cannot make the heart pump a normal cardiac output and maintain mean arterial pressure, the result is **decompensation**.

Given reduced urine production and a normal fluid intake by the patient, the volume of blood in the circulation must increase. Retention of fluid by the kidneys arises from decreased glomerular filtration due to sympathetic vasoconstriction of the afferent ar- terioles, by activation of the renin-angiotensin system (angiotensin II contributes to the sympathetically-mediated increase in total peripheral resistance), and by increased aldo- sterone secretion. The consequence is cardiac volume overload.

Increased volume loading coupled with declining cardiac output can become a vicious cycle.

Because of the high venous pressure, which raises the pressure in the capillaries, there is progressive edema, particularly of the lungs. Accompanying inspiration, the physician typically hears crackling sounds called *rales* and there is also dyspnea ("air hunger"). Death can follow because the blood passing through the lungs cannot be adequately oxygenated, leading to further decline in cardiac performance because the remaining healthy myocardium cannot get enough oxygen from the under-oxygenated blood.

Changes may occur in excitation-contraction coupling, involving reduction of calcium release from the sarcoplasmic reticulum and failure of the sarcoplasmic reticulum to accumulate calcium. Over time, there may be adaptive changes occurring to the left ventricle. One example is wall thickening in response to dilation of the ventricle.

## V. Major Myocardial Infarction—Cardiogenic Shock

Severe consequences usually follow infarction of more than 40% of the myocardium. So much of the myocardium is affected, that death often follows because the body cannot compensate for the sharp drop in cardiac output and mean arterial pressure. Under these conditions, fatality rates can be as high as 80%.

597

## VI. Unilateral Failure of the Left Ventricle

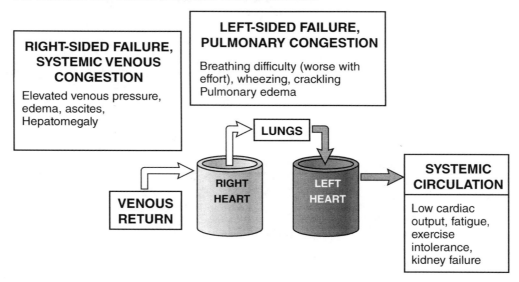

**Figure 28-4.**

While long-term heart failure usually involves both sides of the heart, the initial event is usually right- or left-sided.

When the left ventricle fails and the right ventricle is pumping normally, a very serious situation develops. This is because blood is being pumped at its usual rate into the lungs by the right ventricle, but it is being pumped out of the lungs at a very much reduced rate by the left ventricle.

The result is that there is an increase in pulmonary venous pressure, leading to increased pulmonary capillary pressure and **pulmonary edema**. Cyanosis (blue skin) and shortness of breath are common results. Sometimes, pulmonary edema develops so rapidly that it can cause death by suffocation in 20–30 minutes.

Later, if death has not intervened, there is increased fluid retention by the body as the kidneys fail to function properly, and the situation gets worse as even more blood is pumped into the lungs by the normal right ventricle.

The use of diuretics is helpful in this case. Additionally, substances such as furosemide (Lasix) or bumetide (Bumex) can be administered intravenously in emergency situations. These substances can act quickly to reduce venous pressure by **vasodilation**, even before the onset of **diuresis**.

## VII. Unilateral Failure of the Right Ventricle

Only in rare instances is there a failure on the right side without significant failure on the left. The left is more prone to myocardial ischemia because the walls are thicker, and there is a greater metabolic demand.

Right heart failure can be caused by pulmonary hypertension, and it leads to **peripheral edema**. The left heart continues to pump effectively, but the blood entering the right heart from the venae cavae gets dammed up. This leads to a rise in venous pressure. A rise of venous pressure leads to an increase of pressure at the venous end of the capillaries, and consequently less fluid is withdrawn from the interstitial space. The result is edema.

Edema can lead to accumulation of fluid (ascites) in the abdominal cavity. Edema of the liver increases its size (hepatomegaly).

## VIII. Interventions Designed to Restore the Supply–Demand Mismatch

The rationale for treatment of the ischemic condition is to increase the ratio of coronary blood flow (oxygen supply) to myocardial oxygen demand.

### A. Reduction of Myocardial Oxygen Demand

1. **Rest**

   About 12 hours of bed rest is now the norm, with encouragement for low-level activities including toileting and light ambulation.

2. **Beta-blockers**

   Beta-blockers reduce sympathetic stimulation of the heart, decrease heart rate, mean arterial pressure, and myocardial contractility (cardiac inotropic state), so reducing myocardial oxygen demand. Coronary perfusion may also be increased as a result of the prolongation of diastole.

3. **Reduction of afterload – nitric oxide agonists**

   Nitroglycerin and nitrates provide instant relief for angina.

### B. Increasing Coronary Flow: Reperfusion Strategies

**Prompt restoration of coronary blood flow and myocardial tissue perfusion is the prime goal in early management of MI with S-T segment elevation (STEMI)**. Primary PCI, fibrinolysis and coronary artery bypass grafting are the major approaches.

1. **Percutaneous coronary intervention (PCI), with or without stenting**

   A catheter with a small balloon at its end is inserted into the partially blocked artery, and the balloon is inflated. This compresses the atherosclerotic plaque and stretches the arterial wall.

   A disadvantage of simple PCI is that within four months 30% of patients experience a 70% *restenosed artery.*

   To combat restenosis, there is now increasing use of the stent procedure, which represents 70–90 percent of procedures. Stents are special stainless steel devices (coils or slotted tubes) that are placed over the balloon in the catheter and positioned at the point where the artery is narrowed. The balloon is inflated, the stent expands and is wedged snugly against the wall of the artery. Unfortunately, late (36 month) restenosis rates (20% to 33%) continue to be the most important clinical problem after successful coronary angioplasty. The design of the stent, and whether it is coated with a polymer, seems to be important in preventing restenosis. Drug-eluting stents have come into widespread use in recent years. An unfortunate recent complication, however, is that some patients have developed an allergic reaction to implanted drug-eluting stents.

599

2. **Fibrinolysis**

In the absence of a cath lab and PCI facilities, occlusive thrombi that develop after plaque rupture can be treated by fibrolysis with thrombolytic or "clot-busting" agents. When these compounds are administered intravenously within an hour of the formation of a blood clot in a coronary artery, there is a marked increase in the likelihood of recovery.

Some of these products are manufactured by recombinant DNA technology and belong to the class of compounds known as plasminogen activators. They convert plasminogen trapped in the clot to plasmin, which dissolves the clot.

3. **Aortic-coronary bypass surgery (coronary artery bypass grafting)**

Coronary artery bypass grafting (CABG) involves between one to five grafts using parts of a small vein (usually the long superficial saphenous) or artery to provide connections between the aorta to some of the more peripheral coronary arteries beyond the site of blockage.

4. **Rotational atherectomy**

Mechanical procedures include the use of a rotating "burr" device on the end of a catheter, rather like a Roto-Rooter. The atherosclerotic plaque may also be removed using thermal, laser or ultrasound methods.

5. **Gene therapy – vascular endothelial growth factor (VEGF)**

Gene therapy, using Vascular Endothelial Growth Factor (VEGF) is a new trial approach. The idea is to stimulate growth of new blood vessels in the myocardium.

## C. Medications in the Setting of a Myocardial Infarction

1. **Clotting control and anti-platelet therapies** – platelet aggregation and activation occur in response to plaque rupture and injury to the vessel wall. Aspirin is an important treatment, sometimes combined with an anti-coagulant such as coumadin.

2. **Inotropic** drugs such as *digoxin* (digitalis) increase the cardiac inotropic state (myocardial contractility) by raising intracellular calcium ion concentration. Other inotropic agents include *dopamine* and similar substances such as dobutamine.

3. **Overload reduction: diuretics** – When a congestive heart failure (CHF) patient presents to the emergency department with shortness of breath, one of the first treatment steps is to remove the excess fluid in the body and get the patient back to as "dry" a state as possible. The goal of diuretic therapy is therefore to unload the heart and eliminate the symptoms and physical signs of fluid retention, such as jugular venous distension and/or edema. Diuretics may be accompanied by salt and water restriction.

4. **Overload and TPR reduction: antagonists of the renin-angiotensin-aldosterone system** (also used in antihypertensive therapies) include ACE inhibitors, angiotensin II receptor blockers, renin inhibitors and aldosterone receptor blockers.

5. **Vasodilators to reduce preload and afterload** – the continued activity of the sympathetic nervous system in CHF typically elevates the peripheral vascular resistance, and therefore the afterload. Sympathetic venoconstriction will also reduce venous capacitance, exacerbating the effect of fluid retention and elevating the preload still further.

A vasodilator will reduce the afterload, reducing the systolic pressure, improving the stroke volume and raising the cardiac output.

Many vasodilators also increase the venous capacity by venodilation, so reducing the preload and reducing distension of the left ventricle. Some vasodilators act primarily on the venous system, some act primarily on the arterioles, and others act on both arterioles and veins.

### 1. CONGESTIVE HEART FAILURE
Heart is overloaded and cannot maintain the cardiac output necessary to meet the demands of the tissues.

### 2. UNLOADING THE HEART
Afterload and preload are reduced with diuretics, ACE inhibitors, ARBs, vasodilators

### 3. MINIMIZING HARMFUL SYMPATHETIC EFFECTS ON THE HEART
Slow down and don't overwork - Beta blockers

### 4. ENERGIZING THE HEART, INCREASING ITS INOTROPIC STATE
Inotropes such as digoxin

©Hayden-McNeil, LLC

### 5. OR GET A NEW DONKEY
Heart transplant

**Figure 28-5.**

## D. Current Strategies

1. diuretics initially

2. ACE inhibitors or angiotensin II receptor blockers

3. beta-blockers

4. digoxin or other inotropic drugs if heart failure worsens

# INDEX